P9-BTX-920

# CHEMICAL CONSTITUTION

SOLE DISTRIBUTORS FOR THE UNITED STATES OF NORTH AMERICA:

D. VAN NOSTRAND COMPANY, INC.

*120 Alexander Street, Princeton, N.J. (Principal office)*
*257 Fourth Avenue, New York 10, N.Y.*

SOLE DISTRIBUTORS FOR CANADA:

D. VAN NOSTRAND COMPANY (CANADA), LTD.

*25 Hollinger Road, Toronto 16*

SOLE DISTRIBUTORS FOR THE BRITISH COMMONWEALTH EXCLUDING CANADA:

D. VAN NOSTRAND COMPANY, LTD.

*358 Kensington High Street, London, W. 14*

*Library of Congress Catalog Card Number 58-13592*

# CHEMICAL CONSTITUTION

## AN INTRODUCTION TO THE THEORY OF THE CHEMICAL BOND

BY

J. A. A. KETELAAR

*Professor of Physical Chemistry University of Amsterdam*
*The Netherlands*

SECOND, REVISED EDITION

ELSEVIER PUBLISHING COMPANY

AMSTERDAM LONDON NEW YORK PRINCETON

1958

*1st Dutch edition 1947*
*2nd Dutch edition 1952*
*1st English edition 1953*
*Reprinted 1957*
*2nd English edition 1958*

*With 35 figures and 37 tables*

PRINTED IN THE NETHERLANDS BY N.V. DRUKKERIJ G. J. THIEME, NIJMEGEN

# PREFACE TO THE FIRST EDITION

The interest in theoretical chemistry has increased greatly in the last 25 years. There is now a firm conviction of the necessity of probing deeper into the problems of the constitution of molecules and crystals if there is to be any real insight and understanding with respect to chemical properties and processes.

The chemical constitution of matter comprises both the geometrical structure and the forces acting between the atoms, and also the properties of the molecule or the crystal in the ground state and the interaction with chemical reagents and light.

In the last quarter of the 19th century thermodynamics provided a basis for the systematization of chemistry by evaluating the general interrelationships that the observed physical properties must obey.

The question as to why these properties are shown has only been asked in more recent times, and even now the answers cannot always be given. In attempting to answer, however, the soil is prepared from which new fruitful investigations, both theoretical and experimental, can arise. This new approach to the study of chemical phenomena has now not only found acceptance among scientists but it also has influenced elementary teaching already.

It is anticipated that this introduction provides the chemist with a complement to the usual textbooks of inorganic and organic chemistry, which will enable him to build up the great mass of data into a coherent body.

For the purpose of illustration, recent experimental data are included in the text and in the form of tables so that a considerable amount of chemical information is provided. Reference may be made to the general literature quoted in the text and at the end of each chapter for a more detailed discussion of the subjects.

An attempt is made to make the reader realize that the nature of the chemical bond and chemical constitution, in general, is one single problem that is, however, approached from various sides, the different concepts of which do not include but rather supplement each other. Frequent cross-references may prove to be useful in this respect.

The author believed that he need not hesitate to make use of the ideas and formulae of wave mechanics in many places; for a first reading one can, however, omit some of the more mathematical sections and explanations printed in small type. In this connection I quote with complete approval the statement of EYRING and his co-workers in the preface to their book "Quantum Chemistry":

"No chemist can afford to be uninformed of a theory which systematizes all of chemistry."

Finally I thank all who have assisted me in the preparation of this book, and in particular Dr. J. VAN DRANEN for his comments.

Amsterdam, February 1953 J. A. A. KETELAAR

## PREFACE TO SECOND EDITION

The text of this edition underwent a thorough lingual revision for which I am indebted to Dr. D. K. MYERS and to Mr. R. L. FULTON. Many data were replaced by more recent figures and most tables were completely revised. Apart from numerous corrections and changes of detail, many new topics were included, *e.g.*, polysulphides, colour of inorganic substances, virial theorem, quadrupole coupling constant, stereochemistry of simple compounds, crystal field theory, cyclopentadienyl-metal complexes (ferrocene), etc. Some paragraphs, *e.g.*, on magnetic properties of metals, on the melting point and on the hydrogen bond, were completely rewritten and much extended. A few subjects of minor importance were omitted.

A large number of references to the most recent literature and to review articles has been given in order to enable the reader to extend the study of subjects of special interest. Older literature has only been cited if it is not yet to be found in the general literature cited at the end of each chapter.

I want to thank all who have assisted me by their comments or otherwise in the preparation of this edition.

Amsterdam, October 1958 J. A. A. KETELAAR

CONTENTS

# INTRODUCTION

Matter in all its diversity forms the subject of chemistry while physics finds its task in the study of that which is common to the various manifestations of matter. On the one hand chemistry is, therefore, a descriptive science, a "natural history" of unmoulded, unorganized, non-living matter, but, on the other hand, chemistry as an explanatory science has also the task of reducing this diversity to the multitude of combinations of a very restricted number of elementary concepts.

Although chemistry was practised in Ancient Egypt, as a science it is still young, hardly 150 years old, in contrast again to physics which reached the scientific stage more than 2000 years ago. Although the old laws of physics, *e.g.*, that of ARCHIMEDES, are still valid, the considerations of the alchemists and those of the chemists of the 18th century have little significance now. Consequently, the explanatory theory in chemistry has shown an important development only in the last fifty years.

Exceptions are the brilliant explanation of the composition of compounds on the basis of the atom hypothesis by DALTON (1807) and the development of the structural chemistry of carbon compounds from the ideas of FRANKLAND (1852), COUPER and KEKULÉ (1858), culminating in the hypothesis of the tetrahedral carbon atom by VAN 'T HOFF and LE BEL (1874). It was BUTLEROW (1861) who used for the first time the term chemical structure and who stated that the properties of a compound are determined by its structure. Up to the beginning of this century these theories continued to bear the character of hypotheses, which most people regarded, incorrectly, as being of formal significance only.

The discovery and drafting of the Periodic System of the elements by MENDELÉEFF in 1869 was undoubtedly an extremely important and fruitful generalization but this formal system only acquired significance as an explanatory theory when the meaning of the periodicity could be derived from BOHR's atomic theory.

The aim of modern chemistry can be formulated as the understanding of the properties of substances as functions of the constituent kinds of atoms, that is, stated more accurately, as functions of the atomic numbers which indicate the positions the elements occupy in the Periodic System (Chapter I). The latter is the basis on which the structure of the whole of chemistry should and can be raised. This basis rests in turn on foundations which belong in the realm of physics: the explanation of the Periodic System from the principles of the behaviour of electrons on the one hand and of the nuclei, composed of protons and neutrons, on the other hand.

We are still very far removed from this goal. We still understand very little in chemistry, in spite of the fact that such an overwhelming amount has been achieved experimentally and technically. Thus it is only in the last few years that any insight has arisen into the colour of organic compounds, although tens of thousands of colouring matters have been synthesized since 1856, and although it has even been possible within certain limits to prepare a substance with predetermined properties. A real insight is still almost entirely missing in the territory of the tens of thousands of natural and synthetic physiologically active substances.

The fact that theory lags behind experiment and factual knowledge can only form a stimulus to reduce this gap. The first step in the right direction is made when it is realized that the question as to the essential "why" of chemical properties and reactions is significant even though the complete answer may hardly ever be obtained. The answer, that a substance is an acid because it splits off hydrogen ions in aqueous solutions, was at one time an important generalization of a direct sensory observation, but is now not much more than tautology. The question is: why does sulphuric acid $H_2SO_4$ do this strongly, phenol $C_6H_5OH$ weakly, alcohol $C_2H_5OH$ still much less, and why does methane $CH_4$ not do it at all, though another hydrocarbon such as cyclopentadiene $C_5H_6$ does it more strongly again (see p. 235)? Reference to the consecutively increasing energy of dissociation still forms only a part, though a valuable one, of a thermodynamical description. We want to understand this order on the basis of the interaction between hydrogen atom and oxygen atom or carbon atom and of the influence of the other atoms in the molecule.

Modern chemistry is no longer the "natural history" in which students are told that sodium chloride is by nature just colourless and readily soluble in water, while silver iodide is yellow and insoluble but remarkably enough becomes black in the light. In these cases we can already answer the question why this is so, although a quantitative calculation is frequently still too difficult.

The interaction between the atoms not only determines which compounds are possible but also determines the properties which are exhibited by the individual molecule. The interaction between the molecules, atoms or ions, in turn, determines the macroscopic properties of the phases, whether pure or mixed.

Thus the theory of this interaction, or the theory of the chemical bond, forms the central problem of theoretical chemistry.

The modern use of the term chemical bond no longer implies distinguishing the "chemical" interaction, acting between the atoms of one molecule from the "physical" forces among the saturated molecules themselves. It will be shown that there is no difference in principle between, for example, the interaction between an atom of sodium and an atom of chlorine which leads to the formation of a molecule of sodium chloride or common salt and the interaction which is responsible for the strong cohesion in a crystal of sodium chloride, as appears from the low volatility.

Again the explanation of the "physical" interaction between the atoms of a noble gas follows from the same considerations which are used to explain the union of two hydrogen atoms into a molecule. Similarly, the repulsive forces, which only appear at short distances and which are responsible for the characteristic volume of atoms and molecules, are essentially of the same origin as the bonding forces in the hydrogen molecule.

## LITERATURE

*Historical Development*

E. J. Holmyard, *Alchemy*, London, 1956.
B. Jaffe, *Crucibles; The Story of Chemistry from Ancient Alchemy to Nuclear Fission*, New York, 1948; London, 1950.
H. M. Leicester, *The Historical Background of Chemistry*, New York, 1956.
J. Read, *Through Alchemy to Chemistry*, London, 1957.

*Chemical Constitution in General*

A. E. van Arkel, *Molecules and Crystals in Inorganic Chemistry*, 2nd Ed., London, 1957.
E. Cartmell and G. W. A. Fowles, *Valency and Molecular Structure*, London, 1956.
R. C. Evans, *An Introduction to Crystal Chemistry*, Cambridge, 1946.
H. Hartmann, *Die chemische Bindung*, Berlin, 1955.
L. Pauling, *The Nature of the Chemical Bond*, 2nd Ed., 2nd Impr., Ithaca, 1950.
G. Schwarzenbach, *Allgemeine und anorganische Chemie*, Stuttgart, 1950.
Y. K. Syrkin and M. E. Dyatkina, *Structure of Molecules and the Chemical Bond*, London, 1950.

# I. THE PERIODIC SYSTEM OF THE ELEMENTS
# THE FOUR TYPES OF BONDING

## § 1. THE PERIODIC SYSTEM

The four elements, fire, air, earth and water, as distinguished by ARISTOTLE, had the character of fundamental properties which provided matter with the diversity of its manifestations. The alchemists attached to each of these elements and to the additional properties which they distinguished a representative material which was supposed to exhibit the particular quality in the pure form: thus sulphur represented the principle of fire and mercury the metallic principle (fusible, lustre).

The first indication of the modern concept of an element is given by BOYLE (1627–1691), who was, however, far in advance of his time. LAVOISIER (1743–1794) gave the purely empirical definition of an element, still valid in chemistry, as a substance which cannot be divided or converted by any means. We must make an exception at present only for nuclear processes in which transmutation of the elements can take place. Minute changes can also be brought about by the multiple repetition of physical and chemical processes.

During the course of the 19th century the number of known elements increased greatly. Substances which were first considered to be elements were later found to be further divisible. Thus LAVOISIER still considered calcium oxide, CaO, as an element and in the Rare Earth Group the "element" didymium was only separated into neodymium and praseodymium as late as 1885.

Elements with similar properties were quite early arranged into groups; thus DÖBEREINER arranged the halogens and the alkali metals into groups of three, the so-called triads (1829). However, the honour of having arranged the elements in the Periodic System (Table 1) so that a complete picture was obtained of their mutual relationships is due to MENDELÉEFF (1869), rather than to his predecessors (NEWLANDS, DE CHANCOURTOIS) and contemporaries (L. MEYER).

Arranged according to increasing atomic weight, the elements are divided into short and long periods of 8 and 18 elements, respectively. In this way similar elements are found to be placed in the same vertical column. In order to do this it was necessary to deviate a few times from the normal succession of the weights (for example, Co-Ni, Te-I and Ar-K).

Later it was found that the atomic number of the element is much more important than the atomic weight. This number corresponds to the size of the positive charge of the atomic nucleus, expressed in terms of the elementary charge ($4.80 \cdot 10^{-10}$ E.S.U.) and thus also to the number of electrons of the corresponding neutral atom (VAN DEN BROEK).

The atomic number indicates the number of protons or hydrogen nuclei with charge $+ 1$ in the nucleus, while the atomic weight is given by the sum of the number of protons and neutrons, each of mass 1.

MENDELÉEFF had found himself forced to leave a number of places in his system unoccupied. He correctly believed that elements as yet unknown would find their places in these gaps. His accurate prediction of the properties of these missing elements, which he named eka-boron, eka-aluminium and eka-silicon, was brilliantly confirmed a short time later by the discovery of scandium (21), gallium (31) and germanium (32). The Inert (or Rare) Gases discovered later by RAYLEIGH and RAMSAY could also be readily included in the system. Again, the latest, non-radioactive elements discovered, hafnium (72) (COSTER and VON HEVESY, 1923) and rhenium (75) (NODDACK, 1925), could be discovered because on the basis of the

# TABLE 1

## THE PERIODIC SYSTEM OF THE ELEMENTS

| Preperiod | neutron | H 1 | | | | | | H 1 | | He 2 |
|---|---|---|---|---|---|---|---|---|---|---|
| | 0 | 1 | 2 | 3 | 4 | 5 | 6 | 7 | 8 | 0 |
| 1st period | He 2 | Li 3 | Be 4 | B 5 | C 6 | N 7 | O 8 | F 9 | | Ne 10 |
| 2nd period | Ne 10 | Na 11 | Mg 12 | Al 13 | Si 14 | P 15 | S 16 | Cl 17 | | Ar 18 |
| 3rd period | Ar 18 | K 19<br>Cu 29 | Ca 20<br>Zn 30 | Sc 21<br>Ga 31 | Ti 22<br>Ge 32 | V 23<br>As 33 | Cr 24<br>Se 34 | Mn 25<br>Br 35 | Fe 26 Co 27 Ni 28 | Kr 36 |
| 4th period | Kr 36 | Rb 37<br>Ag 47 | Sr 38<br>Cd 48 | Y 39<br>In 49 | Zr 40<br>Sn 50 | Nb (or Cb) 41<br>Sb 51 | Mo 42<br>Te 52 | Tc 43<br>I 53 | Ru 44 Rh 45 Pd 46 | Xe 54 |
| 5th period | Xe 54 | Cs 55<br>Au 79 | Ba 56<br>Hg 80 | La—Lu 57—71<br>Tl 81 | Hf 72<br>Pb 82 | Ta 73<br>Bi 83 | W 74<br>Po 84 | Re 75<br>At 85 | Os 76 Ir 77 Pt 78 | Rn 86 |
| 6th period | Rn 86 | Fr 87 | Ra 88 | Ac 89 | Th 90 | Pa 91 | U 92 | | | |

| | | | | | | | | | | | | | | | |
|---|---|---|---|---|---|---|---|---|---|---|---|---|---|---|---|
| Lanthanides 4 f-series | La 57 | Ce 58 | Pr 59 | Nd 60 | Pm 61 | Sm 62 | Eu 63 | Gd 64 | Tb 65 | Dy 66 | Ho 67 | Er 68 | Tm 69 | Yb 70 | Lu 71 |
| Actinides 5 f-series | Ac 89 | Th 90 | Pa 91 | U 92 | Np 93 | Pu 94 | Am 95 | Cm 96 | Bk 97 | Cf 98 | Es 99 | Fm 100 | Md 101 | No 102 | |

still unoccupied places in the Periodic System an accurate prediction was possible, both of the properties and of the minerals in which these elements could be sought with some chance of success.

After the two short periods of 8 elements follow the Long Periods of 18, 18 and 32 elements respectively. The elements in the first half of the Long Periods (main series in each column) are grouped together as the A-subgroups, the others (subseries) belong to the B-subgroups. The former are placed at the left, the latter at the right side of the columns (Table 1). Sometimes the subgroups whose properties are most closely related to the corresponding groups of the short periods are also called the main groups (1 A, 2A, 3B, 4B, 5B, 6B, 7B); the others are the subsidiary groups. However, this division is rather arbitrary in the 3rd and especially in the 4th column.

The last three elements of each main series, which are indeed closely related to each other, are brought together in one column (iron, palladium and platinum groups) in order to preserve the regularity.

Finally there was a difficult point; the whole group of the elements of the so-called Rare Earths, lanthanum (57) to lutetium (71), which exhibit almost identical chemical properties, had to be placed in one compartment.

The Periodic System proved to be of great value on continued investigation, among other things on the subject of radioactive phenomena. Thus it was found that all the atoms of one and the same chemical element need not be identical.

With the same nuclear charge and thus the same *atomic number* the chemical properties are also the same because the latter depend exclusively on the electrons, the number of which is then also the same. A difference is, however, possible in the *atomic weight* because nuclei with the same number of protons may contain a different number of neutrons. Such kinds of atoms, or better, kinds of nuclei (nuclides), belong to one element; chemical separation is in fact impossible. The name isotopes (same place) was given to them by SODDY because they occupy the same place in the Periodic System.

Isobaric kinds of atoms, with the same atomic weight but different nuclear charge, for example $^{124}_{50}Sn$ and $^{124}_{52}Te$, are on the other hand not at all related. ($^{124}_{50}Sn$ signifies the nucleus or the atom of tin with a weight 124 and a charge or number 50.)

Isotopes can indeed differ in nuclear properties, *e.g.*, in radio-activity; thus the natural isotope of phosphorus $^{31}_{15}P$ is stable, while the artificially produced isotope $^{32}_{15}P$ emits $\beta$-rays. The easily fissible $^{235}_{92}U$ formed the raw material for the first atomic bomb in contrast to the more stable $^{238}_{92}U$. The atomic weights, really nuclide weights, differ but little from whole numbers, a point to which PROUT had drawn attention (1815), although this cannot, as he thought, be explained by the construction of the elements from hydrogen. Actually this is based on the composition of the nucleus, to which we have already alluded, from protons and neutrons, each with a mass practically equal to one mass unit (M.U. = 1/16 of the atomic weight of oxygen) and thus approximately equal to the atomic weight of a hydrogen atom. The chemical or the physical scale of atomic weights is obtained according as 1/16th part of the atomic weight of the natural mixture of oxygen isotopes (99.76% $^{16}O$, 0.04% $^{17}O$ and 0.20% $^{18}O$) or 1/16th of that of the oxygen isotope $^{16}O$ is taken as the basis: phys. atomic weight = 1.000275 chem, atomic weight.

Thus an element such as chlorine with an atomic weight differing from a whole number, 35.457, consists of 75.4% $^{35}Cl$ and 24.6% $^{37}Cl$.

The packing effect is a small deviation of the atomic (resp. nuclide) weight from the sum of the weights of the component hydrogen atoms (resp. protons) and neutrons. This packing effect is directly connected with the difference in energy between the nucleus and the separate particles according to the well-known EINSTEIN relation $\Delta E = \Delta m \cdot c^2$ (0.001 M.U. = 0.931 Me. V = $21.47 \cdot 10^6$ kcal/mole).

Mass of proton 1.007318 M.U., hydrogen 1.007867 M.U., neutron 1.008705 M.U. chem. scale.

Various physical properties such as diffusion, thermodiffusion and rate of evaporation depend on the mass of the particles and so it has been found possible to separate not only the isotopes of hydrogen and chlorine but also those of uranium by diffusion, in the last case by means of a volatile compound $UF_6$. In some chemical reactions also small isotope effects are found.

It is only in the case of hydrogen H (weight 1) and deuterium D (weight 2), discovered by UREY (1933), that the relative difference is so large that a small but observable difference in all physical and even in chemical properties occurs. Thus pure $D_2$ can be obtained by repeated electrolysis of water, in which the separated hydrogen gas is less rich in the heavy isotope than corresponds to the ratio in the water 1 : 4000. The deuterium therefore accumulates in the residual liquid of technical installations for the electrolytic production of hydrogen.

$D_2O$: melting point +3.8°; boiling point 101.5°; density (20°) 1.10726 (density maximum at 11.2°); viscosity at 25° is 1.23 that of water.

Although the differences in physical and chemical properties are not directly measurable, with other light elements a product with a somewhat modified atomic weight can be obtained by multiple repetition of exchange, for example of $CO_2$ and of $NH_3$, between the gaseous phase and a liquid.

Up till a few years ago four elements (43, 61, 85 and 87) were still missing from the roll-call, although their discovery had been announced repeatedly but always incorrectly. These elements have now all been prepared artifically and they have been found to be radioactive, while there are also grounds for assuming that stable isotopes of these elements cannot exist. The first three of these elements, if they have ever existed, have very probably died out on earth long ago, just as radium (half-life 1620 years) would also have remained unknown to us if it had not been continually generated afresh from the extremely slowly decaying uranium (half-life 4.49 · $10^9$ years). The presence of 87 in extremely small quantities in the decomposition products of actinium was first discovered by PEREY; from her it received the name francium (Fr). The other elements mentioned have been christened: 43 technetium (= artificial) Tc, 61 prometheum (after the titan Prometheus) Pm, 85 astatine (= unstable) At. The elements with higher numbers than uranium (92), the transuranes, have also been obtained only artificially. These are 93 neptunium Np, 94 plutonium Pu (both named after planets), 95 americium (after America), 96 curium Cm (after the CURIE family), 97 berkelium Bk (after the town of Berkeley, where the element was obtained in the large cyclotron), 98 californium Cf (after the State of California in which Berkeley is situated), 99 einsteinium Es, 100 fermium Fm, 101 mendelevium Md, and 102 nobelium No (after the physicists EINSTEIN and FERMI, the chemist, MENDELÉEFF, and the industrialist NOBEL). Most of these have been discovered by SEABORG and his collaborators (PANETH, 1947; HAHN, 1950; SEABORG *et al.*, 1949, 1954; McKAY *et al.*, 1955; LISTER, 1950; SNEED *et al.*, 1953; KATZ and SEABORG, 1957). All these transuranes are radioactive; plutonium, the important nuclear fuel and explosive, has a long half-life of 24,360 years ($^{239}_{94}Pu$). Many tons of this have certainly been prepared in nuclear reactors all over the world.

The explanation of the periodicity in the series of the elements is one of the great triumphs of the quantum theory of atomic structure. According to BOHR the electrons can only move in a discrete number of orbits, characterized by three quantum numbers: the principal quantum number $n$, which can take on the values 1, 2, 3, 4 etc. (also denoted by K, L, M, N, O, ....), the angular quantum number $l$, which can have the values 0, 1, 2, .... $n - 1$ (also denoted by s, p, d, f....) and the magnetic quantum number $m$, which can have the values $-l$, $-(l-1)$ .... $-1$, 0, 1 .... $l-1$, $l$ (p. 124). In each of those orbits there is room for two and not more electrons, which must then have opposite orientations of their spins (UHLENBECK and GOUDSMIT, see page 124). In this way the requirements of the PAULI-principle, that two electrons can never occupy the same quantum state, are satisfied. Wave mechanics has finally thrown light on the essential significance of the formal quantum numbers of the BOHR theory as logically necessary for the description of a stationary state.

The first group or K shell with $n = 1$, $l = 0$ contains only one possible orbit in which therefore two electrons can be placed.

After the element hydrogen follows therefore helium, with which the preperiod ends. In the succeeding L shell ($n = 2$; s-subshell: $l = 0$, $m = 0$, and p-subshell: $l = 1$, $m = -1, 0, +1$) there is room for eight electrons; this is the case with the element neon (10), again an inert gas (Table 2). In the next succeeding M shell ($n = 3$) a similar configuration is reached in the atom of the next inert gas argon (18) after the addition once more of eight electrons. The M shell is, however, not yet completely filled there; there is still room for another 10 electrons d-subshell: $l = 2$, $m = -2, -1, 0, 1, 2$. In the next elements, potassium and calcium, however, the next electrons go straight into the N shell and it is only after this that the $M_d$ shell is filled up from scandium onwards (transition elements Sc-Ni, Y-Pd, La-Pt, with incomplete d-subshells). The further building up of the N shell begins with the element copper. Thus it is only at the eighteenth place after argon that the next inert gas krypton (36) is encountered (Long Period). This is repeated in the next long period up to xenon (54) with an 8-electron configuration again, now in the O-shell.

The fact that a few electrons find a place in the N shell before the $M_d$ shell is completed, a feature which is repeated at the beginning of the other long periods, is connected with the energy differences between the various orbits belonging to one shell, but with different angular quantum numbers. In hydrogen all orbits with the same principal quantum number have the same mean value of $1/r$ and thus also the same energy.

The shape of the elliptical orbit is given by the ratio of major and minor axes, which is equal to $(l + 1)/n$. Therefore the 1s, 2p, 3d and 4f orbits are circles, but just the 3s, 4s and likewise the (5s and 5p) of the M, N and O shells respectively are elongated ellipses. (We shall see later that the charge cloud of all s-electrons is spherically symmetrical (p. 126)). Now in an atom with many electrons this difference in shape means an important difference in energy; indeed in such an elliptical orbit the electron approaches the nucleus very closely at perihelion, so that the field of the nucleus is shielded but little at this point by the other electrons (penetrating orbit). As a result the energy is also much lower than that of an electron in a circular orbit in which the nucleus is always strongly shielded by the inner shells. The energy of the 4s orbit can thus become lower than the 3d orbit, even though the *mean* value of $1/r$ is smaller for the former orbit. If the nuclear charge increases further the 3d orbit wins and the ten transition elements follow. The same consideration provides an explanation for the initial failure to fill the 4f and 5f subshells in favour of the replenishment of the 5p and 6p subshells.

Three places after xenon follows the remarkable group of the Rare Earth elements, because here, beginning with cerium, the $N_f$ or 4f shell ($l = 3$, $m = -3, -2, -1, 0, 1, 2, 3$) becomes filled up. There is thus produced a group of 14 elements from cerium (58) to lutetium (71), which all possess the same electron configuration of the outermost shell as lanthanum and thus also show a great similarity in chemical properties (group of the lanthanides or lanthanons).

From BOHR's theory it could thus be deduced that the element of atomic number 72 cannot be a Rare Earth element, but that it must exhibit a relationship to zirconium. VON HEVESY and COSTER did not look for the missing element in minerals of the Rare Earths as so many others had done, but came across hafnium, as was expected theoretically, in fairly large quantities (about 1%) in the majority of minerals containing zirconium and in all preparations of zirconium which

TA[BLE]

ELECTRON CONFIGURATION[S]

| | K | L | | M | | | N | | | |
|---|---|---|---|---|---|---|---|---|---|---|
| *n* | 1 | 2 | 2 | 3 | 3 | 3 | 4 | 4 | 4 | 4 |
| *l* | 0 | 0 | 1 | 0 | 1 | 2 | 0 | 1 | 2 | 3 |
| | s | s | p | s | p | d | s | p | d | f |
| He | 2 | | | | | | | | | |
| Ne | 2 | 2 | 6 | | | | | | | |
| Ar | 2 | 2 | 6 | 2 | 6 | | | | | |
| K—Ca | 2 | 2 | 6 | 2 | 6 | | 1—2 | | | |
| Sc—Ni | 2 | 2 | 6 | 2 | 6 | 1—8 | 1 or 2 | | | |
| Cu—Kr | 2 | 2 | 6 | 2 | 6 | 10 | 1—2 | 0—6 | | |
| Kr | 2 | 2 | 6 | 2 | 6 | 10 | 2 | 6 | | |
| Rb—Sr | 2 | 2 | 6 | 2 | 6 | 10 | 2 | 6 | | |
| Y—Pd | 2 | 2 | 6 | 2 | 6 | 10 | 2 | 6 | 1—10 | |
| Ag—Xe | 2 | 2 | 6 | 2 | 6 | 10 | 2 | 6 | 10 | |
| Xe | 2 | 2 | 6 | 2 | 6 | 10 | 2 | 6 | 10 | |
| Cs—Ba | 2 | 2 | 6 | 2 | 6 | 10 | 2 | 6 | 10 | |
| La—Lu | 2 | 2 | 6 | 2 | 6 | 10 | 2 | 6 | 10 | 0—14 |
| Hf—Pt | 2 | 2 | 6 | 2 | 6 | 10 | 2 | 6 | 10 | 14 |
| Au—Rn | 2 | 2 | 6 | 2 | 6 | 10 | 2 | 6 | 10 | 14 |
| Rn | 2 | 2 | 6 | 2 | 6 | 10 | 2 | 6 | 10 | 14 |
| Fr—Ra | 2 | 2 | 6 | 2 | 6 | 10 | 2 | 6 | 10 | 14 |
| Ac—No * | 2 | 2 | 6 | 2 | 6 | 10 | 2 | 6 | 10 | 14 |

had been considered pure up till then.

After the lanthanides follows once more a long period which ends with the inert gas radon (86), 32 places after xenon.

A new group of closely related elements, to which the transuranes belong, begins at the end of the Periodic System by the completion of the 5f shell. In the hexavalent state these elements are similar to uranium. In the quadrivalent state, however, they have, like uranium and protactinium in this valency state, externally the inert gas configuration of the thorium ion; in the trivalent state that of the trivalent actinium ion. The name 5f series or actinides is preferred to thorides or uranides.

* There exists no complete certainty yet about the configuration of the elements after Ac; the energies of the 5f and 6d shells lie close together (KATZ and SEABORG, 1957).

LE 2

F THE ELEMENTS

| O | | | | P | | | Q | |
|---|---|---|---|---|---|---|---|---|
| 5<br>0<br>s | 5<br>1<br>p | 5<br>2<br>d | 5<br>3<br>f | 6<br>0<br>s | 6<br>1<br>p | 6<br>2<br>d | 7<br>0<br>s | *n*<br>*l* |
| | | | | | | | | He |
| | | | | | | | | Ne |
| | | | | | | | | Ar |
| | | | | | | | | K—Ca |
| | | | | | | | | Sc—Ni |
| | | | | | | | | Cu—Kr |
| | | | | | | | | Kr |
| 1—2 | | | | | | | | Rb—Sr |
| 0,1 or2 | | | | | | | | Y—Pd |
| 1—2 | 0—6 | | | | | | | Ag—Xe |
| 2 | 6 | | | | | | | Xe |
| 2 | 6 | | | 1—2 | | | | Cs—Ba |
| 2 | 6 | 1 | | 2 | | | | La—Lu |
| 2 | 6 | 2—9 | | 0,1 or2 | | | | Hf—Pt |
| 2 | 6 | 10 | | 1—2 | 0—6 | | | Au—Rn |
| 2 | 6 | 10 | | 2 | 6 | | | Rn |
| 2 | 6 | 10 | | 2 | 6 | | 1—2 | Fr—Ra |
| 2 | 6 | 10 | 0—14 | 2 | 6 | 0, 1 or 2 | 2 | Ac—No |

In the lanthanide series trivalency predominates, with only a few interesting exceptions. Thus cerium occurs not only as a trivalent positive ion, with therefore one electron in the 4f shell, but also as quadrivalent. Evidently it requires but little energy to remove this first electron from the 4f shell. Naturally this $Ce^{4+}$ ion exhibits no similarity to the $La^{3+}$ ion but rather to zirconium which is also quadrivalent. The next element, praeseodymium, still shows some tendency to assume a higher valency, as appears from the existence of an oxide $PrO_2$ and perhaps even of $Pr_2O_5$. The succeeding lanthanides are exclusively trivalent until at europium (63) bivalency and at terbium (65) quadrivalency ($TbO_2$) occur. The reason is here that with gadolinium (64) just seven electrons, half of the maximum number, have been accommodated in the 4f shell. It is known from magnetism among other things that these seven electrons each occupy one of the seven possible states (orbits), all with the spins directed parallel (HUND's rule, p. 156). Evidently this half-filled shell is also characterized by a greater stability, so that the preceding element can readily assume the same configuration in the divalent and the succeeding element in the quadrivalent state. Ytterbium can also be divalent, thus with 14 4f-electrons as in $Lu^{3+}$.

The course of the valency in the 5f series shows some agreement with as well as important differences from that in the 4f series (LISTER, 1950; SEABORG *et al.*, 1949, 1954; MCKAY and MILSTED, 1955; KATZ and SEABORG, 1957). Thorium is (principally) quadrivalent, like cerium. There is, however, no parallel for the higher valencies of uranium, 4, 5 and 6. In the hexavalent state uranium shows a similarity to tungsten, so that it is as much in its place in the 6th column as in the actinide series (Table 1). The transuranes up to and including americium can also be quadri-, quinqui- and hexavalent and in these states of valency correspond to uranium; hence the name uranides. The trivalent form becomes more and more the most stable state of valency in the series of the transuranes. Also americium can be divalent AmO, like europium, and berkelium can indeed occur as quadrivalent, while of curium only the trivalent state is known.

The inert gas configuration with 8 electrons (octet) in the outermost shell is distinguished by special stability, *i.e.*, by the relatively low energy content. This singularity forms the basis of the main types of the chemical bond (p. 20). Atoms of other elements will readily, thus at the cost of little energy, be transformed into positive and negative ions by loss or acceptance of electrons (Chapter II). Thus the halogens in the seventh column form monovalent *negative* ions, the alkali metals in the first column monovalent *positive* ions, etc. Hydrogen forms both a negative ion with a helium configuration (in LiH) and a positive ion. By one or more pairs of electrons held in common and thus forming part of the octets of both partners an atomic bond is realized (Chapter III), *e.g.*,

$Cl_2$ $:\ddot{\underset{..}{Cl}}:\ddot{\underset{..}{Cl}}:$, HCl $H:\ddot{\underset{..}{Cl}}:$, $N_2$ $:N:::N:$ etc.

In the metals of the Short Periods and of the A-subgroups (main series), *e.g.*, the alkali metals, positive ions with the inert gas configurations are also produced, while the surplus electrons form the degenerate "gas" of the conduction electrons. Also the configuration with a filled d-subshell is characterized by a certain preference as is demonstrated by the common 18-electron configuration of many positive ions of the B-subgroups (subseries) *e.g.*,

$Cu^{+}$, $Zn^{2+}$, $Ga^{3+}$, $Ag^{+}$, $Cd^{2+}$, $In^{3+}$, $Au^{+}$, $Hg^{2+}$, $Tl^{3+}$, $Pb^{4+}$, etc.

However, palladium with just 10 electrons in the 4d-subshell around the krypton core is by no means a noble gas.

## § 2. ELECTRONS AS PARTICLES AND AS WAVES

Chemical interaction rests exclusively on the interaction of electrons and it is in fact only the outermost electrons which determine the chemical properties. This interaction is purely of an electrical nature. The magnetic interaction as a result of the spin of the electrons plays no part in the binding energy, although the total magnetic moment of an atom or ion gives a valuable indication of the electron configuration.

The fundamental law of chemical bonding of whatever type is consequently the COULOMB law. In addition to this a description of the behaviour and of the spatial distribution of the electrical particles (nuclei and electrons) is also necessary.

However, the electrons have the character of a wave phenomenon, and also the properties which suggest that they could be considered as charged particles. Their diffraction by crystal lattices is entirely analogous to that of X-rays (p. 112).

Which of the two complementary descriptions is specially suitable for the questions of the chemical bond depends on the wave length of these electron waves in comparison to the interatomic distances.

According to BOHR's theory, in a hydrogen atom, for example, only certain discrete orbits are possible in which the electron can revolve around the nucleus. DE BROGLIE has explained this by stating that the periphery of each stationary orbit must contain a whole number of electron waves. For the state of lowest energy this furnishes $\lambda = 2\pi r$ in which $r = 0.53$ Å, according to BOHR, so that $\lambda = 3.3$ Å. Thus the wave length is in fact of the same order of magnitude as the distances in the molecules. This corresponds with the domain physical optics where HUYGENS' wave theory pre-eminently provides the appropriate interpretation for diffraction, etc..

More generally, the wave length associated with a material particle at constant energy is inversely proportional to $\sqrt{m}$ (p. 114).

For the hydrogen nucleus the wave length is therefore smaller by a factor $\sqrt{1836}$ and is equal to 0.08 Å. The characteristic wave length for this nucleus and *a fortiori* for heavier nuclei is thus very much smaller than the interatomic distances. This corresponds to the domain of geometrical optics with rectilinear propagation according to NEWTON's corpuscular theory.

Thus for electrons the description as a wave phenomenon will be indicated, while for nuclei (and other heavy particles such as ions) one can nearly always be satisfied with the simple representation as charged mass particles.

We have therefore the interaction law of COULOMB on the one hand, and the wave mechanical description of the behaviour of electrons on the other hand, as the fundamentals in chemistry. There can be no doubt about the complete correctness of both, again for the domain of chemistry (corrections resulting from the theory of relativity play no part).

We have in fact only to consider here the time-independent description of this behaviour of the electrons, a restriction therefore to stationary states; this approximation is permissible even with chemical reactions. We can also express this by saying that the velocities of the electrons are, on account of their small mass, so great compared with all other velocities that, for each instantaneous configuration of the nuclei, the corresponding electron state is established rapidly with respect to changes in this nuclear configuration. We can in a certain sense consider the frequencies of the characteristic vibrations as a measure of this "mobility"; the corresponding absorption bands lie in the ultraviolet part of the spectrum ($\sim$ 0.15–0.3$\mu$) for the electronic vibrations, in the infrared part ($\sim$ 3–30 $\mu$) for the molecular vibrations.

The situation is extremely satisfactory, as far as the fundamentals are concerned, so that DIRAC correctly writes:

"The underlying physical laws necessary for the mathematical theory of a large part of physics and *the whole of chemistry* are thus completely known and the difficulty is only that the exact application of these laws leads to equations much too complicated to be soluble".

Thus the problem of the chemical bond can be considered solved from the physical side, whereby the application to special cases is left to the chemists. The exact solution of the above-mentioned equations is still possible for the molecule

$H_2^+$ but for $H_2$ this can be carried out only by successive approximations (Chapter III). In all cases one can, therefore, say that chemists are forced to leave the royal road of the exact theory and take to the winding paths of simplification, schematization and approximation. They will frequently not be able to derive even the indications that they are taking the right direction from the theory itself but have to rely on the agreement of the theoretical results with what is known experimentally.

## § 3. THE FOUR TYPES OF BONDING

The frequently very rough approximations simplify the problems to such an extent that elementary mathematics suffices. However, the approximations which are introduced possess their particular validity only for certain groups of phenomena. For that reason it is desirable to make a classification into types of bonding.

In this classification we divide the elements into electropositive and electronegative elements—an idea already put forward in about 1820 by BERZELIUS* in somewhat different form—as well as indifferent elements. The atoms of the first category, represented by (+), give up one or more electrons more or less readily, those of the second, represented by (—), take up electrons more or less readily, while those of the last category (0) show no tendency to either of the two processes.

The following scheme gives a schematic classification with some characteristic representatives, just as a classification of human character types can be illustrated by historical figures. The type is always idealized; however, the constitution of any substance, which actually occurs, forms a combination in which mostly one of these types clearly predominates.

* BERZELIUS (1779–1848) may indeed be acknowledged as the founder of the theory of ionogenic bonding. That his theory of dualism has fallen so completely into oblivion can be attributed to the vigorous development in the 19th century of organic chemistry to which this theory did not appear to be applicable.

*Four types of bonding*

| | | |
|---|---|---|
| + — ionic bond, especially in solid and liquid state. | CsF, NaCl. | electrostatic attractive forces between charged spheres with quasi-elastic repulsive forces at short distances, non-directed action, high coordination number (classical theory). |
| — — atomic bond, free molecules also in molecular and atomic lattices. | $F_2$, $H_2$, $Cl_2$, organic compounds, diamond. | electron pair bond, exchange forces with directed action, low coordination number (wave mechanical theory). |
| + + metallic bond, only in solid and liquid state. | Li and other metals | electron gas, exchange forces with non-directed action, high coordination number (wave mechanical theory). |
| o o VAN DER WAALS bond, weak, seldom leading to stable compounds; important for the interaction between molecules | Molecular compounds, *e.g.*, hydrates; cohesion of molecular liquids and solids, *e.g.*, liquid inert gases, organic compounds. | VAN DER WAALS-LONDON forces (exchange). In molecules together with possible classical interaction between permanent dipoles (KEESOM) and between permanent and induced dipole (DEBYE). |

Gradual transitions between the first three types are reproduced in Fig. 1.

Although more attention usually is paid to the attractive forces, the repulsive forces between the atoms are of no less importance.

The two *forces* are in fact equal to one another in the equilibrium state, not however the contribution of the two to the *energy* (p. 36).

Originally one was satisfied to take over a model from macroscopic mechanics, namely that of completely hard spheres (b-correction of VAN DER WAALS) or of almost hard spheres (BORN repulsion, p. 36). Interesting results could be obtained with this simple model (the ionic and VAN DER WAALS radii). The work of HEITLER and LONDON on the hydrogen molecule has laid the foundation for a more correct insight in this case (p. 142).

It is, furthermore, still the question in what way experimental clarification can be obtained about the constitution of molecules, *i.e.*, about the nature of the bonds present.

The molecular structure, *i.e.*, the spatial structure, is connected very closely with the constitution. This structure can

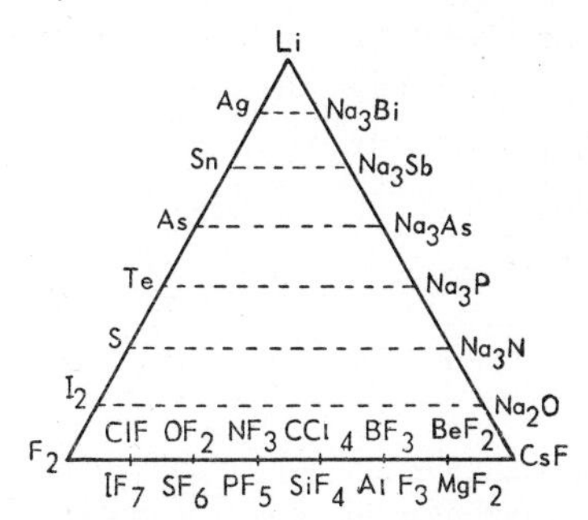


Fig. 1. Transitions between three types of chemical bonding.

often be derived with great accuracy and in all detail from the diffraction of X-rays and electrons by crystals and gases. These data on the structure, particularly the interatomic distances, give important information about the nature of the bonds. Conclusions can be drawn from spectral data (infrared, RAMAN, micro-wave and band spectra, nuclear magnetic resonance) about the forces acting between the atoms; the electric dipole moment and the magnetic properties also furnish important indications.

Finally, all the chemical and physical properties naturally depend on the constitution. However, although the properties can be derived from an insight into the chemical bond once this has been obtained, it is only rarely possible to follow the opposite path with certainty.

The use of the terms heteropolar and homo- or homoio-polar is avoided; in fact, even a pure electron pair bond between elements of different electronegativity or size is polar (see p. 303). The term homopolar should only be used for a particular approximation method used by HEITLER and LONDON (see p. 146) for the atomic bond.

The term covalent referred originally to a bond to which each atom has donated one electron (LEWIS) and has been widely used, but strictly speaking it cannot be applied to those cases where an electron pair bond is formed with both electrons donated by only one of the partners (p. 171).

The term atomic bonding is to be construed as being more general than electron pair bonding and includes, for example, the bonding by one electron, as in $H_2^+$, and by three electrons as in $He_2^+$ and $O_2$ (pp. 154 and 246).

LITERATURE

M. E. WEEKS, *The Discovery of the Elements*, 6th Ed., Eaton Pa., 1956.

*Theory of the Atom*

Y. CAUCHOIS, *Atomes, Spectres, Matière*, Paris, 1952.
W. HUME-ROTHERY, *Atomic Theory for Students of Metallurgy*, London, 1948.
E. RABINOWITSCH and E. THILO, *Periodisches System*, Stuttgart, 1930.
F. O. RICE and E. TELLER, *The Structure of Matter*, New York, 1949.
R. S. SHANKLAND, *Atomic and Nuclear Physics*, New York, 1955.
J. C. SPEAKMAN, *An Introduction to the Electronic Theory of Valency*, 3rd Ed., London, 1955.
S. TOLANSKY, *Introduction to Atomic Physics*, London, 1956.

*Wave Mechanics*

*Introduction:*

W. HEITLER, *Elementary Wave Mechanics*, Oxford, 1956.

*Textbooks:*

H. EYRING, J. WALTER and G. E. KIMBALL, *Quantum Chemistry*, New York, 1944.
H. HARTMANN, *Theorie der Chemischen Bindung auf quantentheoretischer Grundlage*, Berlin, 1954.
H. HELLMANN, *Einführung in die Quantenchemie*, Leipzig, 1937, Ann Arbor, 1944.
W. KAUZMANN, *Quantum Chemistry*, New York, 1957.
L. PAULING and E. B. WILSON, *Introduction to Quantum Mechanics*, New York, 1935.
K. S. PITZER, *Quantum Chemistry*, London, 1953.

REFERENCES

HAHN, O., *New Atoms*, Amsterdam, 1950.
KATZ, J. J. and SEABORG, G. T., *The Chemistry of the Actinide Elements*, London, New York, 1957.
LISTER, M. W., *Quart. Revs. (London)*, *4* (1950) 20.
MCKAY, H. A. C. and MILSTED, J., *Progr. in Nuclear Phys.*, *4* (1955) 287.
PANETH, F. A. *et al.*, *Nature*, *159* (1947) 824.
SEABORG, G. T. and KATZ, J. J., The Actinide Elements, *Natl. Nuclear Energy Ser. Div. IV* 14A, New York, 1954.
SEABORG, G. T., KATZ, J. J. and MANNING, W. M., The Transuranium Elements, *ibid.*, 14 B, New York, 1949.
SNEED, M. C., MAYNARD, J. L. and BRASTED, R. C., *Comprehensive Inorganic Chemistry*, Vol. I, New York, 1953.

## II. THE IONIC BOND

The wave character of the particles plays no part in the bonding between ions since we are concerned with heavy particles in this case. A simple treatment, based on the classical laws of electrostatics, does in fact lead to satisfactory results when the ions are considered as charged, polarizable, almost hard spheres (KOSSEL, VAN ARKEL and DE BOER). Calculations can thus be carried out for the ionic bond and general rules can be readily deduced. The domain in which these rules are valid is very extensive. They are found to hold even in cases where the model of ionic bonding employed certainly cannot be considered as the correct approximation to the constitution. The ionic bond is of paramount importance especially for the solid state.

The value of the theory of the ionic bond is sometimes underestimated because of its clearly approximate nature. However, the approximations introduced in wave mechanical calculations are certainly not less serious, though they are not as easily discerned as such.

When in the gaseous state two free atoms, for example, a sodium and a chlorine atom, are transformed into free ions by the transference of an electron, the ionization energy of the metal atom ($I$ = 118.5 kcal/gr. atom) must be supplied. On the other hand an amount of energy equal to the electron affinity ($E$=85.8 kcal/gr.atom) is set free on adding the electron to the halogen atom. It appears, however, that this balance is always adverse, even for the case of the combination of cesium and fluorine, CsF ($I$ = 89.4, $E$ = 83 kcal/gr. atom). This could give the impression that the ionic bond would be quite exceptional and that a molecule NaCl would be built up of atoms instead of ions. However, when the two oppositely charged ions approach one another, as happens in the formation of a molecule, the potential energy decreases considerably according to COULOMB's law: $U = - e^2/r$. This lowering of the energy is very much smaller for two neutral atoms and consequently the ionic state can represent a lower energy than the atomic state for particles at a small distance (Fig. 2).

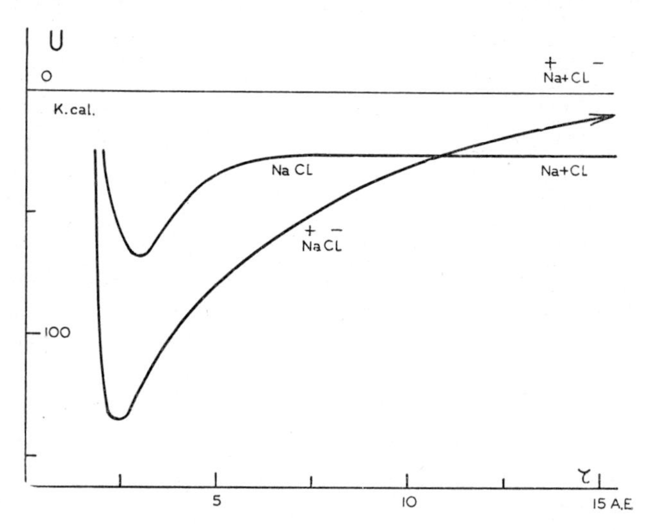


Fig. 2. Potential energy $U$ as a function of the distance $r$ for ions and atoms.

Still more energy is set free in the formation of a crystal of sodium chloride. In a crystal with a lattice of the rock-salt type (Fig. 3) each positive sodium ion is surrounded by not less than six negative chlorine ions and vice versa. It is true that there are also other positive and negative ions in the neighbourhood but these are situated at a greater distance (see p. 35).

For a crystal, built up of molecules, the lattice energy is but small. This is indicated *e.g.*, by the volatility of most organic substances (see, however, p. 169 about diamond, etc.) in contrast to the hardly volatile salt-like compounds which crystallize in an ionic lattice.

It is clear that the ionic bond plays an important role as a type of bonding for the crystalline state.

A molecule or a crystal consisting of oppositely charged ions attracting each other could not exist if repulsive forces did not also act between the ions. In fact, the small compressibility of a sodium chloride crystal indicates that a small

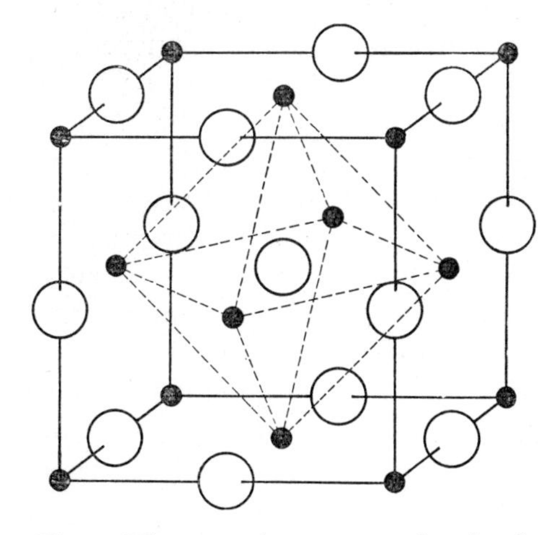

Fig. 3. The crystal structure of rock-salt (octahedral arrangement) • = Na, ○ = Cl.

decrease of the separation of the ions encounters considerable resistance because strongly repulsive forces appear. Attractive and repulsive forces are just equilibrated in the normal crystal but the attraction contributes very much more to the lattice energy (work = force × distance) than the repulsion, which only acts over a very short distance (p. 36 and Fig. 5).

It is not so simple to prove directly that rock-salt, for example, is composed from ions. The melt and the aqueous solution consist of ions, as appears from the conduction of the electric current and electrolysis. This does not prove, however, that this also holds for the solid state, which conducts the current only very slightly.

According to DULONG and PETIT's rule the specific heat per gramatom amounts to about 6 cal/deg. Since the specific heat per grammol. is 11.9 cal/deg for NaCl at 0° C, it follows that there must be two particles per molecule of NaCl. However, the specific heat depends on the temperature, and deviations from this rule, both upwards and downwards, are so numerous that the argument is not very significant. For LiCl, LiH and MgO at 0° C one finds 9.7, 7.8 and 8.4 cal/deg, respectively, for the molecular specific heat; nevertheless these are also ionic lattices.

The strong absorption in the far infrared part of the spectrum (residual ray region LiF: 26 $\mu$, NaCl: 52 $\mu$, KBr: 87 $\mu$, TlBr: 117$\mu$) does in fact prove the presence of vibrating charges, but molecules of a strongly polar nature would also produce a similar absorption.

The direct proof is provided by an extremely accurate crystal structure analysis with X-rays (Ultra-Fourier analysis, BRILL *et al.*, 1939, 1944; WITTE *et al.*, 1955; WEISS, WITTE and WÖLFEL, 1957). By means of this not only is the position of the ions in the crystal determined but also the distribution of the electron density is established.

It can be calculated in this way that in NaCl 10.05 electrons are to be found around a $Na^+$ ion and 17.70 electrons round a $Cl^-$ ion, almost equal to what would be expected for ions, namely 10 and 18 electrons. For a crystal consisting of light atoms and in which the differences in numbers of electrons between an atom and an ion are relatively larger, as in LiF and *a fortiori* in LiH, the existence of ions has been deduced in a simpler way from the X-ray intensities. The reasoning, however, is open to serious criticism (BIJVOET and LONSDALE, 1953).

## § 4. THE IONIC RADIUS

The ions thus behave as almost hard, slightly compressible

spheres which will assume a close packing under the influence of the attractive forces. It seems logical to attribute a definite ionic radius* to the ions, a radius which, on account of the great hardness, will vary but little with differences in the attractive forces, *e.g.*, as a result of difference in charge of the oppositely charged ion, or difference in coordination number, *i.e.*, the number of ions surrounding the one in question (p. 39).

The existence of constant ionic radii is also seen on examining the lattice spacings $a$ of the alkali halides; pairs with the same alkali atom or halogen atom show about constant differences for two different halogens or alkali atoms, respectively.

Thus we have $a_{LiCl} - a_{LiF} = 0.56$ Å, $a_{NaCl} - a_{NaF} = 0.50$Å, $a_{KCl} - a_{KF} = 0.48$ Å (1 Å $= 10^{-8}$ cm).

However, the values of the ionic radii can only be deduced from these differences when the ionic radius is known for one ion. One can decide on the radius of the $I^-$ ion from the consideration that the negative ions will actually touch each other if the positive ion is relatively very small, as in LiI. From their separation (4.24 Å) it follows that $r_I = 2.12$ Å. On the basis of other arguments GOLDSCHMIDT arrived at a value of 1.33 Å for the ionic radius of the fluorine ion as a starting point. PAULING has given a theoretical derivation of the ionic radii, which is based on the idea that the radii of ions with the same electron configuration, such as $Na^+$ and $F^-$, are inversely proportional to the effective charges on the ion. These charges are those which act on the outer electron, that is, the nuclear charge minus the charge of the electrons in the shells multiplied by a screening factor which is deduced experimentally from the spectra. In the above case this effective charge becomes $11 - 4.52 = 6.48$ for $Na^+$ and $9 - 4.52 = 4.48$ for $F^-$, expressed in electron charges. The sum $r_{Na^+} + r_{F^-} =$

* For free ions the concept loses its significance. According to wave mechanics the charge density approaches zero only at large distances. For a $K^+$ ion, about $0.35e$ or 1.95 % of the total electron charge falls outside a sphere with an ionic radius $r = 1.33$ Å.

2.31 Å is therefore divided into $r_{Na^+} = 0.95$ Å and $r_{F^-} =$ 1.36 Å.

Since the ionic radius is an empirical concept and since its value is only approximately constant (p. 39) these differences of a few 0.01 Å have no significance.

Table 3 gives the collected values of the ionic radii as deduced mainly by V. M. GOLDSCHMIDT from numerous X-ray crystal structure determinations and supplemented with numerous newer data (ZACHARIASEN, 1948; AHRENS, 1952). In this table the value 1.45 Å has been attributed to the $O^{2-}$ ion, instead of 1.35 Å as given by GOLDSCHMIDT. The values are valid for a coordination number 6 (p. 39).

TABLE 3

RADII OF IONS IN Å

| A. Ions with inert gas configuration* | | | | | | | | | | |
|---|---|---|---|---|---|---|---|---|---|---|
| | $H^-$ | He | $Li^+$ | $Be^{2+}$ | $B^{3+}$ | $C^{4+}$ | $N^{5+}$ | | | |
| | 1.54 | (1.29) | 0.68 | 0.30 | 0.2 | 0.15 | 0.1 | | | |
| $O^{2-}$ | $F^-$ | Ne | $Na^+$ | $Mg^{2+}$ | $Al^{3+}$ | $Si^{4+}$ | $P^{5+}$ | $S^{6+}$ | $Cl^{7+}$ | |
| 1.45 | 1.33 | (1.60) | 0.98 | 0.65 | 0.45 | 0.38 | 0.35 | 0.3 | 0.25 | |
| $S^{2-}$ | $Cl^-$ | A | $K^+$ | $Ca^{2+}$ | $Sc^{3+}$ | $Ti^{4+}$ | $V^{5+}$ | $Cr^{6+}$ | $Mn^{7+}$ | |
| 1.90 | 1.81 | (1.92) | 1.33 | 0.99 | 0.78 | 0.68 | 0.5 | 0.45 | 0.35 | |
| $Se^{2-}$ | $Br^-$ | Kr | $Rb^+$ | $Sr^{2+}$ | $Y^{3+}$ | $Zr^{4+}$ | $Nb^{5+}$ | $Mo^{6+}$ | Tc | |
| 2.02 | 1.96 | (1.98) | 1.48 | 1.10 | 0.90 | 0.77 | 0.67 | 0.59 | — | |
| $Te^{2-}$ | $I^-$ | X | $Cs^+$ | $Ba^{2+}$ | $La^{3+}$ | $Hf^{4+}$ | $Ta^{5+}$ | $W^{6+}$ | $Re^{7+}$ | $Os^{8+}$ |
| 2.22 | 2.19 | (2.18) | 1.67 | 1.29 | 1.04 | 0.77 | 0.67 | 0.59 | 0.50 | ~0.3 |
| | $At^-$ | Rn | $Fr^+$ | $Ra^{2+}$ | $Ac^{3+}$ | $Th^{4+}$ | $Pa^{5+}$ | $U^{6+}$ | | |
| | (2.27) | — | (1.75) | 1.37 | 1.11 | 0.99 | (0.90) | 0.83 | | |

* The radii of the atoms of the inert gases (in the condensed state) are not directly comparable with the radii of ions (in crystals) because of the much lower cohesion energy in the former case.

B. Ions with 18 electron configuration

| | | | | | | |
|---|---|---|---|---|---|---|
| $Cu^{+}$ 0.95 | $Zn^{2+}$ 0.70 | $Ga^{3+}$ 0.60 | $Ge^{4+}$ 0.54 | $As^{5+}$ 0.45 | $Se^{6+}$ 0.4 | |
| $Ag^{+}$ 1.26 | $Cd^{2+}$ 0.92 | $In^{3+}$ 0.81 | $Sn^{4+}$ 0.71 | $Sb^{5+}$ 0.55 | $Te^{6+}$ 0.5 | $I^{7+}$ 0.45 |
| $Au^{+}$ 1.37 | $Hg^{2+}$ 1.05 | $Tl^{3+}$ 0.91 | $Pb^{4+}$ 0.81 | $Bi^{5+}$ — | $Po^{6+}$ — | $At^{7+}$ — |

C. Ions of the Rare Earth elements

| | | | | | | | |
|---|---|---|---|---|---|---|---|
| $La^{3+}$ 1.04 | $Ce^{3+}$ 1.02 | $Pr^{3+}$ 1.00 | $Nd^{3+}$ 0.99 | $Pm^{3+}$ (0.98) | $Sm^{3+}$ 0.97 | $Eu^{3+}$ 0.97 | $Gd^{3+}$ 0.95 |
| $Tb^{3+}$ 0.94 | $Dy^{3+}$ 0.92 | $Ho^{3+}$ 0.91 | $Er^{3+}$ 0.90 | $Tm^{3+}$ 0.89 | $Yb^{3+}$ 0.87 | $Lu^{3+}$ 0.85 | |

D. Ions of the 5f series and others

| | | | | | | | |
|---|---|---|---|---|---|---|---|
| $Th^{4+}$ 0.95 | $Pa^{4+}$ (0.91) | $U^{4+}$ 0.89 | $Np^{4+}$ 0.88 | $Ce^{4+}$ 0.87 | $Pu^{4+}$ 0.86 | $Pr^{4+}$ 0.85 | $Am^{4+}$ 0.85 |

Trivalent ions 0.15 higher, $U^{3+} \approx La^{3+}$, $Ac^{3+}$: 1.11 Å.

E. Radii of some other ions

| | | | | | | | |
|---|---|---|---|---|---|---|---|
| $OH^{-}$ 1.45 | $CN^{-}$ 1.95 | $NH_4^{+}$ 1.45 | $OH_3^{+}$ 1.40 | $NO^{+}$ 1.40 | $Tl^{+}$ 1.51 | $Mn^{2+}$ 0.80 | $Fe^{2+}$ 0.75 |
| $Co^{2+}$ 0.72 | $Ni^{2+}$ 0.68 | $Pb^{2+}$ 1.17 | $Sm^{2+}$ 1.15 | $Eu^{2+}$ 1.14 | $Cu^{2+}$ 0.69 | $P^{3+}$ $\backsim$0.5 | $As^{3+}$ $\backsim$0.6 |
| $Sb^{3+}$ — | $Bi^{3+}$ 1.16 | $Cr^{3+}$ 0.55 | $Fe^{3+}$ 0.53 | $Se^{4+}$ 0.72 | $Te^{4+}$ 0.84 | | |

From this table one can, as it were, deduce the chemical behaviour of the ions since this behaviour depends in the first place on the ionic radius; the charge, as we shall see, is frequently of subordinate importance in this connection. Thus the small differences in properties between the Rare Earth elements can be attributed to the small differences in ionic radius within this group. In agreement with the value of the ionic radius, although the element yttrium (39) is not a Rare Earth element at all, nevertheless we always encounter it with the Rare Earths and especially the Yttria Earths, in particular the elements dysprosium, holmium and erbium; again $Th^{4+}$ always occurs with $Ce^{3+}$ in the Ceria Earths. Neptunium and plutonium are chemically practically identical with cerium (the second one also in the relative stability of the $3^+$ and $4^+$ valent state). Hafnium always occurs as a companion of zirconium and does not form any typical minerals of its own; this is also a consequence of the almost complete equality in ionic radius. Although hafnium occurs in the earth's crust as extensively as lead and more extensively than cobalt, tin, arsenic or silver, for example, it is nevertheless one of the most recently discovered elements. Although the total amount of germanium in the earth's crust is 150 times greater than that of gold, the former element was nevertheless only discovered quite late and is still very expensive. Because of the similarity in ionic radius germanium was separated from the magma together with silicon and so it occurs very widely distributed in small quantities in all silicates, in quartz, even in coal ash, but practically never in special minerals to any greater extent (Tarnung, camouflage, éléments dispersés). Gallium is also obtained with similar difficulty because it agrees in ionic radius with aluminium.

The radius and not the charge is of decisive significance in the isomorphous replaceability of corresponding elements in the composition of minerals, a very widely occurring phenomenon especially in the silicates. Thus the following replacements occur, for example:

$$Na^+ — Ca^{2+} — Y^{3+},\ Al^{3+} — Si^{4+},\ F^- — OH^- — O^{2-}.$$

Since the radius decreases with increasing charge along a horizontal row (the same electron configuration) and on the other hand increases downwards in a vertical row, we encounter ions with the same radius on the diagonals (GOLD-

SCHMIDT, *diagonal relationship*). The pairs of elements: beryllium and aluminium, lithium and magnesium, are examples of this relationship, the agreement in ionic radii shows itself in numerous properties such as solubility of the various salts, basicity of the hydroxides, etc..

In the group of the Rare Earth elements the ionic radius decreases steadily (Table 3C) with the same external electron configuration (Lanthanide contraction). This happens because the effective charge (p. 27) increases with increasing nuclear charge (= atomic number) through the incomplete screening by the 4f electrons; consequently the outermost shell is contracted. The same phenomenon also appears in the 5f series.

As a result of this lanthanide contraction the radius and therewith the properties of the next elements, hafnium, tantalum, and tungsten, are practically the same as those of the elements zirconium, niobium (columbium), and molybdenum, which are situated above them. The same phenomenon is shown in the similarity of the metals of the platinum group with those of the palladium group.

## § 5. CRYSTAL STRUCTURES

The crystal structure is also determined by the ratio of the ionic radii (GOLDSCHMIDT). In a crystal of the rock-salt type each positive ion is surrounded by six negative ions arranged in an octahedron (Fig. 3) and vice versa. The distance from centre to corner of the octahedron is $^1/_2\, a \sqrt{2}$ when $a$ is the side. In NaCl with a Na-Cl distance 2.81 Å, $a$ is thus equal to 3.98 Å, thus appreciably greater than the sum of the radii of two chlorine ions, so that the latter do not touch one another. If the positive ion now becomes steadily smaller, then the COULOMB attraction increases on account of the smaller lattice spacing. This attraction reaches a maximum when the negative ions just touch each other, that is to say, when:

$$(r_+ + r_-)/2\, r_- = \tfrac{1}{2}\sqrt{2} \text{ or } r_+/r_- = \sqrt{2} - 1 = 0.41.$$

If the positive ion becomes still smaller, *i.e.*, if the ratio $r_+/r_-$ falls below this value of 0.41, then the lattice spacing remains the same and the ion "rattles", as it were, in the octahedron. A structure in which it is surrounded by four negative ions in a tetrahedron soon becomes more advantageous (Fig. 4).

Thus MgTe with $r_+/r_- = 0.29$ and BeO (0.21) possess a tetrahedral arrangement (sphalerite or zinc blende structure), but CaTe (0.42), MgO (0.45) have a rock-salt structure with six surrounding ions. However, MgSe (0.32) has not the ZnS-structure but also the rock-salt structure! The critical value for the transition from six neighbours to eight neighbours (cesium chloride structure) is situated according to a similar geometrical argument at $r_+/r_- = \sqrt{3} - 1 = 0.73$. As we shall see, there are, however, other factors which also influence this crystal type (p. 38).

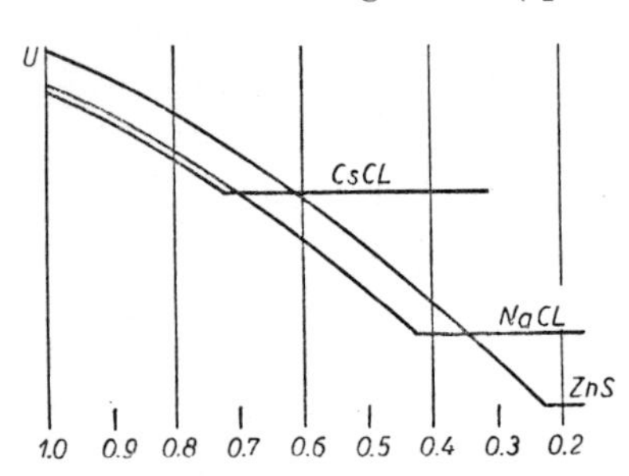


Fig. 4. Lattice energy $U$ as a function of the radii ratio $r_+/r_-$ ($r_-$ is constant).

The influence of $r_+/r_-$ on the structure type is also encountered in compounds $AB_2$.

If we consider the fluorides, for example, which form pure coordination lattices (p. 33), then the fluorides of the alkaline earth metals with the exception of magnesium and beryllium crystallize in the fluorite structure, in which the cation is surrounded by eight fluorine ions; for $CaF_2$ and $CdF_2$, which have the same structure, $r_+/r_-$ is 0.71 and 0.69, respectively, *i.e.*, just at the limit $\sqrt{3} - 1 = 0.73$. The fluorides of other divalent ions, such as Mn, Fe, Co and Ni and also Mg, crystallize in a structure with coordination number six (rutile type). It is only for $BeF_2$ that the ratio $r_+/r_- = 0.23$ lies below the limit of this coordination number and it has a structure similar to that of cristobalite ($SiO_2$) with four neighbours (see also p. 65).

*Layer structures*. In all these structures we encounter a fairly regular surrounding of a positive ion by negative ions and vice versa (coordination lattice). On the basis of COULOMB interaction we cannot indeed expect anything else.

A relative displacement of the centres of positive and negative charge in an atom or ion is produced in an electric field, that is to say the particle becomes polarized, *i.e.*, a dipole moment is induced. As a result, energy is set free by the interaction of this dipole with the inducing field (p. 73). A polarization energy will be produced in addition to the COULOMB attraction in the interaction of a divalent ion, such as $Mg^{2+}$, with $I^-$ ions which are readily polarizable (Table 9, p. 91). If the $I^-$ ion is surrounded evenly by positive ions as in structures of the NaCl, CsCl and $CaF_2$ types then this polarization would be very little in evidence; in fact the field strength would be zero at the position of the centre of the ion. However, the polarization is favoured by a structure where the negative ions are surrounded by positive ions only on the one side and on the other by other negative ions, even though the COULOMB repulsion does indeed act unfavourably. With readily polarizable ions on the one hand and strongly polarizing ions, *i.e.*, ions with high charge and small radius, on the other hand, an energetically favourable structure could nevertheless be produced (layer structure). In such a layer structure the succession of layers is therefore + — — + — — +. According to the type of packing of the larger negative ions present, hexagonal or cubic or more complicated types of closest packing (the $PbI_2$, $CdCl_2$ and $CdI_2$ types*) are produced. With very readily polarizable cations an "anti-layer" structure is also possible with successions of two positive layers, as in $Tl_2S$ (KETELAAR and GORTER, 1939). The particularly easy cleavage parallel to the sheets is characteristic for the layer structures.

* In the alternating structures, *e.g.*, $CdBr_2$ (BIJVOET and NIEUWENKAMP, 1933), $NiBr_2$, etc., intermediate types occur with irregular successions of individually always identical sandwiches — + —. These are not, however, equilibrium states at room temperatures; these are produced by powdering and by dehydration at low temperatures.

Undoubtedly the VAN DER WAALS-LONDON interaction (p. 360) also plays an important part in the production of layer structures.

*Molecular lattices.* When the coordination number is equal to the charge, the free molecule will exhibit the same structure as that expected for the solid substance. We are then dealing with a molecular lattice; we speak of a "shielded" (enveloped) compound. The electrostatic interaction between the neutral molecules, which can however still be composed of ions, is very small; the interaction energy in this case belongs to the VAN DER WAALS type.

*Atomic bonding in crystal lattices.* The crystal structure of the cubic modification of ZnS agrees completely with that of diamond if we disregard the difference between Zn and S atoms. Cuprous halides and AgI also crystallize in the same type (exception CuF). If we compare isoelectronic ion pairs, such as $Na^{+}$—$F^{-}$ with $Mg^{2+}$—$O^{2-}$, we see that the separation decreases rapidly (2.31 Å and 2.10 Å) for the same crystal structure (NaCl type). However, in the series AgI, CdTe, InSb and SnSn (grey tin) the crystal structure is also of the same type (ZnS-diamond type), but the separation does not decrease (2.80 Å, 2.77 Å, 2.79 Å and 2.80 Å). This indicates the increasing occurrence of atomic bonding in this series. This is also seen from the lattice energy (p. 43).

The crystal type, therefore, does not in itself give a sufficient indication regarding the type of bonding. For example NbC, TiC, etc. also crystallize in the NaCl type, and CuZn, AuZn, CuBe, etc., in the CsCl type (see also p. 360).

## § 6. LATTICE ENERGY

According to COULOMB's law the attraction energy per grammolecule for an ion pair or a molecule amounts to $M = -N\frac{e^2}{r}$, where $N$ is AVOGADRO's number, the number of molecules in a grammolecule, and $r$ the distance between the centres of the two ions with charges $+e$ and $-e$.

The COULOMB energy of a crystal lattice, that is to say the electrostatic energy which is set free on formation of the crystal from the free ions, is found by calculating the potential at the position of an ion in the lattice. If this potential is equal to $P_c$ and $P_a$ for the sites of cations and anions then the energy needed to remove two ions from these positions in the lattice is $-eP_c$ and $+eP_a$, respectively. Similarly the energy to break up the lattice completely is $-{}^1/_2\, Ne\,(P_c - P_a)$ per grammolecule, since the first amount is the mutual interaction of the ions with the rest of the ions, and this energy should not be counted twice.

In a simple lattice such as the rock-salt lattice, etc., $P_a$ is equal to $P_c$ (absolute value) since the positions of both kinds of ions are equivalent. In the calculation of the potential the summation must be made over the contributions of all the surrounding ions:

$$-P_a = P_c = -\frac{6e}{r} + \frac{12e}{r\sqrt{2}} - \frac{8e}{r\sqrt{3}} + \frac{6e}{2r} \ldots \text{ etc.}$$

in which $r$ is the shortest distance between anion and cation.

If we represent the result of this summation by $-A \cdot e/r$, then the lattice energy is:

$$U = -N \cdot \frac{Ae^2}{r}$$

MADELUNG has given a method for calculating the factor $A$, the MADELUNG factor. (For a simple method *cf.* EVJEN, 1932; HÖJENDAHL, 1938; PINSKER, 1943; EMERSLEBEN, 1952; BERTAUT, 1952; TEMPLETON, 1955). This $A$ depends only on the type of lattice and has the following values:

| | | |
|---|---|---|
| rock-salt lattice | 1.74756 | |
| cesium chloride lattice | 1.76267 | |
| zinc blende lattice | 1.63806 | |
| wurtzite lattice | 1.641 | |
| calcium fluoride lattice | 5.03878 | (the twofold charge of the cation has been taken into account) |
| rutile lattice | 4.816 | |

Besides this electrostatic attraction there is the repulsion which arises when the ions begin to touch each other. This repulsion originates in the general mutual repulsion of the electron clouds of atoms or ions, which always occurs when the clouds penetrate each other and the electrons do not form any atomic bond with a common electron pair (p. 155). The repulsion is difficult to calculate and so BORN represented the repulsion energy by $B/r^n$, a function which, provided $n$ is large, increases very rapidly with decreasing distance $r$, corresponding to almost hard spheres. $B$ in this expression is a still undetermined factor while the value of the exponent can be deduced from the compressibility; $n$ amounts to about 9.

The total lattice energy is therefore:

$$U = -N\frac{Ae^2}{r} + \frac{B}{r^n}. \qquad (1)$$

In the equilibrium state the energy must be a minimum; thus attractive and repulsive forces compensate one another. This condition furnishes:

$$\frac{dU}{dr} = 0 = N\frac{Ae^2}{r^2} - \frac{nB}{r^{n+1}}. \qquad (2)$$

After eliminating the unknown $B$ we have:

$$U = -N\frac{Ae^2}{r_0}\left(1 - \frac{1}{n}\right). \qquad (3)$$

($r_0$ = equilibrium distance)

As already stated above, the repulsion energy only amounts to about 10% of the attraction energy (Fig. 5).

The compressibility is, by definition

$$\beta = -\frac{1}{V}\left(\frac{\partial V}{\partial P}\right)_T, \quad V = \text{mole volume.}$$

The change of energy on compression, as a consequence of the work done, is

$$dU = -P\,dV$$

(heat effects are small) from which it follows:

$$\frac{d^2U}{dV^2} = -\frac{dP}{dV}$$

or with the first equation above:

$$\frac{d^2U}{dV^2} = - 1/\frac{dV}{dP} = 1/\beta V$$

From equation (1) we obtain:

$$\frac{d^2U}{dr^2} = - N\frac{2Ae^2}{r^3} + \frac{n(n+1)\,B}{r^{n+2}}$$

or after substitution of condition (2) for the equilibrium value of $r$:

$$\frac{d^2U}{dr^2} = + N\frac{Ae^2(n-1)}{r_0^3}$$

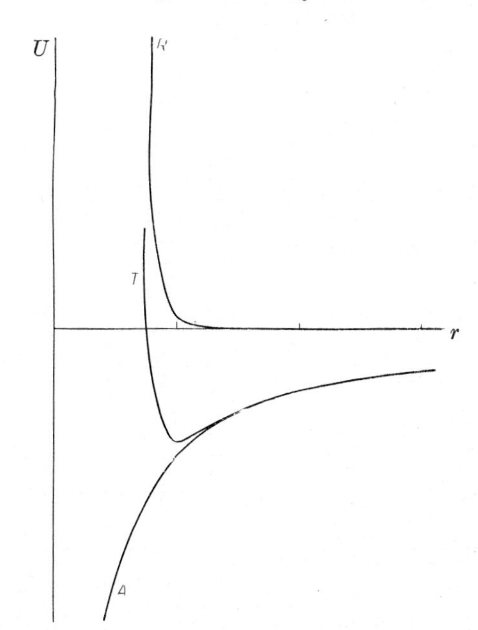


Fig. 5. The total lattice energy *(T)*, composed of the attraction energy *(A)* and the repulsion energy *(R)*.

The relation between the mole volume $V$ and the shortest distance between the ions $r_0$ can be simply represented by $V = CNr_0^3$. $C$ is a constant which depends only on the type of lattice and which includes the number of molecules $Z$ per elementary cell as well as the relation between the side $a$ of the elementary cell and the shortest distance $r_0$ between two ions. For the NaCl type $Z = 4$ and $r_0 = {}^1/_2\, a$ and then $C = 2$.

From the rules of differential calculus and remembering that $\frac{dU}{dr} = 0$, it follows that:

$$\frac{d^2U}{dr^2} = \frac{d^2U}{dV^2}\left(\frac{dV}{dr}\right)^2$$

and then we obtain after substitution and manipulation:

$$\frac{d^2U}{dr^2} = \frac{9NCr_o}{\beta} = +N\frac{Ae^2(n-1)}{r_o^3}$$

$$n - 1 = \frac{9Vr_o}{NAe^2\beta}$$

A value of about 9 for $n$ follows from the compressibility; it is somewhat better to take 5 for ions with the configuration of He; 7, Ne; 9, Ar; 10, Kr; 12, Xe.

BORN and MAYER (BORN and MAYER, 1932; MAYER and HELMHOLZ, 1932; MAYER, 1933) later also employed a formula $Be^{-kr}$ for the repulsion energy. The results, obtained with the two formulae, differ but little; both furnish a repulsive force which decreases rapidly with increasing distance. Similarly to the above calculation we have for this second case:

$$U = -N\frac{Ae^2}{r_o}\left(1 - \frac{1}{kr_o}\right) \text{ and } kr_o - 2 = \frac{9Vr_o}{NAe^2\beta} \text{ with } 1/k \approx 0.345$$

MAYER and HELMHOLZ also take into account the contribution of the VAN DER WAALS-LONDON forces to the lattice energy (p. 360 and Table 6).

This energy is proportional to $\alpha_1\alpha_2/r^6$, so that it is only important for the ions which immediately surround each other; the summation constant, analogous to the MADELUNG constant for the COULOMB energy, can in this case practically be equated to the coordination number. Furthermore, this VAN DER WAALS-LONDON energy is only important if both ions are readily polarizable. In that case, however, this contribution is larger for the CsCl type with eight nearest neighbours than for the NaCl lattice with coordination number 6. Thus the CsCl structure does not occur with KF, CsF, RbCl, etc. ($r^+/r^-$ : 1.00, 1.26 and 0.82) but does with CsCl, CsBr and CsI ($r^+/r^-$ : 0.92, 0.85 and 0.76). The geometrical condition is thus necessary but not sufficient: it is only with Cs that the polarizability is also large enough (Table 9). One can see the contribution of the VAN DER WAALS-LONDON energy quantitatively from Table 6; for the cesium halides it is only 8% (however, see also MAY, 1937). With AgI and with the cuprous halides, which all crystallize in the ZnS structure, the experimental lattice energy is, however, larger than that calculated from the contributions of COULOMB, VAN DER WAALS-LONDON and BORN interactions. This difference must be attributed to the contribution of atomic bonding (p. 34).

We can deduce from our formula for the lattice energy the dependence of the interionic distance on coordination number and charge: the deviations therefore from a constant ionic radius.

The constant $B$ from formula (1) consists, like the factor for the COULOMB energy, of a factor of proportionality $b$ for the repulsive energy of an ion pair: $b/r^n$. In the lattice a kind of MADELUNG factor $K$ also occurs. Since the repulsive energy decreases so rapidly with increasing distance this interaction is practically restricted to the nearest neighbours in the lattice, so that $K$ can, therefore, be put practically equal to the coordination number.

With the two types of lattice $a$ and $b$ with $K_a$ and $K_b$ as coordination numbers, $r_a$ and $r_b$ as ionic distances and equal $n$ we find by applying formula (2):

$$dU/dr = 0 = N\frac{Ae^2}{r^2} - \frac{n\,K\,b}{r^{n+1}}$$

to both cases:

$$[r_a/r_b]^{n-1} = K_a A_b / K_b A_a$$

For the CsCl and the NaCl type $A_a \approx A_b$, $K_a = 8$, $K_b = 6$, and it can be calculated for $n = 9$ that with eight nearest neighbours the ionic distance is 3.6 % greater; with 4 neighbours, ZnS type, the separation will be 4.3 % smaller than with six nearest neighbours (ZACHARIASEN, 1931). This had already been established empirically by GOLDSCHMIDT. Table 3 holds for a coordination number six. If we also apply this argument in the comparison of lattice ($r$) and molecule ($m$), then $K_r = 6$, $A_r = 1.75$ and $K_m = 1$, $A_m = 1$ and so we calculate with $n = 9$ that the distance K—Cl in the KCl molecule is 14.3 % smaller than that in the crystal (p. 94). Actually a reduction of about 14.9 % has been found by means of microwave spectra (HONIG *et al.*, 1954).

We can also express these results by saying that in the transition from molecule to crystal the ionic separations increase because the repulsive forces in the crystal are so much larger through the surrounding of the ions, against which the increase of the attractive COULOMB forces by 75 % offers an incomplete compensation.

The interionic distance is also influenced by the charge. The ionic radii in Table 3 hold for monovalent ions. A correction must be applied for a $z$-valent ion (ZACHARIASEN, 1931).

The lattice energy is therefore the energy which is set free when the crystal lattice is formed from free, gaseous, positive and negative ions.

A direct determination has been carried out in only a few cases, *e.g.*, the direct measurement of the equilibrium in the vapour: NaCl $\rightleftharpoons$ $Na^+$ and $Cl^-$, combined with data on the vapour pressure of solid sodium chloride (Table 4) (HELMHOLZ and MAYER, 1934). We can, however, test the result indirectly by means of a cyclic process due to BORN and HABER, as given below for sodium chloride.

$[Na]_{solid}$, $(^1/_2\,Cl_2)_{gas}$ —— $+S$ (heat of sublimation), $+\,^1/_2\,D$ (heat of dissociation) ——→ Na Cl

$[Na]_{solid}$, $(^1/_2\,Cl_2)_{gas}$ ↓ $-V$ (heat of formation) ↓ $[NaCl]_{crystal}$

Na ↓ $+I$ (ionization energy) ↓ $Na^+$

Cl ↓ $-E$ (electron affinity) ↓ $Cl^-$

$[NaCl]_{crystal}$ ←—— $-U$ (lattice energy) —— $Na^+$ $Cl^-$

TABLE 4

LATTICE ENERGY ALKALI HALIDES IN KCAL/MOLE AT 0° K*

| | $U_{theor.}$ | | $U_{exp.}$ | |
|---|---|---|---|---|
| | Eq. (3) | MAYER and HELMHOLZ, 1932 HUGGINS, 1937** | BORN-HABER cycle | Direct determination*** |
| LiF | 238.9 | 243.6 | 243.6 | |
| LiCl | 192.1 | 200.2 | 200.3 | |
| LiBr | 181.9 | 189.5 | 190.8 | 167.3 |
| LiI | 169.5 | 176.1 | 177.3 | |
| NaF | 213.8 | 215.4 | 216.9 | |
| NaCl | 179.2 | 183.5 | 185.3 | 180.7 |
| NaBr | 170.5 | 175.5 | 176.2 | 175.8 |
| NaI | 159.6 | 164.3 | 164.4 | 166.2 |
| KF | 189.2 | 192.5 | 192.8 | |
| KCl | 163.2 | 167.9 | 168.5 | |
| KBr | 156.6 | 161.3 | 161.2 | 159.4 |
| KI | 147.8 | 152.4 | 151.0 | 151.4 |
| RbF | 180.6 | 183.0 | 185.1 | |
| RbCl | 157.7 | 162.0 | 162.7 | |
| RbBr | 151.3 | 156.1 | 155.9 | 151.2 |
| RbI | 143.0 | 148.0 | 146.6 | 145.5 |
| CsF | 171.6 | 175.7 | 172.7 | |
| CsCl | 147.7 | 153.1 | 155.1 | |
| CsBr | 142.3 | 149.6 | 149.0 | |
| CsI | 134.9 | 142.5 | 140.4 | 141.5 |

* The lattice enthalpy at 298° K is only a few tenth kcal higher than the lattice energy at °K. (RABINOWITSCH and THILO, 1929; SHERMAN, 1932; ROSSINI *et al.*, 1952; PRITCHARD, 1953; MORRIS, 1956; MORRIS and AHRENS, 1956).
** With corrections for VAN DER WAALS-LONDON energy and zero-point energy.
*** HELMHOLZ and MAYER, 1934.

From the process on p. 39 it follows that (absolute values):

$$V = U - I - S + E - {}^1/_2\, D.$$

All the quantities in this equation are known and so the value of $U$ obtained in this way can be compared with that calculated from formula (3) above. A complete agreement is found for the group of the alkali halides, for example, within the limits of accuracy of the data employed (Table 4).

TABLE 5

ENERGY OF IONIZATION $I$, SUBLIMATION $S_0$, DISSOCIATION $^1/_2 D_0$ AND ELECTRON AFFINITY $E_0$ IN KCAL/MOLE AT 0° K

| 1+ | $I_1$ | $S_0$* | 2+ | $I_2$ | $S_0$ | 3+ | $I_3$ | $S_0$ |
|---|---|---|---|---|---|---|---|---|
| H | 313.3 | — | | | | | | |
| Li | 124.4 | 37.1 | Be | 634 | 78 | B | 1640 | ~90 |
| Na | 118.5 | 26.0 | Mg | 522 | 36 | Al | 1230 | 76 |
| K | 100.0 | 21.5 | Ca | 415 | 42 | Sc | 1020 | 93 |
| Rb | 96.1 | 20.5 | Sr | 385 | 39 | Y | 905 | ~103 |
| Cs | 89.7 | 18.8 | Ba | 350 | 42 | La | 830 | 99 |
| Cu | 178.0 | 82 | Zn | 631 | 31.2 | Ga | 1320 | ~55 |
| Ag | 174.7 | 69 | Cd | 597 | 26.8 | In | 1210 | 57 |
| Au | 212.8 | 91 | Hg | 674 | 14.5 | Tl | 1290 | 43 |
| Tl | 141.1 | 43 | Cu | 643 | 82 | | | |
| Ca | 140.8 | 42 | Ag | 668 | 69 | | | |

| | $E_0$ | $^1/_2 D_0$ (gas) | $^1/_2 D_{st}$** | $E_0 - {}^1/_2 D_{st}$ |
|---|---|---|---|---|
| H | 17.2 | 51.61 | 52.09 | —34.9 |
| F | 83 | 18.8 | 19.1 | 64 |
| Cl | 85.8 | 28.60 | 29.0 | 56.8 |
| Br | 80.5 | 22.72 | 26.7 | 53.8 |
| I | 74.2 | 17.77 | 25.5 | 48.7 |
| O | —170 | 58.6 | 59.2 | —229 |
| S | — 90 | 51 | 66 | —156 |

* The difference between the heat of vaporization at 0° K and at 298° K is very small.

** $\Delta H$ for the reaction $\frac{1}{2} X_2$ (standard state) → X(gas) at 298.1° K and 1 at (heat of atomization). $E_0 - \frac{1}{2} D_{st}$ is the electron affinity of the element.

A direct determination of the electron affinity of fluorine gave 82.2 kcal/mole (BERNSTEIN and METLAY, 1951).

The calculation for sodium chloride provides an example:

| | | |
|---|---|---|
| Heat of formation NaCl (298° K) | $V =$ 98.2 | kcal/mole |
| ionization energy Na atom | $I =$ 118.5 | ,, |
| heat of vaporization sodium (298° K) | $S =$ 26.0 | ,, |
| electron affinity chlorine | $E =$ 85.8 | ,, |
| heat of dissociation (atomization) Cl (298° K) | $\frac{1}{2}D =$ 29.0 | ,, |
| hence lattice enthalpy $H$ at 298° K | $H =$ 185.9 | ,, |
| and lattice energy $H_0 = U_0$ at 0° K | $U_0 =$ 185.3 | ,, |

[The quantity $I—E$ has equal values at 0° K and 298° K; thus we can use the spectroscopic values for 0°K.]

The above relation can also be of use for calculating the heat of formation in some instances. The latter does in fact determine the stability of the compound against dissociation into the elements. (Heats of formation, see LONG, 1953).

Thermodynamics shows that it is not the change in the energy $U$ but rather the change in the free energy $F = U — TS$, or in the thermodynamic potential or free enthalpy $G = U — TS + PV$, which determines the position of the equilibrium. In the temperature range with which we are concerned, $TS$ is, however, considerably smaller than $U$ (this holds all the more for $PV$) and in addition the change of entropy $S$ varies little for different compounds.

For NaCl at 298° K we have $\Delta TS = —6.45$ kcal $\Delta PV = —0.30$ kcal for formation from the elements so that the free enthalpy of formation $\Delta G = —91.78$ kcal/mole compared with the heat of formation $\Delta U = —97.93$ kcal and $\Delta H = \Delta U + \Delta PV = —98.23$ kcal.

The change of entropy is in the main caused by the loss of the entropy of the gaseous halogen:

$^1/_2\, S(Cl_2) = 26.64$ cal/deg at 298° K, $TS = 7.94$ kcal.

A calculation of the heat of formation of the completely hypothetical compound ArF, argon fluoride, furnishes $V = —140$ kcal/mole. On the grounds of such a strongly negative heat of formation this compound can be declared impossible. The reason for this lies in the high ionization energy of the argon atom with its inert gas configuration. A compound such as CaCl is also found to be unstable with respect to a dissociation into Ca and $CaCl_2$ (2 CaCl = Ca + $CaCl_2$ + 114 kcal) in spite of a positive heat of formation of 38 kcal/mole. The existence of CaF is probable, that of CaCl is certain (EHRLICH and GENTSCH, 1953, 1954; WEHNER, 1954).

If we compare the elements of the main series (A-subgroups) with those of the subseries (B-subgroups), we see that both the ionization energy and the heat of sublimation are appreciably higher for the latter elements (Table 5). Thus the heat of formation of the compounds of the subseries is lower and the stability is less than that of the compounds of the main series. Thus the silver halides, with the exception of the much more stable AgF (large electron affinity and small ionic radius of fluorine), are decomposed into their elements even by visible light, while this only occurs with the sodium compounds with short wave ultraviolet radiation. Although the ionic radius of $Ag^+$ is even somewhat greater than that of $Na^+$, the ionization energy $I_{Ag} = 174.7$ kcal is much larger than $I_{Na} = 118.7$ kcal. The heats of sublimation are 69 and 26.0 kcal, respectively. The polarizability (Table 9) of the ions of the B-subgroups and therewith the VAN DER WAALS-LONDON energy is also larger (p. 360).

TABLE 6

CONTRIBUTION OF THE VAN DER WAALS-LONDON ENERGY AND THE ATOMIC BONDING ENERGY TO THE LATTICE ENERGY IN KCAL/MOLE*

| Compound | Structure-type | COULOMB-attraction | LONDON-attraction | BORN-repulsion | Zero-point energy | $U_{calc}$ | $U_{exp}$ | $\Delta$ |
|---|---|---|---|---|---|---|---|---|
| AgF | NaCl | 235 | 23.7 | 38.2 | 1.4 | 219 | 218 | —1 |
| AgCl | NaCl | 209 | 29.2 | 34.5 | 1.3 | $202^5$ | $205^5$ | 3 |
| AgBr | NaCl | 202 | 27.4 | 31.9 | 0.9 | 197 | 202 | 5 |
| AgI | ZnS | 193 | 30.7 | 33.1 | 0.7 | 190 | 199 | 9 |
| TlCl | CsCl | 175 | 27.6 | 34.2 | 0.9 | $167^5$ | 170 | $2^5$ |
| TlBr | CsCl | 169 | 27.8 | 32.4 | 0.7 | 164 | $165^5$ | $1^5$ |
| TlI | CsCl | 161 | 30.3 | 31.0 | 0.6 | $159^5$ | 161 | $1^5$ |
| CuCl | ZnS | 232 | 15.2 | 29.8 | 1.2 | 216 | 222 | 6 |
| CuBr | ZnS | 221 | 15.2 | 27.3 | 0.9 | 208 | 216 | 8 |
| CuI | ZnS | 207 | 17.5 | 25.0 | 0.7 | 199 | $213^5$ | $14^5$ |

* MAYER *et al.*, 1933; ALTSHULLER, 1954; MORRIS and AHRENS, 1956.

As we saw, the expression for the heat of formation contains a large number of terms. VAN ARKEL and DE BOER could compose general stability rules by introducing some simplifying assumptions, which are difficult to justify. However, these rules have a practical value as they do seem to give a correct result when tested on a large amount of data. Actually the variation of all terms in the expression for $V$, except those for the lattice energy and the ionization energy, are left out of account in these rules, while the ionization energy is, far from correctly, put inversely proportional to the ionic radius: $I = \frac{z^+e^2}{r^+}$. In this way we obtain*:

$$V = N\frac{Az^+z^-e^2}{r^+ + r^-} - N\frac{z^+e^2}{r^+} + C$$

We see that with these assumptions the heat of formation increases with smaller radius (or higher charge) of the negative

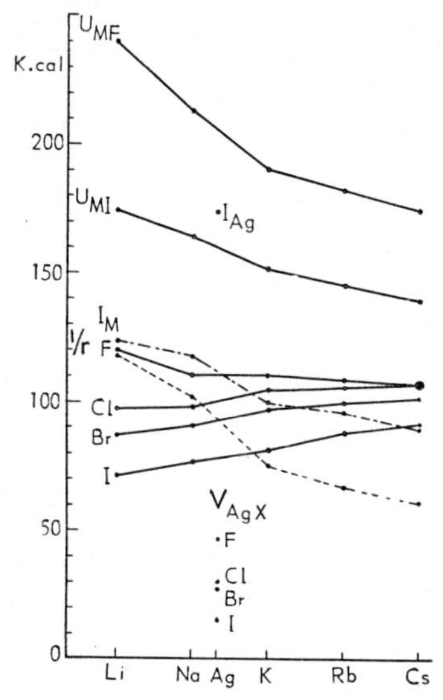


Fig. 6. Heat of formation and lattice energy of the alkali and silver halides (———) and • ; —·—·— = ionization energy, – – – – = 1/radius of positive ions.

ion and decreases with smaller radius (higher charge) of the positive ion, since in the variation of $r^+$ the variation in the ionization energy always predominates because $r^+ < r^-$.

From Fig. 6 it is seen that in the group of the alkali halides

* A more general expression for the lattice energy has been given (KAPUTINSKII, 1933, 1956; TEMPLETON, 1953) in which the MADELUNG constant $A$ is replaced by $\alpha \cdot \frac{\Sigma n}{2}$ with $\Sigma n$ equal to the number of ions per molecule and $\alpha$ a constant equal to about 1.48 – 1.76.

It has also been postulated that the second ionization potential of the alkali metals is proportional to $1/r^+$.

the heat of formation always increases from iodine to fluorine and also from lithium to cesium, this latter with the exception, however, of the fluorides. In this group of fluorides the sequence is just reversed; in this case, in view of the small radius of the negative fluorine ion, the decrease of the lattice energy predominates over that of the ionization energy, which decreases much more slowly than proportional to $1/r^+$.

However, the order of increasing stability with the oxides and sulphides of the alkaline earth metals is Ca > Be > Mg > Sr > Ba and Ca > Sr > Ba > Mg, respectively. These orders do not follow the rule mentioned above; however, it is true that the heat of formation of the oxide is always greater than that of the corresponding sulphide.

These stability rules, applied within restricted groups, do give an insight into many data. As examples we can mention the above-discussed stability of silver fluoride in comparison with the other silver halides, and further the small stability of the azides of the elements of higher valency. The great difference between the azides and oxides (compare also $Ag_2O$ and $Cu_2O$ with the alkali oxides) of the A- and B-subgroup elements is again produced by the difference in ionization energy, which, however, does *not* correspond to an equivalent difference in ionic radius.

The decrease of the stability from $CF_4$ to the very unstable $CI_4$ and the greater stability of the corresponding silicon tetrahalides are also examples in which the facts agree with the stability rules, although it is very doubtful whether the constitution of these compounds does belong predominantly to the ionic type of bonding. (In this connection see p. 149, etc.). There are therefore numerous examples which can be quoted, especially in the complex compounds (p. 58).

This principle is also of technical interest since it furnishes a clue to the experiments of VAN ARKEL and DE BOER on the preparation of pure metals, *e.g.*, titanium, zirconium, hafnium and thorium, by the thermal decomposition of halogen compounds, now employed for the production of these metals.

## § 7. DOUBLE DECOMPOSITIONS

The simplest example of the application of the ideas regarding stability and heat of formation as derived above is given by double decompositions between pairs of solid substances, especially if they are closely related compounds. For example, the following question: given the reaction equation

$$\mathrm{LiBr} + \mathrm{KF} \rightleftharpoons \mathrm{LiF} + \mathrm{KBr}$$

on which side does the equilibrium lie? This equilibrium can be attained experimentally either in contact with the aqueous solution or by fusion. It can never be established by the methods of analytical chemistry which pair of substances is present; this can, however, be carried out very simply by X-ray methods since the powder diagrams of the four substances are all different.

These equilibria are theoretically particularly simple, since the energy of the conversion depends only on the differences in the lattice energies; all other terms in the heat of formation have no influence since these are equal for the substances on the left hand side and on the right hand side of the equation. If in addition the crystal lattice is of the same type for all of them, in this case of the rock-salt type, then the MADELUNG constant is also the same and only the difference of the reciprocal ionic separations has any influence.

$$\Delta U = U(\mathrm{LiF} + \mathrm{KBr}) - U(\mathrm{LiBr} + \mathrm{KF}) = -NAe^2 \left[\frac{1}{r_{\mathrm{LiF}}} + \frac{1}{r_{\mathrm{KBr}}} - \frac{1}{r_{\mathrm{LiBr}}} - \frac{1}{r_{\mathrm{KF}}}\right]$$

The entropy influence may be completely neglected in this case (if no formation of mixed crystals occurs) and thus it is only a question of the sign of $\Delta U$. Negative will mean that the pair of substances on the right is stable, since energy is then set free when the reaction proceeds towards the right.

The interionic distances are equal to the sum of the individual ionic radii, thus $r_{\mathrm{LiF}} = r_{\mathrm{Li}} + r_{\mathrm{F}}$, etc., and the expression in brackets becomes:

$$\frac{1}{r_{Li} + r_F} + \frac{1}{r_K + r_{Br}} - \frac{1}{r_{Li} + r_{Br}} - \frac{1}{r_K + r_F}$$

This is positive, thus $\Delta U$ is negative.

Now it can easily be verified by taking some arbitrary numbers that for four numbers $a$, $b$, $c$ and $d$, combined two and two, $\frac{1}{a + c} + \frac{1}{b + d}$ is always greater than $\frac{1}{a + d} + \frac{1}{b + c}$ if $a < b$ and $c < d$. A general proof can readily be given.

The conclusion can, therefore, be summarized by saying that the pair of substances is always produced in which the two smallest (and hence also the two largest) ions have formed a compound with one another, in this case therefore LiF and KBr.

Within the framework of the alkali halides this rule is indeed found to be confirmed completely by experiment* (THOMAS and WOOD, 1934, 1935, 1936).

The course of many reactions, depending also on a double decomposition, can be regarded from the same point of view. In doing so it must also be borne in mind that the union of the most highly charged (and therefore also of the lowest charged) ions is energetically favourable [$e_1e_3 + e_2e_4 > e_1e_4 + e_2e_3$ if $e_1 < e_2$ and $e_3 < e_4$]. For the same reason the small ions will combine with the most highly charged ions of opposite charge. The influence of the charge generally predominates over that of the radius. In all these cases, however, the structure and hence also the MADELUNG constant is different so that the application of the above-mentioned rules can only have the significance of a global summary.

$2\,NaF + CaCl_2 \rightarrow 2\,NaCl + CaF_2$ radii: $F^- < Cl^-$, $Na^+ \approx Ca^{2+}$
$2\,AgCl + HgI_2 \rightarrow 2\,AgI + HgCl_2$ $Cl^- < I^-$, $Ag^+ \approx Hg^{2+}$
$Na_2S + CaCO_3 \rightarrow Na_2CO_3 + CaS$ $S^{2-} < CO_3^{2-}$, $Na^+ \approx Ca^{2+}$

(LEBLANC soda process).

* In a few cases mixed crystals are formed, *e.g.*, $RbCl + KBr \rightleftharpoons RbBr + KCl$ (WOOD and BREITHAUPT, 1952).

The extension to double decompositions in which other than solid substances take part, can at most be enlightening as a first qualitative orientation. Thus according to VAN ARKEL the following series can be regarded as an illustration of the influence of the competition between the two-fold charged metal ions on the one hand and the very "small" hydrogen ions on the other for the possession of the two-fold negative oxygen ion. The small beryllium ion wins, the larger calcium ion loses the struggle.

$BeCl_2 + H_2O \rightarrow BeO + 2\ HCl$ ($BeCl_2$ fumes in air)
$MgCl_2 + H_2O \rightleftharpoons MgO + 2\ HCl$ (a preparation of HCl)
$CaCl_2 + H_2O \leftarrow CaO + 2\ HCl$

The old "explanation" of the above reaction as depending on the small basicity of the beryllium (hydr)oxide is only a reference to another symptom of the same cause (p. 85), namely the small radius and hence the strong field of the small positive $Be^{2+}$ ion. At the same time we see here that the so-called rule, that a stronger acid (HCl) would displace a weaker acid from its salts, is incorrect. In fact, in its usual application to the reaction of sulphuric acid on common salt, for example, this rule should read: the less volatile acid displaces the more volatile acid.

It should be remembered that in heterogeneous systems reactions will occur which appear to conflict with the above-mentioned rules, but which are due to the slight solubility or greater volatility of one of the components. For example $KI + AgF \rightarrow KF + AgI\downarrow$, HF (anhydrous, less volatile, weak) + $NaCl \rightarrow NaF + HCl\uparrow$ (volatile, stronger).

On the other hand decompositions such as the displacement of a heavier halogen by a lighter one:

$$2\ KBr + Cl_2 \rightarrow 2\ KCl + Br_2$$

must be regarded as a consequence of the lower lattice energy of the chloride compared with that of the bromide, due to the smaller radius of the chlorine ion. The greater electronegativity of chlorine plays little part as this is compensated by the likewise greater dissociation energy: $E—^1/_2\ D$ is almost the same for all halogens.

The easy oxidizability of the iodides compared with the bromides and chlorides—while the reaction takes place in the opposite direction with the fluorides—is likewise a consequence of the increasing stability of the halides with smaller ionic radius.

Such qualitative comparisons regarding the chemical behaviour of corresponding compounds can fruitfully be derived from the theory in its present stage. In view of the numerous factors, often working in opposite directions, caution is still necessary in applying these ideas.

## § 8. COMPLEX COMPOUNDS

Besides a relatively small number of simple compounds, inorganic chemistry includes numerous complex compounds. By complex compounds we mean compounds in which groups of constituent atoms form more or less clearly bounded units, in the solid, liquid or dissolved state.

In contrast to this, no separate groupings can be distinguished in the double salts or mixed compounds generally. MOHR's salt can be mentioned as an example: $FeSO_4.(NH_4)_2\ SO_4.6\ H_2O$ or better $[Fe(H_2O)_6](NH_4)_2(SO_4)_2$ and alum $K_2SO_4.Al_2(SO_4)_3.24\ H_2O$ or $[Al(H_2O)_6]\ [K(H_2O)_6]\ (SO_4)_2$.

Here indeed the $SO_4$ group and the aquo complexes of the metallic ions are complex ions; there is, however, no complex formation of higher order.

Again in a lattice of the perovskite type, such as those of $KMgF_3$ and $CaTiO_3$, no complex groups can be distinguished. The $Mg^{2+}$ ion is indeed surrounded by 6 negative ions and $K^+$ is situated between 12 ions but these negative ions form one regular lattice, in which the positive ions are inserted into the holes. Thus the difference with the lattice of $CaF_2$ or NaCl is merely that in this case there are two kinds of positive ions. It was extremely improbable that $KIO_3$ should belong to this type. A new crystal structure determination showed that $KIO_3$ has a different structure with separate weakly pyramidal $IO_3$ ions (MACGILLAVRY and VAN PANTHALEON VAN ECK, 1943).

Lithium ferrite $LiFeO_2$ is also a typical mixed compound with a lattice the same as that of NaCl in which, in place of the sodium ions, the lithium and iron ions are distributed arbitrarily over the lattice points in question. A curious example of a mixed compound is CaHCl, a hydride chloride with the PbFCl crystal structure (EHRLICH *et al.*, 1956).

The ternary and higher compounds, such as $POCl_3$ etc., are also not complex compounds in the customary sense.

Uncharged complexes exist which are built up from neutral atoms and molecules (carbonyl and molecular compounds, p. 189 and p. 363), or rarely from ions (p. 185). However, the charged complexes are mainly of interest, that is, the complex ions formed from ions together with other ions, atoms or molecules. These complex ions are also described as charged molecules (SCHWARZENBACH), just as the simple ions are charged atoms. However, the corresponding uncharged "molecules" practically never exist, in fact it would be misleading to consider the $SO_3^{2-}$ ion, which is derived from $SO_2$ (with quadrivalent sulphur), as the ion of $SO_3$ (with hexavalent sulphur)*.

Previously a distinction was made between the ordinary salts, such as $Na_2SO_4$, etc., and the complex compounds such as $K_2SiF_6$. This was based on the assumption that the normal valencies should hold with the former compounds, *e.g.*,

```
          O
          ‖
Na—O—S=O
          |
          O
          |
          Na
```

(often incorrectly however, p. 168) with hexavalent sulphur in contrast to the $[SiF_6]^{2-}$-complex in which silicon was considered to carry only four bonds. This difference has now become meaningless since investigations of the crystal structure of the complex compounds have shown that in both compounds separate ions, $[SO_4]^{2-}$ and $[SiF_6]^{2-}$, respectively, occur in the crystals (and in solution) and that the four or six particles arranged around the central atom are bound equivalently. The difference between the principal valency or electro-

* In view also of the predominant construction from ions, complex compounds are seldom stable in the vapour state (p. 24).

Likewise the description of a complex ion as a union of simple ions with neutral molecules is only formally correct. The $SO_4^{2-}$ion does not consist essentially of a $SO_3$ molecule combined with an oxygen ion, as for example $[Ni(NH_3)_6]^{2+}$ consists of ammonia molecules around a double-charged nickel ion.

valency (four in silicon, two in nickel) and the coordinative valency according to WERNER (six in both cases) has, according to our modern ideas, *no* relation to a difference in the *mode* of bonding. It is nothing but a number which, in the case of the principal valency, gives the charge of an ion and thus the number of monovalent ions with which a neutral molecule is formed, or the number of electron pair bonds in a molecule. Thus this principal valency gives the composition of binary compounds. The second, the coordination number, gives simply the number of particles, ions or molecules which are coordinated around the central ion.

A distinction should, however, be made between the charge and the valency in a narrower sense, which is the number of electron pair bonds. The nitrogen atom with a single positive charge is quadrivalent; when neutral it is trivalent. Nitrogen can never be quinquevalent, but can in principle occur as an ion $N^{5+}$ (p. 163); SCHWARZENBACH and others here, however, speak of "Bindigkeit" while "Wertigkeit" with them corresponds to the charge (see also SEEL, 1954).

The term subsidiary valency forces is also used to indicate the interaction through VAN DER WAALS forces, including the hydrogen bond formation (p. 403) in contrast to the stronger atomic and ionic bonding forces. Thus one says that the bonding in one molecule of a polymer is due to principal valency forces; the mutual attraction between the molecules is attributed to the so-called subsidiary valency forces.

Complex compounds can in the first place be divided into three groups:

*a. Complex salts* which are built up of complex ions and as such belong to the typical ionic compounds. This does not, however, prevent the bonds between the particles which compose the complex ion from being electron pair bonds in very many cases. The further classification of the complex ions is as follows:

1. Ion-ion complexes (§ 9, 10). The complex is produced from ions; however, both an ionic bonding as in $[SiF_6]^{2-}$ and an atomic bonding as in $[Fe(CN)_6]^{4-}$ is possible.

2. Ion-dipole complexes (§ 11), from an ion combined with dipole molecules such as water and ammonia. We meet in this case also both the electrostatic bonding, as in the hydrates

$[Mg(H_2O)_6]^{2+}$, and the electron pair bond in the ammoniates, for example, that of trivalent cobalt $[Co(NH_3)_6]^{3+}$.

3. Ion-non-polar molecule (§ 11). The polyhalides such as $KI_3$ belong to this group, at least formally. The bonding can here also be based on electrostatic polarization and on atomic bonding.

*b. Atomic* (*or element*) *complexes* are the complex compounds which, at least formally, can be regarded as consisting of an atom around which molecules are coordinated. In this case it is principally atomic bonds which produce the coherence (p. 177) and in addition VAN DER WAALS forces (p. 360).

*c. Molecular compounds* are complexes of molecules. To these belong both the molecular compounds formed by VAN DER WAALS forces, which readily dissociate (p. 363), but also the very stable aggregates which "unsaturated" molecules can form with suitable partners (§ 25 and p. 369) and also the remarkable "clathrates" (p. 364).

In this chapter we shall discuss the complex salts in so far as these are built up mainly from ions; the other groups follow in Chapter III and V.

## § 9. ION-ION COMPLEXES

One molecule of silicon fluoride reacts readily with two molecules of potassium fluoride to form a compound $2KF.SiF_4$. WERNER has shown for this and innumerable other cases that the formula $K_2[SiF_6]$ is in better agreement with the chemical properties. In fact the normal reactions of the fluorine ion are absent and the unit $[SiF_6]$ is preserved in conversions; the ion gives rise to its own characteristic reactions. Investigation of the crystal structure with X-rays confirmed WERNER's ideas; it was found that the six fluorine atoms were arranged in an octahedron, thus in an equivalent manner, around the silicon atom in the lattice of $K_2[SiF_6]$. For the rest the lattice construction is just the same as that of simple compounds such as $K_2O$ and also fluorite, $CaF_2$; in this case the negative and positive ions are interchanged (antifluorite structure).

Kossel in his fundamental publications on ionic bonding has already answered the question how the formation of complex ions must be explained.

For this purpose let us calculate with Coulomb's law the electrostatic energy which is set free when a varying number of negative ions is added to a four-fold positively charged sphere of the same size with radius $r$. As a result of the mutual repulsion of these latter ions they will arrange themselves in a regular manner such that this repulsion becomes a minimum. Thus a tetrahedral arrangement will have preference over a square.

The following may serve as an example: in surrounding the positive sphere by three monovalent negative ions in an equilateral triangle an attractive energy $-3 \cdot \frac{4e^2}{2r}$ is obtained together with a repulsive energy $+\frac{3e^2}{2r\sqrt{3}}$ since the side of this triangle amounts to $2r\sqrt{3}$.

We see (Table 7) that the quantity of energy liberated is a maximum for six negative ions. Should we wish, therefore, to add a further one or two to this number, then energy would no

TABLE 7

COMPLEX ENERGY OF 4-VALENT ION

| Number | Monovalent ions | Divalent ions |
|---|---|---|
| 1 | —2.00 $e^2/r$ | —4.00 $e^2/r$ |
| 2 | —3.75 | —7.00 |
| 3 | —5.13 | —8.54 |
| 4 | —6.16 | —8.66 |
| 5 | —6.76 | —7.06 |
| 6 | —7.00 | —4.00 |
| 7 | —6.55 | +1.68 |
| 8 | —6.15 | +6.42 |

longer be gained by doing so, rather the contrary. Thus six can be regarded as the maximum coordination number for monovalent ions around a quadrivalent ion. It is clear that this coordination number will be lower for divalent negative ions, as a result of the stronger mutual repulsion; compare $BF_4^-$, $SiF_6^{2-}$ and $PF_6^-$ with $BO_3^{3-}$, $SiO_4^{4-}$ and $PO_4^{3-}$. Thus the following maximum coordination numbers are produced:

MAXIMUM COORDINATION NUMBERS

| Charge on central ion | 1 | 2 | 3 | 4 | 5 | 6 | 7 | 8 |
|---|---|---|---|---|---|---|---|---|
| Monovalent ions | 2 | 4 | 5 | 6 | 8 | 8 | 8 | 12 |
| Divalent ions | 1 | 2 | 3 | 4 | 4 | 5 | 5 | 6 |

The numbers are to be considered as maxima for a regular arrangement, and are valid in so far as spatial factors do not play a role, thus for a large central ion. Indeed the negative ions will touch each other when their number is increased up to a given number. With a further increase of their number the central ion could no longer be in contact with all the negative ions. The attractive energy is influenced by this; moreover the central ion, "rattling" in the cage of negative ions*, would be drawn to one side and consequently the excess of coordinated ions would readily escape. These geometrical factors can be calculated simply from the ratio of the radii which just permits contact between all the ions; (equilateral triangle $(r^+ + r^-)/2r^- = {}^1/_3\sqrt{3}$, $r^+/r^- = {}^2/_3\sqrt{3} - 1 = 0.15$, see also p. 32).

CRITICAL RATIO OF RADII

| Max. coordination number | 2 | 3 | 4 | 6 | 8 | 12 |
|---|---|---|---|---|---|---|
| $r^+/r^-$ | — | 0.15 | 0.22 | 0.41 | 0.73<br>0.64* | 1.00<br>0.90* |

* For an antiprism and an icosahedron respectively (MARTIN, RUNDLE and GOLDEN, 1956).

* This "rattling" seems to be essential for the existence of strong ferro-electric properties at lower temperatures of *e.g.*, barium titanate and $KH_2PO_4$.

The coordination numbers 5 and 7 do not occur here since it can be shown that, when there is a place for five or seven ions, there can also be six or eight around the central ion. This is the reason why these coordination numbers occur extremely rarely (examples: $Na_2FeF_5$, $K_2TaF_7$).

The small chance of a coordination number 5 is strikingly illustrated by the crystal structures of the phosphorus pentahalides. $PBr_5$ appears to be $[PBr_4]Br$ while $PCl_5$ possesses a lattice consisting of the ions $[PCl_4]^+$ and $[PCl_6]^-$ (POWELL and CLARK, 1940, CLARK, POWELL and WELLS, 1942, VAN DRIEL and MACGILLAVRY, 1943). The difference between these two compounds is a consequence of the larger radius of the bromine ion whereby the coordination number six is not possible in the case of $PBr_5$. This also illustrates the occurrence of ions in the solid state with molecules which are formed predominantly by atomic bonds in the gaseous state.

The compound $AsF_3Cl_2$ is $(AsCl_4)^+$ $(AsF_6)^-$ (KOLDITZ, 1955, 1956).

Again a compound $CoCl_2.3$ CsCl is not a complex compound $Cs_3[CoCl_5]$ with coordination number five but on the basis of its crystal structure it is a double salt: $Cs_2[CoCl_4].CsCl$.

The structure of $Tl_2AlF_5$ does not contain $[AlF_5]^{2-}$ groups but there are octahedral groups each with two fluorine ions which belong in common to two groups. $TlAlF_4$ also has a coordination of six fluorine ions around the aluminium ion (p. 71). A coordination number five thus does not occur with certainty, except in free molecules, such as $PCl_5$, $PF_5$, $PF_3Cl_2$. These molecules have the form of a three-sided double pyramid, but the bonding in this case is due to atomic bonds.

The coordination number seven is encountered in $IF_7$ with a five-sided bipyramid and in a group of complex fluorides which includes the following compounds $K_3ZrF_7$, $K_3UO_2F_5$, $K_3TaOF_6$, $K_3WO_2F_5$, $K_3UF_7$, and also $[NH_4]_3$ $[TiO_2F_5]$ (isomorphous replacement of oxygen and fluorine; the last mentioned compound is a peroxide compound of quadrivalent titanium, which appears to be isomorphous with the previous ones). The structure of these compounds is very similar (ZACHARIASEN, 1954) to that with lower symmetry of $K_2NbF_7$ and $K_2TaF_7$; $[NbF_7]^{2-}$ groups are found with seven fluorine ions at approximately equal distances from the $Nb^{5+}$ ion (HOARD, 1939).

The coordination number eight, although geometrically more probable than seven, is still rarer because the total repulsive energy really becomes very large. Octacyanides of molybdenum and tungsten are known: among others $K_4[Mo^{IV}(CN)_8]$, $K_4[W^{IV}(CN)_8]$ and $[K_3W^{V}(CN)_8]$. Here there is, however, certainly no ionic bonding as appears from the diamagnetism of the first two compounds. The shape of the complex ion also points in this direction, namely not a cube or antiprism (cube with upper and lower surface rotated 45°) but a dodecahedron bounded by triangles with the Mo—CN bonds directed towards the eight corners. Five corners form approximately a plane pentagon with further one corner above and two below this plane (HOARD and NORDSIECK, 1939.).

The compound $SbF_5.BrF_3$ is not $SbBrF_8$ but must be formulated as $(BrF_2)^+$ $(SbF_6)^-$ (WOOLF and EMELÉUS, 1949).

It is improbable that a compound $K_3H[PbF_8]$ is correctly formulated in this way; probably there are HF groups in it and the coordination number is lower. The coordination number eight is, however, certain for the volatile $OsF_8$ (b.p. 47·3°) which compound at the same time clearly justifies the place of the platinum metals in the 8th column.

It is this spatial factor which further restricts the coordination number so that the coordination number practically never amounts to more than six for monovalent negative ions. For divalent ions a coordination number greater than four is already improbable on the basis of the above energy calculation. VAN ARKEL and DE BOER quote orthotelluric acid $H_6TeO_6$ and orthoperiodic acid $H_5IO_6$ as examples. One can more correctly speak, however, of a partial coordination of monovalent hydroxyl ions. Under normal circumstances only acid salts such as $Na_4H_2TeO_6$ and $Na_2H_3IO_6$ are formed. $Na_6TeO_6$ is only produced from $Na_2TeO_4$ with $2Na_2O$, and $Na_5IO_6$ can be obtained in the same way. Numerous other compounds with high coordination numbers, for example orthonitrate $Na_3NO_4$, orthoborate $Na_3BO_3$, etc., can be made by this method of preparation (ZINTL and MORAWIETZ, 1938). Since no determinations of structure are known it is not certain if these coordination numbers are really correct. That compounds of orthotelluric acid and orthoperiodic acid such as $Cu_3^{II}TeO_6$, $Zn_3TeO_6$, $Ba_5(IO_6)_2$, $Ag_5IO_6$ can be obtained readily and not those of the alkali metals, argues against the simple formulation of these compounds as salts of orthoacids. The orthoester $Te(OCH_3)_6$ does indeed exist but in this case there is naturally no longer any question of ionic bonding.

In various cases not all coordinated ions are the same, but fluorine and oxygen ions occur side by side, as in the series of isomorphous compounds: $K_3ZrF_7$, $K_3TaOF_6$, $K_3WO_2F_5$, or nitrogen with oxygen in the osmiamates: $K\left[Os\begin{matrix}O_3\\N\end{matrix}\right]$, sulphur with oxygen in the thioarsenates: $Na_3(AsO_4)$, $Na_3(AsO_3S)$, $Na_3(AsO_2S_2)$, $Na_3(AsOS_3)$, $Na_3(AsS_4)$.

A remarkable example, which shows how greatly one can be mistaken in the constitution, is given by the well-known reagent for sodium ions, potassium dihydropyrantimonate $K_2H_2Sb_2O_7 . 5H_2O$. According to an X-ray investigation (BEINTEMA, 1935, 1936) this substance is in fact $K[Sb(OH)_6]$, potassium hexahydroxyantimonate.

Summarizing we can state that the coordination number with respect to oxygen is as a rule 3 for the elements of the first row of the Periodic System, and 4 for the other elements. For monovalent ions these numbers are 4 and 6, respectively.

Lower coordination numbers occur with ions with a small

charge such as: $K[HF_2]$, $K[Ag(CN)_2]$. We shall return to the first example in more detail in the discussion of the formation of the hydrogen bond (p. 418). The $[Ag(CN)_2]^-$ ion is quite certainly not an ionogenic complex.

Low coordination numbers also occur with ions of high valency such as the uranyl ion $[UO_2]^{2+}$ and the corresponding neptunyl and plutonyl ions; here there is also no question of an ionic bond either.

Now it is easy to deduce stability rules starting from the electrostatic picture (VAN ARKEL and DE BOER):

1. The stability of the complex increases with increasing charge and decreasing radius of the central ion.

2. The stability increases with increasing charge (only at lower coordination numbers, see Table 7) and decreasing radius of the coordinated ions.

Thus the stability increases in the series:
$[MgF_6]^{4-}$, $[AlF_6]^{3-}$, $[SiF_6]^{2-}$, $[PF_6]^-$, $SF_6$. The first one does not exist, the last one is an extremely stable, almost inert gas (enveloped or shielded compound, p. 95).

The stability decreases in the series:
$[PO_4]^{3-}$, $[AsO_4]^{3-}$, $[SbO_4]^{3-}$, but the $[NO_4]^{3-}$ occurring in the orthonitrate formed from $Na_2O$ and $NaNO_3$ is hardly stable since the radius of the quinquevalent positive nitrogen ion is too small for a four coordinated arrangement composed of ions.

The influence of the radius of the coordinated ion is seen from the slight stability of the complexes of the other halogens compared with those of fluorine, and of those of sulphur compared with those of oxygen.

The influence of the non-complex ion on the stability has not yet been discussed. In the reaction $2KF + SiF_4 \rightarrow K_2SiF_6$ the energy effect $\Delta U$ is not only determined by the energy of attachment of the fluorine ions to the central ion but also by the lattice energy of the KF. In fact $\Delta U = -2U_{KF} + U_{K_2SiF_6} + W_{SiF}$, in which $U$ represents the respective lattice energies and $W$ the heat of formation of the complex from the free ions. One can also say: the tetrafluoride molecule, as it were, pushes itself in between the potassium and fluorine ions. The influence of the radius of the non-complex ion $K^+$ will be much greater in the first term than in the second; in fact, the formula for lattice energy contains the term $r^+ + r^-$ in the denominator, and the radius of the negative complex ion $[SiF_6]^{2-}$ is always very much greater than that of the negative ion to be coordinated, $F^-$. One can therefore say:

3. The stability increases with decreasing charge and increasing radius of the non-complex ion.

Many examples for this rule can be given, not only for ion-ion complexes but equally for those belonging to the categories yet to be discussed for which the rule holds just as well. In those cases also it is energetically more favourable if the simple compound possesses a small lattice energy (absolute value!).

The rule holds for the decomposition of the sulphates; the sulphates of the trivalent elements aluminium and iron decompose relatively easily; those of the alkaline earth metals decompose appreciably on heating to redness (thus $CaSO_4$ decomposes quantitatively on ignition in the blowpipe flame, barium sulphate only a little); the alkali sulphates are stable. The free acids are much less stable than most of the salts, which is understandable when we regard the hydrogen ion as an extremely small positive ion.

The compounds with non-complex ions of the Subseries (B-subgroups) are less stable than those of the Main Series (A-subgroups). This is not a consequence of the higher ionization energy, as in the case of the decomposition of the simple compounds into the elements, but rather of the higher lattice energy. In the first place these ions have a relatively small radius ($r_{Ag} \approx r_{Na}$) and in addition there is an extra contribution to the lattice energy of the simple compound by LONDON interaction (p. 43) as a result of the large polarizability of these ions.

The contribution of the LONDON energy to the lattice energy is small for the complex ions formed by fluorine and oxygen as a result of the small polarizability.

TABLE 8

DECOMPOSITION TEMPERATURE AND HEAT OF FORMATION OF A NUMBER OF CARBONATES

| Main series | | | Subseries etc. | | |
|---|---|---|---|---|---|
| | Heat of formation from oxide | Decomposition temperature | | Heat of formation from oxide | Decomposition temperature |
| $Li_2CO_3$ | 54.1 kcal | 1270° | $CuCO_3$ | 11.0 kcal | 200° |
| $Na_2CO_3$ | 76.8 | very high | $Ag_2CO_3$ | 19.6 | 218° |
| $K_2CO_3$ | 93.5 | ,, | | | |
| $Rb_2CO_3$ | 96.6 | ,, | | | |
| $Cs_2CO_3$ | 97.4 | ,, | | | |
| $BeCO_3$ | — | 100° | $ZnCO_3$ | 17.0 | 296° |
| $MgCO_3$ | 28.1 | 540° | $MnCO_3$ | 27.8 | 327° |
| $CaCO_3$ | 42.5 | 897° | $FeCO_3$ | 21.0 | 405° |
| $SrCO_3$ | 56.0 | 1189° | | | |
| $BaCO_3$ | 63.8 | 1360° | $PbCO_3$ | 20.9 | 347° |

The complex ions, in which the central ion does not have the inert gas configuration, are very numerous; these are formed especially with readily polarizable ions, such as Cl, (Br, I), CN, CNS and S. In these cases both the polarization and the VAN DER WAALS-LONDON energy can contribute to the heat of formation of the complex. The following are examples: $K_4CdCl_6$, $K_2[Hg(CN)_4]$, $K_3[Ag(SCN)_4]$, $KFeS_2$, etc.

It is, in particular, the ions of the series Ti-Zn, Zr-Cd, Hf-Hg and the ions of the 5f-series which form complexes, the elements of the eighth group being specially prominent. Of no single element are more complexes known than of trivalent cobalt. These central ions form atomic bonds by electron pairs (p. 177) with most ions except fluorine and with most molecules, especially ammonia and other nitrogen derivatives, but much less with water. They are discussed in the next chapter.

Are there also complex ions known in which a negative ion functions as the central ion?

One could regard the ions $NH_4^+$, $PH_4^+$, $OH_3^+$ and $FH_2^+$ as such. The stability decreases in the order given with increasing radius and decreasing charge of the negative central ion. However, the tetrahedral structure as well as the small difference in electronegativity (p. 148), are against an ionogenic constitution of the ammonium ion. For a readily polarizable $N^{3-}$ ion a pyramidal structure would be energetically more favourable in connection with the polarization. The hydrogen nucleus is in fact found wholly within the electron cloud. Atomic bonds are certainly present in the alkyl ammonium ions. However, the ionic bond will certainly be predominant for the fluoronium ion $FH_2^+$ (p. 86), in agreement with the bonding in HF.

The influence of the non-complex ion is demonstrated by the fact that *e.g.*, $PH_4I$ is fairly stable but that $PH_4F$ does not exist. Apparently the stability increases with increasing strength of the acid and with increasing proton affinity or basicity of the hydride. This is not the influence of the radius, as can be seen from the slight stability of $NH_4CN$ compared with $NH_4Br$, although the $CN^-$ion agrees in size with the $Br^-$ ion but HCN is a very much weaker acid than HBr.

When the nitrogen or oxygen atom is bound to the strongly electronegative fluorine atoms as in $NF_3$ or $OF_2$, it has become positive and it still possesses only such a small proton affinity that these molecules no longer form complexes. $OF_2$ is an oxygen fluoride and not a fluorine oxide, if we indicate the anion, the acid residue, by the second part of the name.

Little is (yet) known about other complexes composed of positive ions around a negative ion. Perhaps basic beryllium acetate, $OBe_4(CH_3COO)_6$, is an example in which the oxygen atom is surrounded by the four beryllium atoms which form the corners of a tetrahedron, while the carboxyl groups are situated parallel to the edges in such a way that each beryllium atom is also surrounded by a tetrahedron of oxygen atoms belonging to the acetate groups. Also, 2 $HgCl_2$. HgO is really $[(ClHg)_3O]Cl$ (GRDENIC and SCAVNICAR, 1953, 1955). The formulation $[IAg_3](NO_3)_2$ and $[SAg_3](NO_3)$ might perhaps be correct for these double compounds of $AgNO_3$ (LIESER, 1957).

## § 10. SILICATES AND OTHER POLYNUCLEAR COMPLEXES

The chemical formula give the correct coordination number only when sufficient partners are available for each central ion to realize the maximum coordination. In other cases the coordinated ions will belong to more than one central ion.

In this way polynuclear complexes are produced and, depending on whether the nuclei of the complex anions belong to one or more than one kind of atom, the isopolyacids (iso complexes) and the heteropolyacids (hetero complexes) are formed. One can formulate these compounds also formally as consisting of one molecule of a basic oxide with more than one molecule of acid-forming oxide or with molecules of various oxides. These polynuclear complexes occur as tetrahedra, octahedra or triangles, where one or more atoms at the corners belong conjointly to two groups. In the particularly numerous complexes constructed from oxygen tetrahedra it is clear that, owing to the electrostatic repulsion of the highly charged central ions, corners will be shared but not edges or faces and that one corner will not be shared by more than two groups (PAULING's rules). In $SiS_2$ where the bonds will be ionogenic to a lesser degree, the $SiS_4$ tetrahedra do have common edges. With octahedral groups there is a greater possibility of the sharing of edges because the distance between the central ions does not diminish so greatly then.

When we also take account of the cations which do not belong to the complex ion, we can formulate the following rule:

When as many lines of force start from each cation as correspond to its charge and they are uniformly distributed over the anions around each cation, then a divalent oxygen ion receives two of them and a monovalent anion such as fluorine or hydroxyl receives one. In formula: $z_a = \sum_i \frac{{}_iz_c}{{}_iC_c}$ in which $z_a$ and ${}_iz_c$ are the charges on the anion and cation, respectively, and ${}_iC_c$ is the coordination number of the cation $i$ in question with summation over all the surrounding cations (PAULING,

BRAGG). These rules have proved to be of great value in setting up plausible models for the crystal structures of many complex compounds, in particular of silicates (MACHATSCHKI, BRAGG).

*Silicates.* The most extensive group of polynuclear iso-complexes is the silicates. The structural unit here is always the oxygen tetrahedron around the silicon ion at the centre.* On the basis of what has been said above we can give the formulae of a number of silicates in a simple manner.

However, some complications occur in the application to natural minerals owing to multiple mixed crystal formation. Thus, in particular, a part of the $Si^{4+}$ in the oxygen tetrahedra is often replaced at random by $Al^{3+}$ but there is also aluminium present which does not belong to the tetrahedra of the skeleton. Furthermore, a part of the oxygen ions is sometimes present as $OH^-$, sometimes isomorphously replaced by $F^-$, which has the same size. The $OH^-$ and $F^-$ never form part of the skeleton of oxygen tetrahedra; in fact this would be in contradiction with the above formula for $z_a$, which can only be one in this case. The $OH^-$ions were often incorrectly reckoned as water of crystallization in older chemical analyses and in empirical formulae based on these. The earlier division into metasilicates, orthosilicates, etc, is worthless. Examples: talc was previously classified as a "metasilicate" with the formula $H_2Mg_3(SiO_3)_4$, nevertheless it belongs to the sheet-like lattices (group C) and the formula is $(OH)_2Mg_3(Si_2O_5)_2$; similarly a felspar, leucite, is not $KAl(SiO_3)_2$ but $K(AlSi_2O_6)$ (group D). Also muscovite, a mica, should not be formulated as $H_2KAl_3(SiO_4)_3$, thus as an orthosilicate, but as $(OH)_2KAl_2(AlSi_3O_{10})$ (C).

*a. Spatially restricted groups (Fig. 7)*

1. Separate $SiO_4$ groups $A_4SiO_4$ (orthosilicate, such as olivine $Mg_2SiO_4$, willimite $Zn_2SiO_4$). According to the above-men-

* It has been concluded from X-ray investigation (see p. 26) that the bonding is half ionogenic at least.

tioned rules an oxygen ion will have to belong to one tetrahedron around $Si^{4+}$ with $z_c = 4$, $C_c = 4$ and to the octahedral coordination spheres of three $Mg^{2+}$ions with $C_c = 6$ and $z_c = 2$, so that $z_a = 2$; this is indeed the case with olivine.

2. Combinations of two tetrahedra: $A_6Si_2O_7$, for example, thorveitite $Sc_2[Si_2O_7]$.

3. Ring-shaped complexes from 3, 4 or 6 tetrahedra, thus with formulae $[Si_3O_9]^{6-}$, $[Si_4O_{12}]^{8-}$ and $[Si_6O_{18}]^{12-}$. Since the stoichiometric composition is always $[SiO_3]^{2-}$ in these cases, these silicates were, together with the infinite chain complexes, all classified without distinction among the so-called metasilicates. Examples of the above-mentioned three structures are: wollastonite $Ca_3[Si_3O_9]$, neptunite $Na_2TiFe^{II}[Si_4O_{12}]$ and beryl $Be_3Al_2[Si_6O_{18}]$. The large rings in the last-mentioned crystal lend an open character to the structure so that helium occurs enclosed in beryl.

*b. 1-dimensional infinite groups (chains) (Fig. 7)*

By the formation of an infinite series of tetrahedra connected by common corners, silicates of the (stoichiometric) composition $A_2SiO_3$ are produced. Examples of these structures are to be found in the fibrous silicates, such as diopside, $CaMg(SiO_3)_2$ By the coupling of two parallel chains through common corners into a band, the composition $A_6(Si_4O_{11})$ is produced in the amphiboles, such as tremolite $Ca_2Mg_5(Si_4O_{11})_2(OH, F)_2$, and in chrysotile $Mg_6(Si_4O_{11})$ $(OH)_6 . H_2O$; both minerals are known as asbestos. However, many more types of chains are known (BELOV, 1956).

*c. 2-dimensional infinite groups (sheets) (Fig. 7)*

By repeatedly connecting one tetrahedron to three others, by means of common corners, infinitely extended sheets are produced in two dimensions. One can also think of these as produced by the further extension of the above-mentioned bands. The composition of these complexes is $[Si_2O_5]^{2-}$.

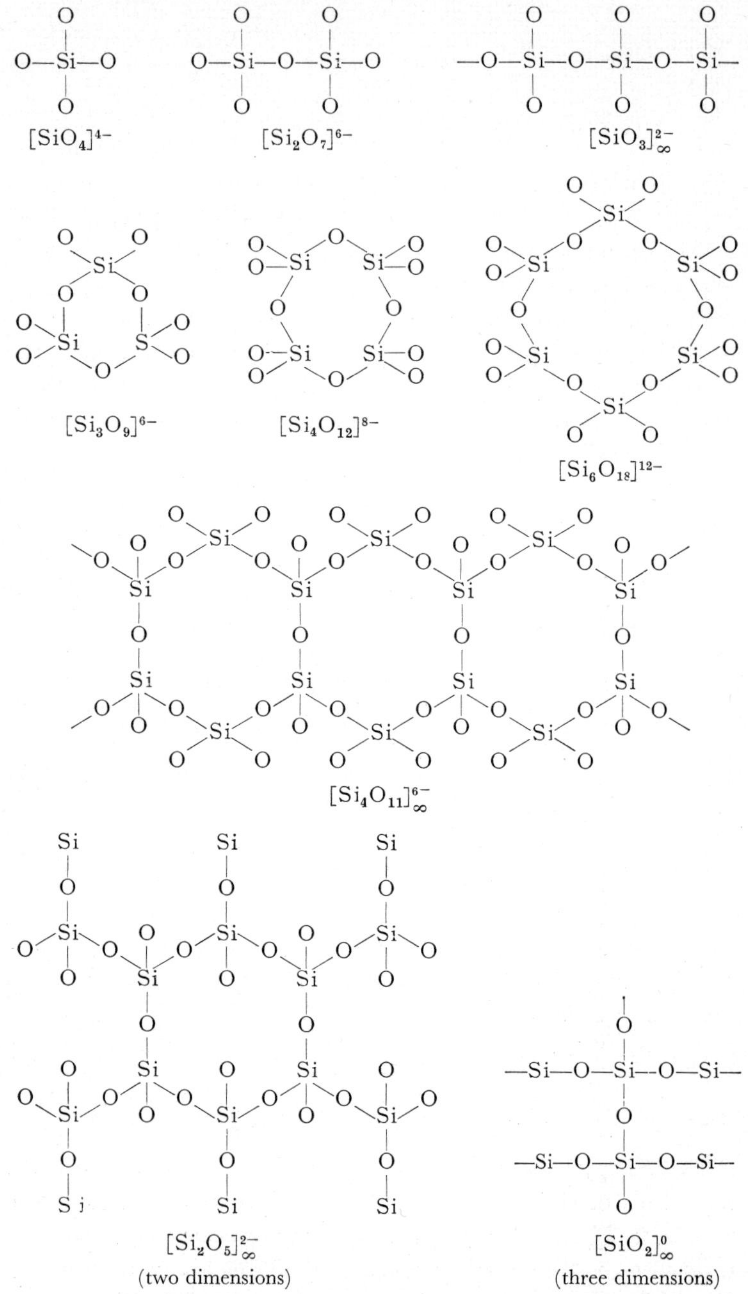

$[SiO_4]^{4-}$

$[Si_2O_7]^{6-}$

$[SiO_3]^{2-}_{\infty}$

$[Si_3O_9]^{6-}$

$[Si_4O_{12}]^{8-}$

$[Si_6O_{18}]^{12-}$

$[Si_4O_{11}]^{6-}_{\infty}$

$[Si_2O_5]^{2-}_{\infty}$
(two dimensions)

$[SiO_2]^{0}_{\infty}$
(three dimensions)

The "free" oxygen atom of each tetrahedron is always directed towards one side of the plane in $[Si_2O_5]$ and $[Si_4O_{11}]$.

Fig. 7. Main types of the complex ions of the silicates.

It is clear that different variations on this theme are possible; thus the free corners of the tetrahedra can all point in the same direction or alternately in opposite directions. The hexagons present in this case also provide, as in beryl, a place for other particles. In addition there are also many variations in the mode of piling of the sheets above each other.

Numerous extremely important minerals, such as the micas, muscovite $(OH)_2KAl_2(AlSi_3O_{10})$ and pyrophylite $(OH)_2Al_2(Si_2O_5)_2$ belong to this group, furthermore talc $Mg_3(Si_4O_{10})(OH)_2$ and especially the so-called clay minerals which mainly form the submicroscopic fraction of the clays and of agricultural soils in general. Besides kaolinite (in kaolin or pipe clay) $Al_2O_3.2SiO_2.\ 2H_2O$ or $Al_2(OH)_4(Si_2O_5)$, montmorillonite $Al(OH)[Si_2O_5].\ nH_2O$ (gross $Al_2O_3.4SiO_2.nH_2O$) is of great agricultural interest; it occurs in fuller's earth and in practically pure form under the name of bentonite. In the soil it is especially the montmorillonite which, besides its water-binding power, determines the fertility by the possibility of base exchange, in particular $K^+ \leftrightharpoons Na^+, Ca^{2+}$, because potassium is thereby fixed in a form available to the plant. We shall not go into details here (see Literature p. 106).

*d. 3-dimensional infinite groups (lattices)*

When a tetrahedron is joined to another at each corner, a three-dimensional network of the composition $SiO_2$ is produced. This is no longer a complex ion, but silicon dioxide. In fact the numerous modifications of $SiO_2$: quartz ($\alpha$ and $\beta$), cristobalite ($\alpha$ and $\beta$) and tridymite ($\alpha$, $\beta$ and $\gamma$) are constructed on this principle. Since now, however, as was mentioned, $Si^{4+}$ is frequently partially replaced by $Al^{3+}$, there are also silicates which belong to this group. These silicates include the leucite already mentioned, the felspars, and in particular the isomorphous series of the plagioclases between albite $Na[AlSi_3O_8]$ and anorthite $Ca[Al_2Si_2O_8]$. Orthoclase is $K[AlSi_3O_8]$ with a closely related structure.

Large spaces are present in the open structure of the felspars in which the alkali ions occur, but there are no continuous canals as in another group of silicates, the zeolites, *e.g.*, natrolite $Na_2[Al_2Si_3O_{10}]2H_2O$. These canals contain water, but zeolites can also absorb numerous gases and vapours with small molecules, such as Ar, $O_2$, $N_2$, $CH_4$, $C_2H_4$, $CO_2$, $NH_3$, methyl and ethyl alcohol and acetic acid, but not, for example, acetone, butyl alcohol and benzene.

Natural and artificial permutites, such as analcime $Na[AlSi_2O_6]H_2O$, belong also to the zeolites in which base exchange occurs, for example $Ca^{2+}$ for $Na^+$ (water softening). The organic permutites, so important nowadays in ion exchange, have the open structure in common with these silicates.

Several species of synthetic zeolites have also been prepared, *e.g.*, $Na_{12}(Al_{12}Si_{12}O_{48}).27H_2O$, in which the oxygen tetrahedra form 8- and 6-membered rings enclosing cavities of 11.4 Å and 6.6 Å diameter. These compounds can act as "molecular sieves" for sharply separating small and large molecules and can be used for this purpose in technical applications also (BARRER, 1949; BRECK *et al.*, 1956; REED and BRECK, 1956).

*e. Glass*

The substances, which can be brought into the state of a glass, can be divided into two groups; the high melting inorganic glasses, composed of oxides mainly, and the low melting organic glasses (p. 421). The inorganic glasses are built up from a three-dimensional irregular network of polyhedra, which are connected by common corners; this is also true for the silicates, the glass-formers par excellence (WARREN, 1940). ZACHARIASEN has now drawn up the conditions which a simple substance must satisfy in order to form a glass. Since the glass structure extends in three dimensions, each of the polyhedra must share at least three corners with others; thus the coordination number must be at least 3. However, a high coordination number (6, 8 or higher) is incompatible with the glassy state, because then the high symmetry facilitates regular arrangement, that is to say, crystallization becomes too easy; thus there remain only triangles and tetrahedra with the coordination numbers 3 and 4. GOLDSCHMIDT had already established empirically that $r^+/r^-$ must lie between 0.2 and 0.4 (p. 32). The coordinated ion must be able to occur as a common corner. With central ions of higher valency this will be the case for oxygen $z_a = 2$ (see p. 61) but not for fluorine, chlorine or $OH^-$.

Of the oxides we have thus only to consider: $MO_2$ and $M_2O_5$ with tetrahedra and $M_2O_3$ with triangles. Thus the following are known in the glassy state: $SiO_2$, $GeO_2$, $P_2O_5$, ($V_2O_5$ with some $P_2O_5$), $As_2O_5$, $B_2O_3$, and $As_2O_3$. Among the fluorides only $BeF_2$ has been obtained as a glass; here we have as an exception the coordination number 4 for fluorine, while the low charge of the $Be^{2+}$ has the consequence that in this case PAULING's condition is just satisfied, *i.e.*, $z_a = 1$ for a $F^-$ ion that belongs to two tetrahedra.

When we add basic oxides, such as $Na_2O$, $K_2O$ or CaO, to $SiO_2$ or quartz glass, where all corners belong in common to two tetrahedra, then the ratio O: Si increases and thus there are now also "free" oxygen corners. The metal ions with a high coordination number find a place in ample cavities as in the felspar structures. Aluminium, which exhibits a coordination number 6 in the oxide, is to be found in the oxygen tetrahedra in glasses, in the same way as in the crystalline silicates. The $B^{3+}$ in the borosilicate glasses has also a coordination number 4; addition of $B_2O_3$ thus decreases the number of "free" oxygen ions and increases that of the "bridge" oxygen ions. In accord with this, properties of borosilicate glasses such as *pyrex* begin to agree with those of quartz glass (*e.g.*, the small coefficient of expansion). It has been found that the ratio of free to bridge oxygen ions determines essentially the properties of a glass (STEVELS, 1948, 1954, MOREY, 1954; HUGGINS, 1955). This ratio can be found from the empirical composition by calculating the ratio of oxygen ions to glass-forming ions.

The network-forming ions, apart from $Si^{4+}$ and $B^{3+}$, are $P^{5+}$, $As^{3+}$, $Ge^{4+}$, $Sb^{3+}$ and usually also $Al^{3+}$, $Ti^{4+}$ and $Sn^{4+}$. Apart from the alkali and alkaline earth oxides, PbO must be mentioned among the basic oxides, which modify the network because it greatly increases the refractive index (high polarizability) of the glass (crystal glass). Ions such as $Fe^{2+}$, $Co^{2+}$ and $Ni^{2+}$ can appear both inside and outside the network, which makes a difference in the coloration of the glass.

In a few inorganic glasses the bonding is partially of a different kind; the coherence of the metaphosphoric acid mentioned below is jointly produced by the formation of hydrogen bonds (p. 403) at a few places between the chains and rings formed by tetrahedra. In glassy selenium there are also chains (p. 340) which are held together by VAN DER WAALS-LONDON forces; this low melting glass ($\sim$ 75°) is associated with the organic glasses, in particular with the high molecular substances.

### *f. Other isopoly complexes*

Although the silicates in particular were discussed in the above paragraph, we meet a corresponding, almost equally great, multiplicity with a number of other elements which can have a coordination number four with oxygen.

It is obvious that the germanates would be very similar to the silicates. This also holds for the phosphates and for the arsenates. Indeed we also encounter (Fig. 8):

$[PO_4]^{3-}$-groups: orthophosphates.

$[P_2O_7]^{4-}$-groups, consisting of two tetrahedra with common corner: pyrophosphates, *e.g.*, $Mg_2P_2O_7$, isomorphous with thorveitite $Sc_2Si_2O_7$.

$[P_3O_{10}]^{5-}$ a chain of three tetrahedra, $Na_5$ $P_3O_{11}$, sodium tripolyphosphate.

$[PO_3]_n^{n-}$-groups, the metaphosphates,
in which ring-shaped complex anions, such as are found in $(NH_4)_4(PO_3)_4$ ammonium tetrametaphosphate (ROMERS, KE-

TELAAR and MACGILLAVRY, 1951), and very long chains, as in glassy metaphosphoric acid, do occur.

A classification of the numerous phosphates which are known already must await the determination of the crystal structures (CALLIS *et al.*, 1954; TOPLEY, 1949). The so-called sodium hexameta phosphate or calgon is not $Na_6(PO_3)_6$ but it has much larger open chains.

Tetrahedra, which have three corners in common, thus with the composition $(P_2O_5)_n$, are represented in the three different modifications of phosphorus pentoxide itself (MACGILLAVRY *et al.*, 1941, 1949).

In the gaseous state, which is the same for all three, there are $P_4O_{10}$ molecules formed of three tetrahedra which form a ring by means of common corners, as in the silicates, while the upper oxygen atoms of these three tetrahedra form a face of the fourth tetrahedron. A compact molecule is produced in this way, in which the phosphorus atoms also lie at the corners of a large tetrahedron ($As_4O_6$ and $P_4O_6$ have a similar structure but then without the "free" oxygen atom of each tetrahedron). The volatile modification ($S_1$) of $P_2O_5$ (triple point 423° C and 380 cm Hg) possesses a molecular lattice constructed of these molecules. This modification is unstable and at higher temperatures the conversion into the stable, very slightly volatile modification ($S_2$, triple point 580° C and 55.5 cm Hg) takes place slowly at 250°, very rapidly at 500°. The structure of this modification is also built up from tetrahedra but now in the form of a three-dimensional network as in the modifications of quartz. The melt of this modification readily gives a glass on cooling. $S_2$ can be considered as a polymer of $S_1$; this modification is very much less hygroscopic than $S_1$; crystals can stay several weeks in water, as a result of which they swell slowly. The "free" oxygen atoms which are responsible for the hygroscopicity are completely built-in in the structure of $S_2$. In the third modification $S_3$, sheets are present, somewhat similar to those in the sheet-like silicates constructed of rings of six tetrahedra.

Just as the three-dimensional type of structure of $SiO_2$ occurs in the felspars as a consequence of isomorphous substitution, phosphates such as $AlPO_4$ and $BPO_4$, in which Al and B both have a coordination number four, also have structures which correspond to those of the $SiO_2$ modifications, quartz and cristobalite, respectively.

If we proceed to the sixth column of the Periodic System, for example, to the elements sulphur, chromium, etc., we also meet polynuclear complexes, built up of tetrahedra, but, since the grouping $[XO_3]$ is neutral, only in the form of restricted groups, *e.g.*, of two tetrahedra, $A_2[S_2O_7]$ pyrosulphates, $A_2[Cr_2O_7]$ dichromates. Trichromates $A_2[Cr_3O_{10}]$ and tetrachromates $A_2[Cr_4O_{13}]$ are, however, also known. Although the structure is not known there are certainly short chains of three and four tetrahedra, respectively.

The structure is known of $N_2O_5.3SO_3$ or $2(NO_2)^+(S_3O_{10})^{2-}$ (ERIKS and MACGILLAVRY, 1954).

Similarly, numerous complex salts are derived from tungsten such as the para- and meta-tungstates, the structures of which are, however, not yet completely elucidated. They are associated with the heteropolyacids, for example, $(NH_4)_6[Mo(MoO_4)_6].4H_2O$, ammonium paramolybdate.

No polynuclear complex ions of the perchlorates $A[ClO_4]$ are conceivable; in fact two tetrahedra, $Cl_2O_7$, form the uncharged oxide.

So far we have spoken of polynuclear (iso) complexes built up from tetrahedra; a similar pattern leads to the formation of complex borates, since the $[BO_3]^{3-}$ group in the shape of an equilateral triangle can also have corners in common with other triangles. Orthoborates, *e.g.*, $ScBO_3$ and $InBO_3$, are isomorphous with $CaCO_3$ and $NaNO_3$ and have separate $BO_3^{3-}$ ions. Metaborates are examples with chains of boron-oxygen triangles each joined through two common corners, as in $Ca(BO_2)_2$. There are also metaborates, in which three triangles form a ring: $K_3(B_3O_6)$. Boron can, however, also possess the coordination number 4, for example in danburite $CaB_2Si_2O_8$, and in $BPO_4$, which has a structure similar to that of cristobalite ($SiO_2$). Complexes which show both four and three nearest neighbours are also known. $B_2O_3$ forms the compound in which all three corners are shared.

*Octahedron complexes.* In the polynuclear complexes built up from octahedra, as already stated, the sharing of edges and even of faces occurs. Since a coordination number six for oxygen is rarely attained, like in compounds *e.g.*, $Ca_3UO_6$, $Ca_3WO_6$ (STEWARD, RUNCIMAN, 1953), these polynuclear octahedron complexes are mainly formed by halogen ions (see also p. 71). There are many octahedron complexes with individual groups such as in the $K_2PtCl_6$ structure, (*e.g.*, $K_2SnCl_6$, $K_2ReF_6$, $Cs_2GeF_6$, $K_2OsBr_6$, $(NH_4)_2PbCl_6$, etc.; the structure of the compounds $A_3BX_6$ also agrees with this: $(NH_4)_3FeF_6$,

$(NH_4)_3AlF_6$ and $(NH_4)_3[MoO_3F_3]$) and further in the cryolite structure, $Na_3AlF_6$.

In addition we have various types of polynuclear complexes. The structure of $Tl_2AlF_5$ exhibits an infinite chain of octahedra, each with two opposite common corners. With four common corners sheets are produced; $TlAlF_4$ is an example of this. There are other possibilities with the complex aluminium fluorides; thus sheets are formed in $Na_5Al_3F_{14}$ with octahedra in which one third have four corners in common while the remainder have only two (BROSSET, 1937, 1938).

In $Cs_3Tl_2Cl_9$, $K_3W_2Cl_9$ and $Cs_2Cr_2Cl_9$ (WESSEL and YDO, 1957) there are groups formed from two octahedra with a common face. Chains formed by octahedra with common edges, thus with composition $BX_4$, are to be found in $K_2[HgCl_4].H_2O$ and $K_2[SnCl_4].H_2O$.

In the structure of tungsten trioxide, $WO_3$, all corners of the octahedra belong to two groups.

*Heteropolyacids* similarly form a group of compounds in which it has only been possible to give the correct stoichiometric composition after the structural principles had become better known by X-ray analysis. The best-known heteropolyacid is phosphomolybdic acid; in fact the test for phosphate ions with ammonium molybdate leads to the formation of the well-known, slightly soluble ammonium phosphomolybdate discovered by BERZELIUS (gross composition after drying: $(NH_4)_3PO_4.12MoO_3$).

The heteropolyacids are formed especially from molybdic and tungstic acid with boron, silicon and phosphorus. The structure consists of $MoO_6$ or $WO_6$ octahedra; 12 of these groups are so arranged around the central ion that this is surrounded tetrahedrally by four oxygen ions. The octahedra have edges and perhaps faces in common with others. In such a way the composition of the precipitate mentioned becomes $(NH_4)_3[P(Mo_3O_{10})_4]$; similarly, we have $[P(W_3O_{10})_4]^{3-}$, or better still $[P(W_{12}O_{40})]^{3-}$ since no quite separate $W_3O_{10}$ groups can be detected. One corner of each octahedron is free, four belong to two and one to three octahedra, so that therefore the ratio O : W = 10/3 : 1. In addition the heteropolyacids and their salts contain a great number of water molecules. In the free acids a part of them is certainly present as hydronium ions $OH_3^+$, for example, borotungstic acid $[OH_3]_5[B(W_3O_{10}]_4].26H_2O$, which is isomorphous with the ammonium salt of corresponding composition $(NH_4)_5[B(W_3O_{10})_4].26H_2O$.

For many compounds the structure is by no means unambiguously established.

## § 11. ION-MOLECULE COMPLEXES

*a. Ion-dipole complexes*

To this group belong the numerous hydrates and ammoniates (ammines) as well as the ion compounds which contain alcohol or ether of crystallization, amines, etc.

The energy of a particle with a (favourably directed) permanent dipole moment $\mu$ in a field, due to an ion with charge $e$ at a distance $r$, is: $U = -e\mu/r^2$ or $-\mu F$, where $F$ is the field strength at the position of the dipole.

In a particle with a polarizability $\alpha$ a dipole moment of size $\mu_i = \alpha F$ is, by definition, induced in a field of strength $F$. (The induced moment is always directed parallel to the inducing field.) The interaction energy here is proportional to $-\mu_i F = -\alpha F^2 = -\alpha e^2/r^4$.

The calculation of the first-mentioned energy of a permanent dipole in a field is simple.

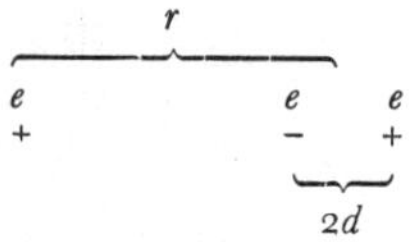

$$\mu \equiv e \cdot 2d$$

$$U = -\frac{e^2}{r-d} + \frac{e^2}{r+d} = -\frac{e^2}{r}\left(\frac{1}{1-d/r} - \frac{1}{1+d/r}\right)$$

or if $d \ll r$

$$U = -\frac{e^2}{r} \cdot \frac{2d}{r} = -\frac{e\mu}{r^2} \qquad (1)$$

In the calculation of the energy of a polarizable particle in a field we must also take into account the fact that energy is required to create the induced dipole in which positive and negative charges are separated by a certain distance. We must bear in mind that, for a dipole, the change of energy $dU$ due to a small change in the field strength $F$ by an amount $dF$ is equal to $\mu dF$. The moment of the dipole may, neglecting terms which are of a higher order of smallness, be considered constant and equal to $\alpha F$: then $dU = -\mu_i iF = \alpha F dF$. The total energy including the creation energy is found by letting the field strength increase from zero to the correct value $F$ and thus we have by integration:

$$U = -\alpha \int_0^F F dF = -\tfrac{1}{2}\,\alpha\, F^2 = -\tfrac{1}{2}\,\frac{\alpha e^2}{r^4} \qquad (2)$$

It can be readily confirmed that the expressions (1) and (2) for $U$ do indeed possess the dimensions of an (electrical) energy, that is, $e^2/L$, charge²/length, when it is remembered that the dimensions of $\mu$ and $\alpha$ are $e.L$ (charge $\times$ length) and $L^3$, (length³), respectively.

Both kinds of interaction energy will always occur between an ion and a particle with a permanent dipole moment, and both contribute to the formation of the complex.

The stability will again increase with increasing charge and decreasing radius of the ion. A large moment or a large polarizability will favour the stability, provided the shortest distance $r$ remains small or at any rate the dipole is situated eccentrically.

*Hydrates* (WELLS, 1954). For the sake of illustration it may be mentioned that about all lithium salts give stable hydrates at room temperature. There are also numerous cases in which the sodium salt gives hydrates or is hygroscopic, in contrast with the corresponding potassium compounds, *e.g.*, sulphate, nitrate.

The ions of higher valency usually bind a large number of water molecules. The mutual electrostatic repulsion of the coordinated neutral water *molecules* is much smaller than that of fluorine or oxygen *ions*, which are of the same size. Thus one finds octammine $[Ba(NH_3)_8]Cl_2$ and ennea-aquo complexes $[La(H_2O)_9](BrO_3)_3$ and even $[Th(H_2O)_{12}](NO_3)_4$. The structure of the hydrate $Na_2S.9H_2O$ corresponds almost to that of a cubic modification of ice. It is therefore really ice in which two $Na^+$ ions, one $HS^-$-ion and one $OH^-$-ion are situated in the cavities in the network formed by eight molecules of water (MACHATSCHKI, 1954). Ice also takes up 10% $NH_4F$ which has the same ratio of protons to negative ions as water (BRILL and ZAROMB, 1954; ZAROMB, 1956).

The influence of the non-complex negative ion on the stability is also manifested in the anhydrous crystallization, for example, of the alkaline earth fluorides in contrast to the other halides. On the other hand sodium perchlorate is $NaClO_4.H_2O$, while the sulphate with the double-charged anion contains $10H_2O$ (Glauber's salt). Here other factors play a part, since the perchlorate in question is hygroscopic and is also very readily soluble.

Similarly most of the hexammine nickel complexes $[Ni(NH_3)_6]X_2$ are very stable, but the fluoride decomposes immediately when one attempts to prepare it from the chloride by double decomposition with AgF.

The question of the hydration of ions in solution (p. 100) is essentially the same as the question of the formation of complex hydrates in the solid state.

*Ammoniates (ammines)*. While ammonia possesses a smaller dipole moment (1.44 D) than water (1.84 D) the polarizability is higher ($\alpha$ is 2.26 and $1.48 \cdot 10^{-24}$ $cm^3$, respectively). Since the bonding energy by polarization (2) is proportional to the square of the field strength, and not directly proportional to the field strength, as in the interaction (1) with a permanent dipole, ammonia will be more strongly bound than water by ions with high field strength, that is, with high charge and small radius (VAN ARKEL and DE BOER). It is a well-known fact that calcium chloride binds ammonia almost as strongly as water vapour (also alcohol). Ammoniates which are stable in aqueous solution, that is to say where ammonia can displace the water around the ion, are not found among the highly charged ions of the Main Series (A-subgroups). However, many ammoniates of the ions of the Subseries (B-subgroups) are known in aqueous solution, *e.g.*, the well-known blue-coloured copper ammonia complexes. Here the influence of the LONDON interaction between two readily polarizable particles stands out; on the other hand these ions also form electron-pair bonds very readily. Thus $[Co(NH_3)_4](NO_3)_2$ probably has a plane structure which, as discussed on p. 187, points with certainty to atomic bonds.

The formation of a complex with the evolution of energy stabilizes the compound formed and thus it is understandable that $Cu(NH_3)_4I_2$, in contrast with $CuI_2$, does exist. Likewise, complex compounds of trivalent copper, divalent silver and monovalent positive iodine are known. Examples are: $K_6H[Cu^{III}(IO_6)_2].10H_2O$ and $[Ag^{II}(pyridine)]\ S_2O_8$, in which the $Ag^{2+}$ ion is paramagnetic in the same way as $Cu^{2+}$. It is doubtful whether there is still any question of an ion-dipole bonding (see p. 375) in $[IPy_2]ClO_4$, since the iodonium compounds, such as $[I(C_6H_5)_2]ClO_4$, are very similar. $K_3[Co(CN)_6]$ (p. 170) is a typical example of the stabilization of $Co^{3+}$ by complex formation. While, for example, $KI_3$ is not stable, hydrates $[K(H_2O)_2]I_3$ are known in the solid state.

*b. Ion-non-polar molecule*

Compounds, such as the polyhalides and polysulphides, formally also the azides, could be regarded as produced by the attachment of one or more neutral non-polar halogen, sulphur or nitrogen molecules to a halogen, sulphide or nitride ion. This way of representation is definitely incorrect for the azides; the azide-ion $N_3^-$ is linear, in contrast to the triangular structure to be expected for ionic bonding.

Van Arkel and De Boer originally considered the polyhalides, such as $I^-_3$, $ICl^-_2$ etc., to be complexes consisting of an ion and a molecule. These complexes are stable, especially in combination with large positive ions outside the complex, *e.g.*, cesium or especially tetra alkylammonium ions; thus even $I_9^-$ ions are known.

However, the $ICl_2^-$ ion is a symmetrical linear ion in which the iodine is situated in the middle. In the thoroughly investigated $ICl_4^-$ the chlorine is arranged in a square around the iodine (Mooney, 1938). It follows from this that halogen molecules as such do not form part of the complex ion. A pure ionic bonding, consisting of a positive iodine ion with two negative halogen ions, is still conceivable and this certainly also contributes to the $X_3^-$ ions. For the higher complexes such as $ICl_4^-$ a constitution

$$\begin{matrix} Cl^- & & Cl^- \\ & I^{3+} & \\ Cl^- & & Cl^- \end{matrix}$$

is excluded on account of the plane structure of these very stable compounds; moreover, owing to the $I^{3+}$, ion it would to have be paramagnetic, which is not the case.

For the 12 bonding electrons (1 for each Cl atom and 8 for the $I^-$ ion outside the filled 4d shell) there are available one 5s orbit, three 5p orbits and thus there must also be an extra two 5d orbits around the central atom (orbitals: p. 157). These six orbitals form by hybridization (p. 160) a set of bonds directed towards the corners of an octahedron. Two of them, at opposite corners, are occupied by two free or lone electron pairs which do not take part in the bonding; the four others are directed towards the chlorine atoms at the corners of a square, so that a plane structure is produced*. However, the ionogenic electron configurations undoubtedly make an important contribution to the stability, especially if the difference in electronegativity is considerable. EMELÉUS has also obtained $KBrF_4$** with the same structure as the $ICl_4^-$ ion (SLY and MARSH, 1957).

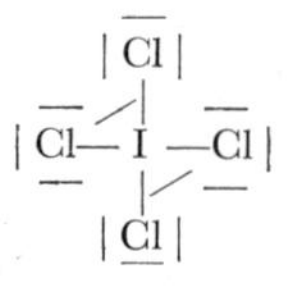

|Cl|
|Cl—I—Cl|
|Cl|

For the $ICl_2^-$ ion a configuration $sp^3d$ would have to be considered for the 10 bonding electrons around the iodine. This furnishes a three-sided double pyramid as the bonding pattern, where the chlorine atoms would occupy the two apexes, and the three non-bonding pairs of electrons the links in the equatorial plane.

X-ray investigation has, however, furnished for $I_3^-$, $I_5^-$, $I_7^-$

* In an alternative possibility the two pairs of non-bonding electrons occupy the 5s and one 5p orbit, while the eight bonding electrons take up the four $5p^2$, $5d^2$ orbitals, which hybridized form four bonds in one plane.

** The existence of polyfluorides, *e.g.* $RbF_3$ and $CsF_3$, needs further confirmation (BODE and KLESPER, 1951).

and $I_9^-$ structures which deviate appreciably from this. $I_3^-$ is indeed linear but an asymmetry was found by MOONEY ($CsI_3$: I-I 2.83 Å and 3.03 Å, TASMAN and BOSWIJK, 1955). With $N(CH_3)_4I_5$ (HACH and RUNDLE, 1951, BROEKEMA, HAVINGA and WIEBENGA, 1957) the iodine atoms lie on a net with almost square meshes (angle 95°); an L-shaped ion $I_5^-$ can be distinguished, formed from an $I^-$ ion at the corner with two $I_2$ molecules at 3.17 Å (I–I: 2.81 Å). The bonding can be regarded as a consequence of resonance between the following configurations:

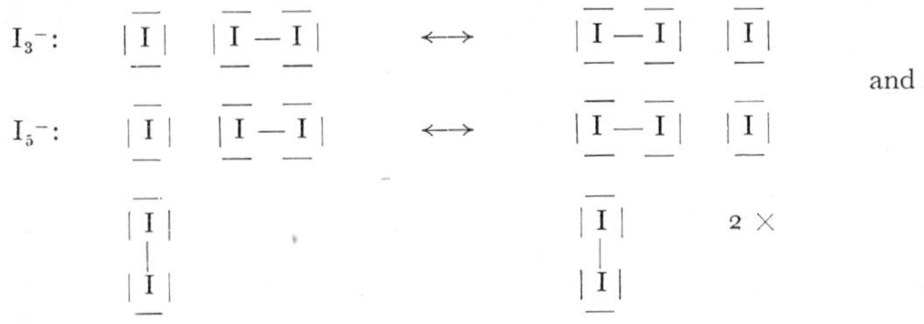

$I_3^-$: |I| |I — I| ⟷ |I — I| |I| and

$I_5^-$: |I| |I — I| ⟷ |I — I| |I|

|I| |I| 2 ×

| |

|I| |I|

With the $I_3^-$ ion the predominance of one of the two configurations can be due to the influence of the positive ion. With the $I_5^-$ ion the configurations are not equivalent *a priori*. The separation in the free $I_2$ molecule is 2.67 Å; this is lengthened in the present case, while the $I^-$–$I_2$ separation is considerably shortened. The shortest distance between different ions is the same as between different molecules in $I_2$ ($I_2$ : 3.54 Å, $I_5^-$ : 3.55 Å). The right angle is a consequence of the angle of 90° between the p-functions concerned; the octet configuration is maintained. With an electrostatic bonding through polarization a linear structure would be expected. The structure of $N(C_2H_5)_4 I_7$ contains (symmetrical) $I_3^-$ ions and $I_2$ molecules; it is thus $N(C_2H_5)_4I_3.2I_2$ (HAVINGA, 1957). The compound $N(CH_3)_4.I_9$ is in fact $N(CH_3)_4.I_5.2I_2$ (JAMES, HACH, FRENCH and RUNDLE, 1955), but with an $I_5^-$ ion with the iodide ion at both ends of the L and surrounded by two other iodine molecules.

$CsI_4$ should be written as $Cs_2I_8$, containing a Z-shaped ion

$I_8^{2-}$ with iodide ions on both corners (HAVINGA, BOSWIJK and WIEBENGA, 1954).

The structure of polysulphides, *e.g.*, $Na_2S$, $Na_2S_4$, $Na_2S_5$, $BaS_4.H_2O$, $Cs_2S_6$, etc., is based on the formation of helical chains from sulphur atoms (ABRAHAMS, 1954; ABRAHAMS and GRISON, 1953) analogous to the chains in the $S_8$ rings in elementary orthorhombic sulphur (ABRAHAMS, 1955).

In the $S_4^{2-}$ ion the two outer S–S distances are 2.026 Å; the inner one is 2.067 Å, with bond angles of 104.5°. In the $S_6^{2-}$ ion alternating S–S distances are found of 2.02 Å and 2.11 Å, again with the small values at both ends and also in the middle (bond angle 108.8°). This effect is probably due to resonance between the configurations

$$|\overset{\ominus}{\underline{\overline{S}}}-\underline{\overline{S}}-\underline{\overline{S}}-\overset{\ominus}{\underline{\overline{S}}}| \quad |\underline{\overline{S}}=\overset{\ominus}{\underline{\overline{S}}}-\underline{\overline{S}}-\overset{\ominus}{\underline{\overline{S}}}| \quad (2\times)| \qquad |\overset{\ominus}{\underline{\overline{S}}}-\overset{\ominus}{\underline{\overline{S}}}=\overset{\oplus}{\underline{\overline{S}}}-\overset{\ominus}{\underline{\overline{S}}}| \quad (2\times)$$

The last configuration is very unlikely as it contains charges of the same sign on neighbouring atoms (adjacent charge rule p. 243). In sulphur itself the S–S bond length is only 2.037 Å (bond angle 107.7°), also due to resonance, involving a group of ten electrons at a sulphur atom (ABRAHAMS, 1955). Analogous chains of sulphur atom are found in the tetra- and pentathionate ion, $S_4O_6^{2-}$ and $S_5O_6^{2-}$, (FOSS, FURBERG and ZACHARIASEN, 1954):

$$\begin{array}{ccccccccc} & & |\overline{O}| & & & & |\overline{O}| & & \\ & & | & & & & | & & \\ |\overline{\underline{O}} & - & S & - & \overline{\underline{S}} & - & S & - & \overline{\underline{O}}| \\ & & | & & & & | & & \\ & & |\underline{O}| & & & & |\underline{O}| & & \end{array}$$

Chains are also found in polysulphides such as the sulphanes $H_2S_n$ and the chlorosulphanes $S_nCl_2$ with $n$ up to 8 (FEHER *et al.*, 1955, 1956, 1957).

## § 12. ELECTROLYTIC DISSOCIATION

A simple compound can decompose not only by dissociation into atoms or molecules, thus into the elements, but also by dissociation into ions. This phenomenon is more complicated because it occurs in (aqueous) solution. On the one hand there is the dissociation energy, and on the other hand there is the energy of interaction of the ions with the molecules of the solvent (hydration energy p. 100).

It follows that strictly speaking no direct relation need exist between the nature of the bonding in the solid state and the dissociation in aqueous solution. However, salts, considered as the group of the compounds of bases and acids, are usually built up from ions in the solid state also (possibly formed from complex ions); in so far as they are soluble in water, they are completely dissociated therein (strong electrolytes). In cases which are exceptions, *e.g.*, the halides of mercury, the atomic bonding forces play an important part; this appears from the formation of special molecular lattices in the solid state.

The cadmium and lead halides are also incompletely dissociated, that is to say, that here in the first place ions $[CdCl]^+$ and $[PbCl]^+$ are formed (dissociation constants are small, of the order of 0.01–0.03; for $CdI^+$ even only 0.004).

From the conductivity in solutions which are not extremely dilute, it appears that ion pairs are formed in numerous other cases (BJERRUM), that is to say, combinations of ions, each still with its hydration sheath, which thus do not correspond with molecules. It is especially the higher valency ions, logically, which exhibit this phenomenon; thus this pair formation occurs, for example, in the alkali sulphates, alkaline earth nitrates and barium hydroxide through the formation of $[MSO_4]^-$, $[MNO_3]^+$ and $[Ba(OH)]^-$ ions, furthermore $[Ce^{4+}(OH)^-]^{3+}$, $[Fe^{3+}(OH)^-]^{2+}$.

In dilute solutions the zinc halides behave entirely as strong electrolytes, but in more concentrated solutions this is otherwise; probably this is a question of the direct formation of higher complexes, for example, $[ZnX_4]^{2-}$, the dissociation of which depends very much more on the concentration than for $[ZnX]^+$.

Some electrolytes seem to be weak although this is actually not so. This always occurs when the (electrolytically) undissociated molecule has little stability and is therefore strongly dissociated non-electrolytically. Aqueous solutions of carbonic acid, sulphurous acid, ammonia, etc., are examples of this.

On the other hand, slight solubility in water or great volatility (see later), thus the absence of a "saltlike" character, does not prove without further argument that ionic bonding is absent.

Although the terms salt and salt-like are frequently used in chemistry, it is impossible to give a good definition of what precisely is now understood by them. This is what happens to historical concepts: the significance becomes vaguer.

Originally one understood by the "sal" of the alchemists a substance which showed an external similarity to common salt. They were substances which were crystalline, readily soluble in water and which were neutral, such as saltpetre (sal petri), sal glauberi ($Na_2SO_4.10H_2O$), sal ammoniac, etc.

According to school textbooks a salt is the product of the reaction of an acidic oxide and a basic oxide, or is produced together with water from an acid and a base, etc. But this definition is not at all satisfactory. Why precisely oxides? Is $Na_2S$ really a salt and $Na_2O$ and $Na_2O_2$ not? Is $SiF_4$ not a salt although it can be thought of as formed from $SiO_2$ and HF? This reaction is not hypothetical, as is that of $Al_2O_3$ and $H_2S$ to yield $Al_2S_3$. $Na_3N$ is certainly a salt, perhaps also $Na_3As$, but $Na_3Sb$ is quite predominantly metallic (Fig. 1, p. 21), although $SbH_3$ is a stronger acid than $NH_3$. It would be more correct to call all compounds which are built up from ions in the solid state salts or salt-like compounds, if it were not that it would certainly be against normal parlance to call NaOH a salt and $HgCl_2$ perhaps not!

The word salt may still be used in the vague sense based on chemical feeling in the intuitive alchemical manner. Regarded in this way salts are certainly built up of ions.

## § 13. STRENGTH OF ACIDS AND BASES

The acids and bases form a special case of the dissociation into ions, so that the question of the strength of acids calls for a further discussion; we shall restrict ourselves here to the inorganic acids and bases. VAN ARKEL and CARRIÈRE (VAN ARKEL and CARRIÈRE, 1937; VAN ARKEL, 1956) followed a greatly simplified scheme for this purpose; they consider the free molecule as constructed wholly from ions and the hydrogen ions as ions with a radius zero. They thus neglect the energy required to bring the molecule of the acid from the normal state of bonding into a purely ionic state. The energy of dissociation was calculated on this ion model for the removal of one or more hydrogen ions. This energy is however certainly not the usual energy of dissociation, since the energy of hydration of the dissociation products (the proton and the anion) is not taken into account. It cannot be directly proved that the sequence of these calculated "absolute" strengths of acids agrees with the actual strengths in aqueous solutions, although this agreement can in general be considered plausible.

The energy of dissociation, calculated in this way, depends only on the charge and radius of the negative ion for the acids derived from the simple negative ions such as those of the halogens, of oxygen, sulphur and homologues and of nitrogen and homologues. Thus it is understandable that the acid strength increases with increasing radius in the series HF, HCl, HBr, HI, likewise in the series $H_2O$, $H_2S$, $H_2Se$, $H_2Te$ and $NH_3$, $PH_3$, $AsH_3$ and $SbH_3$. In agreement with the above-mentioned stability rule, the stability, however, decreases in the same direction. The small acid strength of the hydrogen compounds of oxygen and sulphur, compared with that of the compounds of fluorine and chlorine, must be ascribed to the two-fold negative charge of these first ions, as their ion radii are equal. The hydrogen compounds of the negative trivalent elements, such as nitrogen and phosphorus, have more tendency to accept a proton ($NH_4^+$, $PH_4^+$) than to donate one; thus they are bases in the sense of BRÖNSTED's definition (p. 87).

For the complex acids VAN ARKEL and CARRIÈRE have drawn a number of conclusions from their model arguments regarding the order of acid strength.

1. Oxygen acids are weaker than fluorine acids since in the first case the proton must be separated from a divalent ion, in the second case from a monovalent ion.

Examples: $HB^{3+}F_4$ is a very strong, $H_3B^{3+}O_3$ an extremely weak acid.

2. In the group of the oxygen acids, or of the fluorine acids, a higher charge (or smaller radius) of the central ion gives rise to a stronger acid in view of the stronger repulsion. Thus they explain the well-known rule, that the acid derived from the highest stage of oxidation is the strongest.

Examples: $H_2\overset{6+}{S}O_4$ stronger than $H_2\overset{4+}{S}O_3$, $H\overset{5+}{N}O_3 > H_2\overset{4+}{C}O_3 > H_3\overset{3+}{B}O_3$; $H_2SO_4 > H_2SeO_4 > H_2TeO_4$; $HClO_4 > HClO_3 > HClO_2 > HClO$. The fact that phosphorous acid $H_3PO_3$ is somewhat stronger than phosphoric acid $H_3PO_4$ appears to form an exception. In fact this acid is not derived from trivalent phosphorus, but the anion of this dibasic acid contains a negative hydrogen ion $[H^- \, P^{5+} \, O_3]^{2-}$, whereby the acid must indeed even be stronger than the oxygen acid. The same holds for the anion of monobasic hypophosphorous acid $[H_2^- PO_2]^-$.

3. The difference in the *relative* numbers of coordinated oxygen ions is of much less importance; a larger number of oxygen ions by their combined effect leads to a stronger bonding and thus to smaller acid strength. This is not a question of actual differences in coordination number but of changes in the relative number of oxygen ions per central ion by the formation of polynuclear complex ions.

Thus the explanation of the greater strength of metaphosphoric acid $HPO_3$ compared with orthophosphoric acid $H_3PO_4$ as a consequence of a difference in coordination number is incorrect, since $HPO_3$ as such does not exist but forms polymeric ions built up from complexes of *oxygen tetrahedra* (Fig. 8). There is indeed a difference in the ratio O : P in total.

Naturally the above rules form only a first approximation to the problem and, furthermore, caution is necessary in their application. On the other hand the simple argument provides a striking explanation of the observations in many cases. An example of this is pyrophosphoric acid $H_4P_2O_7$. The successive dissociation stages of a polybasic acid always differ considerably in strength, but this is not the case for the difference between the first and second stages with $H_4P_2O_7$ and still less for that between the third and fourth stages. The explanation is that the $P_2O_7$ ion consists of two tetrahedra with one common corner (Fig. 8). The first proton is split off from one of the two tetrahedra; the second proton will naturally be split off from the other tetrahedron. Thus the energy of separation of this second proton will not differ appreciably from that of the first proton. A third proton must be split off from one of the tetrahedra which are already negatively charged; thus the third stage is very much weaker than the previous two while the fourth stage will again be little weaker than the third stage. In fact the dissociation constants for $H_4P_2O_7$ are:

$K_1 = 1.4 \cdot 10^{-1}$, $K_2 = 1.1 \cdot 10^{-2}$, $K_3 = 2.9 \cdot 10^{-7}$ and $K_4 = 3.6 \cdot 10^{-9}$,

By way of comparison, all three stages differ considerably in size for $H_3PO_4$:

$$K_1 = 0.8 \cdot 10^{-2},\ K_2 = 1.2 \cdot 10^{-7},\ K_3 = 1.8 \cdot 10^{-12}.$$

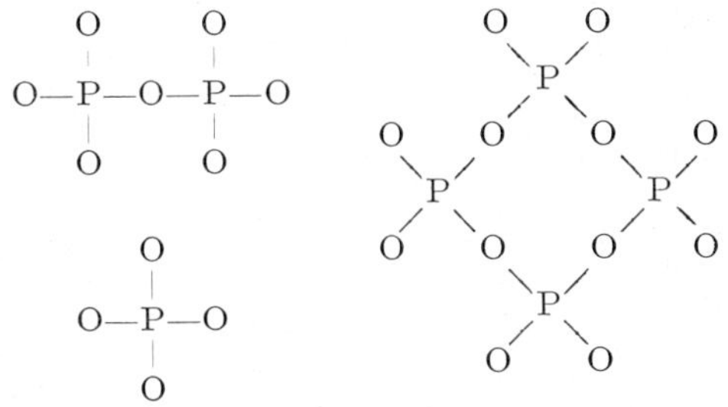

```
  O     O                 O   O
  |     |                  \ /
O—P—O—P—O                   P
  |     |                  / \
  O     O           O   O     O   O
                     \ /       \ /
                      P         P
    O                / \       / \
    |               O   O     O   O
  O—P—O                  \   /
    |                      P
    O                     / \
                         O   O
```

Fig. 8. The anion of ortho-, of pyro-, and of tetrameta-phosphoric acid.

The dissociation of the hydroxides decreases with decreasing radius and increasing charge of the positive metal ion. With increasing charge the repulsion of the proton, on the other hand, becomes greater and the transition to an acid occurs:

$NaOH$, $Mg(OH)_2$, $Al(OH)_3$, $Si(OH)_4$, $P(OH)_5 \rightarrow H_3PO_4$, etc.

The transition, which results in amphoteric hydroxides, can

be found in the Periodic Table along a diagonal since the radius of the metal ion increases in the downward direction (p. 30). Thus HOH, $Be(OH)_2$ and $Al(OH)_3$ are amphoteric, as are also the oxides of titanium, niobium and tungsten. The oxide of the highest stage of oxidation has always the most pronounced acidic properties. Thus $CrO_3$ is exclusively an acid-forming oxide, $Cr_2O_3$ is predominantly basic but nevertheless chromites exist, while CrO is exclusively basic.

KOSSIAKOFF and HARKER (1938) calculated also the electrostatic attraction energy between the hydrogen ion and the different atoms $i$ in the anion of a complex oxygen acid. However, they assigned to each atom the formal charge $q_i$ (p. 165) calculated for the LEWIS configuration of the electron-pair model of the non-resonating molecule (FURBERG, 1955). This repartition of charges may be more adequate than the extreme ionic model of VAN ARKEL and CARRIÈRE.

$H_3PO_4 \rightarrow H^+ + H_2PO_4^-$ : $H^+$ $\ominus|\overline{O}-\overset{\oplus}{P}(-\overline{O}|-H)(-\overline{O}|^{\ominus})-\overline{O}-H$

The initial step of the dissociation process is the removal of a proton at the normal distance of 0.95 Å($r_{i1}$) from its oxygen atom (with a formal charge —1) towards the nearest water molecule (O- - -O distance 2.70 Å) over a distance of 0.80 Å (from one to the other position within the OH . . . O-bridge, $r_{i2}$ = 1.75 Å). An effective dielectric constant $D$ is put equal to 3.0. The transfer of the proton to other water molecules adds very little to the dissociation energy, since, in these further steps, the dielectric constant is assumed to be 80.

The potential energy of dissociation is thus given by:

$$\Delta U = \sum_i \frac{eq_i}{D}\left(\frac{1}{r_{i1}} - \frac{1}{r_{i2}}\right) + C.$$

The other changes in the (free) energy on dissociation are considered to be essentially constant. A structure-dependent entropy term accounts for the number $n_H$ of H atoms which can dissociate and the number $n_O$ of oxygen atoms which can accept an H atom:

$$S = -R \ln n_O/n_H$$

The result is:

$$-RT\ln K = \Delta G = \sum_i \frac{eq_i}{D}\left(\frac{1}{r_{i1}} - \frac{1}{r_{i2}}\right) + RT\ln n_O/n_H + C.$$

The constant $C$ is found by equating the calculated and observed values for $K$ for orthophosphoric acid.

The results are quite satisfactory as is shown in the table:

ACID STRENGTH

$pk = -\log K$ of some inorganic acids

| | calc. | obs. | | calc. | obs. |
|---|---|---|---|---|---|
| $H_3PO_4$ | (2.1) | 2.1 | $H_3AsO_4$ | 2.5 | 2.3 |
| $H_2PO_4^-$ | 6.5 | 6.7 | $H_2AsO_4^-$ | 6.2 | 7.0 |
| $HPO_4^{2-}$ | 11.4 | 11.4 | $HAsO_4^{2-}$ | 10.5 | 9.2 |
| $H_4P_2O_7$ | 1.5 | 0.9 | $H_2SO_3$ | 2.3 | 1.9 |
| $H_3P_2O_7^-$ | 3.8 | 2.0 | $H_2SeO_3$ | 2.9 | 2.3 |
| $H_2P_2O_7^{2-}$ | 7.6 | 6.6 | $H_2TeO_3$ | 3.1 | 2.5 |
| $HP_2O_7^{3-}$ | 10.3 | 8.6 | $HSO_4^-$ | 2.0 | 1.9 |
| | | | $HSO_3^-$ | 7.0 | 7.0 |

However, for molecules where resonance is important, *e.g.*, the carboxylic acids, the observed dissociation energy is much lower than calculated. This is due to the fact that through resonance the charge is spread over the whole molecule and to the lowering of the energy of the anion by the increased possibilities for resonance (p. 210).

Some essential points of both theoretical treatments of acid strength are represented in an empirical expression for the $p_k$ due to PAULING (1947, 1953) and RICCI (1948).

For an acid $H_aMO_b$ the quantities of major influence are the formal charge of the central atom $m$ and the quantity $n = b - a$, the excess of oxygen atoms over the number of replaceable hydrogen atoms.

The acid strength is roughly represented by:

$$p_k = 7.5 - 10\,m + 5\,n$$

This formula expresses the fact that the acid strength of successive dissociation steps of a polybasic acid (with one central atom!) diminishes by about 5 units, However, the acid strength $p_k$ of the first ionization step of different acids also goes down 5 units in a series such as $H_4SiO_4$, $H_3PO_4$, $H_2SO_4$ and $HClO_4$, in which both $m$ and $n$ increase by one unit at a time.

The same electrostatic arguments can also be applied to the dissociation of the hydroxides. As noted above, the strength of the hydroxides decreases with decreasing radius and increasing charge of the metal ion. Thus LiOH is clearly weaker than the other alkali hydroxides; this is evident from the hydrolysis of solutions of lithium salts at higher temperatures. A solution of $MgCl_2$ in water hydrolyses completely on evaporating it down, but with $CaCl_2$ this is hardly the case. Similarly $Si(OH)_4$ is acid, $Ge(OH)_4$ amphoteric, but $Th(OH)_4$ is a base.

The concept base does not, however, include only the hydroxides; according to BRÖNSTED, a base is a proton-acceptor just as an acid is a proton-donor (BRÖNSTED, 1923; LOWRY, 1923). Expressed more precisely, acids and bases are not independent concepts but they indicate the relation of the proton transfer. Thus water behaves as a base with respect to a strong acid and forms the hydronium $OH_3^+$; for example, the hydrate $HClO_4.H_2O$, or better hydronium perchlorate $OH_3(ClO_4)$, is isomorphous with $NH_4(ClO_4)$ in which $NH_3$ is the base. However, in fluoronium perchlorate, HF would fulfil the part of a base: $FH_2[ClO_4]$ (its existence is doubtful, BRAUER and DISTLER, 1954). Phosphoric acid can also behave as a base towards a very strong acid, *e.g.*, $[P(OH)_4]ClO_4$ (ARLMAN, 1937; SIMON and WEIST, 1952).

Water can also react as an acid and thus donates a proton towards the very strong base *e.g.*, $O^{2-}$; this base is much stronger than $OH^-$; in fact $H_2O + Na_2O \rightarrow 2\ NaOH$. Water also behaves as an acid towards weaker bases such as $S^{2-}$ and the acetate ion. The hydrolysis of an acetate solution and the neutralisation of a solution of a strong acid by sodium acetate are thus simple acid-base reactions.

From the electrostatic viewpoint the order in decreasing basicity can be understood directly from charge and radius of the negative ion:
$O^{2-} > S^{2-} > Se^{2-}$, $OH^- > SH^- > SeH^-$, $NH_3 > OH_2 > FH$ and $NH_2^- > OH^-$.

Thus we can formulate the acid-base reaction generally as: acid I + base I $\rightleftharpoons$ acid II + base II; for example:

$$OH_3^+ + OH^- \rightleftharpoons H_2O + H_2O$$
$$HCl + NH_3 \rightleftharpoons NH_4^+ + Cl^-$$
$$HCl + (\text{acetate})^- \rightleftharpoons \text{acetic acid} + Cl^-$$
$$H_2PO_4^- + CO_3^{2-} \rightleftharpoons HCO_3^- + HPO_4^{2-}$$

In the old sense, acids or bases are compounds or ions in aqueous solution which are stronger acids or stronger bases than water. In other solvents, such as liquid ammonia or acetic acid, the division is quite different. In liquid ammonia the $NH_2^-$ ion plays the part of the $OH^-$ ion in aqueous solutions.

According to BRÖNSTED's view, it is no longer necessary to speak of ammonium hydroxide* in aqueous solutions of ammonia. The solution contains $OH^-$ and $NH_4^+$ ions through the equilibrium $NH_3 + H_2O \leftrightharpoons NH_4^+ + OH^-$. The salt formation of $NH_4Cl$ from ammonia and hydrochloric acid can also occur in the gas phase where there is certainly no hydroxide. The same is true for the substituted nitrogen bases; there is no basis for writing $C_6H_5NH_2.HCl$ for aniline hydrochloride; $[C_6H_5NH_3]Cl$ is correct.

A still more general conception of acids and bases is possible (LEWIS), in which bases are compounds or groups such as $O^{2-}$, $OH^-$, $H_2O$, $NH_3$, $NH_2^-$ and $F^-$ with a free electron pair which can take part in a reaction (electron donors or nucleophilic compounds) with an electron acceptor.

Acids are considered to be atoms or groups which can accept an electron pair (acceptors or electrophilic substances), for example, molecules with a sextet configuration (p. 176) such as $BF_3$ and $SO_3$ (and the proton which aims at the helium configuration). Thus the formation of $BF_3.NH_3$ and the formation of $H_2SO_4$ from $SO_3$ and water are acid-base reactions (LUDER and ZUFFANTI, 1946).

Acceptor-donor reactions of this type are very general (see also p. 369) and LEWIS' conception has provided a valuable generalization. However, it is doubtful whether the terms acid and base are still pertinent since these terms have long possessed a particular significance. The service rendered by BRÖNSTED's generalization (BELL, 1947) is that the old term basic substance obtains a meaning in agreement with the original conception but without the emphasis on the hydroxides as the only bases; compare, for example, the alkaloids which certainly do not form hydroxides but which have always been considered as bases.

* It can be proved that this species does not exist (VAN VELDEN and KETELAAR, 1947; BRIEGLEB, 1942). However, there is a hydrate $HOH...NH_3$ with formation of a hydrogen bond as in the solid state (SIEMONS and TEMPLETON, 1954).

## § 14. VOLATILITY

The equilibrium between vapour and liquid or solid is also determined by the thermodynamic potential or free enthalpy $G$ ($G = U + PV - TS = H - TS$, p. 42). At equilibrium this quantity is equal in both phases, $\Delta G = 0$.

According to thermodynamics the dependence of the free enthalpy of the gaseous phase on the pressure is determined by the term $RT \ln p$.

Thus we have:

$$-RT \ln p = \Delta H_0 - T \Delta S_0$$

in which $\Delta H_0$ is the latent heat of evaporation (at constant pressure) and $\Delta S_0$ the entropy of evaporation at 1 atmosphere.

(This expression is also produced from the well-known vapour pressure formula of CLAPEYRON:

$$\frac{1}{p}\frac{dp}{dT} = \frac{Q}{RT^2}, \text{ by integration to } \ln p = -\frac{Q}{RT} + C$$

in which $Q = \Delta H$, the latent heat of evaporation, assumed independent of the temperature).

When the pressure $p$ is expressed in atmospheres, then at the boiling point $T_b$ the pressure $p = 1$ and thus $C \cdot R = \Delta H / T_b = \Delta S_0$. In this last expression we meet the latent heat of evaporation at constant pressure, divided by the boiling point temperature on the absolute scale; according to TROUTON's rule this quotient has an approximately constant value of about 22 for "normal" liquids. This means, therefore, that the entropy of evaporation (at 1 atm) also amounts to approximately 22 cal/mole degree (alkali halides 24 cal/mole degree).

The corresponding rule of LE CHATELIER and MATIGNON holds for the sublimation equilibrium: $\Delta S_0 \approx 32$ cal/mole degree.

Actually the "constants" are somewhat dependent on the temperature; nevertheless, we shall thus be able to draw conclusions on the order of the boiling points as experimentally well-known quantities from the theoretical order of the latent heat of evaporation within a group of similar compounds.

From a simple cycle we have for the heat of sublimation: $Q = U - M$. Since the latent heat of fusion is smaller and varies approximately in step with the latent heat of evaporation, the sequence of the heat of evaporation of solid and liquid is the same for various compounds; thus conclusions regarding the heat of sublimation can be compared with the data regarding the boiling points.

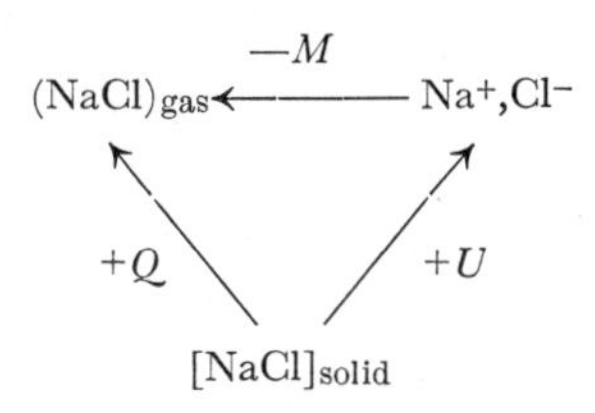


We have already derived an expression for the lattice energy $U$ ((3), p. 36); in quite the same way it follows for the molecular energy:

$$M = -N \frac{e^2}{r^+ + r^-} (1 - 1/n),$$

since here the MADELUNG constant is naturally equal to 1.

$$Q = U - M = N \cdot \frac{Ae^2 (1 - 1/n)}{r^+ + r^-} - N \cdot \frac{e^2 (1 - 1/n)}{r^+ + r^-} =$$

$$= N (A - 1) \frac{e^2}{r^+ + r^-} (1 - 1/n).$$

It follows that the boiling point, for example, in the group of the alkali halides will decrease with increasing radius of the ions. In fact, the boiling point of the fluorides decreases on going from LiF to CsF and similarly the boiling point decreases for the halides of each alkali metal (with the exception of cesium) on going from the fluorides to the iodides. With increasing charge the volatility and likewise the fusibility decreases very strongly: compare NaF, CaO, $Y_3O_3$ and $ThO_2$;

the last oxide is used as a very highly refractory material (similarly $ZrO_2$).

If we examine the groups of the chlorides, bromides, and iodides, we find that the order is quite different and more complicated than for the fluorides. The expression used for the molecular energy $M = N \frac{e^2}{r^+ + r^-}$ is incomplete (FAJANS, VAN ARKEL and DE BOER). The ions behave not only as a charge but they are polarizable as well, thus under the influence of an external field (for example from the other ion) a dipole is induced by displacement of the negative and positive charge. It is mainly the negative charge, represented by the outermost electron shell, which is displaceable. For the large ions, especially where this shell is more removed from the influence of the nuclear charge, the polarizability is large. On the other hand the polarizability of the positive ions, with the exception of cesium and of the ions of the subseries (B-subgroups), is very small. To the expression for the COULOMB energy must be added a term for the attraction between the positive ion and the induced dipole in the negative ion.

When the distance between the midpoints of the positive and the negative ion is $r^+ + r^-$ and the induced dipole is considered to be in the centre of the negative ion, then the interaction energy (see p. 73) $-\frac{1}{2} \alpha F^2 = \frac{-\alpha e^2}{2(r^+ + r^-)^4}$. The molecular energy, calculated per grammolecule, thus becomes:

$$-\frac{e^2 N}{r^+ + r^-} (1 - 1/n) - \frac{\alpha e^2 N}{2 (r^+ + r^-)^4}.$$

For the heat of sublimation we then have:

$$Q = \frac{e^2 N}{r^+ + r^-} \left[ (A - 1) (1 - 1/n) - \frac{\alpha}{2 (r^+ + r^-)^3} \right].$$

As the result of the influence of the very great polarizability of the iodide ion, the order of the boiling points of the alkali iodides is just such that lithium iodide shows the lowest boiling

TABLE 9

POLARIZABILITY α OF SOME IONS*, ATOMS AND GROUPS**
IN $10^{-24}$ cm$^3$

| | | | | | | | |
|---|---|---|---|---|---|---|---|
| $Li^+$ | 0.03 | $Be^{2+}$ | 0.01 | $Ag^+$ | 1.9 | $F^-$ | 0.81 |
| $Na^+$ | 0.24 | $Mg^{2+}$ | 0.10 | $Tl^+$ | 3.9 | $Cl^-$ | 2.98 |
| $K^+$ | 1.00 | $Ca^{2+}$ | 0.60 | $Zn^{2+}$ | 0.5 | $Br^-$ | 4.24 |
| $Rb^+$ | 1.50 | $Sr^{2+}$ | 0.90 | $Cd^{2+}$ | 1.15 | $I^-$ | 6.45 |
| $Cs^+$ | 2.40 | $Ba^{2+}$ | 1.69 | $Hg^{2+}$ | 2.45 | $OH^-$ | 1.89 |
| $NH^{4+}$ | 1.65 | $La^{3+}$ | 1.3 | $Pb^{2+}$ | 3.6 | $O^{2-}$ | 3 |

| | | | | | |
|---|---|---|---|---|---|
| F | 0.38 | O (hydroxyl) | 0.59 | H | 0.42 |
| Cl | 2.28 | O (ether) | 0.64 | C | 0.93 |
| Br | 3.34 | O (carbonyl) | 0.84 | $CH_2$ | 1.77 |
| I | 5.11 | N (primary) | 0.87 | double bond | 0.58 extra |
| CN | 2.12 | N (secondary) | 0.93 | triple bond | 0.86 extra |
| H | 0.42 | N (tertiary) | 1.03 | $—C_6H_5$ | 9.38 |

* From the refractivity (see p. 380) according to FAJANS and HEYDWEILLER, and BÖTTCHER (BÖTTCHER, 1946; BÖTTCHER and SCHOLTE, 1951).
** From refractivity for $\lambda \rightarrow \infty$.

point. Similarly, the boiling point of CsF is lower than that of CsCl because in the first case the cesium ion is polarized by the smaller fluorine ion, while in the latter case, the chlorine ion polarizes the cesium ion to a much lesser extent. The same holds to a still greater degree for thallium compounds (Fig. 9, Table 9).

Furthermore, it is incorrect to use the same value for the distance between the ions in the solid and in the vapour state. By the influence of the difference in coordination number (p. 39) respectively, 6 and 1, the ionic separation in the gaseous molecule will be 14% smaller, which is confirmed experimentally by electron diffraction (p. 39 and Table 10, KETELAAR, 1938; VERWEY and DE BOER, 1940).

PAULING (PAULING, *Chemical Bond*, p. 355; HUGGINS, 1933, 1937; WASASTJERNA, 1935), however, has given quite a different explanation for the same discrepancies in the course of the boiling points from a regular dependence of the ionic radii. Whereas the origin of the irregularities was sought above in the energy of the gas molecule, PAULING introduces a correction of the lattice energy which is dependent on the ratio of radii of positive and negative ions.

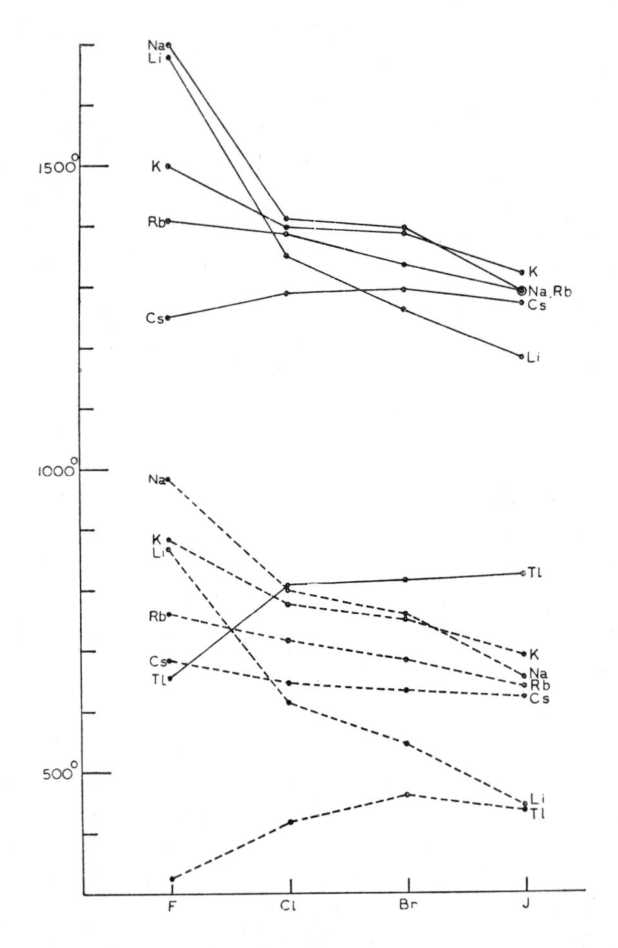


Fig. 9. Boiling points —, and melting points ······ of the alkali halides.

The sum of the radii is much smaller than the observed distances in the crystal for LiCl, LiBr and LiI, due to the contact of anions (p. 27).

| | $r^+ + r^-$ (calc.) | $d_{MX}$ (obs.) |
|---|---|---|
| LiF | 2.01 A | 2.01 A |
| LiCl | 2.49 | 2.57 |
| LiBr | 2.64 | 2.75 |
| LiI | 2.87 | 3.02 |

Thus the sublimation energy of these substances will be considerably lower than for a "normal" radius ratio. This will lower the heat effects at the melting point, and at the boiling point. For the corresponding sodium salts the effect is much smaller, and for the other salts it is of no importance at all.

In the lattice of LiF, NaBr and NaI ($r^+/r^-$ near the critical value of 0.414, p. 32) there will be contact both between anions and cations and between anions, and thus the repulsive energy will be greater than in the case of the other salts with either the first or the second kind of contacts (double repulsion). Owing to double repulsion the boiling points and melting points will thus for LiF, etc., also be slightly lower than expected from ionic sizes.

The behaviour of the thallium halides, where the ratio of the radii is the same as in the rubidium compounds, must certainly be explained from the polarization of the positive, readily polarizable thallium by the small fluorine ion.

Since the melting points show qualitatively the same course as the boiling points a discrepant behaviour of the vapour molecules alone seems inadequate to explain these phenomena.

The small influence of the polarization is apparent from the quoted calculation (p. 39, Table 10) of the decrease of interionic distance in the transition from lattice to vapour molecule where only the COULOMB attraction and the BORN repulsion were taken into account. The dipole moments of the molecules of the alkali halides point to a lower value than that corresponding to *e.d.* This is a consequence of the polarization; in fact the discrepancy is greatest for the lithium halides and CsF. The value of the dipole moment calculated including polarization (RITTNER, 1951), corresponds well with the observed values (Table 10). It is difficult, both experimentally and theoretically, to distinguish the influence of purely elec-

TABLE 10

DIPOLE MOMENT AND BOND DISTANCE OF THE ALKALI HALIDES MOLECULES (KETELAAR, 1938; RITTNER, 1951; HONIG, MANDEL, STITCH AND TOWNES, 1954).

| | $d_{obs.}$ | $d_{calc.}$ | $\mu_{obs.}$ | $e.d$ | $\mu_{calc.}$ |
|---|---|---|---|---|---|
| LiBr | 2.170 Å | 2.24 Å | 6.19 D | 10.42 D | 5.14 D |
| LiI | 2.392 | 2.52 | 6.25 | 11.48 | 5.37 |
| NaCl | 2.361 | 2.38 | 8.5 | 11.33 | 7.77 |
| KF | (2.17) | 2.16 | 8.62 | 10.42 | 8.06 |
| KCl | 2.667 | 2.70 | 10.0 | 12.80 | 9.18 |
| KBr | 2.821 | 2.85 | 10.61 | 13.54 | 9.58 |
| KI | 3.048 | 3.07 | 11.05 | 14.63 | 9.92 |
| RbBr | 2.945 | 2.99 | 10 | 14.14 | 9.92 |
| CsF | 2.345 | 2.56 | 7.88 | 11.26 | 7.28 |
| CsCl | 2.906 | 3.03 | 10.40 | 13.95 | 9.36 |
| CsBr | 3.072 | 3.19 | – | 14.74 | 9.97 |
| CsI | 3.315 | 3.44 | 12.1 | 15.91 | 10.61 |

trostatic polarization from that of the transition from purely ionic bonding to partial atomic bonding (see also p. 150).

Beside the very little volatile halides, oxides, sulphides, etc., which clearly have a salt-like character, stand the volatile, low melting compounds of the higher valent elements, which are non-conducting in the melt.

The transition from non-volatile to volatile, for example between $AlF_3$ and $SiF_4$, is frequently but incorrectly attributed to the transition from ionic bonding to atomic bonding.

We saw that the monovalent sodium ion is surrounded in the lattice by six chlorine or fluorine ions; the coordination number is six. On passing to more highly charged ions such as $Mg^{2+}$, $Al^{3+}$ and $Si^{4+}$, the radius decreases and the coordination number falls to four. When the coordination number becomes equal to the charge, then molecules can be distinguished in the lattice although they consist of ions. In the rock-salt lattice a sodium ion with its surroundings of six chlorine ions is not a neutral whole; only the whole lattice is neutral. In silicon tetrafluoride each molecule of $SiF_4$ is an electrically neutral complex; thus the forces, which it exerts on neighbouring molecules can only be very small. These belong to the type of the VAN DER WAALS interaction (Chapter V).

Silicon tetrafluoride is thus a volatile compound because the molecule is enveloped or "shielded" in the gas phase, that is to say, the charge has already reached the coordination number, in contrast, for example, with sodium fluoride, where this ratio is only 1 against 6, magnesium fluoride and aluminium fluoride, where this ratio is respectively 2 and 3 against 6.

For the same positive ion the shielding sets in earlier with large than with smaller negative ions. Thus aluminium fluoride

TABLE 11

BOILING POINTS AND MELTING POINTS OF FLUORIDES AND OXIDES

| | $NaF$ | $MgF_2$ | $AlF_3$ | $SiF_4$ | $PF_5$ | $SF_6$ | $IF_7$ |
|---|---|---|---|---|---|---|---|
| m.p. | 992 | 1266 | — | —90.3 | —93.7 | —56 | +5.5 |
| b.p. | 1700 | 2227 | 1257 (subl.) | —95.5 (subl.) | —84.5 | —63.8 (subl.) | +4.5 (subl.) |
| | $Na_2O$ | $MgO$ | $Al_2O_3$ | $SiO_2$ | $P_2O_5$ | $SO_3$ | $Cl_2O_7$ |
| m.p. | — | 2800 | 2050 | 1725 | 580 | +16.8 | —91.5 |
| b.p. | 1275 (subl.) | 2850 | 3300 | 2590 | 594 | +44.8 | +82 |

$AlF_3$ is still typically a slightly volatile, non-shielded compound, while aluminium chloride and *a fortiori* the bromide and iodide are volatile shielded compounds.

With these aluminium halides still other complications occur, because the coordination number amounts to four (and not three as is still the case for boron). The molecules consist in the gas phase, as in the liquid phase, of $Al_2X_6$, *i.e.*, two tetrahedra with a common edge. These molecules are also present in the solid state with the bromide and iodide, not, however, for the chloride, which still possesses a coordination lattice similar to that of chromium chloride (KETELAAR, MACGILLAVRY and RENES, 1947). Aluminium chloride thus just forms the transition.

The rules that determine the volatility of the shielded compounds will be discussed in Chapter V. Likewise the volatility of the hydrogen compounds will be dealt with there.

The electrical conductivity in the liquid state of the halides, *e.g.*, the chlorides, also provides a well-marked difference between the non-conducting shielded compounds and the good-conducting non-shielded compounds with free ions in the melt (BILTZ and KLEMM, see *e.g.*, W. HÜCKEL, book). Aluminium chloride also forms a special case here in so far that the solid substance (coordination lattice), quite exceptionally has a higher conductivity than the liquid (molecules $Al_2Cl_6$).

## § 15. HARDNESS AND COLOUR

*Hardness.* Hardness is a property which can be immediately observed but which can only be determined in an exact manner with great difficulty. The usual figures according to MOH's scale only give the correct order, determined by the possibility of scratching the compound with the standard substances of this scale. The relation between hardness and attraction energy, thus naturally qualitative, is nevertheless very clear. Higher charge and smaller distance result in greater hardness.

Very great hardness would thus be expected in nitrides and carbides in which, on the assumption of ionic bonding, tri- and quadrivalent negative ions would be present. In fact the extremely hard substances, belong to these groups, *e.g.*, carborundum SiC, as well as BN, AlN, TiN, TiC and WC.

However, the converse conclusion, that it would also be plausible that these lattices are built up from ions, is certainly incorrect, since diamond, the hardest substance of all, is certainly not built up of quadrivalent negative and positive ions. Atomic bonding, which predominates in diamond, SiC, BN and AlN leads to extreme hardness; this is also encountered in the last-mentioned metallic interstitial compounds (p. 351).

The agreement between theory and experiment may only

TABLE 12

HARDNESS IN DEPENDENCE ON CHARGE AND DISTANCE

| Compound | Hardness | Distance | Compound | Hardness | Distance | Compound | Hardness | Distance |
|---|---|---|---|---|---|---|---|---|
| BeO | 9.0 | 1.65 Å | CaO | 4.5 | 2.40 Å | NaF | 3.2 | 2.31 Å |
| MgO | 6.5 | 2.10 | CaS | 4.0 | 2.84 | MgO | 6.5 | 2.10 |
| CaO | 4.5 | 2.40 | CaSe | 3.2 | 2.96 | ScN | 7—8 | 2.22 |
| SrO | 3.5 | 2.57 | CaTe | 2.9 | 3.17 | TiC | 8—9 | 2.16 |
| BaO | 3.3 | 2.77 | | | | | | |
| | | | | | | LiBr | 2.5 | 2.75 |
| | | | | | | MgSe | 3.5 | 2.73 |

be put forward as a complete confirmation of the theory if it can be shown that other theories would lead to an essentially different result.

*Colour.* A substance is coloured when visible light is absorbed, *i.e.*, when electronic transitions are possible with an energy difference corresponding to a quantum of light with a wavelength in the visible part of the spectrum (p. 257).

In dilute solutions of inorganic salts the light absorption is found to be independent of concentration, *i.e.*, the molar extinction coefficient $\varepsilon$ is constant and thus Lambert-Beer's law is obeyed. The absorption is additively composed from the contribution of the ions. These facts constitute the most convincing proof that the strong electrolytes are completely dissociated. There are, however, exceptions; thus a concentrated solution of cupric chloride $CuCl_2$ is green instead of blue; it even becomes yellow on the addition of HCl, due to the formation of complex ions $CuCl_4^{2+}$ and not of undissociated molecules. Solutions of ferric salts are yellow to brown but the colour disappears almost completely on addition of a strong non-complexing acid, such as $HNO_3$, as the colour was due to ions formed by hydrolysis, *e.g.*, $Fe(OH)^{2+}$, $Fe(OH)_2^+$ or even colloidal $Fe(OH)_3$. With ferric chloride the yellow colour persists on addition of HCl because of complex formation. In solution the ions with an inert gas electron configuration or an 18-electron configuration are all colourless. Colour is shown by the ions of the transition metals and by the lanthanide and actinide ions and in general by ions with incomplete configurations, *e.g.*, $Cu^{2+}$. Only in these cases are electronic levels available sufficiently close to the ground state to cause absorption in the visible.

The colour exhibited by the solution is in most cases not that of the free ions but rather of the hydrated ions. There is often a difference between the colour of the solution and the fully hydrated solid salt and the colour of the anhydrous salt. Thus *e.g.*, anhydrous nickel fluoride, chloride, bromide and iodide, are green, yellow, brown and black, respectively, but cobalt fluoride, chloride, bromide and iodide are light pink, pale blue, bright green and black; anhydrous cupric sulphate is white, mostly quite different from the well-known colours of the solutions of these ions: green, pink and blue.

The colour of solid inorganic compounds depends strongly on the interaction of the coloured ion with its surroundings. In general the characteristic absorption moves to longer wave lengths with increasing polarization (Fajans) and increasing atomic character of the bonding (Pitzer and Hildebrand, 1941; Donohue and Helmholz, 1944). Both the energy of the upper state and of the ground state of the transition is decreased by polarization. However, this decrease is larger for the upper state with the higher polarizability causing both levels to approach one another.

The nickel and cobalt halides mentioned above form such series with increasing polarization, where the fluorides with pure ionic bonds with little polarization have the same colour as the hydrated ions in which the water molecules are also bound by ion-dipole forces. The iodides resemble elementary iodine very much in colour. The ammines of the transition metals, *e.g.*, those of trivalent cobalt, have predominantly atomic bonding (p. 184), contrary to the hydrates; they show all kinds of lively colours.

A more detailed quantitative study has been made of the behaviour of the electronic levels of the central atom under the influence of the ligands. Especially the splitting of degenerate levels of d-electrons in the free ion due to the cubic electric field arising from the octahedrally arranged surrounding ions or dipole molecules has been studied. (Crystal field theory; HARTMANN *et al.*, 1951, 1955; HARTMANN, 1954, book § 142; ORGEL, 1952, 1955; GRIFFITH and ORGEL, 1957.)

Both colour and magnetic moment furnish experimental evidence of the change in electronic levels and electronic distribution with the change of strength and type of bonding in the complex (p. 185).

Compounds with free or nearly free electrons giving rise to electron conduction in the solid state are black or darkly coloured; the reverse is also true in many cases. Solid compounds containing one element in two valency states are as a rule also darkly coloured because transfer of an electron from the lower to the higher oxidized state is possible in most cases without much change in the energy of the system. It is clear that this is not the case, for instance, in an extreme ionic configuration, *e.g.*, the colourless thiosulphate ion $S_2O_3^{2-}$ or $[S^{6+}(O_3^{2-}S^{2-})]^{2-}$. A striking example is the black colour of the precipitate formed by adding ammonia to a mixture of ferrous and ferric salts, whereas the hydroxides of the two pure salts are rather lightly coloured.

## § 16. SOLUBILITY AND HYDRATION

Owing to the historical development of chemistry from analysis, the solubility of a compound, and especially the solubility in water, is still an important characteristic.

The solubility of organic compounds, the inert gases and such are dealt with in Chapter V; here we will discuss the solubility of the typical ionic lattices.

The fact that many compounds are dissociated into ions in aqueous solution is incorrectly put forward as sufficient proof that these substances must also be constructed from ions in the solid state. It is equally incorrect to conclude from non-solubility that the bonding is not ionogenic.

A purely energetic argument is quite inadequate since heat is absorbed when most salts dissolve, while heat is liberated with only a few, but certainly not exceptionally soluble, compounds, such as $Na_2SO_4$ (anhydrous), $CaSO_4$, etc.

Cases are also known in which the heat effect is greatly variable, and even changes sign, on change of the concentration ($CaCl_2$ 2aq, LiCl, etc.).

The driving force in the solution process and likewise in evaporation, is the pursuit, despite the opposing influence of the change of energy, of a state of higher entropy. That is to say, the system tries to assume a state which has a greater probability as a result of the very much greater number of ways (configurations or states) of realizing the system as regards position and velocity of the molecules in the gas phase or in the solution than in the pure solid phase.

However, the entropy change on solution, in contrast to evaporation, is not independent of the nature of the substance. The magnitude of the heat of solution has no direct connection with the magnitude of the solubility. We also see in a graph of the solubility of various salts as a function of the temperature that intersection of the curves frequently occurs, *i.e.*, the sequence of solubilities changes with the temperature. At low temperatures the salt with a large heat of solution (the amount of heat absorbed) is indeed less soluble, but at higher temperatures this is reversed. The heat of solution is the difference between lattice energy and hydration energy, but it is small in comparison with each of these latter amounts of energy.

The lattice energy for 0° K has to be corrected to 298.16° K for the difference in the specific heats of the crystal and of the gas of free ions. Thus for KCl : $U_0 = H_0 = -168.5$ kcal/mole; $H_{298} = 169.0$ kcal/mole; heat of solution is $\Delta H_{sol} = +4.1$ kcal/mole; and thus the total heat of hydration is $H_{\mathrm{H}} = H_{298.1} + \Delta H_{sol} = -164.9$ kcal/mole can be calculated.

The lattice energy of the silver halides (with the exception of the fluoride) is increased by the contribution of the VAN DER WAALS-LONDON attraction between the readily polarizable cations and anions; the hydration energy remains normal on account of the small polarizability of water. The hydration entropy will also be quite comparable with that of the alkali halides; thus the small solubility of these silver compounds can rightly be attributed to the LONDON contribution to the lattice energy. The silver halides are indeed more readily soluble in the better polarizable liquid ammonia, but NaF for example is only very slightly soluble on account of the smaller dipole of $NH_3$. Silver fluoride and the silver salts of complex oxygen acids are again all quite soluble in water. The same holds for the cuprous and lead salts. Also for the pairs $Tl^+$—$K^+$, $Cd^{2+}$—$Ca^{2+}$, which possess approximately equal hydration energies and hydration entropies, the fluorides of the polarizable non-inert gas ions are always the most readily soluble, the iodides the least soluble.

The small solubility of divalent and higher compounds, such as MgO, CuS, $BaSO_4$, $AlPO_4$, ($Mg_3N_2$), etc., must be attributed to the large lattice energy.

It is, however, not justifiable to discuss small relative differences in solubility in a similar, purely energetic way.

Why, for instance, are the salts of the heavier alkali metals $K^+$, $Rb^+$, $Cs^+$ (but also $NH^+$) with large complex negative ions, such as the perchlorates, silicofluorides, etc., less soluble than those of the lighter alkali metals? In general the salts of these former metals are more soluble; compare LiF with KF. VAN ARKEL relates this to the high acid strength of these acids from which he concludes a generally smaller attraction energy for positive ions.

On the other hand the heat of hydration increases $\propto 1/r^+$ with decreasing radius of the positive ion; the lattice energy also increases but $\propto 1/(r^+ + r^-)$. The latter influence will be small for large negative ions, thus explaining the different sequence in solubility in the series of the alkali salts with small anions ($F^-$) and with large anions ($ClO_4^-$, $SiF_6$, $PF_6^-$, $PtCl_6^{2-}$). With non-polarizable anions $Ag^+$ behaves quite analogously to $Na^+$, with about the same radius (comp. Table 13). The insolubility of $Ag_3PO_4$ as compared with $Na_3PO_4$ must be ascribed to a deviation from pure ionic bonding in the first substance as corroborated by its yellow colour (p. 98). Owing to the lack of sufficient knowledge of the heats and entropies of solution such a conclusion is difficult to justify although the phenomenon is conspicuous. It may be remembered that the difference in entropy of solution $\Delta S_H$ between, for example, $F^-$ and $I^-$ is 23 cal/deg. mole. This causes at room temperature (T = 298° K) a difference of 6.9 kcal in the free energy at constant pressure or free enthalpy of solution $\Delta G$, with a difference in heat of solution $\Delta H$ between NaF and NaI of only 2.4 kcal ($\Delta G = \Delta H - T\Delta S$).

The number of water molecules bound by an ion, *i.e.*, the hydration number, is not well defined. Divergent results are obtained by different methods, *e.g.*, transference, mobility entropy, volume change on solution, specific heat, etc.

The number of tightly bound molecules of water (primary hydration) as calculated from the hydration entropy (values from the mobility in brackets) are (EUCKEN, 1948, BOCKRIS, 1949; HAASE, 1958):

HYDRATION NUMBERS

| | | | | | |
|---|---|---|---|---|---|
| $Li^+$ | 5 (6) | $Mg^{2+}$ | 10 (14) | $F^-$ | 5 (2) |
| $Na^+$ | 4 (4) | $Ca^{2+}$ | 7 (12) | $Cl^-$ | 2 (0.9) |
| $K^+$ | 2 (1.5) | $Ba^{2+}$ | 6 (10) | $Br^-$ | 1.5 (0.6) |
| $Cs^+$ | 1 (1) | | | $I^-$ | 0.5 (0.2) |

In order to calculate the hydration energy, *i.e.* the change of the energy of an ion when the latter is brought from vacuum into water, the simplest way is to consider the water, according to BORN, as a continuous medium with a dielectric constant $D$ equal to 80. According to the laws of electrostatics the amount of energy in question is $U_H = -\frac{1}{2}\frac{e^2}{r}\left(1 - \frac{1}{D}\right)$, the energy of a charged sphere in a medium with dielectric constant $D$ being $\frac{1}{2}\frac{e^2}{rD}$. Thus one obtains for $K^+$ with $r = 1.33$ Å $U_H =$ $= -122$ kcal/g ion; for $Cl^-$ with $r = 1.81$ Å $U_H = -89$ kcal/g ion. The separate hydration energies cannot be determined directly from experiment, but the sum is known from the lattice energy and the heat of solution of a salt, as discussed. For KCl the total hydration energy is 164.4 kcal/mole (p. 100), considerably less than that just calculated; *i.e.*, 211 kcal.

Now this calculation is undoubtedly very rough and the macroscopic picture of a continuous medium is certainly incorrect. The dielectric constant in the immediate neighbourhood of the ion will be very much less than 80, because the water molecules will be strongly orientated there by the field and this hydrate "envelope" is therefore much less polarizable than "free" water.

The experimental values of the total heat (enthalpy) of hydration at 298.1° K of the alkali halides show constant differences, just as in the case of interionic distances (p. 27) *e.g.*:

| | | | | | |
|---|---|---|---|---|---|
| NaCl | 185.0 | kcal | NaBr | 176.9 | kcal |
| KCl | 164.9 | ,, | KBr | 156.7 | ,, |
| Diff. | 20.1 | ,, | Diff. | 20.2 | ,, |

Thus single ionic heats of hydration (Table 13) can be obtained, once one value has been found.

It can be expected that the heat of hydration will be proportional to $1/r$ (in general $z^2/r$) just as many other phenomena related to hydration.

An approximately straight line is obtained if we plot the total hydration energy, *e.g.*, of all the sodium halides, as a function of $1/r_-$ of the negative ion. The intersection with the vertical axis ($1/r = 0$) then gives the heat of hydration of the sodium ion (in combination with an imaginary anion with infinite radius). Somewhat better results are obtained if $r_- + a_-$ (and $r_+ + a_+$) are used instead of the crystal radii proper. The values of the parameters $a_-$ and $a_+$ chosen to obtain straight lines are 0.10 Å and 0.85 Å for anions and cations, respectively. Table 13 gives a set of values for the heat (enthalpy) of hydration (VAN ARKEL and DE BOER, book § 37; VAN ARKEL, *Molecules and Crystals*, 1949, 1957; VOET, 1936, LATIMER, 1936, 1938, 1952, 1955; LATIMER *et al.*, 1939; VERWEY, 1940, 1942; ELEY and EVANS, 1938; EUCKEN, 1949; STREHLOW, 1952; BENJAMIN and GOLD, 1954; RUNDLES, 1956).

With $K^+$ and $F^-$, the hydration energy with 75 kcal and 122 kcal respectively is greater for the negative ion although these ions have the same radius. This is due to the eccentric situation of the positive centres of charge of the water molecule (see also the hydrogen bond, § 45). This result can be calculated when accurate account is taken of the structure and charge distribution of the water molecule (VERWEY, 1941).

X-ray investigation has shown that in very concentrated salt solutions of high valent ions, for example of $Th(NO_3)_4$, the strongly hydrated $Th^{4+}$ ions have bound practically all the water, so that an almost regular arrangement of these ions is produced (PRINS, 1935; LATIMER *et al.*, 1939; EUCKEN, 1949; STREHLOW, 1952; BENJAMIN and GOLD, 1954).

The hydration entropy can also be deduced experimentally (LATIMER, 1936) as the difference between the standard entropy of the hydrated ions (deduced from measurements of the specific heat on the basis of NERNST's Heat Theorem or the Third Law of Thermodynamics) and the theoretically calculated absolute entropy of the gaseous ion, both reckoned per unit volume at equal concentration. The hydration entropy can also be calculated theoretically (ELEY and EVANS, 1938).

It appears (Table 13) that loss of entropy, frequently considerable, occurs on hydration and that this loss is roughly proportional to the hydration energy; both run parallel to $z^2/r$, where $z$ is the valency. This can be readily understood, since through the strong bonding of the water molecules to the ion, the possibilities of movement of these water molecules are greatly restricted, which means a reduction of the entropy (formation of an "iceberg" round the ion). It can also be interpreted in such a way that the hydration of an ion corresponds to a large internal pressure on the surrounding water which also brings with it a diminution of entropy.

The free energy of the hydration at constant pressure ($\Delta g_H = \Delta H_H - T\Delta S_H$) can now be calculated also. It is this

TABLE 13

HYDRATION ENTHALPY AND ENTROPY* AT 25° C

in kcal/mole and cal/degree · mole respectively

| | $-\Delta H_H$ | $-\Delta S_H$ | | $-\Delta H_H$ | $-\Delta S_H$ | | $-\Delta H_H$ | $-\Delta S_H$ |
|---|---|---|---|---|---|---|---|---|
| $H^+$ | 259 | 24.3 | $Mg^{2+}$ | 456 | 66.5 | $OH^-$ | 87 | 26 |
| $Li^+$ | 121.3 | 26.7 | $Ca^{2+}$ | 377 | 53 | $F^-$ | 122 | 26 |
| $Na^+$ | 95.2 | 19.2 | $Sr^{2+}$ | 342 | 51 | $Cl^-$ | 89.8 | 12.5 |
| $K^+$ | 75.0 | 10.7 | $Ba^{2+}$ | 308 | 41 | $Br^-$ | 81.7 | 8.8 |
| $Rb^+$ | 69.1 | 7.8 | $Zn^{2+}$ | 485 | 67 | $I^-$ | 71.3 | 3.3 |
| $Cs^+$ | 61.2 | 7.1 | $Cd^{2+}$ | 428 | 57.5 | $CN^-$ | – | 0 |
| $Ag^+$ | 111.9 | 20.6 | $Hg^{2+}$ | 435 | 49 | $NO_3^-$ | – | –8 |
| $Tl^+$ | 76.2 | 9.7 | $Fe^{2+}$ | 455 | 68 | $SO_4^{2-}$ | – | 20 |
| $NH_4^+$ | 74 | 6.5 | $Al^{3+}$ | 1110 | 118 | $CO_3^{2-}$ | – | 36 |
| | | | $Fe^{3+}$ | 1042 | 119 | $S^{2-}$ | – | 16 |

* The change in entropy on the transfer from the standard gas state (1 atm) to the ideal solution at 0.041 *M*, *i.e.*, in general at the same volume concentration in both states. For a concentration of 1 *M*, $\Delta S_H$ (again with respect to the gas at 1 atm) is 6.33 cal/degr·mole lower.

quantity and not the energy itself which must be compared with the electrical energy according to BORN; the differences are, however, not great. In general, changes in the hydration enthalpy and the hydration entropy thus oppose one another in the free energy. General conclusions on solubility and electrochemical potential are not possible, therefore. In particular the electrochemical potential does not show a direct parallelism with the ionisation potential of the metal atom.

We have seen that the electrostatic theory of ionic bonding is able to give an account of the properties of large groups of, in particular, inorganic compounds. It is also of great interest that the work of KOSSEL, BORN, GOLDSCHMIDT, VAN ARKEL and DE BOER, PAULING, ZACHARIASEN, MAYER and others has raised the question of the explanation of the properties of compounds. Only on this basis is a further development of theoretical chemistry possible. Here also curiosity forms the beginning of science.

## LITERATURE

J. M. BIJVOET, N. H. KOLKMEYER and C. H. MACGILLAVRY, *X-ray Analysis of Crystals*, London, 1951, 2nd ed., 1952.
H. J. EMELÉUS and J. S. ANDERSON, *Modern Aspects of Inorganic Chemistry*, London, 1938, 2nd ed., 1952.
R. C. EVANS, *An Introduction to Crystal Chemistry*, Cambridge, 1946.
J. E. HILLER, *Grundrisz der Kristallchemie*, Berlin, 1952.
W. HÜCKEL, *Anorganische Strukturchemie*, Stuttgart, 1948; also *Structural Chemistry of Inorganic Compounds*, I, II, Amsterdam, 1950, 1951.
N. V. SIDGWICK, *Chemical Elements and Their Compounds*, I, II, Oxford, 1950.
A. E. VAN ARKEL, *Molecules and Crystals*, London, 1949, 2nd ed., 1957.
A. E. VAN ARKEL and J. H. DE BOER, *Die Chemische Bindung als Elektrostatische Erscheinung*, Leipzig, 1931; *La Valence et l'Electrostatique*, Paris, 1936.
A. F. WELLS, *Structural Inorganic Chemistry*, Oxford, 2nd ed., 1950.

## REFERENCES

ABRAHAMS, S. C., *Acta Cryst.*, *7* (1954) 423; *8* (1955) 661.
ABRAHAMS, S. C. and GRISON, E., *Acta Cryst.*, *6* (1953) 206.
AHRENS, L. H., *Geochim. et Cosmochim. Acta*, *2* (1952) 155.
ALTSHULLER, A. P., *J. Chem. Phys.*, *21* (1954) 1136.
ARLMAN, E. J., *Rec. trav. chim.*, *56* (1937) 919.

BARRER, R. M., *Quart. Revs. (London)*, *3* (1949) 293.
BEINTEMA, J., *Koninkl. Ned. Akad. Wetenschap. Proc.*, *38* (1935) 1015; *39* (1936) 652.
BELL, R. P., *Quart. Revs. (London)*, *1* (1947) 113.
BELOV, N. V., *Acta Cryst.*, *10* (1956) 757.
BENJAMIN, L. and GOLD, V., *Trans. Faraday Soc.*, *50* (1954) 797.
BERNSTEIN, R. B. and METLAY, M., *J. Chem. Phys.*, *19* (1951) 1612.
BERTAUT, F., *J. phys. radium*, *13* (1952) 499.
BOCKRIS, J. O'M., *Quart. Revs. (London)*, *3* (1949) 173.
BODE, H. and KLESPER, E., *Z. anorg. u. allgem. Chem.*, *267* (1951) 97.
BORN, M. and MAYER, J. E., *Z. Physik*, *75* (1932) 1.
BÖTTCHER, C. J. F., *Rec. trav. chim.*, *65* (1946) 19, 91.
BÖTTCHER, C. J. F. and SCHOLTE, TH. G., *Rec. trav. chim.*, *70* (1951) 209.
BRAUER, G. and DISTLER, H., *Z. anorg. u. allgem. Chem.*, *275* (1954) 157.
BRECK, D. W. *et al.*, *J. Am. Chem. Soc.*, *78* (1956) 5963.
BRIEGLEB, G., *Naturwissenschaften*, *30* (1942) 506.
BRILL, R., GRIMM, H. G., HERMANS, C. and PETERS, CL., *Ann. Physik*, (5) *34* (1939) 393.
BRILL, R. and ZAROMB, S., *Nature*, *173* (1954) 316.
BRILL, R. *et al.*, *Naturwissenschaften*, *32* (1944) 33.
BROEKEMA, J., HAVINGA, E. E. and WIEBENGA, E. H., *Acta Cryst.*, *10* (1957) 596.
BRÖNSTED, J. N., *Rec. trav. chim.*, *42* (1923) 718.
BROSSET, C., *Z. anorg. u. allgem. Chem.*, *235* (1937) 139; *238* (1938) 201; *239* (1938) 301.
BIJVOET, J. M. and LONSDALE, K., *Phil. Mag.*, [7] *44* (1953) 204.
BIJVOET, J. M. and NIEUWENKAMP, W., *Z. Krist.*, *86* (1933) 466.

CALLIS, C. F., VAN WAZER, J. R. and ARVAN, P. G., *Chem. Revs.*, *54* (1954) 777.
CLARK, D., POWELL, H. M. and WELLS, A. F., *J. Chem. Soc.*, (1942) 642.

DONOHUE, J. and HELMHOLTZ, L., *J. Am. Chem. Soc.*, *66* (1944) 295.

EHRLICH, P. and GENTSCH, L., *Naturwissenschaften, 40* (1953) 460; *41* (1954) 211.
EHRLICH, P. *et al.*, *Z. anorg. u. allgem. Chem.*, *283* (1956) 58; *288* (1956) 146, 156.
ELEY, D. D. and EVANS ,M. G., *Trans. Faraday Soc.*, *34* (1938) 1093.
EMERSLEBEN, O., *Z. physik. Chem. (Leipzig)*, *199* (1952) 170.
ERIKS, K. and MACGILLAVRY, C. H., *Acta Cryst.*, *7* (1954) 430.
EUCKEN, A., *Z. Electrochem.*, *51* (1948) 6.
EUCKEN, A., *Lehrbuch der chemischen Physik*, 3rd Ed., Bd. II 2, Leipzig, 1949, p. 991.
EVJEN, H. M., *Phys. Rev.*, *39* (1932) 675.

FEHER, F. *et al.*, *Z. anorg. u. allgem. Chem.*, *281* (1955) 151, 161; *286* (1956) 45; *288* (1956) 103, 113, 123; *292* (1957) 203, 210.
FOSS, O., FURBERG, S. and ZACHARIASEN, W. H., *Acta Chem. Scand.*, *8* (1954) 459, 873.
FURBERG, S., *Acta Chem. Scand.*, *9* (1955) 1557.

GRDENIC, D. and SCAVNICAR, S., *Nature, 172* (1953) 584; *Acta Cryst.*, *8* (1955) 275.
GRIFFITH, J. S. and ORGEL, L. E., *Quart. Revs. (London)*, *11* (1957) 381.

HAASE, R., *Z. Elektrochem.*, *62* (1958) 62.
HACH, R. J. and RUNDLE, R. E., *J. Am. Chem. Soc.*, *73* (1951) 3538, 4321.
HARTMANN, H., *Theorie der chemischen Bindung auf quantentheoretischer Grundlage*, Berlin, 1954, cited on p. 22.
HARTMANN, H. *et al.*, *Z. physik. Chem. (Leipzig)*, *197* (1951) 116, 239; *Z. physik. Chem. (Frankfurt)*, *4* (1955) 376.
HAVINGA, E. E., *Thesis*, Groningen, 1957.
HAVINGA, E. E., BOSWIJK, K. H. and WIEBENGA, E. H., *Acta Cryst.*, *7* (1954) 487.
HELMHOLZ, L. and MAYER, J. E., *J. Chem. Phys.*, *2* (1934) 245.
HOARD, J. L., *J. Am. Chem. Soc.*, *61* (1939) 1252.
HOARD, J. L. and NORDSIECK, H. H., *J. Am. Chem. Soc.*, *61* (1939) 2853.
HÖJENDAHL, K., *Kgl. Danske Videnskab. Selskab, Mat. fys. Medd.*, *16* (1938) 133.
HONIG, A., MANDEL, M., STITCH, M. L. and TOWNES, C. H., *Phys. Rev.*, *96* (1954) 629.
HUGGINS, M. L., *J. Chem. Phys.*, *1* (1933) 643; *5* (1937) 143.
HUGGINS, M. L., *J. Am. Ceram. Soc.*, *38* (1955) 172.

JAMES, W. J., HACH, R. J., FRENCH, D. and RUNDLE, R. E., *Acta Cryst.*, *8* (1955) 814.

KAPUTINSKII, A. F., *Z. physik. Chem. (Leipzig)*, *B 22* (1933) 257; *Quart. Revs. (London)*, 10 (1956) 283.
KETELAAR, J. A. A., *Ned. Tijdschr. Natuurk.*, *5* (1938) 233.
KETELAAR, J. A. A. and GORTER, E. W., *Z. Krist.*, *101* (1939) 367.
KETELAAR, J. A. A., MACGILLAVRY, C. H. and RENES, P. A., *Rec. trav. chim.*, *66* (1947) 501.
KOLDITZ, L., *Z. anorg. u. allgem. Chem.*, *280* (1955) 313; *Angew. Chem.*, *68* (1956) 154.
KOSSIAKOFF, A. and HARKER, D., *J. Am. Chem. Soc.*, *60* (1938) 2047.

LATIMER, W. M., *The Oxidation States of the Elements and Their Potentials in Aqueous Solutions*, New York, 1952.
LATIMER, W. M., *J. Chem. Phys.*, *23* (1955) 90.
LATIMER, W. M., PITZER, K. S. and SLANSKY, C. M., *J. Chem. Phys.*, *7* (1939) 108.
LATIMER, W. M. *et al.*, *Chem. Revs.*, *18* (1936) 349; *J. Am. Chem. Soc.*, *60* (1938) 1829.

LIESER, K. H., *Z. anorg. u. allgem. Chem.*, *292* (1957) 114.
LONG, L. H., *Quart. Revs. (London)*, *7* (1953) 134.
LOWRY, T. M., *Chemistry & Industry*, *42* (1923) 43.
LUDER, W. F. and ZUFFANTI, S., *The Electronic Theory of Acids and Bases*, New York, 1946.

MACGILLAVRY, C. H. and DEDECKER, H. C. J., *Rec. trav. chim.*, *60* (1941) 153.
MACGILLAVRY, C. H., DEDECKER, H. C. J. and NIJLAND, L., *Nature*, *164* (1949) 448.
MACGILLAVRY, C. H. and VAN PANTHALEON VAN ECK, C. L., *Rec. trav. chim.*, *62* (1943) 729.
MACHATSCHKI, F., oral communication, 1954.
MARTIN, D. S., RUNDLE, R. E. and GOLDEN, S. A., *J. Chem. Phys.*, *24* (1956) 1114.
MAY, A., *Phys. Rev.*, *52* (1937) 339.
MAYER, J. E., *J. Chem. Phys.*, *1* (1933) 270.
MAYER, J. E. and HELMHOLZ, L., *Z. Physik*, *75* (1932) 19.
MAYER, J. E. *et al.*, *J. Chem. Phys.*, *1* (1933) 327, 647.
MOONEY, R. C. L., *Z. Krist.*, *98* (1938) 377.
MOREY, G. W., *The Properties of Glass*, 2nd Ed., New York, 1954.
MORRIS, D. C. F., *Acta Cryst.*, *9* (1956) 197.
MORRIS, D. C. F. and AHRENS, L. H., *J. Inorg. & Nuclear Chem.*, *3* (1956) 263.

ORGEL, L. E., *J. Chem. Soc.*, (1952) 4756; *J. Chem. Phys.*, *23* (1955) 1004.

PAULING, L., *General Chemistry*, San Francisco, 1947.
PAULING, L., *School Science and Mathematics*, 1953, p. 429.
PINSKER, G., *Acta Physicochim. U.R.S.S.*, *18* (1943) 311.
PITZER, K. S. and HILDEBRAND, J. H., *J. Am. Chem. Soc.*, *63* (1941) 2471.
POWELL, H. M. and CLARK, D., *Nature*, *145* (1940) 971.
PRINS, J. A., *J. Chem. Phys.*, *3* (1935) 72, 362.
PRITCHARD, H., *Chem. Revs.*, *52* (1953) 529.

RABINOWITSCH, E. and THILO, E., *Z. physik. Chem. (Leipzig)*, *B 6* (1929) 284.
REED, T. B. and BRECK, D. W., *J. Am. Chem. Soc.*, *78* (1956) 5972.
RICCI, J. E., *J. Am. Chem. Soc.*, *70* (1948) 109.
RITTNER, E. J., *J. Chem. Phys.*, *19* (1951) 1030.
ROMERS, C., KETELAAR, J. A. A. and MACGILLAVRY, C. H., *Acta Cryst.*, *4* (1951) 114.
ROSSINI, F. D. *et al.*, *Selected Values of Chemical Thermodynamic Properties*, N.B.S. Circ. 500, Washington, 1952.
RUNDLES, J. E. B., *Trans. Faraday Soc.*, *52* (1956) 1573.

SEEL, F., *Angew. Chem.*, *66* (1954) 581.
SHERMAN, J., *Chem. Revs.*, *11* (1932) 93.
SIEMONS, W. J. and TEMPLETON, D. H., *Acta Cryst.*, *7* (1954) 194.
SIMON, A. and WEIST, M., *Z. anorg. u. allgem. Chem.*, *268* (1952) 301.
SLY, W. G. and MARSH, R. E., *Acta Cryst.*, *10* (1957) 378.
STEVELS, J. M., *Progress in the Theory of the Physical Properties of Glass*, Amsterdam 1948.
STEVELS, J. M., *Glass Ind.*, *35* (1954) 135.
STEWARD, E. G. and RUNCIMAN, W. A., *Nature*, *172* (1953) 75.
STREHLOW, H., *Z. Electrochem.*, *56* (1952) 119.
TASMAN, H. A. and BOSWIJK, K. H., *Acta Cryst.*, *8* (1955) 59, 587.

TEMPLETON, D. H., *J. Chem. Phys.*, *21* (1953) 2097.
TEMPLETON, D. H., *J. Chem. Phys.*, *23* (1955) 1629.
THOMAS, E. B. and WOOD, L. J., *J. Am. Chem. Soc.*, *56* (1934) 92; *57* (1935) 82; *58* (1936) 1341.
TOPLEY, B., *Quart. Revs. (London)*, *3* (1949) 345.

VAN ARKEL, A. E. *Molecules and Crystals*, London 1949, 1957.
VAN ARKEL, A. E. and CARRIÈRE, G., *Chem. Weekblad*, *33* (1937) 182.
VAN DRIEL, M. and MACGILLAVRY, C. H., *Rec. trav. chim.*, *62* (1943) 167.
VAN VELDEN, P. F. and KETELAAR, J. A. A., *Chem. Weekblad*, *43* (1947) 401.
VERWEY, E. J. W., *Rec. trav. chim.*, *60* (1941) 887.
VERWEY, E. J. W., *Rec. trav. chim.*, *61* (1942) 127; *Chem. Weekblad*, *37* (1940) 530.
VERWEY, E. J. W. and DE BOER, J. H., *Rec. trav. chim.*, *59* (1940), 633.
VOET, A., *Trans. Faraday Soc.*, *32* (1936) 1301.

WARREN, B. E., *Chem. Revs.*, *26* (1940) 237.
WASASTJERNA, J. A., *Soc. Sci. Fennica Commentationes Phys.-Math.*, *8* (1935) 21.
WEHNER, G., *Z. anorg. u. allgem. Chem.*, *276* (1954) 72.
WEISS, A., WITTE, H. and WÖLFEL, E., *Z. physik. Chem. (Frankfurt)*, *10* (1957) 98.
WELLS, A. F., *Quart. Revs. (London)*, *8* (1954) 380
WESSEL, G. and YDO, D. J. W., *Acta Cryst.*, *10* (1957) 466.
WITTE, H. and WÖLFEL, E., *Z. physik. Chem. (Frankfurt)*, *3* (1955) 296.
WOOD, L. J. and BREITHAUPT, L. J., *J. Am. Chem. Soc.*, *74* (1952) 727.
WOOLF, A. A. and EMELÉUS, H. J., *J. Chem. Soc.*, (1949) 2865.

ZACHARIASEN, W. H., *Z. Krist.*, *80* (1931) 137.
ZACHARIASEN, W. H., *Acta Cryst.*, *1* (1948) 265; *Phys. Rev.*, *73* (1948) 1104; *J. Chem. Phys.*, *16* (1948) 254.
ZACHARIASEN, W. H., *Acta Cryst.*, *7* (1954) 783, 792.
ZAROMB, S., *J. Chem. Phys.*, *25* (1956) 350.
ZINTL, E. and MORAWIETZ, W., *Z. anorg. u. allgem. Chem.*, *236* (1938) 372.

# III. THE ATOMIC BOND

Although valency strokes have been customary in chemical formulae for a century, no conception of their true significance could be formed until recently. One operated with them on the patient paper as with hooks which were undone, rotated, etc. at will. Even the RUTHERFORD-BOHR theory of the atom did not furnish an explanation, not even for the bonding of two hydrogen atoms to form a hydrogen molecule. The successful octet theory and the LEWIS and LANGMUIR theory of the electron-pair bond were still purely formal, but later were seen to be essentially correct.

The calculation of the energy of the hydrogen molecule by HEITLER and LONDON (1927), together with the conception of the spatial model of the carbon atom by VAN 'T HOFF and LE BEL, must be considered as the most important contribution to theoretical chemistry, since the advent of DALTON's atomic hypothesis. However, we shall let the treatment of the hydrogen molecule itself be preceded by the discussion of the hydrogen molecule ion $H_2^+$, since this problem with only one electron is simpler than that of the $H_2$ molecule itself.

The first step soon led to a fundamentally new insight into the constitution of benzene and other aromatic molecules. A correct conception regarding the molecular structure had been obtained quite early in organic chemistry by inductive intuitive method, but this was not the case with the constitution of aromatic molecules. It was the quantum mechanical theory which first gave the solution of the benzene problem. The same ideas also laid the foundation for a better understanding of conjugation and of the relation between colour and constitution of organic compounds.

## § 17. PARTICLES AND WAVES

According to the views of the majority of physicists in the 17th and 18th centuries, the simple phenomena of (geometrical) optics, such as rectilinear propagation, reflection and refraction, found a completely acceptable explanation in the corpuscular theory of NEWTON. The Dutchman HUYGENS suggested, however, that light was a vibrational phenomenon and he proposed his wave theory (or undulatory theory) with which he could explain rectilinear propagation as well as reflection and refraction. The initially slight success of this latter theory is obvious when one remembers how much simpler it is to explain rectilinear propagation, as exhibited in the formation of shadow, by NEWTON's hypothesis of flying corpuscles than by the much more complicated considerations of HUYGENS on wave fronts.

The controversy was settled in favour of the wave theory because the latter could immediately give a reasonable explanation of interference and diffraction phenomena. Moreover, the observation (FOUCAULT) that the velocity of propagation of light in a medium is less than in a vacuum was in contradiction to the corpuscular emission theory.

However, in the 20th century a discontinuous character was again attributed to light in the quantum hypothesis of PLANCK where light was regarded as a stream of energy quanta. It does indeed exert a pressure on a surface; this effect had already been looked for in 1754 but was experimentally established as late as 1900 (LEBEDEW). EINSTEIN in particular drew the corpuscular character of light quanta or photons into the foreground; this representation was confirmed in a brilliant fashion by the photoelectric effect and the COMPTON effect (p. 113).

The two views on light, the wave theory and the corpuscular quantum theory, in no way exclude one another; both are capable of correctly explaining all the phenomena. For some phenomena the one theory, for others the alternative theory gives the simplest and most obvious interpretation, without contradiction being produced. Following BOHR one speaks of complementary theories.

When HITTORF (1869) (and later GOLDSTEIN (1876)) carried out experiments with a discharge tube and thereby saw the formation of a shadow by a metal cross in this tube, he, just like NEWTON and his contemporaries, drew the obvious conclusion that he must have been dealing with a corpuscular radiation. The name electrons was later given to these particles by STONEY (1891).

It was not difficult to explain various phenomena discovered later, on the basis of this corpuscular conception of cathode rays, phenomena such as the deflection in magnetic and electric fields from which the value of $e/m$ could be deduced.

It was only in 1927 that the experiments of DAVISSON and GERMER, and of G. P. THOMSON showed that these electron beams exhibit exactly the same diffraction phenomena as those which VON LAUE, FRIEDRICH and KNIPPING had observed with X-rays in 1912. The diffraction of X-rays was in agreement with the prevailing conception of the nature of these rays. With electrons, however, this wave character appeared to be completely in conflict with the ideas which had been supported for more than 50 years; however, DE BROGLIE had published his fundamental hypothesis on the wave nature of electrons in his thesis (1924) only three years previously.

What would have been the development of physics if HITTORF, GOLDSTEIN or LENARD had just put a gold foil in the path of the cathode rays instead of a massive cross? Would they not have regarded the diffraction phenomena as an incontestable proof of the wave nature of the cathode rays?

PLANCK's fundamental formula in quantum theory is as follows:

$$E = h\nu \tag{1}$$

A not less fundamental formula is that of EINSTEIN:

$$E = mc^2 \tag{2}$$

in which the equivalence of energy and mass is expressed.

When the two formulae are combined we have:

$$mc^2 = h\nu \qquad (3)$$

or, by replacing the frequency $\nu$ by the wave length $\lambda$ *in vacuo* by means of the relation $\nu = c/\lambda$ we have

$$\lambda = \frac{h}{mc} = \frac{h}{p} \qquad (4)$$

in which $p$ represents the momentum of the light quantum of mass $m$ and velocity $c$.

The relation between the mass (or momentum) of the light quantum and the wave length of the radiation is confirmed experimentally by the observation of the COMPTON effect. In this effect, *i.e.*, the change of the wave length of X-rays when the latter are scattered by an electron, the experimental result can be calculated simply when both the electron and the quantum of radiation are treated as material particles colliding with one another.

In the derivation the laws of collision, the law of the conservation of energy and the law of the conservation of momentum, are applied exactly as in a mechanical collision problem, for example, of billiard balls.

Let us consider a central collision between a light quantum, with frequency $\nu$ and mass $\frac{h\nu}{c^2}$, and a free electron of mass $m_0$. We derive the formula here for the simplest case, namely that of scattering through 180°, *i.e.*, the light quantum after the collision moves in exactly the opposite direction and with a frequency $\nu'$, while the electron has received a velocity $v$ in the original direction.

Law of conservation of energy:

$$h\nu = h\nu' + {}^1/_2\, m_0 v^2 \qquad (5)$$

Law of conservation of momentum:

$$mc = -\, m'c + m_0 v \qquad (6)$$

in which $m = \frac{h\nu}{c^2}$ and $m' = \frac{h\nu'}{c^2}$ are the masses of the light quanta before and after the collision. Thus

$$\frac{h\nu}{c} = -\frac{h\nu'}{c} + m_0 v \qquad (6')$$

(The negative sign in (6) and (6′) is necessary on account of the opposite direction after scattering.)

From (6′) we have:

$m_0 v = \frac{2\,h\nu}{c}$ when $\nu + \nu' \approx 2\,\nu$ is assumed since the relative change of frequency is only small.

From (5) we then have $h(\nu - \nu') = \frac{1}{2\,m_0} \cdot \frac{4\,h^2\nu^2}{c^2}$ or $c(\nu - \nu')/\nu^2 = 2\,h/m_0c$.
By a simple transformation (with the approximation $\lambda\lambda' \approx \lambda^2$) we have:

$$\lambda' - \lambda = \Delta\lambda = 2\,h/m_0c = 2\,\lambda_0 \qquad (7)$$

(The general formula is $\Delta\lambda = 2\lambda_0 \sin^2\vartheta/2$ in which $\vartheta$ is the angle of deviation.)
The COMPTON wave length: $\lambda_0 = h/m_0c = 0.024$ Å is a universal constant, which represents the wave length of a light quantum with a mass equal to that of the electron.

It is only for X-rays of short wave length that $\Delta\lambda$ is a measurable amount; in other words, only for such radiation is the mass of the light quantum appreciable compared with the rest mass of the electron $m_0$. A particulate nature is thus added to the wave nature of the radiation in the complementary theory and vice versa, according to equation (4).

DE BROGLIE (1924) now made the step of also adding a wave phenomenon to the particulate nature of a moving electron, led by considerations of symmetry and by the need for a generalization of the fundamental concepts of nature. DE BROGLIE's relation is similar to (4):

$$\lambda = \frac{h}{p} = \frac{h}{mv} \qquad (4')$$

in which $m$ and $v$ are now the (rest) mass and the velocity of the electron (we always neglect relativity corrections here).

This relation found a direct experimental confirmation in the experiments (already mentioned) of DAVISSON and GERMER and of THOMSON on the diffraction of electron beams by crystal lattices. For electrons which have traversed a potential difference $P$, the energy is $eP = {}^1/_2 mv^2$, the kinetic energy; thus $(mv)^2 = 2\,meP$ and:

$$\lambda = \frac{h}{\sqrt{2\,m\,e\,P}}$$

After inserting the values of the universal constants and expressing the potential difference in volts, we have:

$$\lambda = \sqrt{\frac{150}{V}}\ \text{Å}$$

For a potential difference of 150 V and 60,000 V we have therefore $\lambda = 1$ Å and 0.05 Å respectively; this agrees with the experiments carried out by DAVISSON and GERMER with nickel single crystals or by THOMSON with gold foil. With the observed angles of deviation the wave length could be calculated from the lattice spacings in the same way as with X-rays. We can therefore look upon (4′) also as a purely experimental result from which the wave nature of the electron and the correctness of equation (4′) appear empirically.

The wave nature is not connected only with electrons but with all matter. However, this does not appear in the macroscopic world because, in view of the large mass, the wave length is so small compared with all other dimensions. Even with light, diffraction phenomena do in fact only occur when the dimensions of hole or obstacle are of the order of magnitude of the wave length. For protons of the same energy the wave length is $\sqrt{1{,}836}$ times smaller than for electrons. Nevertheless diffraction phenomena have been obtained with protons, helium nuclei and lithium ions. Neutrons also give diffraction phenomena in a crystal lattice (BACON, 1955; LONSDALE, 1951; RUNDLE, 1951; PETERSON and LEVY, 1951); with thermal neutrons, $\frac{1}{2}mv^2 = 3/2\,kT$ and thus the wave length at 298° K is equal to 1.46 Å.

DE BROGLIE was able to draw a very important conclusion from his relation (4′) regarding the stationary states of a hydrogen atom. His result agreed with that of BOHR. However, in BOHR's theory the stationary states were introduced completely *ad hoc* to explain the spectra, while they follow logically and obviously from the basic hypothesis of DE BROGLIE.

A stationary state of an electron, considered as a wave phenomenon, signifies a stationary wave motion, whereby the perimeter of the orbit must therefore be a whole number of waves long. Thus discrete orbits of length $\lambda$, $2\lambda$, $3\lambda$, etc. are "obviously" produced as a result of which whole numbers already occur. However $\lambda$ is not equal for the different energy states on account of the connection between the wave length of the electron and the momentum, *i.e.*, $\lambda$ depends on the energy.

The condition for a stable circular orbit of rank $n$ and radius $a_n$ is according to (4′):

$$2\,\pi a_n = n\,\lambda_n = \frac{nh}{mv} \tag{8}$$

In a circular motion around a nucleus with charge $Ze$ the centripetal force is provided by the COULOMB force:

$$\frac{mv^2}{a_n} = \frac{Ze^2}{a_n^{\,2}} \tag{9}$$

From (8) and (9),

$$a_n = \frac{n^2h^2}{4\,\pi^2e^2mZ} \tag{10}$$

This result is exactly the same as that of BOHR. For the total energy = potential energy + kinetic energy we have for the case of this circular motion:

$$W = -\frac{Ze^2}{a_n} + {}^1/_2\,mv^2 = -{}^1/_2\,\frac{Ze^2}{a_n}$$

or after substitution of the expression (10)

$$W = -\frac{2\,\pi^2\,e^4mZ^2}{h^2\,n^2} \tag{11}$$

This expression is again the same as that of BOHR but the significance of the (principal) quantum number $n$ as an integer has now become clear as logically necessary for a stationary state.

## § 18. WAVE FUNCTION AND WAVE EQUATION

The fruitfulness of the attribution of a wave nature to the electron has thus become apparent; the wave mechanical description should be completed by setting up a general equation which the behaviour of an electron satisfies according to this conception.

The characteristic quantity in any wave phenomenon is the wave function $\varphi$, the amplitude as a function of the spatial coordinates and of the time. We shall, however, leave the time dependence out of consideration; in chemistry, even in chemical reactions, we are always dealing with stationary states. It is only in phenomena such as the emission of radiation, etc., that this time dependence comes into the discussion.

This amplitude itself is no more accessible to measurement than in visible light. In both cases it is the intensity, related to the quantity $\varphi^2$, which can be determined physically and which has thus a physical significance.

In general $\varphi$ is not real but complex; $\varphi\varphi^*$ then occurs throughout instead of $\varphi^2$, in which $\varphi^*$ is the complex conjugate of $\varphi$. However, $\varphi$ can be regarded as real in the problems which interest us particularly here, so that this refinement of the notation is omitted.

Now the intensity of light in the quantum theory is amenable to two interpretations, which are, however, essentially equivalent since no experiment can be conceived which would permit a decision in favour of one of them. We can regard the intensity as the density of light quanta at the point under consideration, *i.e.*, the number of quanta per unit volume, or as the probability of encountering a light quantum in this element. In the wave mechanics of an electron, similarly $\varphi^2$ signifies both the charge density (in atomic units, otherwise it is $e\varphi^2$) and the probability of finding the electron there. In the first case the electron is, as it were, thought of as spread out over the space; in the second, statistical conception, the idea of an individual discrete electron is fundamental. Since however only statistical data can be collected, that is to say measured, this has not the consequence that one can say: the electron is there at a given instant, or not; we only know the probability $\varphi^2$ of encountering it.

What must be the answer to the question: What actually undulates?

In the 19th century, people were so definitely convinced that any understanding of natural events consisted in reduction to a mechanical picture that they created an aether in order to be able to answer this question for light; however, any physical reality is denied to this aether. Both for light and for electrons the analogy to mechanical waves (vibrating strings, organ pipes, etc.) does not go further than the fact that $\varphi$ behaves mathematically in a similar way to the physical, actually real, amplitude in the mechanical analogy. The classical language used, *e.g.*, wave, particle, orbit, is metaphorical.

$\varphi$ can be called a probability amplitude; it is not itself observable but without it no single natural law relating to microscopic, atomic events can be formulated.

The question whether this wave picture corresponds to objective reality or is a product of the human brain with its limited powers—or the question whether the electron is really somewhere or not when we only know the probability of observing it there—is a philosophical question; it is a question of "belief" but not of science, since there is no experiment which furnishes results which could not be predicted on the basis of the probability picture (or of that of the spread-out electron) (BORN, 1955).

It is also clear that there can no longer be any question of a strict causality according to 19th century ideas. The natural laws for the microcosmos have a statistical character; therefore the laws valid for the macrocosmos which follow from the former, will bear essentially the same character although it is more difficult to demonstrate this character by direct experiment in the macroscosmos.

The wave function $\varphi$ must satisfy a number of conditions which arise from the requirement that the function must be physically significant. Here we will only mention that the wave function must be zero at infinity; at finite distances $\varphi$ will usually be different from zero, that is to say, the charge cloud extends to infinity in contrast to the picture of the electron as a charged sphere.

Since $\varphi^2$ is a probability or charge density it will be desirable to provide the solution for the wave function of one electron always with a factor (to be determined from the succeeding condition) such that integration over the whole space results in one, *i.e.*, $\int \varphi^2 dv = 1$. In other words the probability of finding the electron in infinite space is one, or otherwise stated the total charge in the whole space must amount to one (in atomic units). The condition is called the normalization condition; the wave function which satisfies it is normalized.

A consideration exclusively of the intensity can never lead to an explanation of interference phenomena, for example, in which light + light can indeed give darkness. The amplitudes of the two interfering waves are opposite in such a case. It is also necessary in the discussion of electrons to start always from the wave function $\varphi$, and we shall see that it is similarly of essential importance whether two wave functions have the same or opposite sign.

The total sign of a wave function is naturally without significance because only $\varphi^2$ has essential significance.

The stationary states, to which we restrict ourselves here, correspond to stationary waves in vibration theory; loops correspond to high charge density and nodes to a charge density of zero.

The wave function is governed by a differential equation which can also be written in the same form for light; this is the (time-independent) wave equation of SCHRÖDINGER (1926):

$$\nabla^2 \varphi + \frac{8 \pi^2 m}{h^2} (W - V) \varphi = 0.$$

$W$ = total energy and is therefore a constant parameter (for a definite state).

$V$ = potential energy, a function of the coordinates.

$\nabla^2\varphi$ = an abbreviated notation for

$$\frac{\partial^2 \varphi}{\partial x^2} + \frac{\partial^2 \varphi}{\partial y^2} + \frac{\partial^2 \varphi}{\partial z^2}.$$

One can accept this equation as a fundamental natural law of the mechanics of electrons, the correctness of which has been tested many times by experiment, just as NEWTON's law of attraction is a fundamental law of macroscopic mechanics. DE BROGLIE's relation is then a special result of this equation.

It can also be shown that SCHRÖDINGER's wave equation is none other than a form of the classical differential equation for a wave phenomenon; the new feature is to be found in its application to electrons by means of the experimentally verified DE BROGLIE relation. As seen above, this relation, in turn follows from a combination of the fundamental relations of PLANCK and EINSTEIN in the form $h\nu = mc^2$ (p. 112).

A plane wave which is propagated along the $x$ direction has the following equation for the amplitude $U$:

$$U = A \sin 2\pi (x/\lambda - \nu t)$$

(or alternatively this expression with a cosine, which gives the same wave with a phase difference of 90°).

The differential equation for this wave is obtained by double differentiation with respect to the coordinate $x$ and the time $t$ respectively.

$$\frac{\partial^2 U}{\partial x^2} = -\frac{4\pi^2}{\lambda^2} U \tag{2}$$

$$\frac{\partial^2 U}{\partial t^2} = -4\pi^2 \nu^2 U \tag{3}$$

The stationary states, such as are studied in quantum chemistry, correspond to stationary waves for which we have:

$$U = A \sin 2\pi x/\lambda \cdot \cos 2\pi \nu t$$

(or with sine and cosine interchanged).

The time-independent part which interests us

$$U = A \sin 2\pi x/\lambda \text{ (or} = A \cos 2\pi x/\lambda)$$

satisfies the differential equation (2).

Equation (2) is thus the characteristic time-independent wave equation which we shall now apply to an electron by means of DE BROGLIE's relation:

$$\lambda = \frac{h}{m v}$$

We then have:

$$\frac{\partial^2 U}{\partial x^2} + \frac{4\pi^2 m^2 v^2}{h^2} \cdot U = 0.$$

or by introducing the kinetic energy $T = {}^1/_2 mv^2$:

$$\frac{\partial^2 U}{\partial x^2} + \frac{8\pi^2 m T}{h^2} \cdot U = 0. \tag{4}$$

Now, in general, the kinetic energy $T$ of an electron that moves in an electric field will change under the influence of the field; the total energy $W$, however, will not change. This total energy is the sum of the kinetic and the potential energy:

$$W = T + V$$

We thus obtain the final form of the (time-independent) wave equation (in one dimension):

$$\frac{\partial^2 U}{\partial x^2} + \frac{8\pi^2 m}{h^2}(W - V)\,U = 0 \tag{5}$$

This equation is completely analogous to the SCHRÖDINGER wave equation.

To obtain the complete solutions, the solutions of this wave equation must then be multiplied by $\cos 2\pi\nu t$ (see above) in which the frequency $\nu$ is naturally connected with the wave length $\lambda$.

In three dimensions, we replace the amplitude $U$ by $\varphi$ and the equation becomes:

$$\nabla^2\varphi + \frac{8\pi^2 m}{h^2}(W - V)\,\varphi = 0 \tag{6}$$

$$\left(\nabla^2\varphi \equiv \frac{\partial^2\varphi}{\partial x^2} + \frac{\partial^2\varphi}{\partial y^2} + \frac{\partial^2\varphi}{\partial z^2}\right)$$

SCHRÖDINGER's equation governs the electrons even in the most complicated cases just as the motion of planets and moons is determined by NEWTON's law. The trick in both cases is to solve the equation!

A solution can be written down directly for a single simple case, a free electron *in vacuo* ($V = 0$) moving along the $x$ axis.

The differential equation is then satisfied by:

$$\varphi = A\cos 2\pi\, x/\lambda, \quad \text{or} \quad \varphi = A\sin 2\pi\, x/\lambda$$

Thus we have:

$$(2\pi/\lambda)^2 = \frac{8\pi^2 m}{h^2} W \quad \text{or} \quad \lambda = \frac{h}{\sqrt{2mW}}$$

(The more general solution is given by $\varphi = Ae^{-2\pi i x/\lambda}$.)

The solution thus represents a wave along the $x$ axis with a wave length which agrees with that determined in the experiments of DAVISSON and GERMER and of G. P. THOMSON (see p. 114); if the electrons have traversed a potential difference $P$ then the total energy $W = eP$.

For an electron in a space in which $V \neq 0$ we have:

$$\lambda' = \frac{h}{\sqrt{2m(W-V)}}$$

When therefore a beam of electrons passes from a vacuum into a crystal in which there is a potential $P_i$ (thus $V = -eP_i$) then a change of wave length takes place. That is to say, there is a refractive index:

$$n = \lambda/\lambda' = \sqrt{(W-V)/W} = \sqrt{(P+P_i)/P}$$

We therefore have refraction just as occurs for light in passing into an optically denser medium.

Now $P_i$ is of the order of 10–25 V, so that this effect of the refraction was clearly seen in the experiments of DAVISSON and GERMER with $P$ equal to 30–300 V, but not in those of THOMSON with $P \approx 30{,}000$ V.

The problem of an electron in a box is treated later in Chapter IV.

The correspondence between wave mechanics and classical mechanics can be clearly demonstrated by a transformation of equation (6).

In classical mechanics we have:

$$W = T + V = \frac{1}{2m}(p_x^2 + p_y^2 + p_z^2) + V(x, y, z) \tag{7}$$

Actually the kinetic energy is: $T = {}^1/_2\, mv^2 = \frac{1}{2m}(p_x^2 + p_y^2 + p_z^2)$ and the potential energy is a function only of the positional coordinates $x$, $y$, and $z$.

We may also write:

$$W = H(p, q), \tag{8}$$

since the total energy is a function of the moments $p$ and the coordinates $q$. This form is called the HAMILTONIAN, hence the letter $H$.

The wave equation (6) can now be written as:

$$W.\varphi = -\frac{1}{2m}\left(\frac{h}{2\pi}\right)^2\left(\frac{\partial^2}{\partial x^2} + \frac{\partial^2}{\partial y^2} + \frac{\partial^2}{\partial z^2}\right)\varphi + V.\varphi \tag{9}$$

Formally (7) and (9) correspond if we merely replace the quantity $p_x$ in (7) by the operator $\frac{h}{2\pi i}\cdot\frac{\partial}{\partial x}$ acting on the wave function $\varphi$; in fact $p^2$ as twice the operation then corresponds to $-\left(\frac{h}{2\pi}\right)^2\frac{\partial^2}{\partial x^2}$.

That is to say, the quantity $p$ from classical mechanics is thus replaced in wave mechanics by an operator. Likewise the potential energy is also replaced by an operator, namely the multiplication of the function of the potential energy $V$ by the wave function $\varphi$.

In place of the classical equation (8) we can now also write for the wave equation:

$$W\cdot\varphi = H\varphi \tag{10}$$

$H$ is now a symbol not for a quantity but for an operation to be applied to the wave function $\varphi$ (see p. 129); $H$ is called the HAMILTONIAN operator. This *operator H*, therefore, has the same form as the *function H* in classical mechanics when the above-mentioned formal rules are borne in mind.

In the calculation of the total energy $W$ (p. 129) as well as other dynamical quantities which can be written classically as a function of $p$ and $q$, the method of calculation in wave mechanics is to be found by means of the transformation to the corresponding operators according to the same rules.

## § 19. THE HYDROGEN ATOM

For the hydrogen atom we have simply $V = -e^2/r$ and the equation is then soluble although some mathematical dexterity is needed. It appears that a solution is only possible for certain values of the total energy $W$; thus the discrete energy states, which were assumed *ad hoc* in BOHR's theory, are produced "automatically". These states are characterized by certain quantities which must be whole numbers, the quantum numbers; thus these numbers follow immediately from the mathematical behaviour of the equation. One finds for the wave function of the ground state of the hydrogen atom:

$$\varphi = \frac{1}{\sqrt{\pi}}\left(\frac{1}{a}\right)^{3/2} e^{-r/a} \text{ with } a = \frac{h^2}{4\pi^2 m e^2} = 0.529\text{Å},$$

the radius of the orbit according to BOHR, and for the energy:

$$W_H = -\frac{2\pi^2 e^4 m}{h^2} = -\frac{1}{2}\frac{e^2}{a},$$

as had already been derived directly (p. 116).

Solutions of the wave equations for higher states are:

1s $n = 1$ (K-Shell) $l = 0$ $m = 0$: $\varphi = \frac{1}{\sqrt{\pi}} \left(\frac{1}{a}\right)^{3/2} e^{-r/a}$

2s $n = 2$ (L-Shell) $l = 0$ $m = 0$: $\varphi = \frac{1}{4\sqrt{2\pi}} \left(\frac{1}{a}\right)^{3/2} (2 - r/a)\, e^{-r/2a}$

$2p_z$ ,, ,, $l = 1$ $m = 0$: $\varphi =$ ,, ,, $r/a\, e^{-r/2a} \cos \vartheta$

$2p_x$ ,, ,, ,, $m = -1$: $\varphi =$ ,, ,, $r/a\, e^{-r/2a} \sin \vartheta \cos \varphi$

$2p_y$ ,, ,, ,, $m = +1$: $\varphi =$ ,, ,, $r/a\, e^{-r/2a} \sin \vartheta \sin \varphi$

The angles $\vartheta$ and $\varphi$ as polar coordinates correspond to the geographical latitude and longitude respectively, while $r$ is the distance from the centre, the nucleus. For the energy of the higher states we have the same formula as in BOHR's theory.

$$W_H = -\,{}^1/_2\, \frac{e^2}{a} \cdot \frac{1}{n^2}$$

In the hydrogen atom the energy is the same for the 2s and the three 2p states. In an atom with more electrons the energy is still the same for the three 2p states, but then the 2s state has a lower energy (penetrating orbits, p. 13).

The principal quantum number $n$, the angular momentum quantum number $l$, which can take the values 0, 1 ... up to $(n - 1)$, the magnetic quantum number $m$ with the values $-l$, $-(l-1) \ldots 0 \ldots (l - 1), l$, all follow directly from the wave mechanical theory. Each state can further be occupied by two electrons, on account of the spin quantum number $s$, which can have the values $+ {}^1/_2$ and $-{}^1/_2$.

SCHRÖDINGER's wave equation for the hydrogen atom is solved by separating the equation into three equations, each of which depends on only one of the variables. The simplest one is that dependent on $\varphi$, the geographical longitude in polar coordinates. This equation is $\frac{1}{\phi} \frac{\partial^2 \phi}{\partial \varphi^2} =$ constant or $\frac{\partial^2 \phi}{\partial \varphi^2} = -m^2 \phi$, in which $m$ is a constant. A solution of this simple equation is $\phi = A \sin m \varphi$. Now this solution is only physically significant when by increasing the argument $\varphi$ by $2\pi$, that is to say, after one whole revolution, the function again possesses the same value. It is clear that this will only be the case when $m$ is a positive or negative whole number including zero. The magnetic quantum number of BOHR's theory thus makes its appearance as a necessarily whole number.

The factor $A$ follows from the normalizing condition $\int_0^{2\pi} \phi^2\, dv = 1$, thus we have $A = 1/\sqrt{\pi}$, except for $m = 0$, when $A = 1/\sqrt{2\pi}$.

The more general solution of the above differential equation is $A\,e^{im\varphi}$ or equally $A\,e^{-im\varphi}$ and thus linear combinations of them also form solutions, this fact can be used to obtain real in place of complex solutions:

$$^1/_2\, A\,(e^{im\varphi} + e^{-im\varphi}) = A \cos |m|\, \varphi \text{ and } \frac{1}{2i}\, A\,(e^{im\varphi} - e^{-im\varphi}) = A \sin |m|\, \varphi.$$

For the 2p states with $m = 0, \pm 1$ we have as solutions

$$\frac{1}{\sqrt{2\pi}},\ \frac{1}{\sqrt{\pi}} \cos \varphi \text{ and } \frac{1}{\sqrt{\pi}} \sin \varphi \text{ respectively.}$$

Let us examine the wave function of the lowest state, the 1s state of the electron. This function depends only on the distance $r$ and not on the angles; in other words this function $\varphi$, and therefore also the charge distribution $e\varphi^2$, is spherically symmetrical. The radial distribution function $4\pi r^2\varphi^2$ is more suitable for conveying information than the function $\varphi^2$; the function $\varphi^2$ is proportional to the probability of finding the electron in a unit volume at distance $r$, while the former function is proportional to the probability of finding the electron at a distance $r$, thus in a spherical shell of radius $r$ and thickness $dr$. If the number of hits $n$ per unit area is uniformly distributed over a target, the probability at a distance $r$ from the bull's eye is proportional to $2\pi rn$.

This radial density distribution has a maximum at $r = a$ (Fig. 10).

According to BOHR's theory the electron in this state ($n = 1$, K shell) describes a circular orbit with a radius $a = \dfrac{h^2}{4\pi^2 me^2}$. What therefore follows from the wave mechanical description is that this value is the most *probable* value for the distance of the electron from the nucleus; according to BOHR the electron could *only* occur at this particular distance from the nucleus. According to the new conception the orbit of the electron is smeared out.

Furthermore the charge is now seen to be spherically distributed; thus another difficulty in BOHR's theory is again removed automatically, namely, that of the so-called spatial quantization. An electron which moves in a plane orbit, would represent a magnetic orbital moment; this is in conflict with experience. To eliminate this difficulty BOHR had at the time to make new hypotheses.

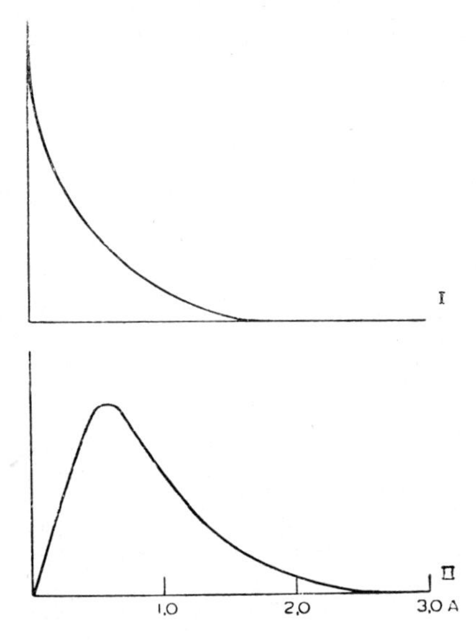


Fig. 10. Wave function $\varphi$ (I) and radial charge distribution $4\pi r^2 \varphi^2$ (II) as functions of the distance for the hydrogen atom in the ground state (1s).

On examining the wave function for the 2s state ($n = 2$, M shell), it is seen that this is also spherically symmetrical. This is the case for all s-states ($l = 0$) in general, independent of the principal quantum number. The density distribution shows two maxima for $n = 2$, three for $n = 3$, etc.

Let us now consider the 2p states. From the occurrence of the angles $\varphi$ and $\vartheta$ it is immediately seen that in these states the charge distribution can no longer be spherical. We shall now investigate this angular dependence in more detail, that is the functions cos $\vartheta$, sin $\vartheta \cdot$ cos $\varphi$ and sin $\vartheta \cdot$ sin $\varphi$.

A graph of cos $\vartheta$ as a function of $\vartheta$ as an angle in a plane results in a combination of two circles (Fig. 11). It should be remembered that, in the better known representation of cos $\alpha$ as sinussoidal curve, the angle is not plotted as such but as a linear coordinate. In the case of the $p_z$ function the factor depending on angle is a combination of two spheres along the Z axis; in the upper part the sign is positive, in the lower negative. We call the $p_z$ function antisymmetrical with regard to reflection in the horizontal plane as one half is the mirror image of the other half, but with opposite sign; the s function is symmetrical. The charge distribution, the function $\varphi^2$, is also dumb-bell shaped extended along the Z axis, but symmetrical.

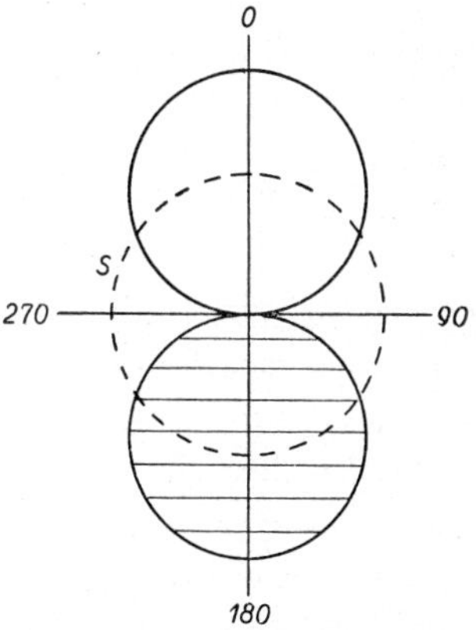

Fig. 11. Cos $\vartheta$ as a function of the angular coordinate $\vartheta$ and part of p-function dependent on angle —. Part of s-function dependent on angle - - -.

An examination of the two other functions shows that these functions have precisely the same shape but now directed along the X axis and the Y axis. Through their strong directional dependence these p-functions play a special part in the formation of directed bonds (p. 157).

A general property which plays an important role is the orthogonality, *i.e.*, $\int \varphi_1 \varphi_2 \, dv = 0$ of wave functions of different character. Thus *e.g.*, $\int \varphi_s \varphi_{pz} \, dv = 0$ as the integral extended over the space above the horizontal plane (positive $z$ values) is equal but opposite in sign to the integral over the lower half (negative $z$ values) (p. 161 and 212).

A remarkable property is worthy of mention: the charge distribution of three electrons, one each in the $p_x$, $p_y$ and $p_z$ states, is naturally given by ${\varphi_{px}}^2 + {\varphi_{py}}^2 + {\varphi_{pz}}^2$. If thus we add together the squares of the above-mentioned functions dependent on angle: $\cos^2\varphi \sin^2\vartheta + \sin^2\varphi \sin^2\vartheta + \cos^2\vartheta$, then a simple transformation shows that this expression is equal to one. This combined charge distribution of the three electrons is thus once more independent of $\varphi$ and $\vartheta$; in other words it is spherical.

Thus we find that the charge distribution in a nitrogen atom, with two electrons in the 1s state, two electrons in the 2s state and also three electrons, one in each of the three 2p levels, must be spherical. This must also hold for neon where two electrons are present in each of the three 2p states. Similarly to neon, all the ions with a neon configuration, such as $Na^+$, $Mg^{2+}$, $Al^{3+}$, $F^-$ and $O^{2-}$ have therefore a purely spherical charge distribution. Thus the representation of these atoms and ions as spheres is justified.

This result can be further generalized: the charge distribution of a filled subdivision (all states with one value of $l$) and of each closed principal quantum state or shell (one value of $n$) is spherically symmetrical. All atoms and ions with an inert gas electron configuration, and also all ions with an 18-electron configuration, such as $Cu^+$, $Ag^+$, $Zn^{2+}$, $Ga^{3+}$, etc., (in which a d-subdivision is completely filled), therefore have spherical symmetry.

Again a half-filled shell, such as in $Gd^{3+}$, with seven electrons in the 4f shell, is spherically symmetrical; the stability is connected with this (p. 15).

Now it is easy to calculate the potential energy, for example, of the electron in the 1s state by means of the solution obtained. For this purpose let us calculate what we could call the average value of this quantity. We then take the sum each time of the value of the quantity $-\frac{e^2}{r}$ for a particular distance $r$ multiplied by the probability $\varphi^2$ that an electron is at this distance, and divide this expression by the sum of all the probabilities $\varphi^2$.

The expression after changing from summation to integration becomes:

$$\frac{\int\limits_{r=0}^{r=\infty} -\frac{e^2}{r}\varphi^2\,4\,\pi r^2 dr}{\int\limits_{r=0}^{r=\infty} \varphi^2\,4\,\pi r^2 dr} = -\frac{e^2}{a} = -\frac{4\,\pi^2 m e^4}{h^2}$$

On account of the normalization the denominator will be equal to 1; the volume element is a spherical shell $4\pi r^2 dr$. The result is the same as that of BOHR's theory, where $a$ is the radius of the orbit and $-\frac{e^2}{a}$ the potential energy.

The calculation of the total energy (and in general that of all dynamical quantities) is somewhat more complicated in wave mechanics than the calculation of static quantities, such as $\overline{r}$ and $\overline{1/r}$ (see also p. 123).

The wave equation is often written as:

$$H\varphi = W\cdot\varphi \tag{1}$$

The left hand side $H\varphi$ (note: without a full stop in between, since it is not a multiplication) is then a symbolic method of writing:

$$-\frac{h^2}{8\pi^2 m}\nabla\varphi^2 + V\cdot\varphi \tag{2}$$

Here $H$ is thus a symbol not for a quantity but for an operation to be carried out on the function $\varphi$, similar to log and $d/dx$ for example; here, however, the operation is composed of a double differentiation of $\varphi$ multiplied by a constant factor and a multiplication of $\varphi$ by an expression for the potential energy (p. 123). The calculation of the total energy is as follows: multiply both sides of the equation $H\varphi = W\cdot\varphi$ by $\varphi$ and integrate left and right sides over all space. We then have on the right $\int W\cdot\varphi^2 dv = W$, on account of the normalizing condition $\int\varphi^2 dv = 1$ and because the total energy $W$ is a constant parameter.

According to this procedure the equation for the energy is as follows: $\int \varphi \cdot H\varphi dv = W$. For the calculation of $W$ it is thus first necessary to know the wave function $\varphi$ or at least an approximation to it, on which the operation, symbolized by $H$, must then be carried out, followed by integration.

Example: hydrogen in the ground state. We must now substitute $V = -e^2/r$ in the above development (2) of the left hand side $H\varphi$ of the wave equation, and the following value of $\varphi$ for the ground state (p. 124):

$$\varphi = \frac{1}{\sqrt{\pi}}\left(\frac{1}{a}\right)^{3/2} e^{-r/a}.$$

Here we use polar coordinates with the restriction to $r$ on account of the spherical symmetry of $\varphi_{1s}$; we then have

$$\nabla^2 \varphi = \frac{1}{r^2}\frac{\partial}{\partial r}\left(r^2 \frac{\partial \varphi}{\partial r}\right).$$

After substituting and carrying out the differentiation we have:

$$\nabla^2 \varphi = \frac{1}{a^2} - \frac{2}{ar}\varphi.$$

On substitution in (2) and with $V \cdot \varphi =$

$$-\frac{e^2}{r}\varphi = -\frac{h^2}{8\pi^2 m}\cdot\frac{2}{ar}\cdot\varphi$$

we obtain:

$$H\varphi = -\frac{h^2}{8\pi^2 m a^2}\varphi.$$

Multiplied by $\varphi$ and integrated ($dv = 4\pi r^2 dr$) this gives:

$$W_H = \int \varphi \cdot H\varphi\, dv = -\frac{h^2}{8\pi^2 m a^2} = -{}^1/_2 \frac{e^2}{a} \text{ with } a = \frac{h^2}{4\pi^2 m e^2}.$$

This result for the energy is the same as that in BOHR's theory.

## § 20. THE HYDROGEN MOLECULE ION $H_2^+$

The simplest conceivable molecule is $H_2^+$, the hydrogen molecule ion with two nuclei and one electron. It is true it does not occur in chemical compounds but a spectrum can be observed in discharges in hydrogen gas which must be attributed to $H_2^+$. The heat of dissociation and the nuclear separation are known from the spectrum.

For this hydrogen molecule ion $H_2^+$ we must substitute in the wave equation:

$$V = + e^2/r_{AB} - e^2/r_A - e^2/r_B\,;$$

in fact there is now the repulsion of the two nuclei $A$ and $B$ at a distance $r_{AB}$ and the attraction between the one electron and either of the nuclei at distances $r_A$ and $r_B$. The equation that arises in this way is still directly soluble but we shall use, rather, an approximation method which is necessary for the hydrogen molecule.

a. *Qualitative discussion*

We shall first attempt to find the solution by a qualitative discussion.

For very large distances between the two nuclei a solution of the equation can readily be given.

Furthermore it is plausible to employ this solution, which is valid for very large nuclear distances, as a first approximation for smaller distances.

At large nuclear distances we have simply a system of a proton and a hydrogen atom at an appreciable distance from one another. The charge distribution of this latter atom is, in these circumstances, the same as that of a separate hydrogen atom. The charge distribution can be written $\varphi_{\mathrm{I}}^2 = \varphi_A^2\,(1)$, that is to say electron (1) moves around nucleus $A$ as in the ground state (1s) of a hydrogen atom.

It is fundamental and characteristic of quantum mechanics, in contrast to classical mechanics, that one must say that the above statement is incomplete. In fact the electron can just as well be found around nucleus $B$ (this configuration possesses the same energy): $\varphi_{\mathrm{II}}^2 = \varphi_B^2\,(1)$. The hydrogen molecule ion can thus be formulated both as $H_A H_B^+$ and as $H_A^+ H_B$. The two configurations are equivalent and as the probability of finding the electron at a large distance from the nucleus is small but not zero, that is to say the electron can jump; both configurations will therefore contribute equally to the actual stationary state. The charge distribution which is found with long observation times will be $\Phi^2 = (\varphi_I^2 + \varphi_{II}^2)/2$ (Fig. 12, for a much larger internuclear distance).

What about $\Phi$ itself? Here an ambiguity arises; actually $\Phi_S = (\varphi_I + \varphi_{II})/\sqrt{2}$ and $\Phi_A = (\varphi_I - \varphi_{II})/\sqrt{2}$ both satisfy the

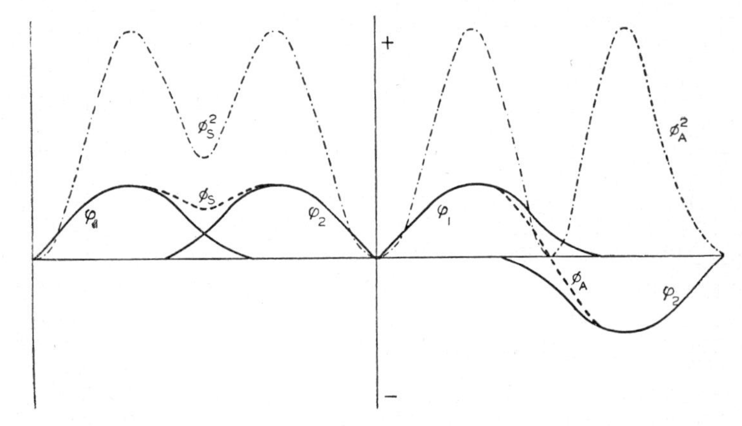


Fig. 12. Symmetrical ($\Phi_A$)and antisymmetrical ($\Phi_B$) solutions for the wave function and charge distributions (–·–·–) for an intermediate internuclear distance.

conditions. [At large distances $2\varphi_I\varphi_{II}$ will be very small because then *either* $\varphi_I$ or $\varphi_{II}$ will be nearly zero at every point (Fig. 12, also for a much larger distance).]

At smaller nuclear distances $\Phi_S$ and $\Phi_A$ are different and the corresponding energy will also be different; in fact, the symmetrical state $S$ with the piling up of negative charge between the two positive nuclei will possess a lower energy than the antisymmetrical state $A$*; for very small nuclear distances,

* A wave function is symmetrical (with respect to interchange) if it remains the same on interchange of equal particles, in this case the nuclei, antisymmetrical if it changes sign thereby.

however, the repulsion of the nuclei will be predominant in both cases.

In this way we have already obtained two approximate solutions for our $H_2^+$ ion. The variation of energy as a function of the nuclear distance is given for both of them in Fig. 13. We see that the symmetrical solution $S$ (with the same signs) yields attraction with the formation of a stable molecule, the antisymmetrical $A$ (with opposite signs) gives only repulsion. The heat of dissociation $D$ and the nuclear distance $r_0$ of $H_2^+$ can be read off directly from the figure. Without any knowledge of numerical data other than the values of the fundamental constants, $h$, $e$, and $m$, we could thus to a first approximation calculate $D$ as 40.7 kcal and $r_0$ as 1.21Å. Experimentally we find: $D = 63.81$ kcal, $r_0 = 1.06$ Å. The exact solution gives $D = 63.933$ kcal, $r_0 = 1.06$ Å. Here the stage has been reached where the calculated value is more reliable than the measured figure, as is always the case in geometry.

We have already pointed out the analogy between the wave function and the amplitude of light and other vibrational phenomena. There is now also a mechanical analogue of the two wave functions $\Phi_S$ and $\Phi_A$ as described above.

Let us take two equal pendulums which oscillate independently of one another and in the same way as a separate pendulum (as with $\varphi_I$ and $\varphi_{II}$ above) with frequencies $\nu_I = \nu_{II}$. If we apply a weak coupling in the form of a weak spring between the two extremities of the pendulums, we see that the motions which this complex can carry out are more complicated. On analysing them, two kinds of motion can be recognized: in the one, the quicker motion, the pendulums move oppositely, the restoring force is increased and the frequency raised: $\nu_A > \nu_I = \nu_{II}$, and the other, the slower motion, with the pendulums in the same phase has a frequency $\nu_S < \nu_I = \nu_{II}$*.

This analysis is significant if the coupling is weak; similarly

* In the special case of mathematical pendulums and a spring in this last case, we have $\nu_s = \nu_I = \nu_{II}$, because the period of oscillation is independent of the masses and is determined only by the length of the pendulum.

our wave functions $\varphi_{I} \pm \varphi_{II}$ can only be considered a good approximation for not too small distances between the nuclei. The formal analogy with the wave functions in the hydrogen molecule ion is complete; the symmetrical motion with the same phase $\varphi_{I} + \varphi_{II}$ also has the lowest energy, that is to say, according to PLANCK's relation, the lowest frequency. In one respect there is a difference: there is no temperature in the mechanical model but there is one in the physical. The two types of motion, the symmetrical and the antisymmetrical have the same probability in the mechanical model; in the physical model, however, the occupation of the antisymmetrical state will be related to that of the symmetrical state as $e^{-\delta W/kT}$ to 1 (according to BOLTZMANN's law when $\delta W = h(\nu_A - \nu_S)$ is the difference of energy between the two states). If $\delta W \gg kT$ the molecules will be found exclusively in the lowest state, *i.e.*, the symmetrical state and so we see that *in this case* there is a decrease of energy equal to $\delta W/2$ with respect to one separate state such as is realized for very large nuclear distances. If $\delta W \ll kT$, the molecules will be distributed evenly over both states and the total energy is equal to that of the separate state.

With stronger coupling of the two pendulums the frequency difference or $\delta W$ increases. With electron configurations this coupling is nearly always so large that we do have $\delta W \gg kT$.

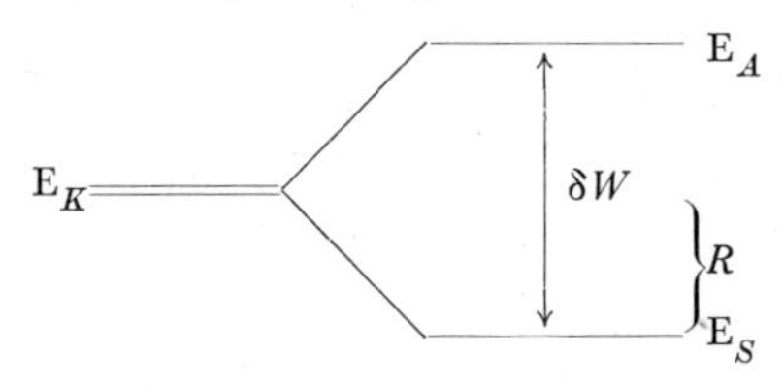


This decrease of energy $^1/_2\, \delta W$ is also called the resonance energy $R$. This quantity forms the bonding energy of the molecule, or at least the part which is not included in the classical electrostatic interaction (in $H_2^+$ leading to repulsion, see curve $K$ in Fig. 13).

The difference in frequency $\nu_A - \nu_S$ can also be made visible in the model of the coupled pendulums. If we set one pendulum in motion, its motion will be slowly damped while the other pendulum will be set in oscillation, after which the same sequence will be repeated in the opposite direction, etc. This transition frequency is now $(\nu_A - \nu_S)$. It is tempting to interpret the frequency difference in the $H_2^+$ ion in an analogous way as the frequency (to which, however, no physical

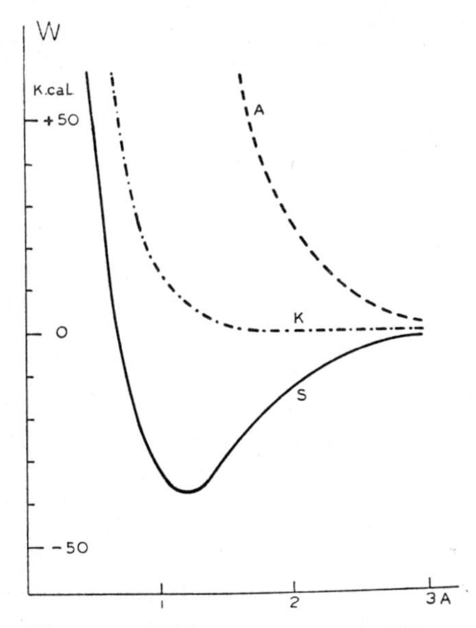


Fig. 13. Energy as a function of the nuclear separation of $H_2^+$, —— symmetrical, – – – antisymmetrical state, – · – · – classical interaction.

meaning can be attached) with which the electron is, as it were, interchanged, that is to say the frequency of the exchange $HH^+ \longleftrightarrow H^+H$. This frequency difference is of the order of magnitude of the electron vibrations, and thus of the ultraviolet light waves with a wavelength of about 0.2 $\mu$.

It is necessary here to go further into the real significance of the above results. When we reproduce in mathematics the results in words, we use words such as "sphere", not only in three dimensions but also in more dimensions; these words are metaphors borrowed from objects of daily life, in this case a ball, which show a correspondence in certain aspects only. It is the same in physics and particularly in wave mechanics. When we speak of light vibrations or electron waves, we are alluding to the analogy between certain mathematical formulae for these phenomena and the formulae valid for mechanical vibrations; however, this certainly does not imply that a complete agreement exists in other aspects also.

Thus the amplitude of a tuning fork has a real physical significance; this amplitude is susceptible to experimental measurement. However, this is not the case with the amplitude of light or electrons.

When we speak of resonance and in this connection of the exchange $HH^+ \leftrightarrow H^+H$, then we are only illustrating our abstract reasoning with a picture derived from classical mechanics. When one wishes to avoid all association with the mechanical phenomenon in question, one also speaks of *mesomerism* (= between parts, INGOLD).

The separate configurations $HH^+$ and $H^+H$ are mental pictures which have no physical significance themselves (and neither has the exchange) since they can never be the subject of physical investigation; this in contrast to the stationary state.

Essentially only the total wave function $\Phi$ has a meaning because it describes the stationary state. The division of $\Phi$ into $\varphi_I \pm \varphi_{II}$ is artificial and is only a means of finding an approximate solution of the wave equation, thus a necessary consequence of our mathematical incapacity. Resonance is therefore also not a real physical phenomenon but a human mnemonic. In the same way we say of a child, "just like his mother" and later "just like his father". We do not really mean that the character or personality of the child alternates, "resonates", between that of mother and father or that these latter are present as parts. We try to describe his personality to a first approximation as a sum of two other entities. Similarly an analysis of an entity such as a human being into intelligence, character, etc., can be very useful but is not based on the presence of distinct parts which are themselves the subject of investigation.

Also, one cannot speak of an equilibrium between two forms $HH^+$ and $H^+H$. A thermodynamic equilibrium can only exist if each form has a lifetime at least of the order of the time between two collisions. This is a time which is many thousand times greater than the above-mentioned "time of exchange" $1/(\nu_A - \nu_S)$.

We have found that the energy of the hydrogen molecule ion is lower than that calculated on the basis of classical interaction $H^+H$ (Fig. 13 K); this result was a consequence of the fact that we also took the configuration $HH^+$ into account, that is to say, it was a consequence of the view that the stationary state was considered to be built up of two electron configurations, between which transition was possible*. The bonding in the $H_2^+$ ion depends on this resonance or exchange and the bonding energy is essentially the resonance energy. As we shall see, the same is true for atomic bonding in general (p. 154) and for "aromatic bonding" in particular (p. 217).

Nevertheless, only the classical COULOMB law was applied to the interaction; the special feature of the atomic bond thus does not depend on a special non-classical interaction but on the particular wave-mechanical behaviour of the electrons. As a result of this wave character negative charge can be piled up (in the symmetrical state) at a place where the potential energy for the electrons is low. In the individual configuration $H^+H$ the repulsion of the two nuclei predominates, as can be seen from Fig. 13 K, over the attraction of the one proton for the "cloud" of negative charge around the other proton at all distances.

We can generalize these results with the following theorem:

*The stationary state of an electron system, for which various con-*

---

* See for example p. 211; here there is a difference from previous ideas on valency tautomerism (WIELAND).

*figurations are conceivable between which transitions are allowed, can be described as a combination of these separate configurations in which the energy is lower than that of the configuration(s) with the lowest energy; this difference in energy is known as the resonance energy.*

We have interpreted the bonding as being due to a decrease in the potential energy; but what about the kinetic energy? A very general theorem, the virial theorem (PITZER, book p. 139 and 426, KAUZMANN, book p. 229, 244 and 437), applied to a system in which the forces are the electrostatic interaction of charges, states:

$$2\,\overline{T} = -\overline{V} \text{ or } W = \overline{T} + \overline{V} = -\overline{T} = {}^1/_2\,\overline{V},$$

in which $W$ is the total energy and $\overline{T}$ and $\overline{V}$ are the (time average) kinetic and potential energies respectively. Thus the lower total energy of the molecule $H_2^+$ compared to the energy of the proton plus the hydrogen atom is indeed due to a decrease in the potential energy in spite of an increase of the kinetic energy. A possible alternative description of the bonding energy, namely as "energy of enlargement" results from considering the lowering of the kinetic (zero-point) energy on enlarging the space available to the electrons (p. 324). It can be shown, however, that this lowering of the kinetic energy (and consequently an increase in potential energy) occurs only at distances larger than two or three times the equilibrium distance in the molecule.

The reliability of a given wave function can be tested by calculating $\overline{T}$ and $\overline{V}$ separately and checking whether or not $W = {}^1/_2\,\overline{V} = -\,\overline{T}$.

The values calculated for $W$ and $\overline{V}$ for the hydrogen atom (pp. 129, 130) pass this test.

The first approximations for the wave functions used on p. 139 and p. 144 for $H_2^+$ and $H_2$ give large divergences. However, when an effective charge $Z$ is introduced in the variation function (p. 142 and p. 145) the virial theorem is obeyed.

### b. *Quantitative treatment*

The approximation methods which are used in wave-mechanical calculations are the perturbation method and the variation method. The first method starts with a simple case for which the solution (unperturbed state) is known, in our case the hydrogen atom. Then the actual situation is regarded as a consequence of a (small) perturbation of the first-mentioned state, in our case the perturbation by the field of the second proton.

The variation method starts with an (in principle) arbitrary function, the parameters of which are varied until the agreement with the correct solution with respect to a particular criterion, here the energy, is as good as possible.

The first method was developed for the calculation of planetary orbits but has also found much application in the wave mechanics of the atom. The second method is sometimes physically less clear but in most cases this method leads with less calculation more rapidly and more accurately to the end result than the former method. The variation method is mainly used in the wave-mechanical treatment of molecules.

We shall now apply the variation method to the $H_2^+$ ion. We choose a, for the time being, arbitrary function $\phi$, in which one or more parameters occur to which we shall now give such values that this variation function $\phi$ agrees as well as possible with the correct but still unknown wave function $\varphi$. What is the criterion for this? It is furnished by the calculation of the quantity which corresponds to the total energy: $E = \int \phi \cdot H\phi \, dv$. The lower this result is for small variations in the parameters, the better $\phi$ approximates to the correct $\varphi$; indeed it is plausible that every deviation from $\varphi$, that is to say, every charge distribution differing from the correct one, will be associated with a higher energy. It will naturally be necessary so to choose the function $\phi$ that there is a chance of approaching the end closely by the variation of a small number of parameters. In the case of $H_2^+$ this choice is simple.

In most cases one chooses as the variation function $\phi$ a linear combination of wave functions which are correct to a certain approximation, for example, for large nuclear separations. In this case we choose (see p. 132): $\phi = c_1\varphi_I + c_2\varphi_{II}$ ($\varphi_I$ and $\varphi_{II}$ are hydrogen 1s wave functions).

Values must now be sought for the coefficients $c_1$ and $c_2$ such that the (apparent) energy $E$ corresponding to the variation function $\phi$ is as low as possible. We find the conditions for this by differentiating $E$ with respect to $c_1$ or $c_2$, since we have for the minimum value of $E$ with respect to $c_1$ or $c_2$:

$$\frac{\partial E}{\partial c_1} = \frac{\partial E}{\partial c_2} = 0.$$

The above-mentioned quantity $\int \phi \cdot H \phi \, dv$ must still be divided by $\int \phi^2 \, dv$ since $\phi$ is not normalized but $\varphi$ is. The expression for the energy becomes (p. 130):

$$E = \frac{\int \phi \cdot H \phi \, dv}{\int \phi^2 \, dv}; \text{ or } E \int \phi^2 \, dv = \int \phi \cdot H \phi \, dv.$$

After substitution of $\phi$ the expression is differentiated with respect to $c_1$ and to $c_2$. In the first case we have (and similarly for $c_2$):

$$\frac{\partial E}{\partial c_1} [c_1^2 \int \varphi_I^2 \, dv + 2c_1c_2 \int \varphi_I\varphi_{II} \, dv + c_2^2 \int \varphi_{II}^2 \, dv] +$$
$$+ E [2c_1 \int \varphi_I^2 \, dv + 2c_2 \int \varphi_I\varphi_{II} \, dv] =$$
$$= 2 c_1 \int \varphi_I \cdot H \varphi_I dv + c_2 \int \varphi_I \cdot H \varphi_{II} \, dv + c_2 \int \varphi_{II} \cdot H \varphi_I \, dv.$$

Application of the minimum conditions for $E$ gives: $\dfrac{\partial E}{\partial c_1} = \dfrac{\partial E}{\partial c_2} = 0.$

This gives two linear homogeneous equations for the two unknowns $c_1$ and $c_2$:

$$c_1 [Q - E] + c_2[\beta - \Delta E] = 0. \quad (1)$$

$$c_1 [\beta - \Delta E] + c_2 [Q - E] = 0. \quad (2)$$

Here we have put $\int \varphi_I^2 \, dv = \int \varphi_{II}^2 \, dv = 1$ on account of the normalization, and the following abbreviations have been introduced:

$$\int \varphi_I \, \varphi_{II} \, dv = \Delta, \; \int \varphi_I \cdot H \, \varphi_I dv = \int \varphi_{II} \cdot H \, \varphi_{II} \, dv = Q$$

$$\text{and } \int \varphi_I \cdot H \, \varphi_{II} \, dv = \int \varphi_{II} \cdot H \, \varphi_I \, dv = \beta$$

since $\varphi_I$ and $\varphi_{II}$ are essentially equivalent. They are both equal wave functions for an electron, moving around proton $A$ or $B$ respectively; the operator $H$ is symmetric in the nuclei A and B, *i.e.*, it does not change sign on interchanging A and B.

This system of equations (1) and (2) has only a solution—differing from zero and so physically significant—when the equations are not contradictory (but dependent). The conditions for this in a system of linear homogeneous equations:

$$a\,x + b\,y = 0$$

$$c\,x + d\,y = 0$$

is naturally that $a/c = b/d$ or $ad - bc = 0$.

Mathematically this condition for solubility in the general sense is that the determinant of the coefficients must be equal to zero.

This determinant, or the condition derived from it corresponding to the above statement, is:

$$\begin{vmatrix} Q - E & \beta - \Delta E \\ \beta - \Delta E & Q - E \end{vmatrix} = 0 \text{ or } (Q - E)^2 = (\beta - \Delta E)^2. \quad (3)$$

On working out (3) two solutions for $E$ are obtained.

Only for these values of the energy is a physically significant stationary state possible.

These solutions are:

$$E_S = \frac{Q + \beta}{1 + \Delta} \text{ and } E_A = \frac{Q - \beta}{1 - \Delta} \quad (4)$$

It is now easy to find the unknowns $c_1$ and $c_2$ after substitution of $E_A$ and $E_S$ in the set of equations (1) and (2). One obtains respectively $c_1 = -c_2$ and $c_1 = c_2$. The absolute values are fixed by applying the normalization condition to the wave functions $\phi_S$ and $\phi_A$; $c_1 = c_2 = \dfrac{1}{\sqrt{2(1 + \Delta)}}$ (symmetrical solution) or $c_1 = -c_2 = \dfrac{1}{\sqrt{2(1 - \Delta)}}$ (antisymmetrical solution).

What now is the essential meaning of these results for $E_A$ and $E_S$? It is necessary to examine in more detail the meaning of the quantities represented by the symbols $Q$, $\beta$ and $\Delta$*. $Q$ is, by definition:

$$Q = \int \varphi_I \cdot H \, \varphi_I \, dv = \int \varphi_{II} \cdot H \, \varphi_{II} \, dv.$$

* See for example L. PAULING and E. B. WILSON; H. EYRING, J. WALTER and G. E. KIMBALL; K. S. PITZER; W. KAUZMANN, cited on p. 22.

The Hamiltonian $H$ is the same as that for hydrogen, increased by the new terms in the potential energy for the interaction of the electron with the other nucleus and of the nuclei with one another.

$$H\varphi_I = -\frac{h^2}{8\pi^2 m}\nabla^2\varphi_I - \left(\frac{e^2}{r_A} + \frac{e^2}{r_B} - \frac{e^2}{r_{AB}}\right)\varphi_I$$

On carrying out the integration we have:

$$Q = \int \varphi_I \cdot H\varphi_I dv = \int \varphi_I\left(-\frac{h^2}{8\pi^2 m}\nabla^2\varphi_I - \frac{e^2}{r_A}\varphi_I\right) dv -$$

$$-\int \frac{e^2}{r_B}\varphi_I^2\, dv + \int \frac{e^2}{r_{AB}}\varphi_I^2\, dv$$

The first term is the same as that for the hydrogen atom and thus equal to $W_H$; in the third term $r_{AB}$ is a parameter and not a function of the coordinates of the electron around nucleus $A$, so that the integration is restricted to $\int \varphi_I^2\, dv = 1$ (on account of normalization) and therefore

$$Q = W_H + \mathcal{J} + \frac{e^2}{r_{AB}}, \text{ in which } \mathcal{J} = -\int \frac{e^2}{r_B}\varphi_I^2\, dv,$$

The quantity $\mathcal{J}$ is in fact the classical COULOMB interaction between a proton $B$ and electron cloud given by $\varphi_I^2$ around nucleus $A$. The last term is the mutual COULOMB repulsion of the two nuclei. The whole quantity $Q$ is indeed called the COULOMB energy and forms the classical energy (Fig. 13 K). The quantity $\Delta = \int\varphi_I\varphi_{II} dv$ indicates the extent to which the wave functions of a hydrogen atom $A$ and $B$ overlap; hence the name "overlap" integral.

The integral $\beta = \int\varphi_I \cdot H\varphi_{II}\, dv$ is particularly important. Working it out we have: $\beta = \Delta \cdot W_H + K + \Delta \cdot \frac{e^2}{r_{AB}}$ in which $K = -\int \frac{e^2}{r_B}\varphi_I \cdot \varphi_{II}\, dv.$

Thus we have:

$$E_S = W_H + \frac{e^2}{r_{AB}} + \frac{\mathcal{J} + K}{1 + \Delta} \approx Q + K;$$

$$E_A = W_H + \frac{e^2}{r_{AB}} + \frac{\mathcal{J} - K}{1 - \Delta} \approx Q - K$$

From the sign it follows that $K$ is an attraction energy. This energy integral $K$ is the exchange energy and typical of the wave-mechanical theory, because here both $\varphi_I$ and $\varphi_{II}$ occur in the integral, that is to say this energy depends on the exchange of the electron between the two nuclei $A$ and $B$. The energy $K$ is practically the bonding energy. For larger nuclear separations, $\Delta \ll 1$ and to a first approximation we have $E_S \approx Q + K$ and $E_A \approx Q - K$.

In comparison with p. 134, the resonance energy $R$ is then $1/2\, \delta W = K$ (see Fig. 13).

The variation function $\phi$ can be provided with more parameters so that the energy can also be minimized with respect to these parameters; thus the agreement with the correct energy can be continually improved. The introduction of an effective nuclear charge $Z$ into the hydrogen functions $\varphi_1$ and $\varphi_2$ instead of the nuclear charge 1 forms one of these extensions.

## § 21. THE HYDROGEN MOLECULE $H_2^+$

What about the hydrogen molecule itself? Can we perhaps also write more than one wave function for it? Here we are dealing with two electrons 1 and 2 as well as the two nuclei *A* and *B*. What does the wave function look like when the nuclear separation is so large that electron 1 moves as in a free hydrogen atom around nucleus $A[\varphi_A\ (1)]$ and electron 2 around nucleus $B\ [\varphi_B\ (2)]$? It appears that the product $\varphi_A(1) \cdot \varphi_B(2)$ is sufficient; on substitution in the wave equation, this equation separates into two parts, which are each identical with the equation of a separate hydrogen atom. The two parts represent electron 1 around *A* and 2 around *B*; the total energy is also separated into two parts.

On substituting $\phi = \varphi_A\ (1) \cdot \varphi_B\ (2)$ in the wave equation, we have $\nabla^2 \phi = \varphi_B(2)\ \nabla_1^2\ \varphi_A(1) + \varphi_A(1)\ \nabla_2^2\ \varphi_B\ (2)$; in fact $\nabla^2 = \frac{\partial^2}{\partial x_1^2} + \ldots \frac{\partial^2}{\partial x_2^2} + \ldots . = \nabla_1^2 + \nabla_2^2$ and $\varphi_A\ (1)$ and $\nabla_1^2$ only contain the coordinates *x*, *y* and *z* of the first, $\varphi_B\ (2)$ and $\nabla_2^2$ only those of the second electron. For large distances the potential energy *V* also splits in $V_1 + V_2 = -\frac{e^2}{r_{1A}} - \frac{e^2}{r_{2B}}$; $1/r_{1B}$, $1/r_{2A}$ and $1/r_{AB}$ can be neglected ($r_{1B}$ is the distance of electron 1 from nucleus *B* etc.). After separating *W* into $W_1$ and $W_2$ the whole equation separates into two parts, the one depending only on the coordinates of electron (1) and the other of electron (2):

$$\varphi_B\ (2)\ [\nabla_1^2\ \varphi_A\ (1) + \frac{8\,\pi^2 m}{h^2}(W_1 - V_1)\ \varphi_A\ (1)] + \varphi_A\ (1)\ [\nabla_2^2\ \varphi_B\ (2) + \\ + \frac{8\,\pi^2 m}{h^2}(W_2 - V_2)\ \varphi_B\ (2)] = 0$$

After division by $\varphi_A\ (1) \cdot \varphi_B\ (2)$ we have an equation with two terms which are functions exclusively of the coordinates of electron (1) or exclusively of those of (2).

Each part can also be put separately equal to zero, so that in fact two wave equations for two separate hydrogen atoms are obtained. Thus the product function appears to have been chosen correctly.

However, the function $\varphi_A(1) \cdot \varphi_B(2)$ is also not the only possibility in this case. We can just as correctly put forward $\varphi_B(1) \cdot \varphi_A(2)$ as the solution for the wave function which describes the two hydrogen atoms at a large distance. The difference between the two solutions is more subtle than in the case of the hydrogen molecule ion, where the difference could also be made manifest in a chemical formula. The difference

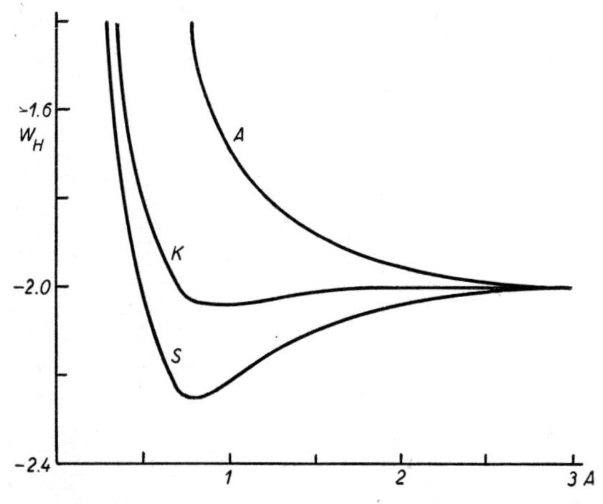


Fig. 14. Energy as a function of the nuclear separation for $H_2$; *A* antisymmetrical, *S* symmetrical state, *K* classical (COULOMB) interaction. $W_H = 313.7$ kcal $= 13.60$ e.V.

in $H_2^+$ represented an *exchange* of the one electron between two nuclei, here it is an *interchange* of the two electrons (1) and (2). In the function $\varphi_A(1) \cdot \varphi_B(2)$ electron (1) belongs to *A* and (2) to *B*, in the function $\varphi_B(1) \cdot \varphi_A(2)$ electron (1) belongs instead to nucleus *B* and (2) to *A*.

Naturally both functions are completely equivalent as far as energy is concerned; in fact, one could even say that there is no difference whatsoever, but this will be discussed later (p. 152).

For smaller distances of the two nuclei it will again, as in the case of $H_2^+$, be obvious to choose as the variation function:

$$\phi = c_I \varphi_A(1) \ \varphi_B(2) + c_{II} \varphi_B(1) \ \varphi_A(2).$$

From the equivalence of both terms it is immediately clear that $|c_I| = |c_{II}|$, so that there are two possibilities:

$$\phi_S = n\,[\varphi_A(1) \ \varphi_B(2) + \varphi_B(1) \ \varphi_A(2)]$$
$$\text{and } \phi_A = n'[\varphi_A(1) \ \varphi_B(2) - \varphi_B(1) \ \varphi_A(2)]$$
$$(n, \ n' = \text{normalizing factor}).$$

It is now possible to calculate the energy for the symmetrical and for the antisymmetrical solutions after much numerical work. The symmetrical solution again gives a potential curve with a minimum and thus corresponds with the formation of a stable molecule, while the antisymmetrical solution gives repulsion for all distances (Fig. 14).

The classical interaction, that is, without the exchange effect, here gives a very slight attraction; however, this would lead to a heat of dissociation of only about 10 kcal.

In Table 14 are reported the results of the first approximation and of the final calculation which are obtained with variation functions with more parameters. The exact result has been reached within the limits indicated; the agreement with the experimental data is perfect.

The solution for the hydrogen molecule strongly resembles that for $H_2^+$; in fact, the variation function can be written in essentially the same form in both cases:

$\phi = c_1 \ \varphi_I + c_2 \ \varphi_{II}$, now with $\varphi_I = \varphi_A(1) \, \varphi_B(2)$ and $\varphi_{II} = \varphi_B(1) \, \varphi_A(2)$.

Thus two solutions are also produced:

$$E_S = \frac{Q + \beta}{1 + \Delta} \text{ and } E_A = \frac{Q - \beta}{1 - \Delta}$$

The significance of the symbols $Q$, $\Delta$ and $\beta$ is now different however; the Hamiltonian is also more complicated:

$$H\varphi = -\frac{h^2}{8\pi^2 m} \nabla_1^2 \varphi - \frac{h^2}{8\pi^2 m} \nabla_2^2 \varphi - \left( \frac{e^2}{r_{1A}} + \frac{e^2}{r_{2A}} + \frac{e^2}{r_{1B}} + \right.$$
$$\left. + \frac{e^2}{r_{2B}} - \frac{e^2}{r_{AB}} - \frac{e^2}{r_{12}} \right) \varphi$$

in which $\nabla_1^2$, $\nabla_2^2$ refer to the coordinates of electrons (1) and (2) respectively; the potential energy now involves the distances of two electrons from the two nuclei and from one another.

The development proceeds in principle as with $H_2^+$:

$$E_S = 2\, W_H + \frac{e^2}{r_{AB}} + \frac{J' + K'}{1 + \Delta} \approx Q + K'$$

$$E_A = 2\, W_H + \frac{e^2}{r_{AB}} + \frac{J' - K'}{1 - \Delta} \approx Q - K'$$

$J'$ is here again a Coulomb term, containing the same integral $J$ for the interaction of a nucleus with the electron around the other nucleus and vice versa, (thus $B$ with $\varphi_A$ (1) and $A$ with $\varphi_B$ (2)), and, in addition, an integral over the electrostatic interaction of the two electrons, *i.e.*, the mutual interference of the two electron clouds:

$$J'' = \int\int \frac{e^2}{r_{12}}\, \varphi_A^2\,(1)\, \varphi_B^2\,(2)\, dv_1\, dv_2$$

The term $K'$ includes the exchange energy; besides the same integral as in $H_2^+$ there is also a double exchange integral:

$$K'' = \int\int \frac{e^2}{r_{12}}\, \varphi_A\,(1)\, \varphi_B\,(2)\, \varphi_B\,(1)\, \varphi_A\,(2)\, dv_1\, dv_2,$$

which is the most difficult one to calculate (Sugiura).

The result with this simple variation function is not so good (Table 14, first line); nevertheless, this calculation of Heitler and London was a revelation at the time because the theories of that period gave no explanation whatever for the bonding in $H_2$.

Wave functions with effective nuclear charges, and finally more or less extensive polynomials as variation functions, give complete agreement with experiment (Table 14).

## TABLE 14

CALCULATION OF HYDROGEN MOLECULE

| Type of variation function | Dissociation energy* | Distance (Å) |
|---|---|---|
| Heitler-London, hydrogen functions . . . . . | 72.3 kcal | 0.80 |
| Wang, *idem* with effective nuclear charge . . . | 86.6 | 0.76 |
| Weinbaum, with ionic terms . . . . . . . . . | 92.1 | 0.77 |
| Weinbaum, *idem* with polarization . . . . . . | 94.4 | — |
| James-Coolidge, polynomial 5 terms . . . . . | 103.7 | 0.77 |
| ,, ,, ,, 11 ,, . . . . . | 107.85 | — |
| ,, ,, ,, 13 ,, . . . . . | 108.15 | — |
| ,, ,, estimated influence of further terms . . . . . . . . . . . | 108.70 ± 0.3 | 0.74 |
| Observed . . . . . . . . . . . . . . . . . | 108.65 | 0.7395 |

* This is the depth of the potential curve; to obtain the experimental dissociation energy (Table 18 )the zero point energy $^1/_2\, h\nu$ has to be subtracted.

In addition to the two equivalent functions $\varphi_A$ (1) $\varphi_B$ (2) and $\varphi_B$ (1) $\varphi_A$ (2), two other mutually equivalent functions are also possible, which are also valid at large distances, namely $\varphi_A$ (1) $\varphi_A$ (2) and $\varphi_B$ (1) $\varphi_B$ (2). While the first two correspond to the formula HH, the latter pair corresponds to the ionogenic configurations $H^-H^+$ and $H^+H^-$, *i.e.*, both electrons are to be found with nucleus *A* or with nucleus *B*. The ionogenic configurations have, however, an energy content, which lies I—E = 296 kcal above that of the atomic configuration. An improved variational function will therefore be (WEINBAUM):

$$\phi = c_{\mathrm{I}}\varphi_A(1)\varphi_B(2) + c_{\mathrm{II}}\varphi_B(1)\varphi_A(2) + c_{\mathrm{III}}\varphi_A(1)\varphi_A(2) + c_{\mathrm{IV}}\varphi_B(1)\varphi_B(2),$$

in which $|c_{\mathrm{I}}| = |c_{\mathrm{II}}|$ and $|c_{\mathrm{III}}| = |c_{\mathrm{IV}}|$, but in which $c_{\mathrm{III}} \ll c_{\mathrm{I}}$. That is to say, the hydrogen molecule has predominantly atomic bonding; but nevertheless, the ionogenic configurations do contribute to the stationary state. The ionogenic model is, therefore, partly applicable even here, though only to a small extent. The total contribution of the two ionogenic configurations is 6%.

This observation is especially intended to show how the wave-mechanical picture contains all transitions from a purely homopolar picture (considering only I and II) to a purely heteropolar picture (taking only III and IV into account). With unequal nuclei, *i.e.*, with unequal degrees of electronegativity, one of the two ionic configurations will become more important, while the other hardly counts any longer. Thus the bonding becomes polar even though the contribution of the atomic configurations (homopolar terms) still predominates. In extreme cases the heteropolar terms can be large and a bonding of predominantly ionic bond type is produced*.

* We speak of ionic bond and atomic bond (also frequently called covalent bond) and not of heteropolar in contrast to homopolar (or homeo-) bond, since the last terms only have a meaning in characterizing the method of approximating the real wave functions, used by KOSSEL (VAN ARKEL and DE BOER) and by HEITLER and LONDON. With unequal atoms, even the homopolar approximation leads to a bond which possesses an electric moment on account of the difference in electronegativity, and which is thus (hetero)polar.

How can the relative values of the homopolar coefficient ($c_I$ always equal to $c_{II}$) compared with $c_{III}$ or $c_{IV}$ (according to whether $A^-B^+$, or $A^+B^-$ represents the lower energy) be determined experimentally? This is a fundamental question concerning the constitution of the molecules, *i.e.*, concerning the nature of the bonds. Some material can be collected in an indirect way only.

One obtains a very rough estimate, neglecting the influence of polarization, by comparing the observed electric moment of a bond with the moment which would be found for ions at the same distance (p. 93). The moment of HCl is 1.03 D, in comparison with the theoretical moment $e \cdot d = 4.80 \times 1.28 \times 10^{-18}$ $= 6.07$ D for a molecule consisting of unpolarizable ions; an amount of 17% of ionic configuration would follow. These values probably give the order of magnitude and are suitable for comparisons. Thus one finds in the series HF, HCl, HBr and HI the values 43%, 17%, 11% and 5%.

If we adopt for the wave function

$$\varphi = \varphi_{at.} + \lambda \varphi_{ion.}$$

the charge distribution $\varphi^2$ in zeroth approximation, neglecting overlap (p. 293), is a superposition of $\varphi_{at.}^2$ without a dipole moment (this is certainly incorrect, see p. 303) and of $\lambda^2 \varphi_{ion.}^2$ with a dipole moment $e \cdot d$ for the charge distribution of the ionic configuration. The estimate of the ionic character from the dipole moment mentioned above is related to the parameter $\lambda$ by:

$$\% \text{ ionic character} = 100 \cdot \frac{\lambda^2}{1 + \lambda^2}.$$

For the hydrogen halides we obtain for $\lambda$: 0.86, 0.45, 0.36 and 0.25 (see also p. 149).

The contribution of the ionic configurations is also evident in another property. PAULING postulates that the heat of dissociation is additive for pure atomic bonds or covalent bonds, *i.e.*: $D_{AB}^{theor.} = (D_{AA} + D_{BB})/2$.* The deviation from the theoretical value $\Delta_{AB} = D_{AB}^{exp.} - (D_{AA} + D_{BB})/2$ which will always have to be positive, will find its origin in the resonance

* There is reason, however, to prefer the geometric mean $\sqrt{D_{AA} \cdot D_{BB}}$ rather than the arithmetic mean.

energy resulting from the contribution of ionic configurations $A^+B^-$ (or $A^-B^+$). This $\Delta_{AB}$ is also the heat of reaction of the reaction $^1/_2\, A_2 + {}^1/_2\, B_2 = AB + \Delta_{AB}$. PAULING has based a scale of electronegativity $x$ ("The power of an atom in a molecule to attract electrons to itself") on these differences. He puts:

$$(x_A - x_B) = 0.208\, \sqrt{\Delta_{AB}}\ (\Delta_{AB} \text{ in kcal}).$$

(Fig. 15 and Table 15)

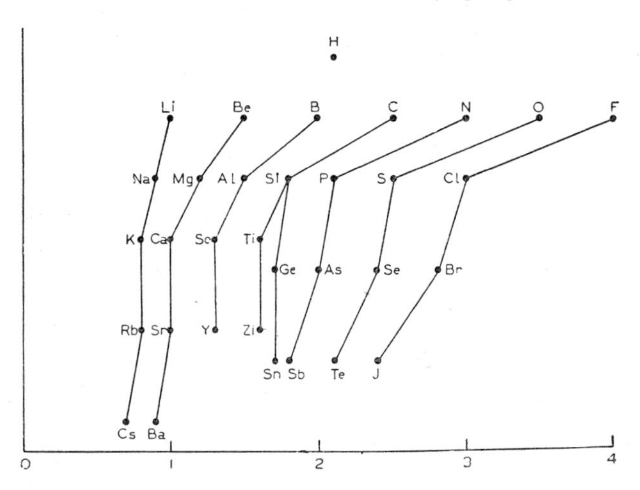


Fig. 15. Electronegativity scale according to PAULING.

(PAULING, book; HAISSINSKY, 1949; HUGGINS, 1953; PRITCHARD and SKINNER, 1955; GORDY and THOMAS, 1956). A formula was derived for the electronegativity (GORDY, 1946):

$$x = 0.31\ (n + 1)/r + 0.50$$

in which $n$ is the number of electrons in the valence shell, and $r$ is the single bond atomic radius in Å (p. 199).

The dipole moment of a bond $AB$ is roughly equal to the difference $x_A - x_B$ on this scale, *e.g.*, HF, HCl, HBr and HI with $\mu$ 1.91, 1.03, 0.78 and 0.38, whereas $x_A - x_B$: 1.9, 0.9, 0.8 and 0.4.

The amount of the ionic configuration can be deduced from

the difference in position on this scale. In this way we have for the series C — H, N — H, O — H and F — H; 4%, 19%, 39% and 60% and for C — F, C — Cl, C — Br and C — I: 43%, 11%, 3% and 0%. With the carbon-halogen bonds these amounts are much smaller than would be expected on the basis of the fairly large dipole moments. The reason for this is probably that even a purely atomic bond can be polar (p. 303).

As noted above, the heat of reaction, which is therefore the heat of formation of the compound *AB*, is determined by the amount of ionic configuration even if the bond *AB* is predominantly of atomic nature; this is important in connection with the apparently large region of validity of the theory of ionic bonding.

Mulliken has arrived at an electronegativity scale by another and better way; the values agree well with those of Pauling (Table 15 A).

TABLE 15 A

ELECTRONEGATIVITY SCALE

| | | | |
|---|---|---|---|
| | | | H<br>2.1 |
| C<br>2.5 | N<br>3.0 | O<br>3.5 | F<br>3.9 |
| Si<br>1.8 | P<br>2.1 | S<br>2.5 | Cl<br>3.0 |
| Ge<br>1.8 | As<br>2.0 | Se<br>2.4 | Br<br>2.8 |

I 2.5; B 1.8–2.0; Li 1.0; Na 0.9; K 0.8; Cs 0.7.

To transform an atom *A* and an atom *B* into $A^+ + B^-$ an energy $I_A - E_B$ the sum of ionization energy and electron affinity, is required. However, in order to obtain $A^- + B^+$, the energy $-E_A + I_B$ is necessary. Mulliken now postulates that *A* and *B* are of equal electronegativity when these two energies are the same, thus $I_A - E_B = -E_A + I_B$, or $I_A + E_A = I_B + E_B$. When *A* is more strongly electronegative than $B$, *i.e.*, when it is easier to form $A^-B^+$, then $I_A + E_A > I_B + E_B$. In other words $x_M = I_A + E_A$ is a measure of the electronegativity.

MULLIKEN does not use the quantities observed with free atoms but makes allowance for the valency state of the atom as it occurs in a molecule. Also the hybridization (p. 160) has an influence; thus for the carbon atom the electronegativity follows the sequence $sp > sp^2 > sp^3$ (MOFFITT, 1950). The relation of MULLIKEN's scale $x_M$ to that of PAULING's $x_P$ is best given by: $x_M/3.15 = x_P$ (PRITCHARD and SKINNER, 1955).

The best method to-day to evaluate the ionic-atomic character of a bond is based on the nuclear quadrupole coupling constant (GORDY, 1951; GORDY *et al.*, 1953).

The coupling constant $Q$ is determined from the hyperfine splitting in the microwave spectrum. The coupling between the nuclear spin and the surrounding electron cloud is caused by the deviation from spherical symmetry of the electric field of the cloud acting on the nucleus. For a chloride ion, as for all ions with closed shells, the coupling constant $Q = 0$. For a chlorine atom with an unpaired p electron $Q = -110$ Mc/sec. For a pure atomic bond with a pure p character the same value would be expected; this is very nearly realized in the chlorine molecule $Q = -108.5$ Mc/sec. (The difference indicates 1% s-character of the Cl–Cl bond.)

The value of $Q_{observed}/Q_{atomic}$ (with for $Q_{atomic}$ the value for $Cl_2$) can be taken as a measure of the atomic bond character or $1-Q_{obs.}/Q_{at.}$ for the ionic character. GORDY assumes this latter quantity equal to $(x_A - x_B)/2$.

| | $1 - Q_{obs.}/Q_{at.}$ | $(x_A - x_B)/2$ | | $Q_{obs.}/Q_{at.}$ |
|---|---|---|---|---|
| $Cl_2$ | (0.00) | 0 | LiBr | 0.048 |
| BrCl | 0.05 | 0.10 | LiI | 0.086 |
| ICl | 0.24 | 0.25 | NaCl | 0.01 |
| $CH_3Cl$ | 0.30 | 0.25 | NaBr | 0.075 |
| $SiH_3Cl$ | 0.63 | 0.60 | NaI | 0.113 |
| $GeH_3Cl$ | 0.58 | 0.60 | KCl | 0.004 |
| | | | KBr | 0.013 |
| | | | KI | 0.026 |

The difficulty is to distinguish between some s-character and some ionic contribution.

The values for the alkali halides indicate indeed nearly pure ionic character with, as expected, some decrease of ionic character in going from chloride to iodide (TOWNES and DAILEY, 1949, HONIG *et al.*, 1954). However, the electrostatic polarization will give rise to a change in the same direction (p. 93).

The relation between the chemical shift from nuclear magnetic resonance and electronegativity is not yet clarified in general.

## § 22. THE ELECTRON SPIN

It may seem surprising that in the preceding paragraphs we have never been concerned with the electron spin and the electron pair.

Actually, the interaction of the electron spins is without any direct significance for our considerations on bond energy since this magnetic energy is small. We saw that bonding or repulsion of two hydrogen atoms is determined by the COULOMB interaction of the charge cloud, condensed or rarified in the region between the nuclei according to whether the two hydrogen atom functions were of the same or opposite sign (same or opposite phases). The electron spin produces a phenomenon which is symptomatic for the behaviour of the wave function, but not of vital importance for the energy.

The PAULI principle was formulated in the older quantum theory as the prohibition of two electrons in one and the same quantum state (that is, having the same set of quantum numbers). This principle is equally valid in the wave mechanical theory but it is frequently formulated differently. If two electrons occupied exactly the same state, then interchange of the two would produce no difference. The PAULI principle in the modern formulation is as follows: On interchange of two electrons (in general, of two similar particles with odd spin, thus also hydrogen nuclei, etc.) the total wave function must change sign.

The total wave function is not only a function of the positional coordinates of the electrons but also contains their spin orientation. The symmetrical (orbital) wave function of the hydrogen molecule:

$$\phi_s = \varphi_A(1)\,\varphi_B(2) + \varphi_B(1)\,\varphi_A(2)$$

is transformed into itself on interchange of (1) and (2); on the other hand, the antisymmetrical (orbital) wave function:

$$\phi_A = \varphi_A(1)\,\varphi_B(2) - \varphi_B(1)\,\varphi_A(2)$$

changes sign. To satisfy the PAULI principle the spin functions of the two electrons (which bear only the character + or —, *i.e.*, dextro or laevo rotatory) must obviously be different in the first case; in the case of the antisymmetrical (orbital) function, on the other hand, the spin functions must be the same. This means that in the symmetrical attractive state the two electrons have oppositely directed spins; in the repulsive state the spins are parallel. However, the atoms attract one another not because the spins of the electrons are oppositely directed but because the electrons are piled up between the nuclei in the symmetrical state. The patient is ill not because the mercury stands high in the thermometer capillary but because certain biochemical processes are in progress which result in a rise in temperature.

Also with the older formulation of the Pauli principle we can understand that a penetration of the electron orbits, as in the attractive state, whereby the two electrons can, as it were, meet at one place, is only possible when there is a difference in spin orientation.

As already pointed out, terms such as wave function, electron orbit, resonance, etc., are used to describe the formulations and results of wave mechanics; these terms are borrowed from classical mechanics of matter in which concepts occur which, in certain respects at least, show a correspondence to the wave mechanical concepts in question. The same is true for the electron spin. Uhlenbeck and Goudsmit's hypothesis of the electron spin meant the introduction of a fourth quantum number $s$, which can only take on the values $+^1/_2$ and $-^1/_2$ into Bohr's quantum theory. In wave mechanics it means that the total wave function, besides the orbital function, contains another factor, the spin function. This spin function can be represented by $\alpha$ or $\beta$, whereby, for example, $\alpha$ describes the state $s = +^1/_2$ and $\beta$ that with $s = -^1/_2$. There is correspondence with the mechanical analogy, the top, from which the name "spin" has been borrowed; the correspondence is simply that a top can rotate to the right or to the left, *i.e.*, the axis of rotation (*e.g.*, clockwise) can point in the +

or — direction. A magnetic moment and a mechanical angular momentum can be attributed to the electron, but the relation between the two is different from that for a circular current like an electron in its orbit; this again points to the formal and restricted character of the correspondence between the concepts from classical mechanics and wave mechanics.

With two electrons 1 and 2 we can compose the following four spin functions:

$$\alpha(1)\ \alpha(2)$$
$$\beta(1)\ \beta(2)$$
$$\alpha(1)\ \beta(2) + \beta(1)\ \alpha(2)$$
$$\alpha(1)\ \beta(2) - \beta(1)\ \alpha(2)$$

$\alpha(1)\ \beta(2)$ alone would not be sufficient because electrons 1 and 2 are essentially indistinguishable; we must take linear combinations here as we did above with the orbital functions.

It is clear that the first three are symmetrical with respect to interchange of the electrons (1) and (2). Only the last is antisymmetrical, *i.e.*, changes sign on interchange of (1) and (2), and therefore only this one can be combined with the symmetrical orbital function of the bonding state, which thus has a total spin moment $S = 0$. The other three spin functions, multiplied by the antisymmetrical orbital function of the repulsive state, also give three different total wave functions. These three functions correspond to three states of equal energy (threefold degeneracy) with the total spin moment $S = 1$.

The degeneracy would be removed in a magnetic field and three levels, corresponding to the above three spin functions, would result according as the projection of the spin moment in the direction of the field is $+1$, $-1$, or 0. The attractive state is thus a singlet, the repulsive state a triplet state, and the probabilities of the two states are in the ratio of the statistical weights $(2S + 1)$, *i.e.* as 1 : 3.

Since the proton also has a (nuclear) spin $^1/_2$, one single combination antisymmetrical in the nuclear spins and three combinations symmetrical in the nuclear spins are possible in the hydrogen molecule. Since the antiparallel nuclear spin combination cannot be transformed into a parallel combination (except for example, in a magnetic field), there are therefore actually two kind of hydrogen molecules; the first has received the name para-hydrogen, the other combination the name ortho-hydrogen. Because, in this case, the ratio of the statistical weights is 1 : 3, normal hydrogen consists of 25% para- and 75% ortho-hydrogen. Apart from an extremely small difference in magnetic behaviour there would be no difference between the two kinds of molecule, if it were not that the para $H_2$-molecules (with antiparallel nuclear spins) occur exclusively in the even rotational levels, including the 0 level, the ortho $H_2$-molecules (with parallel nuclear spins) only in the odd levels, thus with 1 as the lowest, for the rotation of the whole molecule. This again is connected with the symmetrical character of the even rotational functions and the antisymmetrical character of the odd rotational functions, *i.e.* the latter change sign on rotation over 180° whereby the two nuclei are interchanged. Thus the energy of a para-molecule in the lowest rotational state 0 is lower than that of the ortho-molecule in its lowest attainable rotational level 1, and at low temperatures the true equilibrium lies entirely on the side of the para-molecules.

There is no difference in chemical and physical properties between para- and ortho-hydrogen except at low temperatures as regards specific heat and thermal conductivity. The transformation into para-$H_2$ at low temperatures only takes place after adsorption on charcoal. The reverse reaction occurs at room temperature in the presence of catalysts, in particular paramagnetic molecules (oxygen, free radicals, ions of the Rare Earths Elements); the reaction takes place spontaneously at high temperatures at which some dissociation occurs.

## § 23. ONE, TWO AND THREE ELECTRON BOND AND BORN REPULSION

In the $H_2^+$ ion the bonding is a consequence of the (place) *ex*change of one electron. In the hydrogen molecule the bonding depends on the *inter*change of two electrons which form an electron pair with antiparallel spins. In the $He_2^+$ ion with two nuclei and three electrons we have a three electron bond. As in the case of $H_2^+$, this depends on (place) *ex*change or, otherwise stated, on resonance between $HeHe^+$ and $He^+He$. Here an electron pair is exchanged for a separate electron.

The bonding energy in these three cases is:

| | |
|---|---|
| $H_2^+$ | 64 kcal |
| $H_2$ | 108 kcal |
| $He_2^+$ | 58 kcal |

It is evident from these figures that the electron pair bond is stronger than the two other types. In fact these other types hardly ever occur in stable molecules (exception $O_2$, p. 246).

However, there is another important reason for the preference for the electron pair bond. As shown in the case of a molecule $AB$, the energy of either $A^+B^-$ or $A^-B^+$ will always lie very much lower than that of the other configuration. Place *ex*change is, therefore, greatly hampered and one of the configurations will appear in the wave function with only a small coefficient. In *inter*change this difficulty does not occur; thus the electron pair bond will predominate still more strongly in bonding between dissimilar atoms. In the extreme case of a large difference between $A^+B^-$ and $A^-B^+$, we shall obtain an ionic bond in which only one of these configurations occurs in the wave function.

If we go another step forward and consider a molecule which

would be formed from two helium atoms (in the ground state), we find that there is no longer any possibility of place exchange or of interchange without coming into conflict with the PAULI principle. Thus only one single wave function without any resonance possibilities can be written down. Thus there is always repulsion between the two helium atoms. (The VAN DER WAALS-LONDON attraction is a relatively weak effect that is only obtained by a more accurate calculation, p. 358.)

The electron clouds of the two helium atoms cannot penetrate one another; this would be in contradiction with the PAULI principle (precisely as in the antisymmetrical orbital function of $H_2$) since the spins are always parallel two and two.

Here one sees the cause of the general repulsion, first, of all ions with closed electron configurations but, in addition, of all atoms which are not bound to each other by an electron pair. Indeed with two hydrogen atoms the probability is *a priori* 3 for the repulsive state against 1 for the attractive symmetrical state with antiparallel spins (p. 153).

The interaction of two hydrogen atoms with arbitrary relative spin orientation is thus $^3/_4$ repulsion $+$ $^1/_4$ attraction. According to the calculations for hydrogen (curve $A$ and $S$, Fig. 14) the one was approximately $Q - K'$, the other $Q + K'$ (p. 145); this sum is therefore $Q - {}^1/_2\, K'$. This is a repulsion since $^1/_2\, K'$ is negative and $Q$ does not decrease much for smaller distances (curve $K$). Repulsion will also exist between two hydrogen atoms of different hydrocarbon molecules and for that matter between two hydrogen atoms attached to the same carbon atom since there is no bonding between the hydrogen atoms and therefore also no spin orientation.

We can thus write for the total energy: $E = E_{atoms} + \Sigma$ (over all electrons) $Q'_{ij} + \Sigma$ (paired e.) $K'_{ij} - {}^1/_2\, \Sigma$ (non-paired e.) $K'_{ij} - \Sigma$ (e. with parallel spins) $K'_{ij}$. ($Q'$ is the quantity $Q$ of p. 141 minus the atomic energy $W_H$.) Again $H_3^+$ is possible but not $H_3$ because the third electron would always be parallel to one of the other two; thus there is repulsion.

This general repulsion of non-bonded atoms forms the basis

of the small compressibility of condensed phases, a conception which had already been introduced *ad hoc* by BORN (p. 36).

The repulsion between atoms which are not attached to each other also finds its expression in the VAN DER WAALS radius of an atom (p. 201).

The repulsion of the electrons not taking part in the bonding is the reason that atomic radii (p. 199) exist with atomic bonding, somewhat similar to the ionic radii with ionic bonding.

Moreover, in this chapter we shall always attempt to arrange the electrons in the *molecules* as far as possible in pairs, either as bonding pairs, or as "lone" pairs belonging to one atom, to obtain the lowest energy. Naturally in molecules with an odd number of electrons, such as NO, $NO_2$, $FeCl_3$, HgCl, free radicals, etc., it is impossible to arrange all electrons in pairs; however, dimers are then frequently produced in which this is possible. Oxygen is the only exception to this rule, apart from a few complicated biradical molecules (p. 266). Except for these odd compounds, $O_2$, and the salts and complexes of paramagnetic ions and atoms, all compounds are diamagnetic.

The descriptive theory of G. N. LEWIS and I. LANGMUIR on atomic bonding is based on the formation of electron pairs; each atom at the same time forms as far as possible an octet of eight electrons (only hydrogen merely two, He configuration) in connection with the stability of the inert gas configuration (Octet theory).

Electrons with parallel spins tend to avoid one another; thus in this case there is less mutual repulsion (correlation energy) than with electrons in the same orbit with antiparallel spins. Consequently, other things being equal, the energy will be lowest for the configuration with the electron spins parallel as far as possible. Thus an atom with electrons in degenerate energy levels (three p-levels, five d-levels, seven f-levels) will attain the configuration with maximum total spin number (HUND's rule, *e.g.*, N : $^4S$; $Fe^{3+}$: $^6S$; $Gd^{3+}$: $^8S$, with 3, 5 and 7 electrons with parallel spins respectively, see also p. 185). In ferromagnetic crystals the state having parallel spins also has the lowest energy ($K'$ is positive).

## § 24. DIRECTED VALENCY. HYBRIDIZATION

We have seen that the bond between two atoms through an electron pair is brought about by the overlapping of the wave functions of the two electrons with opposite spins and the consequent accumulation of charge between the nuclei which results in a negative exchange energy $K'$. The exchange integral between non-bonding electrons which are not paired with one another is positive and leads to repulsion. The COULOMB energy, consisting of the repulsion of the nuclei and the COULOMB interaction between electrons and *other* nuclei and the interaction between electrons themselves, is small and negative but becomes strongly positive for somewhat smaller distances.

It is now obvious, as PAULING was the first to suggest, that the bonding will take place so that the overlapping in question will be a maximum.

For a spherical wave function of an electron in an s state (with an s-type wave function or s orbital) there is naturally no preferred direction*. However, this is quite different for a p orbital which has as far as the angular dependence is concerned the shape of a dumb-bell consisting of two spheres on one another, directed along the $x$, $y$ or $z$ axis (Fig. 11). The charge distribution, $\varphi_p^2$, has the shape of a figure 8.

Let us now successively consider each of the atoms of the first row of the Periodic System as regards the compounds which they can form with hydrogen atoms, especially as far as the spatial arrangement is concerned.

*Fluorine* | ↑↓ | ↑↓ | ↑↓ | ↑ | ground state ($^2$P)

2s 2p$_x$ 2p$_y$ 2p$_z$

Two of the nine electrons of the fluorine atom are to be found in the (thereby) closed K shell while of the 7 L electrons two in the 2s level and four in two 2p levels form lone pairs. The last electron is unpaired and is likewise in a 2p level. It is plausible that on bonding the overlapping will tend to be-

* Bonds formed from s functions are in general weak, comp. Na — Na 17.3 kcal. An exception is $H_2$ with 103.2 kcal; but here the distance can be very small since there are no inner shells of electrons.

come as great as is possible without bringing the nuclei, which repel one another, closer together. The hydrogen atom with a spherical charge cloud will, therefore, attach itself to the fluorine atom along the dumb-bell axis: $:\ddot{\underset{\cdot\cdot}{F}}:H$

*Oxygen* | ↑↓ | ↑↓ | ↑ | ↑ | ground state ($^3P$)

2s 2p$x$ 2p$y$ 2p$z$

In the oxygen atom, there are two unpaired electrons in the lowest energy state, each in a different p level. The electrons available for bonding, therefore, form two dumb-bells along mutually perpendicular axes. A rectangular structure

$$\begin{array}{c} :\ddot{\underset{\cdot\cdot}{O}}:H \\ H \end{array}$$

is thus produced as the molecular model for water $H_2O$. Secondary influences, *e.g.*, the mutual repulsion of the partially positively charged hydrogen atoms and the repulsion of the two pairs of bonding electrons, produce a small increase in the bond angle from 90° to 104° 27′ (p. 170). For other bonds with the oxygen atom, *e.g.*, F—O—F in $F_2O$ and C—O—C, the bond angle is also of the same order, namely 101.5° and 110°, respectively.

With sulphur, selenium and tellurium the angle is still closer to 90° ($H_2S$ 92.3°, $H_2Se$ 91°, $H_2Te$ 89.5°) because here the electrostatic repulsion and the exchange repulsion, are smaller on account of the larger S—H or Se—H distance.

*Nitrogen* | ↑↓ | ↑ | ↑ | ↑ | ground state ($^4S$)

2s 2p$x$ 2p$y$ 2p$z$

$$\begin{array}{c} H \\ :\ddot{\underset{\cdot\cdot}{N}}:H \\ H \end{array}$$

The bonding of three hydrogen atoms with nitrogen to form $NH_3$, ammonia, takes place though three unpaired p electrons along three mutually perpendicular axes. The molecular structure of ammonia is indeed that of a three-sided pyramid; for the same reason as in the water molecule the valency angle is increased in this case to 106.75°.

The valency angle is again lower for $PH_3$, namely 93.8°; $AsH_3$ 91.6°, $SbH_3$ 91.5°. With $NF_3$ the bond angle of 102.2° is smaller than in $NH_3$ because of the much larger F—F distance and smaller repulsion.

| *Carbon* | ↑↓ | ↑ | ↑ | | ground state ($^3P$) |
|---|---|---|---|---|---|
| | 2s | 2p*x* | 2p*y* | | |

Now what happens with the carbon atom? In the ground state the four L electrons are distributed over a lone pair in the lowest energy state (2s), and one unpaired bonding electron in each of two p levels. Thus one would expect $CH_2$ as the normal hydrogen compound with a structure like that of water. Actually methylene exists only as a very unstable product formed, for example, in the decomposition of ketene, $CH_2=C=O$, but carbon is nevertheless predominantly quadrivalent. How can this be explained?

| ↑ | ↑ | ↑ | ↑ | excited state ($^5S$) |
|---|---|---|---|---|
| 2s | 2p*x* | 2p*y* | 2p*z* | |

Other electron configurations are also possible in addition to the above-mentioned ground state, for example, one ($^5S$) in which the four electrons are all unpaired and distributed over the 2s and the three 2p levels. Thus carbon will indeed react as quadrivalent if the energy necessary to promote the atom from the divalent ground state to this quadrivalent state finds sufficient compensation in the extra bond energy of the two new bonds. These four bonds would, however, not all be equivalent; in fact, three would be p bonds, the fourth a probably weaker s bond.

For the same nuclear distance and thus the same repulsion, the overlapping and, therefore, according to PAULING (see however also below), the bonding energy will be greater for the combination of a 2p function than for a 2s function with the 1s function of the hydrogen atom (Fig. 11).

The overlap integral $s = \int \varphi_A \varphi_B dv$ (pp. 141, 292) is a much better criterion than the original concept of PAULING of the product of the maximal values of both orbitals for given $r$. According to PAULING the $sp^3$ bond would be strongest, contrary to the experimental data given below.

C—H BOND

| Type | Molecule | Length | Diss. energy | Force constant |
|---|---|---|---|---|
| sp | acetylene | 1.065 Å | ~ 121 kcal | 5.88 $10^5$ dyne/cm |
| $sp^2$ | ethylene | 1.071 | ~ 104 | 5.05 |
| $sp^3$ | methane | 1.095 | ~ 101 | 4.88 |
| p | CH radical | 1.120 | 80 | 4.09 |

This sequence is completely in accordance with the change in the overlap integral with hybridization (WALSH, 1947, MACCOLL, 1950, HERZBERG, and STOICHEFF, 1955).

The wave equation obviously furnishes one s and three p functions as the solution for the carbon atom in the $^5S$ state; however, a linear combination of these four functions will also be a solution (hybridization, hybrid orbital).

Now PAULING has posed the question: what four new wave functions are produced by taking such linear combinations of one s and three p functions when the demand is made that these new functions should be equivalent? Each of these hybrid $sp^3$ functions is occupied by one electron ($sp^3$ means a combination of one s state and three p states, $d^2sp^3$ the same in combination with two d states of a lower situated shell).

It appears that in this way four functions are produced which have peaks along the four directions from the centre to the corners of a tetrahedron, making an angle of 109°28′ with each other. Thus the tetrahedral molecular model will indeed be produced for $CH_4$ as had been postulated by VAN 'T HOFF and LE BEL as early as 1874.* This structure is, however, not as obvious as one might perhaps expect. Indeed when the four bonds are not occupied by four similar atoms, the hybridiza-

* The final experimental proof of the tetrahedral model was given by the brilliant determination of the absolute configuration of the asymmetric carbon atom in optical-active compounds by BIJVOET (BIJVOET, 1949, BIJVOET, PEERDEMANS and VAN BOMMEL, 1951).

tion need no longer be *a priori* equivalent for the four bonds. This would give rise to deviations in the bond angles, but experimentally such deviations appear to be extremely small or zero.

| | | |
|---|---|---|
| $CH_3F$ | $\angle$ HCH | 110.0° |
| $CH_3Cl$ | $\angle$ HCH | 110.2° |
| $CH_2Cl_2$ | $\angle$ ClCCl | 111.8° |
| $CHCl_3$ | $\angle$ ClCCl | 110.4° |
| $CHF_3$ | $\angle$ FCF | 108.6° |

Hybridization is simpler for the sp case, thus between one s and one p function, than for $sp^3$.

The two new functions are in general:

$$\varphi_1 = C_{11}\varphi_s + C_{12}\varphi_p$$
$$\varphi_2 = C_{21}\varphi_s + C_{22}\varphi_p$$

On account of the normalizing of $\varphi_1$ and $\varphi_2$ we must have:

$$C_{11}^2 + C_{12}^2 = 1$$
$$C_{21}^2 + C_{22}^2 = 1$$

since $\int \varphi_s \, \varphi_p \, dv = 0$ (orthogonal functions p. 127).

We also have
$$C_{11}^2 + C_{21}^2 = 1$$
$$C_{12}^2 + C_{22}^2 = 1$$

since there is only one s and one p function which are divided over $\varphi_1$ and $\varphi_2$. We further assume that both new functions are equivalent, *e.g.* the s-function equally divided between both or $|C_{11}| = |C_{21}|$.

These four equations give:

$|C_{11}| = |C_{12}| = |C_{21}| = |C_{22}| = \frac{1}{\sqrt{2}}$; with $C_{11} = C_{21}$ arbitrarily chosen positive, then $C_{12} = +\frac{1}{\sqrt{2}}$ and $C_{22} = -\frac{1}{\sqrt{2}}$ (or vice versa).

If we only consider the angular dependent parts, we have $\varphi_s = \frac{1}{\sqrt{4\pi}}$ and $\varphi_{pz} = \frac{\sqrt{3}}{\sqrt{4\pi}} \cos \vartheta$, in which the factors are determined by the normalizing condition:

$$\int_0^{\pi} \int_0^{2\pi} \varphi^2 \sin \vartheta \, d\vartheta \, d\varphi = 1.$$

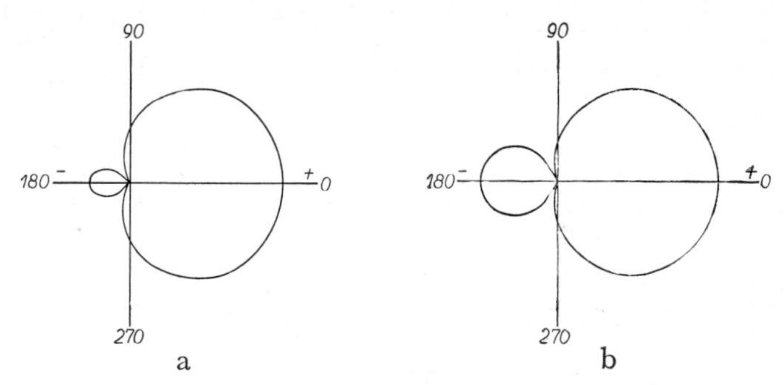


Fig. 16. Hybrid wave functions (angular dependence).

a. $\varphi\,(sp) = \frac{1}{\sqrt{2}}(s+p) = \frac{1}{\sqrt{4\pi}}\frac{1}{\sqrt{2}}(1+\sqrt{3}\cos\vartheta)$, one of the two digonal functions.

b. $\varphi\,(sp^3) = \frac{1}{2}(s+p\sqrt{3}) = \frac{1}{\sqrt{4\pi}}\frac{1}{2}(1+3\cos\vartheta)$, one of the four tetrahedral functions.

The sp functions are:

$$\varphi_1 = \frac{1}{\sqrt{2}}\varphi_s + \frac{1}{\sqrt{2}}\varphi_p = \frac{1}{\sqrt{4\pi}}\frac{1}{\sqrt{2}}(1+\sqrt{3}\cos\vartheta)$$

$$\varphi_2 = \frac{1}{\sqrt{2}}\varphi_s - \frac{1}{\sqrt{2}}\varphi_p = \frac{1}{\sqrt{4\pi}}\frac{1}{\sqrt{2}}(1-\sqrt{3}\cos\vartheta)$$

The one sp function is depicted in Fig. 16a as far as angular dependence is concerned, the other is equivalent to this but points in the opposite direction. This type of hybridization is present in the linear molecules of $HgCl_2$ and $HgBr_2$.

In a similar way three functions are found for the $sp^2$ hybridization which lie in a plane and make an angle of 120° with each other. Apart from the above-mentioned normalization conditions there are also the orthogonality conditions which these hybrid functions must also satisfy: $\int \varphi_i \varphi_k \, dv = 0$, which give further equations for the coefficients. Since nevertheless the number of unknowns for $sp^3$ is found to be greater than the number of equations (16 unknowns and 14 equations) a further condition is still necessary and PAULING has assumed the mutual equivalence of the functions. The four $sp^3$ functions are:

$$\varphi_1 = \frac{1}{2}s + \frac{\sqrt{3}}{2}p_x \quad ; \varphi_3 = \frac{1}{2}s - \frac{1}{2\sqrt{3}}p_x + \frac{1}{\sqrt{2}}p_y - \frac{1}{\sqrt{6}}p_z$$

$$\varphi_2 = \frac{1}{2}s - \frac{1}{2\sqrt{3}}p_x + \frac{\sqrt{2}}{\sqrt{3}}p_z; \varphi_4 = \frac{1}{2}s - \frac{1}{2\sqrt{3}}p_x - \frac{1}{\sqrt{2}}p_y - \frac{1}{\sqrt{6}}p_z \; *$$

* Or after rotating the system of axes:

$\varphi_1 = 1/2\,(s + p_x + p_y + p_z)$ ; $\varphi_3 = 1/2\,(s - p_x - p_y + p_z)$
$\varphi_2 = 1/2\,(s + p_x - p_y - p_z)$ ; $\varphi_4 = 1/2\,(s - p_x + p_y - p_z)$;

from which the equivalence of the functions is seen directly.

We find the same $sp^3$ hybridization with tetrahedral bonds. for the other elements of the 4th column, such as silicon, germanium and tin.

*Boron*

For boron, with three electrons in the L shell, the trivalency results from the $sp^2$ hybridization with three bonds in a plane at angles of 120°. This is the case in $BF_3$, $B(CH_3)_3$ etc.

| ↑ | ↑ | ↑ | |
|---|---|---|---|
| 2s | $2p_x$ | $2p_y$ | $2p_z$ |

excited state ($^4P$)

The constitution of the boron hydrides is, however, a separate question as $BH_3$ does not exist (p. 247).

Since the L shell can only contain eight electrons it is clear that the highest number of electron pairs and thus also the maximum valence of any atom in the first row of the Periodic System, can only amount to four. Nitrogen with five atomic bonds, *i.e.*, five valence strokes, is therefore impossible. Structural formulae which use this should be rejected and replaced by correct formulations of the constitution.

Thus ammonium chloride is not

```
    H
    |  Cl
H—N<             but    [     H     ]+
    |  H                [     |     ]
    H                   [ H—N—H ]  Cl⁻;
                        [     |     ]
                        [     H     ]
```

ammonium chloride does not exist at all as a free molecule.

Nitric acid and nitrates are still formulated incorrectly as:

```
O              O
 ⪢N—O—H   or    ⪢N—O—Na
O              O
```

This should be

```
 _
|O\
    N—O—H
|O/
 ‾
```

in resonance with

```
|O\                    |O\
    N—O—H  and a little     N=O—H   (see p. 210),
 O=                    |O/
```

(N—O 1.22 Å, N—OH 1.41 Å), or for the nitrate ion (N—O 1.21 A):

```
   |O|             |O̅|             |O̅|
   ||              |               |
   N     ⟷        N       ⟷      N
  / \             // \             / \\
|O̲| |O̲|        |O̲| |O̲|        |O̲| |O̲|
```

In general, each atom will be surrounded by four electron pairs (octet theory), either bonding or lone-pair electrons (hydrogen by two electrons). A bond stroke in the formulae always represents a common electron pair while the lone pairs are likewise represented by transverse strokes. The older representation by dots is, however, still largely employed.

In elementary teaching it would be well to refrain from reproducing structural formulae with valency strokes for inorganic compounds unless one goes into the matter in detail after dealing with the atomic bond and resonance in aromatic compounds. However, the construction of inorganic substances from ions can be given without special difficulties; structures such as $[N^{3-}H_4^{+}]\ Cl^{-}$ and $Na^{+}[N^{5+}O_3^{2-}]$ are undoubtedly far removed from the truth, but these are at any rate not incorrect in principle, like the above-mentioned valency structures.

Atomic bonds can be formed between neutral atoms as in methylamine.

```
    H
    |
H—C—N̅—H
    |  |
    H  H
```

However, the singly positively charged nitrogen $N^{+}$ is isoelectronic with carbon and thus this will form bonds of the same kind. Methane is isoelectronic with the tetrahedrally built ammonium ion. These bonds are of quite the same nature as those between formally neutral atoms (see § 25, onium compounds).

$$\begin{array}{c} \text{H} \\ |\oplus \\ \text{H—N—H} \\ | \\ \text{H} \end{array}$$

The *formal charge* of the atoms is found by halving each bonding pair and then comparing the total number of electrons with that of the neutral atom. Thus in the nitrate ion the formal charge of the nitrogen atom is equal to + 1, that of $\underline{\overline{O}}=$ to zero and that of $|\underline{\overline{O}}—$ to — 1. This formal charge only partially determines the actual charge distribution, which is also determined by the differences in electronegativity; thus in the ammonium ion the positive charge will quite certainly, for a considerable part, reside on the hydrogen atoms, in spite of their formal charge 0 compared with + 1 or the nitrogen atom.

We always indicate this formal charge by $\oplus$ or $\ominus$. The algebraic sum of these formal charges is equal to the charge of the molecule or ion concerned.

For the atoms of the second and higher periods of the Periodic System, the octet rule is no longer strictly valid.

In the first place, to begin with the M shell, there are the d electrons. Moreover, the occurrence of the transition elements after calcium indicates that the energy difference between the 4s (N shell) and the 3d (M shell) state is small; the spectra also show that the energy differences between the transitions 4s—3s and 4s—3p are much smaller than between 3s—2s and 3s—2p.

Furthermore, the ionization potential of the elements of the second row is smaller than that of the first row, thus the configurations in which the atom carries a positive formal charge can occur more readily. Thus a large number of configurations always occur here simultaneously and resonance will occur (see p. 210).

*Phosphorus*

The normal valency of the element phosphorus is three, as

with nitrogen: $PH_3$, $PCl_3$, etc. In the singly positively charged state it is quadrivalent; $P^+$ occurs not only in the phosphonium compounds like $PH_4I$ but also in the LEWIS-LANGMUIR configurations of the acids:

```
       |O̅|⊖
        |                        |O̅|⊖                        |O̅|⊖
H—O̅—P⊕—O̅—H                        |                            |
   _    |    _               H—O̅—P⊕—O̅—H                  H—P⊕—O̅—H
       |O|                      _   |   _                     |   _
        |                           H                         H
        H
ortho (pyro and meta)          phosphorous              hypophosphorous
  phosphoric acid                 acid                       acid
```

However, by promoting the 3s electron to 3d (or perhaps also 4s) the possibility of the formation of 5 electron pair bonds results, in contrast to nitrogen.

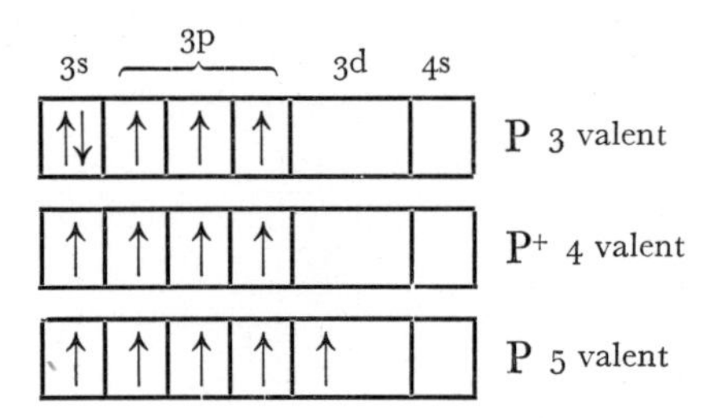


We meet this state in $PCl_5$, $PBr_5$ etc., in which a trigonal bipyramid can result by the hybridization $sp^3d$. This quinquevalency also appears in other possible electronic configurations of the phosphoric acids; this is responsible for the fact that the "free" oxygen atoms have an appreciably smaller bond distance in the tetrametaphosphate ion (p. 83) and in orthophosphoric acid itself (FURBERG, 1955).

```
      |O|                        |O|
       ||                         ||
|O̅—P—O̅—P   and   H—O̅—P—O̅—H
 _     |   _                _     |   _
      |O|  (2×)                  |O|
       |                          |
       P                          H
```

The bond length of the free and hydroxyl oxygen atoms in $H_3PO_4$ are 1.57 Å and 1.52 Å respectively. In the orthophosphate ion, $PO_4^{3-}$, the same configurations occur as in the isoelectronic sulphate and perchlorate ion.

With strongly electronegative ions, in particular fluorine,

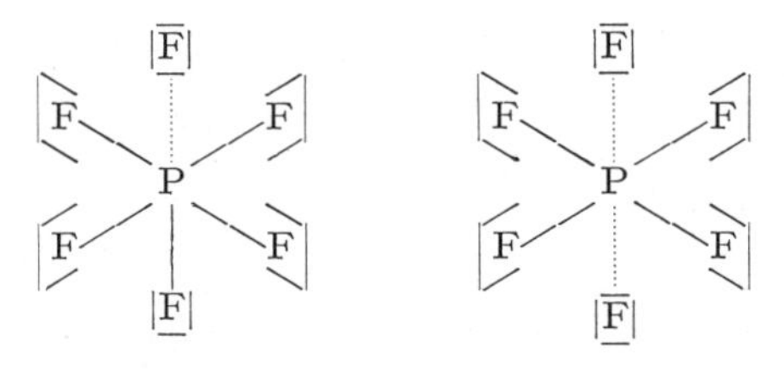


hexavalency, $PF_6^-$, occurs as well. This ion is isoelectronic with $SF_6$, to which the following statements also apply. There is resonance between configurations with four atomic bonds and two ionic bonds or five atomic and one ionic bond as the most probable constitution, and further a configuration with the six octahedral $sp^3d^2$ bonds; by this resonance six equivalent bonds are produced. With $PF_5$, but not with $PCl_5$ and $PBr_5$, there is certainly an appreciable contribution of configurations with 4 atomic bonds and one ionic bond.

*Sulphur*

The uncharged sulphur atom in the ground state is able to form two bonds as in $H_2S$ (see above).

As $S^+$, isoelectronic for the outer electrons with nitrogen, sulphur can form three bonds as in the sulphonium compounds

| 3s | 3p | | | |
|---|---|---|---|---|
| ↑↓ | ↑↓ | ↑ | ↑ | S |
| ↑↓ | ↑ | ↑ | ↑ | $S^+$ |
| ↑ | ↑ | ↑ | ↑ | $S^{2+}$ |

(p. 174), but also in $SO_3^{2-}$ and $SO_2$. The bond angle of $SO_2$:

119° 30′, is in agreement with the expected angle of 120°—125° for a bond arrangement similar to that around the carbon atom in $C_2H_4$ ($sp^2$ hybridization, p. 162) but with the lone pair of electrons occupying the same orbital as one of the C—H bonding pairs.

$SO_3^{2-}$:

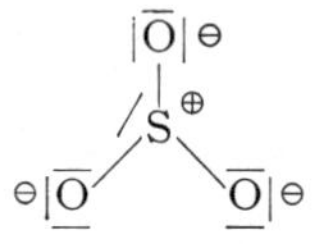

$SO_2$:

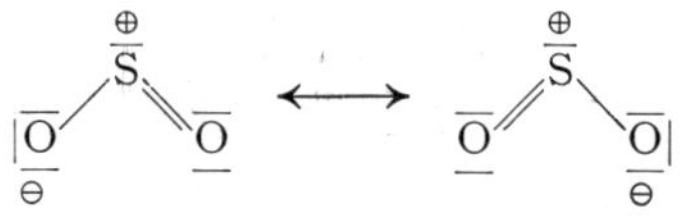

The atom $S^{2+}$, isoelectronic with $N^+$ and C, can form a plane molecule with three atoms by $sp^2$ hybridization; the resulting constitution for $SO_3$ is similar to $NO_3^-$ and $CO_3^{2-}$ with similar configurations for all three:

$SO_3$:

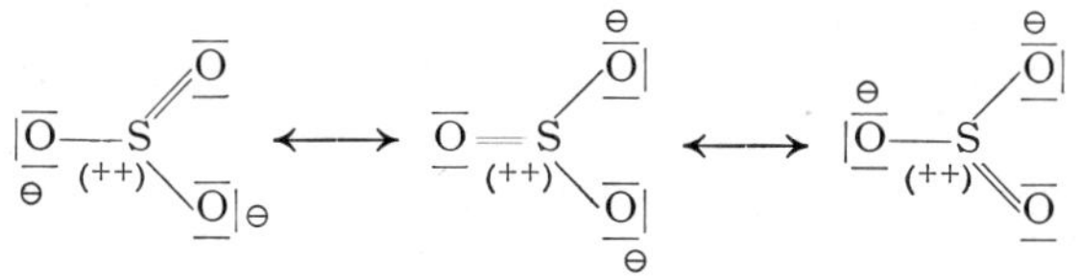

The S—O bond distance of 1.43 Å, both in $SO_2$ and in $SO_3$, is even shorter than 1.49 Å, the value to be expected for a $S^+{=}O$ bond (p. 199). Thus certainly configurations with the use of 3d orbitals

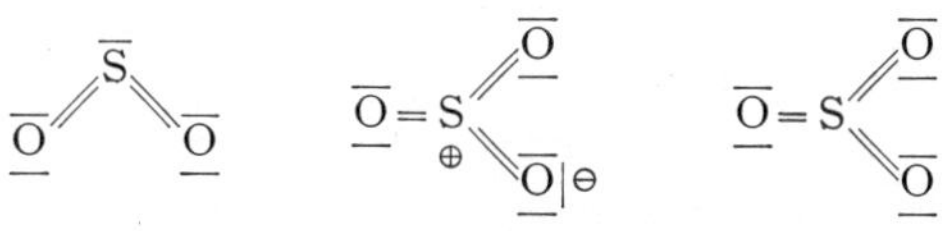

do largely contribute. Configurations with five and six bonds will also contribute to the electron configuration of the sulphate ion with a S—O distance of 1.51 Å.

```
      |O|⊖                  |O|⊖                  |O|⊖
  ⊖    |    ⊖           ⊖    |                ⊖    |
 |O—S—O|               |O—S=O                |O—S=O
       | (++)                | ⊕                   ||
      |O|⊖                  |O|⊖                  |O|
```

It is not yet possible to estimate well the relative importance of the contributions from these configurations.

Atomic bonding is not restricted to the bonding of atoms to form separate molecules but also gives rise to the formation of lattices, *i.e.*, giant three-dimensional molecules .

Diamond is a prototype of this group of solid substances, similarly boron, silicon, germanium, carborundum SiC, aluminium and boron nitride (AlN and BN) and in a certain sense the modifications of $SiO_2$. To some extent the binding in ZnS (zinc blende, wurtzite) is also due to atomic bonds (p. 34).

As can be expected from the high bond energy (in analogy to the C—C bond), these substances are extremely hard and have extremely small volatility (p. 96).

Graphite can be considered as a giant two-dimensional molecule from the series of condensed rings; the bonding between the separate layers is very weak, being due, as in molecular lattices, to VAN DER WAALS-LONDON interaction. The now infinite system of $\pi$ electrons results in metallic conduction, however, in the plane of the rings! Boron nitride has recently been obtained also in a diamond-like form called borazon (WENTORF, 1957) as well as in the common graphite-like modification (p. 252).

The starting point of the above considerations was the ground state of the free atom. However, another approach is also feasible, based on the observation that a given number of pairs of electrons in a valency shell, irrespective of whether they are bonding pairs or lone-pairs, are always arranged in about the same way (SIDGWICK and POWELL, 1940). Thus we have the following arrangements for non-transitional elements: two pairs, linear; three, plane triangle; four, tetrahedron; five, trigonal bipyramid; six, octahedron; seven, pentagonal bipyramid. (Table 15B, GILLESPIE and NYHOLM, 1957).

The hydrides of the first row elements $CH_4$, $NH_3$, $OH_2$ and FH are iso-electronic with neon. The neon atom can be considered the unified atom of these molecules if we let the protons approach the central nucleus. In neon there are 8 electrons in the M shell. These electrons can be divided into two groups of four

## TABLE 15 B

SHAPE OF MOLECULES (SINGLE BONDS)

| Total number of pairs | Hybridization | Number of bonding pairs | Shape of molecule | Example |
|---|---|---|---|---|
| 2 | sp | 2 | linear | $HgCl_2$ |
| 3 | $sp^2$ | 3 | plane triangle | $BF_3$ |
| ,, | ,, | 2 | V-shape (120°) | $SnCl_2$ |
| 4 | $sp^3$ | 4 | tetrahedron | $CH_4$ |
| ,, | ,, | 3 | trig. pyramid | $NH_3$ |
| ,, | ,, | 2 | V-shape (109.5°) | $OH_2$ |
| ,, | ,, | 1 | linear | FH |
| 5 | $sp^3d$ | 5 | trig. bipyramid | $PCl_5$(gas) |
| ,, | ,, | 4 | irr. tetrahedron | $SCl_4$ |
| ,, | ,, | 3 | T-shape | $ClF_3$ |
| ,, | ,, | 2 | linear | $[ICl_2]^-$ |
| 6 | $sp^3d^2$ | 6 | octahedron | $SF_6$, $[PF_6]^-$ |
| ,, | ,, | 5 | square pyramid | $IF_5$ |
| ,, | ,, | 4 | square | $[ICl_4]^-$ |
| 7 | $sp^3d^3$ | 7 | pentag. bipyramid | $IF_7$ |
| ,, | ,, | 6 | irr. octahedron | $[SbBr_6]^{2-}$ |

electrons, one group with one spin orientation and the other with the opposite spin orientation. Owing to the PAULI or exclusion principle (p. 152) the most probable arrangement within each set is with the electrons at the corners of a tetrahedron (LENNARD-JONES, 1954, DAUDEL *et al.*, 1954, 1955). However, there is no correlation between the two sets, with equal probability for any relative orientation; thus the spherical symmetry (p. 128) is preserved in the neon atom.

The same tetrahedral arrangement will be found in molecules with four pairs of electrons, either bonding pairs or lone pairs in the L shell. However, because now one (or more) bonding pair is orientated along the bond the two tetrahedra now have a fixed, identical, orientation in the molecule. Starting from the unified neon atom one would expect bond angles of 109°28′ for the set of iso-electronic hydrides $CH_4$—FH. However, because the centre of the charge cloud of a bonding pair will be situated at a larger distance from the central atom than the centre of a lone-pair charge cloud, the lone-pair—lone-pair repulsion will be higher than lone-pair— bonding pair and bonding pair— bonding pair repulsion. This will lead to a decrease of the bond angle below the tetrahedral value as observed in $NH_3$(106.75°) and still more in $OH_2$ (104.5°).

The centres of the charge distribution in the water molecule will thus nearly form a tetrahedron with two negative and two positive corners. This charge distribution determines, *e.g.*, the crystal structure of ice (p. 420), the dipole moment (p. 303) and the association through hydrogen bonds (p. 420).

For elements in the second and higher rows of the periodic systems this decrease is expected to be still larger (compare p. 158) because of larger differences in electron pair repulsion energy.

If we replace hydrogen by the more electro-negative and larger fluorine atom, the bond angle will be still smaller ($NF_3$: 102.1°; $OF_2$ : 101.5°).

The change of bond angles will be accompanied by a related change in the hybridization. One can conclude that for the first row hydrides the bonding pairs occupy orbitals which are closer in character to $sp^3$— than to pure p-orbitals (p. 157) but that the contrary is true for second and higher row elements. Both points of view thus have their special merits in particular fields but they merge in higher approximation.

In shells with more than eight electrons d-orbitals are used (p. 166, 170). Later we shall discuss the bond formation of the transition elements, also involving d-orbitals (p. 180).

## § 25. ONIUM COMPOUNDS

We know that in the ionic compounds there is no essential difference between the principal valency and the subsidiary or coordinative valency; this is evident from the symmetrical arrangement in the coordination compounds of WERNER, for example in $[SiF_6]^{2-}$, $[BF_4]^-$, $[SO_4]^{2-}$, etc. In atomic bonding the bond number (the "Bindigkeit"), the number of valencies from the central atom, may also be greater than the normal valency. In organic chemistry the so-called onium compounds belong to this class: ammonium, oxonium, sulphonium, phosphonium and iodonium compounds, etc. (see also p. 60). The central atom in these cases (N, O, S, P or I) has one or more lone electron pairs in the normal valency state, which can become bonding pairs; the central atom then gets a formal positive charge of + 1, sometimes even higher.

In these cases, *e.g.*, in the ammonium ion or in an amine oxide,

$$R_3\overset{\oplus}{N}-\overline{\underline{O}}|^{\ominus}$$

the bonding pair is supplied by only one of the two partners but this does not affect the essential nature of the bond.

LOWRY and SIDGWICK designated this bond between nitrogen and oxygen as "semi-polar double bond" (covalent bond + ionic bond) or "coordinate link" and used the symbol →.

The direction of the arrow indicates the direction of the electron transfer, thus

$$\begin{array}{c} R \\ | \\ R{-}N \rightarrow O \\ | \\ R \end{array}$$

We reject these terms and symbols as misleading and superfluous.

The older formula

$$\begin{array}{c} R \\ | \\ R{-}N{=}O \\ | \\ R \end{array}$$

is, of course, completely incorrect (p. 163). The N—O bond in these amine oxides is similar in its properties (length 1.36 Å) to a "normal" single bond.

The simplest case is the attachment of a proton to the nitrogen atom of the ammonia molecule:

$$\begin{array}{c} H \\ | \\ H{-}N| \\ | \\ H \end{array} + H^+, Cl^- \longrightarrow \left[\begin{array}{c} H \\ | \\ H{-}N{-}H \\ | \\ H \end{array}\right]^+ Cl^- \quad \text{ammonium chloride}$$

The phosphonium and hydronium salts are similar (hydronium salt (p. 86)).

The existence of the hydronium ion in the solid state is well established (CONWAY, BOCKRIS and LINTON, 1955). Both infrared and Raman spectra (FERRISO and HORNIG, 1953, 1955; BETHELL and SHEPPARD, 1953; MULLHAUPT and HORNIG, 1956; TAYLOR and VIDALE, 1956) and also nuclear magnetic resonance (RICHARDS and SMITH, 1951) indicate the presence of the $OH_3$ -ion in the solid hydrates of strong acids. However, until recently the infrared spectra of liquid solutions did not reveal the presence of the hydronium ion.

It was even thought that this failure would indicate that the lifetime of the hydronium ion is too small. However, recently FALK and GIGUÈRE (FALK and GIGUÈRE, 1957) have shown that the infra-red spectra of aqueous solutions of mineral acids *e.g.*, HCl, $HNO_3$, $HClO_4$, $H_2SO_4$ and $H_3PO_4$ do show the bands arising from the $OH_3^+$ ion; thus its lifetime must be longer than $10^{-13}$ second.

From the vibration frequencies of the $NH_4^+$ ion, it appears that this ion possesses a tetrahedral structure; all the bonds are therefore the same. As stated above, $sp^3$ hybridization occurs.

This formation of ammonium compounds by the addition of a proton takes place in the same way in the substituted primary, secondary and tertiary aliphatic and aromatic amines. There is certainly no reason for writing $NH_4Cl$ but still indicating aniline hydrochloride, pyridine hydrochloride, etc. as $C_6H_5NH_2.HCl$ and $C_6H_5N.HCl$ in place of writing $[C_6H_5NH_3]Cl$ and $[C_5H_5NH]Cl$, *i.e.*, anilinium and pyridinium chloride.

The formation of ammonium salts can also take place intramolecularly, as in the amino acids:

$$R{-}\overline{N}(R){-}CH_2{-}COOH \rightarrow R{-}N^{\oplus}(H)(R){-}CH_2{-}COO^{\ominus} \quad \text{"zwitter" ion}$$

In the formation of peralkylammonium salts one can think of an intermediate step in which an alkyl ion occurs.

$$R{-}\underset{R}{\overset{R}{N}}| + C_2H_5I \rightarrow \left[R{-}\underset{R}{\overset{R}{N}}{-}C_2H_5\right]^+ I^- \quad \text{tetra-alkyl-ammonium iodide}$$

Similarly the betaines are the intramolecular peralkylammonium salts in analogy with the "zwitter" ion formation with the amino acids.

$$(CH_3)_3N^{\oplus}{-}CH_2{-}COO^{\ominus} \quad \text{betaine}$$

It does not have a ring structure as was suggested by previous formulae.

Similar alkyloxonium compounds are produced from oxygen compounds:

$$CH_3{-}\overset{CH_3}{\underline{O}}| + C_2H_5F \rightarrow \left[CH_3{-}\overset{CH_3}{\underline{O}}{-}C_2H_5\right]^+ F^-$$

This compound is stabilized when a complex ion $BF_4^-$ is also produced as the negative ion by the simultaneous addition of $BF_3$.

On the other hand the ether-hydrochloric acid compound $(CH_3)_2O.HCl$ does not have a salt-like character and is not a typical oxonium compound; the bond is here produced by VAN DER WAALS forces (hydrogen bond, p. 417).

On account of the greater electronegativity of oxygen compared with nitrogen, oxonium compounds are produced much more rarely than ammonium compounds since the central atom thereby formally obtains a positive charge.

On the other hand, owing to the lower electronegativity of S and I, the sulphonium and iodonium salts are more stable.

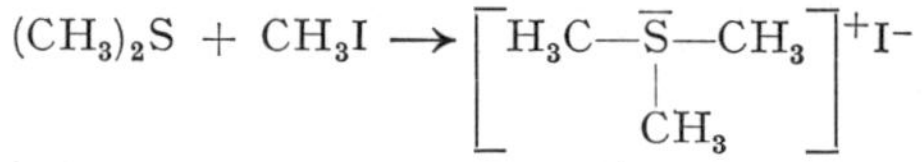

$$(CH_3)_2S + CH_3I \rightarrow \left[\begin{array}{c} H_3C-\overline{S}-CH_3 \\ | \\ CH_3 \end{array}\right]^+ I^- \quad \text{sulphonium salt}$$

$$[|\underline{I}\,(C_6H_5)_2]^+ I^- \quad \text{diphenyliodonium iodide}$$

An atom with a lone electron pair, as above, can only react with atoms, ions or molecules which lack an electron pair, that is to say, which have an electron sextet. (The hydrogen ion, of course, likewise lacks one electron pair from the closed configuration of the K shell.)

Above we dealt with examples in which positive ions, (hydrogen ions and alkyl ions) were bonded; similar reactions occur with uncharged molecules and atoms with an electron sextet. As regards LEWIS's idea that these reactions are acid-base reactions*, see p. 87.

The boron atom, for example, has in its normal compounds, such as boron trifluoride and boric acid, only a sextet. These substances will therefore form compounds with molecules which contain atoms with lone electron pairs, *e.g.*, oxygen or nitrogen. In particular, numerous stable compounds with boron trifluoride are known:

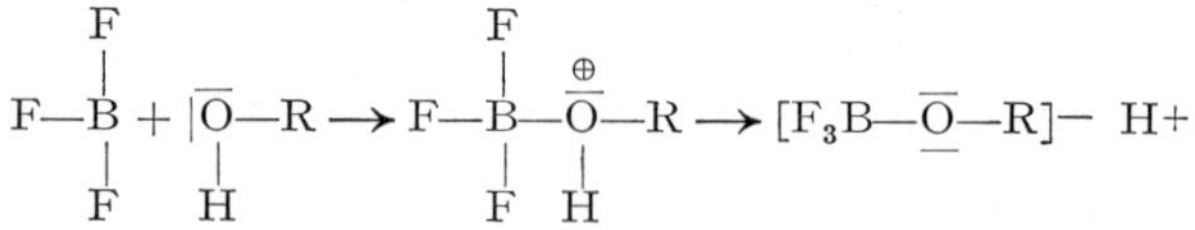

$$\begin{array}{c} F \\ | \\ F-B \\ | \\ F \end{array} + \begin{array}{c} \\ \\ |\overline{O}-R \\ | \\ H \end{array} \rightarrow \begin{array}{c} F \\ | \\ F-B \\ | \\ F \end{array}\!\!\begin{array}{c} \\ \oplus \\ -\overline{O}-R \\ | \\ H \end{array} \rightarrow [F_3B-\underline{\overline{O}}-R]^- \; H^+$$

* For a similar general concept of acid-base reactions of USSANOWITSCH, see GEHLEN, 1954.

As a result of the formal positive charge which the oxygen atom acquires, this compound of boron fluoride with alcohol is a much stronger acid than alcohol itself. The same holds for the addition products with carboxylic acids. Boron trifluoride, and similarly aluminium chloride, are active catalysts for many reactions, among others, polymerization and substitution. Polar configurations of the double bond (p. 279) with a lone pair on a carbon atom are stabilized by attachment of a boron or aluminium atom with a sextet configuration.

The constitution of the fairly strong complex acids formed from alkyl borates and alcohol and of esters of boric acid with polyalcohols with hydroxyl groups in the *cis* position (Boeseken, 1933) must be similar:

```
     OR                      OR              ┌      OR         ┐ −
     |                       |               │      |          │
RO—B  + |Ō—R ⟶ RO—B—Ō—R ⟶ │ RO—B—Ō—R  │ H+
     |      |                |  |            │      |    ‾     │
     OR     H                OR H            └      OR         ┘

        ┌R                   R┐ −
        │  \                /  │
        │ R—C—Ō\      /Ō—C—R   │
        │    |  ‾  B  ‾  |     │ H+
        │ R—C—Ō/      \Ō—C—R   │
        │  /   ‾      ‾    \   │
        └R                   R┘
```

It is not the esterification as such which causes the increase of the acid strength but the addition of the oxygen atom with its lone pair to the boron atom with a sextet. This is evident from the very weak acid strength of the compound of one molecule of diol with one molecule of boric acid (Hermans, 1925).

```
                  R
                 /
           /Ō—C—R
H—Ō—B   ‾   |
   ‾     \Ō—C—R
          ‾    \
                R
```

The strong tendency to fill up the electron sextet is evident from the formation of complexes of boron trifluoride with argon although neither of the two components possesses a dipole moment (compare p. 369). So-called hydrates are produced with water; $BF_3.H_2O$ is, however, $H(BF_3OH)$ and $BF_3.2H_2O$ is really $(OH_3)$ $(BF_3OH)$, isomorphous with the corresponding fluoborates and perchlorates (Klinkenberg and Ketelaar 1935, Greenwood *et al.*, 1951, 1958). Complex compounds are also produced, *e.g.*, with potassium sulphate, such as

$$K_2(O-\overset{O}{\underset{O}{S}}-O-\overset{F}{\underset{F}{B}}-F)$$

This compound corresponds to pyrosulphate; the boron fluoride therefore reacts analogously to $SO_3$. This analogy of $SO_3$ with $BF_3$ and also the formation of polymers point to the electron-accepting tendency of the sulphur atom in $SO_3$ in forming ten and twelve electron configurations (p. 168).

Both in the ring-shaped $(SO_3)_3$ trimeric molecules of the volatile ice-like modification and in the chain polymers of the asbestos-like $\beta$ and $\gamma$ modifications the oxygen atoms are arranged tetrahedrally around the sulphur atoms. However, the S—O—S distances in the chain are 1.60, 1.61 Å, whereas the distance to the two free oxygen atoms are 1.40, 1.41 Å respectively; the latter bonds are thus more nearly S = O links, the former S—O single bonds (Westrik and MacGillavry, 1941, 1954). In the vapour the molecules are single with a plane structure; in the liquid there is an equilibrium between monomeric and trimeric molecules (Gerding *et al.*, 1937).

The compound $SO_3.NH_3$ is better known as amidosulphonic or sulphamic acid: $H_2NSO_2(OH)$. In the very stable $BF_3.NH_3$ ($\Delta H$–42 kcal) there is no transfer of hydrogen; the B—N distance is 1.60 Å (sum of the radii 1.58 Å) (Hoard, 1951).

Atoms, other than a proton, with an incomplete octet can likewise form bonds with atoms with lone electron pairs. Thus similarly to the onium compounds, the amine oxides, the sulphoxides and sulphones are produced by addition of an oxygen atom to the nitrogen or sulphur atom of amines or sulphides.

$$R_3N| + \overline{\underline{O}}| \rightarrow R_3N^{\oplus}—\overline{\underline{O}}|^{\ominus} \qquad \text{amine oxide}$$

$$R_2|S| + \overline{\underline{O}}| \rightarrow R_2|S^{\oplus}—\overline{\underline{O}}|^{\ominus} \qquad \text{sulphoxide}$$

$$R_2|S| + 2\,\overline{\underline{O}}| \rightarrow {}^{\ominus}|\overline{\underline{O}}—S^{(2+)}R_2—\overline{\underline{O}}|^{\ominus} \qquad \text{sulphone}$$

In all these cases the oxygen atom has a negative formal charge, while the nitrogen or sulphur atom carries a corresponding positive charge. Double bonds were written in the older formulae, later also semipolar double bonds; however, there is here no essential difference from the normal single electron pair bond.

All these examples demonstrate for the elements of the first row the strong tendency to the formation of complete octets as required by the LEWIS-LANGMUIR theory (see also p. 215), owing to the relative stability of the inert gas configuration. For second row elements there is, moreover, a tendency to form five or six bonds (p. 165).

## § 26. COMPLEX COMPOUNDS*

In Chapter II we discussed complexes in which the electrostatic forces of the ionic bonding predominated; these are also numerous complexes in which the coordination is brought about by electron pairs. This type of complex is usually formed

* *General literature:* BJERRUM, 1950; BURKIN, 1951; QUAGLIANO and SCHUBERT, 1952; HEIN, 1950; MARTELL and CALVIN, 1952; BAILAR, 1956; also *Proc. Conf. Coordination Compounds*, Copenhagen, 1953; Amsterdam, 1955; or *Rec. trav. chim.*, 75 (1956) 557; GILLESPIE and NYHOLM, 1957.

from slightly electropositive atoms with a large ionization energy and which do not form ions with an inert gas configuration (transition metals), combined with weak electronegative, readily polarizable ions such as the halogens Cl, Br, I, the pseudo halogens, CN and CNS or $O_2^{2-}$ and $S^{2-}$. Non-ionic complex formation also takes place with some less polarizable ions such as $NO^+$, $OH^-$, $NO_2^-$, oxalate, etc. Also in the formation of electron pair bonds it is not essential that the coordinated groups should all be ions: they can also be neutral molecules with free electron pairs with or without a dipole moment, such as $NH_3$, $H_2O$, NO, CO and ethylenediamine ($H_2NCH_2CH_2NH_2$).* The special stability of these complexes with a non-inert gas ion as central ion was formerly explained on the basis of the strong electrostatic polarization by the central ion to which an extra strong COULOMB field had then been attributed; however, this is incorrect (see p. 186). Let us compare, for example, the compound $SO_4[Fe(H_2O)]_7$ with $K_4[Fe(CN)_6]$. Ferrous sulphate is paramagnetic with a moment equal to that expected on the basis of the presence of $Fe^{2+}$ ions; potassium ferrocyanide is, however, diamagnetic. This result proves that the configuration of the electron spins in the $Fe^{2+}$ ion with four unpaired electrons with parallel spins has been radically changed in the ferrocyanide. In the bonding of the six cyanide ions, in themselves diamagnetic, new electron pairs have been formed in such a way that unpaired electrons no longer occur.

---

* The stability of complexes of $z$-valent cations with anions can be expected to follow a function of the potential $z/r$. However, the stability of complexes of divalent ions of the transition metals with molecules as ligands, *e.g.*, $NH_3$, ethylene diamine, salicylic aldehyde, will largely depend on the polarization of the molecule (p. 73). The ionization potential ($I = I_1 + I_2$ for $Me \rightarrow Me^{2+} + 2e$ or $I_2$ for $Me^+ \rightarrow Me^{2+} + e$) is a measure of the attraction of electrons by the cation. The well known sequence in the stability $Mn^{2+} < Fe^{2+} < Co^{2+} < Ni^{2+} < Cu^{2+} < Zn^{2+}$ (IRVING and WILLIAMS, 1948, 1953; AHRENS, 1952) is the same as that of $I_2$ (less well that of I). A quantitative relation is given by: $\log K + p\,(I—q)$ where $K$ is the equilibrium constant for $Me^{2+} + A \rightleftharpoons [MeA]^{2+}$ and $p$ and $q$ are constants depending on the nature of the ligand, the temperature and the solvent (VAN PANTHALEON VAN ECK, 1953). The relations cannot be expected to hold if the total spin of the cation is changed on complex formation (p. 184).

This contrast is quite fundamental. We have, it is true, shown that a transition between a purely atomic bond and a purely ionic bond is possible (p. 146) but this continuity exists, according to the principles of the wave mechanics, only if the total spin moment of both states is the same (see also p. 211). A transition and thus resonance (p. 210) between the atomic bonding in the ferrocyanide complex and an ionogenic bonding would only be possible for a state in which the $Fe^{2+}$ ion had a total spin moment zero; however, the energy of this state lies far above the ground state. Conversely, the transition of the ionic bonding into atomic bonding with four parallel spins and yet six bonding pairs would likewise represent a very highly excited state. Thus the magnetic behaviour of the complex is in many cases an extremely important characteristic of state of bonding. It may be pointed out again that even a purely atomic bond through electron pairs can be polar and that this will be the case if the bonded atoms differ appreciably in electronegativity (p. 303).

Although there is a fundamental qualitative difference between ionic and atomic bonds, the formation of electron pairs as such is a symptom and not the cause of the bonding.

Indeed one can not say which part of the bond energy is of electrostatic origin and which part depends on exchange.

Unfortunately we have no data at our disposal from which we can deduce the character of a bond even approximately for molecules and ions which possess no dipole moment by reason of their symmetry. The intensities of the infrared-absorption bands (Mecke, 1950; Lippert and Mecke, 1951; Bell, Thompson and Vago, 1948; Hornig and McKean, 1955), the quadrupole coupling constants (p. 150) and paramagnetic resonance can probably give important indications on partial dipole moments and on the extent to which electrons are shared between atoms.

Let us consider the nature of the bonds in $[Fe(CN)_6]^{4-}$ somewhat further. The electron configuration of $Fe^{2+}$ (Fig. 17) contains the argon configuration and a further six electrons in the five available levels of the 3d sub-shell, four unpaired and two paired.

The cyanide ion $|C\equiv N|$ has a single non-bonding electron pair available on the formally negatively charged carbon atom. There are thus altogether $6 + 6 \cdot 2 = 18$ outer electrons or 9 pairs to be accomodated; 12 electrons are bonding electrons, so that the remaining 6, as non-bonding pairs, will first of all occupy the three lowest available 3d levels of the iron

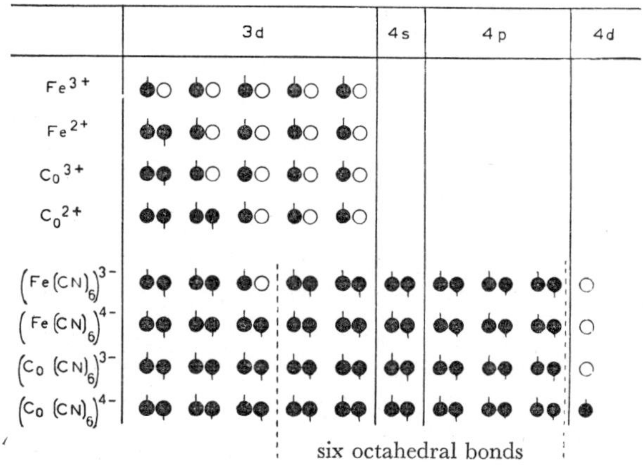

3d 4s 4p 4d

$Fe^{3+}$
$Fe^{2+}$
$Co^{3+}$
$Co^{2+}$
$(Fe(CN)_6)^{3-}$
$(Fe(CN)_6)^{4-}$
$(Co(CN)_6)^{3-}$
$(Co(CN)_6)^{4-}$

six octahedral bonds

Fig. 17. Electron configurations of di- and tri-valent iron and cobalt in the free ion state and in the cyanide complexes (PAULING). (The electron in 4d might also be in 5s stead).

atom. The remaining 12 bonding electrons will find the two other 3d levels and one 4s and three 4p levels in the N shell available. Thus the configuration of krypton is produced; this is, therefore, diamagnetic and, according to the theory of hybridized wave functions (p. 161), the bonds of the central ion, which are formed from two d, one s and three p functions (symbol $d^2sp^3$) are directed towards the corners of an octahedron.

In $K_3[Fe(CN)_6]$ the situation is similar; however, there is one electron less so that one electron remains unpaired and potassium ferricyanide shows a corresponding magnetism. The free $Fe^{3+}$ ion, present *e.g.* in $K_3FeF_6$, has, however, a much larger moment corresponding to five spins.

It is interesting to compare the configurations of the complex cyanides of di- and tri-valent cobalt and iron (Fig. 17).

The free $Co^{3+}$ ion accepts an electron so readily that it only exists as $CoF_3$ (it is very strongly oxidizing and liberates oxygen from water) but $Co^{2+}$ is stable. However, the situation is just the opposite with the hexacyanides. Here $K_3[Co^{3+}(CN)_6]$ with a krypton configuration is very stable and $K_4[Co^{2+}(CN)_6]$ with an electron too many is a strong reducing agent, which even reduces water to hydrogen. If we mix concentrated solutions of KCN and a cobalt salt, for example $Co^{2+}$ acetate, then an evolution of hydrogen takes place in the same way as occurs when an alkali metal is brought into contact with water. In fact, the general method of formation of the $Co^{3+}$ complexes depends on oxidation by air after the complex-forming components are added.

The paramagnetism of atoms and molecules has two causes: the spin of the electrons and the magnetic moment of the motion of the electron in its orbit (SELWOOD, 1956). The magnetic moment of the electron is usually expressed in the BOHR magneton ($B.M. = eh/4\pi mc$) as unit. (The magnetic moment connected with the spin of the atomic nucleus is very small, since the BOHR nuclear magneton is $m_e/m_H$ smaller).

The magnetic moment resulting from the spin for $n$ unpaired electrons with spin quantum number $s$ ($|s| = 1/2$), and the total spin quantum $S = n \cdot s = 1/2\ n$, is given by $\mu = 2 \cdot \sqrt{S(S+1)} = \sqrt{n(n+2)}\ B.M.$

The contribution of the orbital motion of one electron depends on the angular momentum quantum number $l$: $\mu = \sqrt{l(l+1)}\ B.M.$ There is thus no contribution from the orbital motion of an s electron. With more electrons, the total quantum number $L$ appears, resulting from the vector summation of the individual $l$ values.

In general, however, the magnetic moment depends on the

total angular momentum of the electron system which is obtained by combining $S$ and $L$ to form $J$. The magnetic moment is then $\mu = g\sqrt{J(J+1)}$ $B.M.$

An ion such as $Ce^{3+}$ with one electron besides closed shells with $S = 1/2$, $L = 3$ (f electron) has a total angular moment $J = 5/2$ in the lowest state represented by the symbol $^2F_{5/2}$. The magnetic moment will be $g\sqrt{5/2 \cdot 7/2}$, with $g = 6/7$, thus $\mu = 2.54$ $B.M.$; exp. value 2.37—2.77. The factor $g$, the LANDÉ factor, is a function of the values of $J$, $L$ and $S$, and has a value of the order of 1.

With the paramagnetic ions of the transition metals things are somewhat different since we are not concerned with the magnetic behaviour of free gaseous ions but of hydrated ions or ions interacting with other ions in a crystal lattice. The electric fields of the surroundings disturb the orbits in such a way that the orbital magnetism disappears almost completely. Thus practically only the spin magnetism remains, since the spin is scarcely influenced by an electric field but does respond to a magnetic field. The $g$ factor for spin magnetism is always 2 and for all these ions the magnetic moment is directly connected with the total number of unpaired spins; according to the above formula, $\mu = \sqrt{n(n+2)}$.

In this way we obtain the following values:

MAGNETIC MOMENT IN SOLUTION

| Ion | 3d Electrons | Unpaired | Moment | |
|---|---|---|---|---|
| | | | calc. | obs. |
| $K^+$, $Ca^{2+}$, $Sc^{3+}$, $Ti^{4+}$ | 0 | 0 | 0.00 | 0.00 |
| $Ti^{3+}$, $V^{4+}$ | 1 | 1 | 1.73 | 1.7 |
| $V^{3+}$ | 2 | 2 | 2.83 | 2.4 |
| $V^{2+}$, $Cr^{3+}$ | 3 | 3 | 3.88 | 3.8—3.9 |
| $Cr^{2+}$, $Mn^{3+}$ | 4 | 4 | 4.90 | 4.8—4.9 |
| $Mn^{2+}$, $Fe^{3+}$ | 5 | 5 | 5.92 | 5.9 |
| $Fe^{2+}$, $Co^{3+}$ | 6 | 4 | 4.90 | 5.3 |
| $Co^{2+}$ | 7 | 3 | 3.88 | 5.0—5.2 |
| $Ni^{2+}$ | 8 | 2 | 2.83 | 3.2 |
| $Cu^{2+}$ | 9 | 1 | 1.73 | 1.9—2.0 |
| $Cu^+$, $Zn^{2+}$, $Ga^{3+}$ | 10 | 0 | 0.00 | 0.00 |

The confirmation of the structure of the cyanide complexes is found in the following magnetic moments:

| | $\mu$ obs. | calc. |
|---|---|---|
| $[Fe^{2+}(H_2O)_6]\ (NH_4)_2(SO_4)_2$ | 5·3 | 4·90 |
| $K_4Fe^{2+}(CN)_6$; $K_3Co^{3+}(CN)_6$ | 0 | 0 |
| $(NH_4)_3Fe^{3+}F_6$ | 5·9 | 5·92 |
| $K_3Fe^{3+}(CN)_6$ | 2·33 | 1·73 |
| $K_3Co^{3+}F_6$ | 5·3 | 4·90 |
| $[Co^{2+}(H_2O)_6]\ (NH_4)_2(SO_4)_2$ | 5·1 | 3·88 |
| $[Co^{3+}(NH_3)_6]\ Cl_3$ | 0 | 0 |

The iron in oxyhaemoglobin shows the same $d^2sp^3$ octahedral arrangement as in the cyanides with the six bonds to the four nitrogen atoms of the porphyrin, one nitrogen atom of the globin and the oxygen molecule (or other groups such as CO); the ferrous compound is also diamagnetic while the ferric compound has a magnetic moment $\mu = 2.5$ (calc. 1.73) like $K_3Fe(CN)_6$.

The above examples were complexes with a coordination number 6; those with a coordination number 4 are also interesting. In this case we can have plane or tetrahedral complexes; the former with $dsp^2$ bonds directed towards the corners of a square, the latter with $sp^3$ bonds directed towards the corners of a tetrahedron.

The $Ni^{2+}$ ion has eight 3d electrons; in the complex $[Ni(CN)_4]^{2-}$ there are, therefore, $8 + 4 \times 2 = 16$ electrons to be considered. There are four 3d levels for the non-bonding electron pairs; for the four bonding pairs there are one 3d, one 4s and two 4p levels available. Thus a plane diamagnetic complex is produced; this is confirmed by X-ray analysis. The well known nickel dimethylglyoxime also belongs to this same group, as well as $K_2Pd(CN)_4$, $K_2PdCl_4$.

However, the complexes $[Ni(H_2O)_4]^{2+}$, $[Ni(NH_3)_4]^{2+}$ etc. are paramagnetic with $\mu = 2.6$—3.2. Here, therefore, the bonding is obviously different. The moment indicates the presence of ion-dipole bonding with the same electron structure as the $Ni^{2+}$ ion, or the formation of 4 bonds using the

4s and the three 4p levels with the 8 non-bonding electrons in the five 3d levels. In both cases a tetrahedral arrangement with two unpaired electrons is to be expected.

Even in magnetic ions a difference in the nature of the bonding cannot always be detected. Thus a $Cr^{3+}$ ion with six neighbours will have three unpaired 3d electrons either with ionic bonding or with $d^2sp^3$ atomic bonds. Resonance will, therefore, not be excluded in this case.

In the formations of electron pair bonds it is not essential that the coordinated groups be all ions, or all neutral molecules. Thus $[Fe^{2+}(CN)_5NH_3]^{3-}$ is diamagnetic and analogous to potassium ferrocyanide.

However, the bond between water molecules and iron, or divalent cobalt is ionic since oxygen has a high electronegativity. Trivalent cobalt forms electron pair bonds with all ions and groups mentioned, as appears from the diamagnetism, analogous to that of $K_3[Co(CN)_6]$. With fluorine, however, a strongly paramagnetic complex, $K_3CoF_6$ (4 spins) is produced by ionic bonding.

The negative cyanide ion $[|C{\equiv}N|]^-$ can be replaced by the isoelectronic nitrosyl ion $[|N{\equiv}O|]^+$ whereby the bond relationships remain unchanged. Thus $Na_2[Fe(CN)_5(NO)]$, sodium nitroprusside, is diamagnetic, analogous to $K_4[Fe(CN)_6]$.

The nitrosyl ion also occurs independently, *e.g.*, in $NO(ClO_4)$, $NOPF_6$, $(NO)AlCl_4$ and $(NO)_2SnCl_6$, in which the latter appears to be isomorphous with other complex stannichlorides so that the formula 2 $NOCl.SnCl_4$ does not correctly reproduce the construction from the ions $NO^+$ and $SnCl_6^{2-}$. This also holds for compounds such as $NOSbF_6$ and $NOSbCl_6$; the former does not decompose even at very high temperatures. Also the "Lead Chamber" crystal $NO[HSO_4]$ is a nitrosyl salt.

The CO molecule is likewise isoelectronic with $[|C{\equiv}N|]^-$, the configurations $|C{\equiv}O|$ and $|C{=}\overline{O}$ contributing to it (p. 244). Thus $K_3[Fe^{2+}(CN)_5CO]$ is isomorphous with $K_3$ $[Fe^{3+}(CN)_6]$.

Mixed complexes occur very generally, for example, the series from hexammine cobalt (III) chloride $[Co(NH_3)_6]Cl_3$—by replacement of more and more ammonia molecules by nitrite ions—to $K_3[Co(NO_2]_6]$ potassium hexanitrito cobaltiate. The middle member $[Co(NH_3)_3(NO_2)_3]$ is a non-electrolyte since the complex is now uncharged.

Isomers are known of hydrated chromic chloride, among others: $[Cr(H_2O)_6Cl_3]$ violet, and $[Cr(H_2O)_4Cl_2]Cl \cdot 2\ H_2O$ dark green. In the first compound three chlorine ions can be precipitated with silver nitrate, in the second compound only one.

Also *cis-trans* isomerism occurs with complex compounds of suitable composition, *e.g.*, *cis* and *trans*, or from the colours praseo (green) and violeo, $[Co(NH_3)_4Cl_2]^-$, with the two chlorines on one edge or at opposite corners of an octahedron. Optical isomers were already discovered by WERNER in 1911. Here two mirror images are obtained with one, two or three groups which fill two coordination positions such as the ethylene diamine and the oxalate groups but with different single groups such as $NH_3$, $Cl^-$ or $NO_2^-$ at the other positions.

*Crystal field theory*. A different approach to the formation of complexes of the transition metals is given by the crystal field or better ligand-field theory (HARTMANN *et al.*, 1951, 1955; ORGEL, 1952, 1955; BJERRUM *et al.*, 1954, 1956; especially ORGEL, 1952, 1955; ORGEL and SUTTON, 1954; and GRIFFITH and ORGEL, 1957).

In an octahedral complex the transition-metal ion is subjected to an electric field with cubic symmetry. The five degenerate d-levels of equal symmetry in the free ion are split into two levels, a lower triplet ($t_{2g}$) and an upper doublet ($e_g$). The orbitals of the triplet correspond to a high electron density between the lines joining the central ion and the ligands; the doublet to a high density along these lines thus giving rise to repulsion by the negative charges or the negative poles of the dipole of the ligands.

With 1, 2 or 3 d-electrons the electrons will find a place in the triplet levels with parallel spins. With 4 to 7 d-electrons two cases have to be considered. With a small splitting, in the case of weak fields, the electrons will fill both the triplet and the doublet levels with parallel spins as far as possible (high-spin complexes), whereas in a strong field the triplet levels are filled first, and only in the case of 7 d-electrons does one electron occupy one of the doublet levels (low-spin complexes). There is no difference in the arrangement of spins for 8 and 9 d-electrons.

The energy difference $\Delta$ between doublet and triplet levels is, *e.g.*, for hydrated bivalent ions 7500–12500 $cm^{-1}$, for hydrated trivalent ions 13500–21000 $cm^{-1}$. The colour of the complex ions (p. 98) is in general due to transitions from the

| Number of d-electrons | Weak field High-spin | | Strong field Low-spin | |
|---|---|---|---|---|
| | $t_{2g}$ | $e_g$ | $t_{2g}$ | $e_g$ |
| 1 | ↑ | — | ↑ | — |
| 2 | ↑ ↑ | — | ↑ ↑ | — |
| 3 | ↑ ↑ ↑ | — | ↑ ↑ ↑ | — |
| 4 | ↑ ↑ ↑ | ↑ | ↑↓ ↑ ↑ | — |
| 5 | ↑ ↑ ↑ | ↑ ↑ | ↑↓ ↑↓ ↑ | — |
| 6 | ↑↓ ↑ ↑ | ↑ ↑ | ↑↓ ↑↓ ↑↓ | — |
| 7 | ↑↓ ↑↓ ↑ | ↑ ↑ | ↑↓ ↑↓ ↑↓ | ↑ |
| 8 | ↑↓ ↑↓ ↑↓ | ↑ ↑ | ↑↓ ↑↓ ↑↓ | ↑ ↑ |
| 9 | ↑↓ ↑↓ ↑↓ | ↑↓ ↑ | ↑↓ ↑↓ ↑↓ | ↑↓ ↑↓ |

triplet to the doublet levels. The arrangement of electrons with 4, 6, 5 and 7 electrons in the low-spin complexes gives rise to an important gain in energy equal to $\Delta$, 2 $\Delta$, 2$\Delta$ and $\Delta$ respectively, compared with the high-spin arrangement in the free ion.

The sequence of increasing strength of the ligand-field as derived from the increasing value of $\Delta$ is given by $I^-$, $Br^-$, $Cl^-$, $F^-$, $H_2O$, oxalate, pyridine, $NH_3$, $NO_2$, $CN^-$.

Examples of the strong-field or low-spin complexes are $[Fe(CN)_6]^{4+}$ and $[Fe(CN)_6]^{3+}$ with six and five electrons respectively in the triplet levels, in correspondence with the magnetic moment observed (p. 183). With $[Co(NH_3)_6]^{3+}$, $[Co(NH_3)_6]^{2+}$ and $[Ni(NH_3)_6]^{2+}$ there are 0, 1 and 2 electrons respectively in the doublet levels.

Examples of the weak-field case are the hydrated $Mn^{2+}$ and $Fe^{3+}$ ions, which are low-spin complexes with five d-electrons with parallel spins.

The distinction between high-spin and low-spin complexes of the ligand-field theory corresponds to the distinction of ionic and atomic (covalent) complexes of PAULING, discussed above; both distinctions are based on the same magnetic criterion.

According to both the ligand-field and the valence-bond theory the doublet ($e_g$) levels may be used for the formation of $d^2sp^3$ bonds. However, the ligand-field theory postulates that electrons may go into the (anti-bonding) doublet orbitals without an essential change in the nature of the bonds. For typical covalent complexes of $Co^{2+}$, *e.g.*, $[Co(CN)_6]^{4-}$, the valence-bond theory assumes promotion of an electron to a 5s level (which has a lower energy than the 4d level indicated in Fig. 17, p. 180). According to the ligand-field theory ionic bonds with one electron in the doublet levels are equally possible. According to the valence-bond theory there is a sharp change from atomic bonding to ionic bonding. The ligand-field theory postulates a gradual change with increasing importance of atomic bonds with decreasing number of electrons in the doublet levels.

The ligand field is indeed essentially an electric field as all interaction of electrons is electrostatic in nature (p. 137). However, this field is only to a very small extent due to the classical forces from the theory of the ionic bond, acting between a charged central ion and the charges or the dipoles of the ligands. This is obvious from the sequence of increasing strength of the ligand field given above.

The COULOMB attraction between the cation and a fluorine ion with a unit negative charge will be certainly very much stronger than the attraction of the cation with the small dipole moment of $NH_3$, with an effective negative charge of the negative pole equal to only a very small fraction of an electron charge.

Apparently electrostatic polarization in the classical sense is also of slight influence as $CN^-$ is not much more polarizable than $I^-$. The increasing strength of the ligand field indeed signifies increasing transfer of electronic charge from the ligand to the central ion by the formation of atomic bonds, as opposed to formation of ionic bonds without exchange of electrons. Thus again the strong-field case in general corresponds to atomic bonding and ligand-field theory and valence-bond theory are not very seriously at variance. However, the former theory is very valuable in explaining details of the spectra, hydration energies, etc.

The complexes of nickel and palladium with a coordination number four mentioned above, are interesting because a plane configuration occurs which is inexplicable on the basis of the electrostatic theory of the ionic bond; the latter leads to a tetrahedral model. The diamagnetism also points to the formation of electron pairs in the bonding. The occurrence of *cis* and *trans* isomers is in agreement with a plane structure but incompatible with a tetrahedral arrangement.

In the complexes between non-magnetic ions, *i.e.*, as in most of the ions outside the iron group, the magnetic behaviour fails to be a point of difference between the two types of bonding.

In many cases the same complex or molecule can be described equally well on the basis of an ionic model as of an atomic model. On the one hand, atomic bonding is assured for the extremely stable complexes with weakly electronegative, large groups such as cyanide, NO, CO, ammonia, etc. On the other hand complex ions such as $AlF_6^{3-}$ and $SiF_6^{2-}$ are certainly predominantly built up from ions, since a purely atomic bonding, breaking the octet rule by the use of the levels of the 3d shell, is energetically less probable. The other fluorine complexes will, in general, belong to the same category. The atomic distances in $SiF_4$, for example, also indicate partial ionic binding. This is much more probable than the assumption of a partial double bond character in order to explain the observed shortening of the Si—F distance (sum of atomic radii: PAULING 1.81 Å, STEVENSON and SCHOMAKER 1.69 Å; obs. 1.54 Å). The sum of ionic radii is 1.52 Å calculated from

Zachariasen's univalent radii (p. 39) with corrections for charge and coordination number.

It is not possible at the present stage to reach a decision regarding the predominant type in the numerous oxygen complexes; both contribute. From a didactic point of view, the ionogenic conception will frequently offer the advantage of simpler formulations than the atomic bonding type with multiple resonance possibilities. In the discussion of the constitution of organic molecules, on the other hand, a correct understanding cannot be obtained without the discussion of resonance. Again in cases where ions with a configuration different from an inert gas must be assumed, the atomic bonding frequently appears more acceptable. Zachariasen's rule, according to which complexes of central ions without inert gas configurations have an asymmetrical structure, follows directly from the presence of a non-bonding electron pair on the central atom (compare p. 168). Thus, for example, the sulphite ion (and likewise $[ClO_3]^-$, $[IO_3]^-$ etc.)

```
                 |Ō|
                  |
[SO3]2-   |Ō—S|
                  |
                 |O|
```

is pyramidal. However, a plane structure would be probable for the ionic model since the polarizability of the central ion is small.

On the other hand, according to both conceptions of a bond, with an arrangement of three atoms round the center, plane structures are to be expected, and with an arrangement of four atoms round the center, tetrahedral structures, when there are respectively $3 \times 8$ or $4 \times 8$ electrons available outside the closed shell so that no non-bonding pair occurs on the central atom. The possibility of a formulation as ions with inert gas configurations is always present in these cases. Thus $NO_3^-$, $CO_3^{2-}$ and $SO_3$ are indeed plane (see pp. 164 and 168).

Up to this point we have discussed complex compounds in which the complex as a whole is an ion (and hence are also called complex salts). The complex itself may be wholly or partially constructed from ions or neutral molecules and the bonds may be ionic (§ 8–11) or atomic (this § and § 25).

In atomic or element complexes and also in the molecular complexes to be discussed in Chapter V the complexes are neutral particles.

The best known atomic complexes are the carbonyl compounds (Cable and Sheline, 1956; Anderson, 1947) and the related nitrosyl compounds formed especially by the metals of the iron group.

Nickel carbonyl, $Ni(CO)_4$, is diamagnetic in contrast to the nickel atom (and ion). Outside the argon configuration there are eight 3d and two 4s electrons; together with the eight bonding electrons of the CO, there thus result 18 electrons which fill five 3d, one 4s and three 4p orbitals, that is to say, a krypton configuration. In $Fe(CO)_5$ and $Cr(CO)_6$, the metal atom possesses two and four electrons less respectively, but in total they have the same electron configuration; the intermediate elements cobalt and manganese cannot form these simple carbonyl compounds.

Pauling concludes from the short metal-carbon distance that besides the single bond $>Ni—C{\equiv}O|$ the configurations $>Ni{=}C{=}\overline{O}$ would also play a part. The evidence does not appear very strong; the C—O distance points to $—C{\equiv}O$.

The carbonyls of chromium and iron correspond exactly with the similarly constituted compounds of the homologous elements Mo, W and Ru, Os. However, no carbonyl compounds are known from Pd and Pt, the homologues of Ni.

They are all relatively volatile compounds: $Ni(CO)_4$ b.p. 43° C, $Fe(CO)_5$ b.p. 103° C.

There are, however, also numerous multinuclear carbonyl compounds. Since $Co(CO)_4$ would have one electron less than the above-mentioned krypton configuration, this molecule itself does not exist but the dimer $Co_2(CO)_8$ does, just as two Br atoms form a $Br_2$ molecule with krypton configurations (there are analogous compounds of Ir and Rh).

Of manganese the compound $Mn_2(CO)_{10}$ is known, and similarly $Re_2(CO)_{10}$. The existence of the manganese carbonyl can be understood on comparison with $Fe(CO)_5$ as discussed above for cobalt carbonyl.

Of iron (and of ruthenium), however, there is also known $Fe_2(CO)_9$ [and $Fe_3(CO)_{12}$]. An investigation of the crystal structure furnishes the following picture with threefold symmetry about the Fe—Fe axis. A Fe—Fe bond is present here, since the diamagnetism points to the spins of the electrons in the iron atoms being paired.

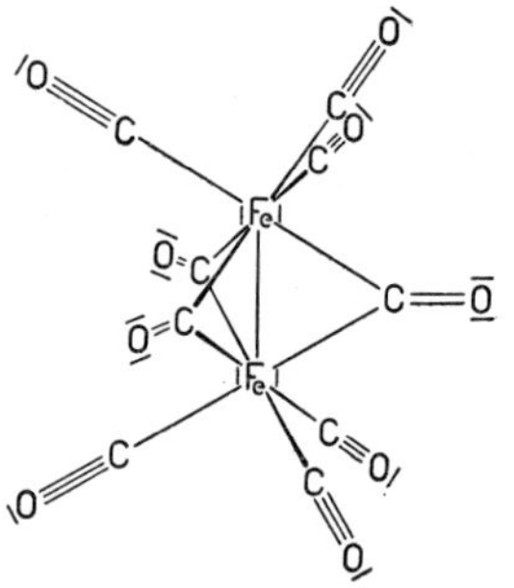

There are two non-bonding electron pairs in 3d together with seven bonding pairs in $d^3sp^3$ around an iron atom.

The general electron configuration of carbonyl hydrogen compounds such as $H_2Fe(CO)_4$, must be similar to $Fe(CO)_5$; in fact two H atoms contribute two electrons precisely like one CO molecule. It also follows that $HCo(CO)_4$ will exist, formally analogous to HBr. The spatial configuration of these compounds is the same as that of $Ni(CO)_4$; the four CO molecules are placed tetrahedrally around the metal hydrogen group or the nickel atom ($sp^3$ bonds).

It is probably not correct to think of the hydrogen atoms as directly bound to the metal atom but rather to the CO group, thus Me—C$\equiv$O—H. This is an unusual bonding with a twofold positive formal charge on the oxygen atom, but the hydrogen is readily replaceable by metals and the carbonyl hydride can be regenerated with acids.

When NO donates the odd electron to the central atom the $NO^+$ ion is produced which can replace the isoelectronic CO. Compare the isoelectronic compounds $Ni(CO)_4$, $Co(CO)_3NO$ and $Fe(CO)_2(NO)_2$, all with the same spatial structure. These, therefore, correspond with the above-mentioned carbonyl hydrides.

An interesting class of complex compounds are the stable compounds of transition metals with the cyclopentadienyl-anion $C_5H_5^-$ (WILKINSON *et al.*, 1954; PAUSON, 1955b; COTTON, 1955) and with the benzene molecule (FISCHER and HAFNER, 1955, 1956), which were recently discovered. The first representative found was ferrocene, $Fe(C_5H_5)_2$, an orange-coloured extremely stable compound. Related compounds are *e.g.*, $Co(C_5H_5)_2$, $Ni(C_5H_5)_2$, $Ru(C_5H_5)_2$, $Mn(C_5H_5)_2$, $Cr(C_5H_5)_2$, $V(C_5H_5)_2$, $[Ni(C_5H_5)_2]^+$, $[Fe(C_5H_5)_2]^+$, $[Ti(C_5H_5)_2]^{2+}$, $[Ta(C_5H_5)_2]^{3+}$, $Y(C_5H_5)_3$, etc. With benzene $Cr(C_6H_6)_2$, $[Cr(C_6H_6)_2]^+$ and $Mo(C_6H_6)_2$ are known.

In all these complexes both the cyclopentadienyl-ion and the benzene molecule are completely aromatic in their chemical reactions. The investigations of the crystal structure have shown that all* have a sandwich structure, with the metal atom between the two parallel rings at equal distances to all carbon atoms. In the cyclopentadienyl compounds the two regular pentagons are arranged in alternating positions with the symmetry $D_{5d}$ with a center of symmetry at the position of the metal atom. The C—C distance of 1.40 Å is only slightly larger than in benzene (1.38 Å) (DUNITZ, ORGEL and RICH, 1956). The force constants for the C—H and C—C stretching movements derived from the infrared absorption spectrum (LIPPINCOTT and NELSON, 1958) also indicate that the constitution of the cyclopentadienyl-anion is very nearly equal to that in benzene (p. 235).

Several theories have been given to account for the bonding

* Exceptions are the tri-cyclopentadienyl compounds of the metals of the third group and the Rare Earth elements; these have an ionic character and hydrolyze easily, in contrast to most of the other compounds.

in these substances, very much along the same lines as for the bonding in the cyanide- and carbonyl-complexes. The simplest description is to consider that in the diamagnetic $Fe(C_5H_5)_2$ the iron atom has again obtained a krypton configuration with the ten $\pi$ electrons, just as in $[Fe(CN)_6]^{4-}$ and in $Fe(CO)_5$.

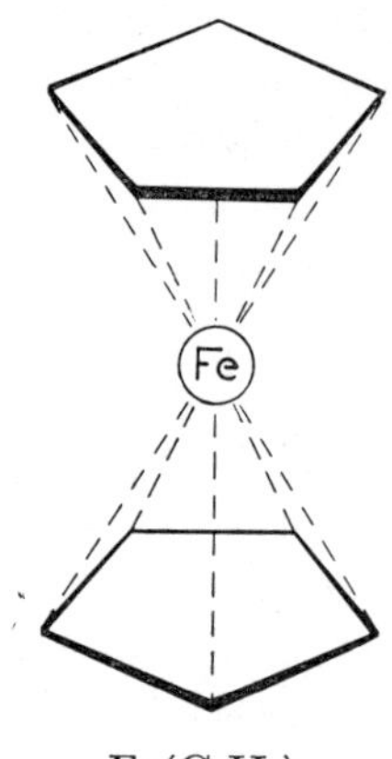


$Fe(C_5H_5)_2$

The same configuration will be possible for $Cr(C_6H_6)_2$ with twelve electrons supplied to the chromium atom (FISCHER and PFAB, 1952; RUCH and FISCHER, 1952; RUCH, 1956).

In the corresponding cobaltocene and nickelocene there are one and two electrons more, whereas in $Mn(C_5H_5)_2$ and $[Fe(C_5H_5)_2]^+$ there is one less, in $Cr(C_5H_5)_2$ two less than the krypton configuration. Indeed these compounds are all paramagnetic with a moment corresponding to 1, 2, 1 and 2 unpaired electrons respectively. However, one has to assume that the two extra electrons in $Ni(C_5H_5)_2$ are placed in two different 4d sublevels, whereas the 5s level has a lower energy, but there they would have to be paired. Also, it is not easy to understand why the bonding within the cyclopentadienyl ion and in the benzene molecule is hardly changed on complex formation.

Elaborate descriptions based on a molecular orbital

description with two dπ–pπ single bonds have been given (*e.g.*, DUNITZ and ORGEL, 1953; COTTON and WILKINSON, 1954; CRAIG *et al.*, 1954, and especially MOFFITT, 1954).

However, the existence of the benzene complexes provides an argument in favour of the concept of FISCHER and RUCH; as does the existence of carbonyl compounds, *e.g.*, $V(C_5H_5)(CO)_4$, $Mn(C_5H_5)(CO)_3$, $Co(C_5H_5)(CO)_2$ and $Ni(C_5H_5)NO$ with again a krypton configuration (LINNETT, 1956; ORGEL, 1956).

Little is known about the structure of other atomic complexes such as the alkali metal and alkaline earth metal-ammonia complexes, *e.g.*, $Li(NH_3)_4$ and $Ca(NH_3)_6$. The latter especially is very stable. These substances have an electronic conductivity like the well-known blue solution of sodium in liquid ammonia. Metal ions, $Li^+$ and $Ca^{2+}$, are present which are solvated by ammonia molecules through ion-dipole forces; free electrons are also present.

$K_4[Ni(CN)_4]$ also belongs to this group; it is produced from potassium in liquid ammonia and normal $K_2[Ni(CN)_4]$. The former can perhaps be regarded as a complex, built up from a nickel atom and four CN ions; thus it will have $10 + 4 \times 2$ electrons around the central atom in a krypton configuration as in $Ni(CO)_4$, instead of $8 + 4 \times 2$ as in the ordinary complex of $Ni^{2+}$. One would have to expect tetrahedral $sp^3$ bonding as opposed to the normal $dsp^2$ bonding in $K_2[Ni(CN)_4]$; the crystal structure is not known, however.

## § 27. THE MULTIPLE BOND

In VAN 'T HOFF and LE BEL's hypothesis the double bond between two carbon atoms was represented by two tetrahedra with a common edge. This model can account for the *cis-trans* isomerism of the 1,2-derivatives of ethylene and it also leads to a plane molecular model. The suggested equivalence of the two bonds is, however, incorrect.

The wave-mechanical theory of the atomic bond leads to a

more detailed picture of the multiple bond (PENNEY) which is no longer based on a tetrahedral model.

What will be the state of bonding in the methyl radical $CH_3$?

For the production of three bonds, the carbon atom will have to be brought into the excited configuration mentioned on p. 159. When three equivalent bonds are formed with the electrons of the hydrogen atoms, one electron naturally remains unpaired. The three electron pairs will occupy the functions with the lowest energy, *i.e.*, $2s + 2 \times 2p$, for example $2s + 2p_x + 2p_y$, thus we have $sp^2$ hybridization and bond angles of 120°. The lone electron is then a $p_z$ electron. The radical will then have a plane structure with the dumb-bell-shaped wave function of the lone electron perpendicular to the plane and antisymmetrical with regard to reflection in the plane.

We speak of a $\pi$ wave function and of a $\pi$ electron when the wave function is antisymmetrical with respect to reflection in the plane of the molecule, of a $\sigma$ function and of a $\sigma$ electron when the latter is symmetrical. The six bonding electrons are therefore all $\sigma$ electrons, the lone electron a $\pi$ electron. A $\pi$ function has a node with a value zero in the plane, a $\sigma$ function has a large value in this plane.

One can regard ethane as derived from two methane molecules where the C—C bond takes the place of two CH bonds and preserves the bond relations, as is seen from the unchanged bond angles; similarly one can also derive ethylene from two methyl radicals.

In this picture the two plane groups are bound by one C—C bond ($\sigma$—$\sigma$ bond). The two $\pi$ electrons can now form a second C—C bond ($\pi$—$\pi$ bond), if their orbital functions are combined in such a way that the resulting function is symmetrical with respect to interchange of both electrons (just as in the bonding state of $H_2$), that is to say pointing with their positive halves in the same direction (Fig. 18). The spins of both $\pi$-electrons are anti-parallel. This second bond will have a smaller bond energy than the first one because the overlap is less fa-

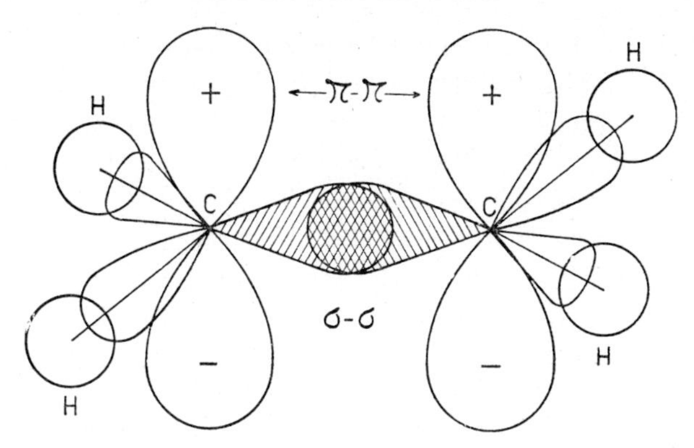


Fig. 18. Wave functions of the bonding electrons in the molecule of ethylene, $C_2H_4$.

vourable (bond energy C—C 83.0 kcal, C=C 146.4 kcal). Rotation of the two halves of the molecule with respect to one another would make this overlap still more unfavourable and would involve increase of energy. With 180° rotation the interaction of the $\pi$ electrons would lead to a repulsion (antisymmetric orbital functions, parallel spins).

A direct conversion of *cis* and *trans* isomers would thus demand a very high activation energy. Thus the transformation in the case of dichloroethylene occurs by the catalytic action of bromine *atoms*, and the first step is addition of an atom with the formation of a radical with a single rotatable bond.

In contrast with older ideas, we find that the double bond is stronger than a single carbon-carbon bond; this appears from the behaviour of saturated and unsaturated hydrocarbons on dissociation and pyrolysis.

On the other hand, this double bond is very reactive; for example, hydrogen, halogen and hydrogen halides can be added. The energy balance of this process equals the bond energy of two single bonds between the carbon atoms and the added atoms minus the heat of dissociation of the added molecule and the energy required to break the second bond of the double bond. Roughly speaking, when we treat all single bonds alike, the ability to add atoms can be attributed to the fact that the second bond of the double bond is weaker than the first. In the addition of iodine to ethylene only a small amount of energy is set free, however, (13.4 kcal) as a result of the small C—I bond energy (Table 18). Thus diiodoethane readily liberates iodine again.

As a result of the stronger bond, the bond length for a double bond is 87% of the length of the single bond; C—C: 1.54 Å, C=C: 1.34 Å (Table 16).

Other double bonds, such as $R_1R_2C{=}\overline{O}$, $R\overline{N}{=}\overline{N}R$, are similarly constituted from a $\sigma$—$\sigma$ and a $\pi$—$\pi$ bond. The same *cis-trans* isomerism does, in fact, occur in the azo compounds as in the ethylene derivatives (azobenzene).

In the molecule of acetylene with a triple carbon-carbon bond, the first C—C bond and the C—H bond lie in one line (sp hybridization), so that the molecule is linear. The second and third bonds are $\pi$—$\pi$ bonds similar to the second bond in ethylene. The bond length of 1.20 Å is only 78% of that of the single bond.

We find the same triple bond in $|N{\equiv}N|$, $H{-}C{\equiv}N|$, $Cl{-}C{\equiv}N|$, etc.; these molecules are linear like acetylene.

A multiple bond does not necessarily possess an unsaturated character; this is illustrated by the nitrogen molecule. The very strong triple bond leads to the result that compounds with single or double bound pairs of nitrogen atoms, such as hydrazine $R_1R_2N{-}NR_3R_4$ and azocompounds $R_1N{=}NR_2$, decompose rather easily with the evolution of nitrogen. Conversely, the addition of hydrogen to nitrogen leads readily to ammonia but not to hydrazine, on account of the small energy of the N—N bond.

The striking decrease of the single bond energy in the series C—C, N—N, O—O, (F—F), is explained by PITZER (PITZER, 1948) as caused by the mutual repulsion of the lone pair(s) in the valence shells. For the elements in the second (and higher) row, there is, moreover, the repulsion of the inner shells which explains the absence of stable multiple bonds except for first row elements.

The hybridization ratio is not necessarily the same for all bonds with dissimilar substituents.

We have supposed that in ethylene the two CH bonds and the $\sigma$—$\sigma$ C—C bond all have the same $sp^2$ character, that is to say $^1/_3$s and $^2/_3$p, with angles of 120° for HCH and HCC. If we assume that the C—H bonds have the same $^1/_4$s and $^3/_4$p character as in methane, then the C—C bond is, therefore $^1/_2$s + $^1/_2$p and the angle HCH is 109°28′ and the angle HCC 125°16′*. In fact an intermediate value is found in ethylene and its derivatives, ∠ HCC is equal to 121°—124°; the bond character will, therefore, lie between the two cases.

The C—H bond in acetylene (and HCN) deviates from that in methane; this is evident from the short length of 1.065 Å compared with 1.095 Å, and from the positive charge of the hydrogen atom in both cases (see p. 240). The C—H distance in ethylene is 1.071 Å. The molecule of allene, $CH_2{=}C{=}CH_2$, is no longer plane in its entirety; we can no longer strictly speak of $\sigma$ and $\pi$ electrons; nevertheless the electrons in the separate bonds retain this character. The two $\sigma$—$\sigma$ C—C bonds lie in one line and the two $\pi$—$\pi$ bonds lie in two mutually perpendicular planes through this axis**. The $CH_2$ groups again lie in planes perpendicular to those of the neighbouring $\pi$—$\pi$ bond. Optical isomerism in derivatives has been discovered in 1935, but the possibility was already pointed out by VAN 'T HOFF in 1874. In ketene $CH_2{=}C{=}O$ and in carbon dioxide $O{=}C{=}O$ the configuration is similar.

A system of cumulative double bonds leads to a loss in stability. The heat of hydrogenation of allene is 71.3 kcal; higher than the value of about 58–60 kcal to be expected for two non-conjugated double bonds.

However, carbon dioxide is 26 kcal more stable than expected for two ketonic C=O bonds. This is probably to be ascribed to resonance (p. 244).

---

* The smaller C=C distance as compared with the C—C distances, *e.g.*, in tetramethylethylene, will favour a higher amount of s character in the former.

** Restricted to an individual bond the definition of a $\sigma$ function is a function cylinder-symmetrical round the bond axis (angular moment zero); a $\pi$ function has a component of unity along this axis; comp. s and p states with values for the angular momentum quantum number $l$ equal to 0 and 1, respectively (p. 124).

## § 28. ATOMIC RADII

In analogy with ionic radii, a table of atomic radii can be made for the calculation of the bond length for electron pair bonds (Table 16). As a starting point, we can simply use the observed distances between similar atoms, *e.g.*, the halogens, carbon, nitrogen, etc. However, it makes a difference whether a single, a double or a triple bond is present. Thus the C—C length is 1.54 Å both in diamond and in the saturated aliphatic hydrocarbons but the C=C length is 1.34 Å and the C≡C 1.20 Å*. The atomic radius of carbon for single bonds is therefore 0.77 Å. Similarly the values for the halogens are equal to half the nuclear separation in these molecules.

There is no sound theoretical foundation at the basis of the concept of the atomic radius. It is only an empirically established fact that the distances between dissimilar atoms calculated from these atomic radii usually agree well with the values found (within ± 0.02 Å).

In PAULING's original table (Table 16) the values for N, O and F of 0.70, 0.66 and 0.64 Å were taken from the distances in bonds with carbon. Later investigations on hydrazine, hydrogen peroxide and fluorine furnished values for these radii of 0.74, 0.74 and 0.72 Å, respectively. In $H_2$ itself the distance is 0.74 Å and the radius should therefore be 0.37 Å. However, the atomic radius for hydrogen is found to vary considerably; 0.29 Å is an average value for compounds.

A revision of PAULING's table has been proposed (SCHOMAKER and STEVENSON, 1941); the strict additivity has been abandoned and the influence of the polarity has been taken into account, simultaneously with the above alteration in the radii for N, O and F (see footnote to Table 16).

In most cases, in particular for organic molecules, this improved formula gives results which differ but little from those derived from the original table.

* More accurate values are ethane 1.543 Å, ethylene 1.353 Å, acetylene 1.207 Å (HERZBERG and STOICHEFF, 1955).

TABLE 16

ATOMIC RADII ACCORDING TO PAULING, IN Å*

| | | | | |
|---|---|---|---|---|
| | | | | H 0.29 |
| B 0.88 | C 0.77 | N 0.70 | O 0.66 | F 0.64 |
| | Si 1.17 | P 1.10 | S 1.04 | Cl 0.99 |
| | Ge 1.22 | As 1.21 | Se 1.17 | Br 1.14 |
| | Sn 1.40 | Sb 1.41 | Te 1.37 | I 1.33 |

| | |
|---|---|
| Factor for double bond | 0.87 (2nd row 0.91) |
| Factor for triple bond | 0.78 (2nd row 0.85) |

* For atoms with a formal charge +1 the radius is reduced to a value halfway between the normal value and that of the next atom; with a charge —1 the radius is increased to halfway between the normal value and that of the previous atom.

In a revision, in place of additivity a formula is given $r_{AB} = r_A + r_B - 0.09 (x_A - x_B)$, in which the difference in electronegativity $x_A - x_B$ (p. 148) plays a part. In addition the values for N, O and F of 0.74, 0.74 and 0.72 have to be inserted for use with this new formula.

Appreciable differences between the observed bond length and the sum of the radii indicate that the character of the bond under consideration is different, for example, as a result of resonance with structures with double bonds (pp. 225 and 230).

The relation between atomic separation and bond type (p. 225) for the C—C bond was originally established empirically by plotting 1.54 Å for a single bond, 1.39 Å in benzene and 1.34 Å for a double bond against 0, $^1/_2$ and 1 for the double bond character. A fourth point is formed by the distance 1.42 Å for graphite, which has $^1/_3$ double bond character (Fig. 19). A similar empirical curve can be produced if, in place of the double bond character according to PAULING, another criterion such as the "bond order" (p. 299) is used to characterize the constitution of the C—C bond.

A theoretical explanation for this relation can be given; thus this type of curve, deformed proportionally, can also be used for other bonds.

It should be pointed out that the atomic radius, in contrast to the ionic radius, does not correspond to the radius of a sphere; it is only a partial bond length. However, these values can be used for calculations which are of particular importance as an indication of the bond character, and can also be used for calculation of molecular models, in particular, of organic compounds. The distance to which atoms not directly

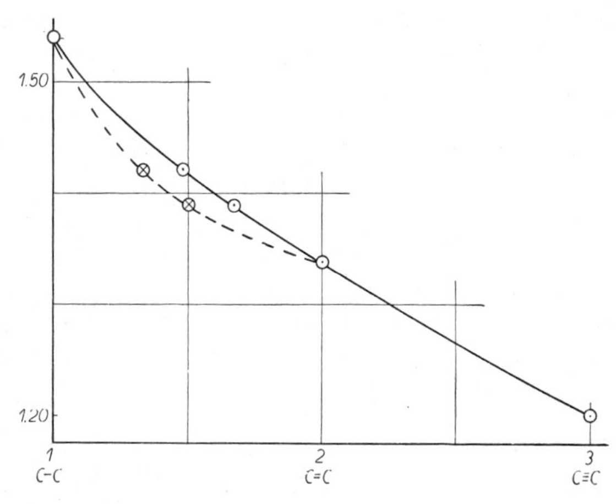


Fig. 19. Bond length of the carbon bond as a function of bond character (PAULING) - - - and (total) bond order (COULSON)—.

bound to each other can approach each other is found from the values of the VAN DER WAALS radii (Table 17). Between these atoms only the VAN DER WAALS forces are active; hence the name. These radii agree fairly well with the ionic radii; that is to say, a halogen ion behaves externally just like a covalent bound halogen atom. This is connected with the fact that in both cases the radii depend on the BORN repulsion and this, in turn, depends on the interaction of an 8-electron configuration which is practically the same for the ion $|\overline{\underline{Cl}}$ and for the atom $|\overline{\underline{Cl}}-$.

TABLE 17

EXTERNAL OR VAN DER WAALS RADII, IN Å

| | | |
|---|---|---|
| | | H<br>1.2 |
| N<br>1.5 | O<br>1.40 | F<br>1.35 |
| P<br>1.9 | S<br>1.85 | Cl<br>1.80 |
| As<br>2.0 | Se<br>2.00 | Br<br>1.95 |
| Sb<br>2.2 | Te<br>2.20 | I<br>2.15 |

Methyl group $CH_3$ and methylene $CH_2$: 2.0.
Half thickness of aromatic nucleus 1.85.

These VAN DER WAALS radii are useful for calculating distances in molecules in connection with the possibility of steric hindrance, etc. Models which correctly reproduce both the bond lengths and the spatial filling can be made from spheres with radii proportional to the VAN DER WAALS radii when segments are removed from the spheres in such a way that both the bond lengths and bond angles take on their correct values (STUART, "Kalotten" model or space-filling model).

## § 29. BOND ENERGY

The bond energy of a diatomic molecule is the heat of dissociation into two atoms in the ground state. Photochemical dissociation, however, sometimes leads (for example, in the halogens) to two atoms, one of which is in an excited state.

With polyatomic molecules and in particular with carbon compounds, it is difficult to give a correct definition (SZWARC and EVANS, 1950; SZWARC, 1950).

What is the C—H bond energy in methane? We can understand by it one fourth of the total bond energy, *i.e.*, one fourth of the energy required to divide $CH_4$ into C + 4H (heat of atomization). This bond energy is not, however, the energy required to remove one hydrogen atom from methane, thus the heat of dissociation in the reaction $CH_4 \rightarrow CH_3 + H$. In fact, a rearrangement of the electron distribution will take place in the methyl radical so formed (transition from $sp^3$ hybridization to $sp^2$, p. 194); consequently the energy required for this reaction is smaller than that for the removal of one hydrogen atom, while the other C—H bonds remain unchanged. This third energy could also be considered to be the C—H bond energy in $CH_4$.

The (average) bond energy, as first defined as a part of the total binding energy, has a great practical advantage, since this total bond energy can be readily derived from the heats of combustion; these are well known for many compounds*. For the dissociation energy according to the other definitions, spectroscopic data and ionization potentials or appearance potentials are required and these are not so well known. The second definition is that of the (equilibrium) dissociation energy; the third one that of the "vertical" dissociation energy.

However, with the (average) bond energy there are still two difficulties. (*a*) In the reaction $CH_4 \rightarrow C + 4H$, free carbon atoms are produced; therefore it is necessary to know the heat of vaporization of graphite. Must we now use the values of the energy for $CH_4 \rightarrow$ C (valency state) + 4H or for $CH_4 \rightarrow$ C (ground state $^3P$) + 4H? We have seen indeed that carbon is quadrivalent in an excited state which, on account of the hybridization, is not equal in energy to the spectroscopically well-known state $^5S$ (PAULING, 1949). Now it does not matter what starting point is chosen for the comparison of bond energies; the absolute values do change however. The bond energies given in Table 18, are relative to the carbon atom in

* The heat of combustion itself can also be expressed as an additive function of atom or group contributions. No fundamental significance, however, can be attached to the atom or group values (WHELAND, 1945, 1955; KLAGES, 1949; FRANKLIN, 1949, 1950).

the ground state and with 170.9 kcal as the value of the heat of vaporization of graphite*. The calculation of the bond energy for $CH_4$ is as follows.

There is the cycle:

$$\begin{array}{ccc} CH_4 & \xrightarrow{\quad 4\,E_{CH} \quad} & C + 4\,H \\ \downarrow -Q_{CH_4} & & \uparrow S_C + 2\,D_{H_2} \\ CO_2 + 2\,H_2O & \xrightarrow[Q_C + 2\,Q_{H_2}]{} & C_{gr.} + 2\,H_2 \end{array}$$

Here the $Q$'s are the heats of combustion, $S_C$ the heat of sublimation of carbon and $D_{H_2}$ the heat of dissociation of hydrogen respectively, all at constant pressure ($Q = -\Delta H$) and at 298.15°K (25°C).** It follows that:

$$4\,E_{CH} = -\,Q_{CH_4} + 2\,Q_{H_2} + Q_C + S_C + 2\,D_{H_2}$$

or

$$4\,E_{CH} = -\,212.8 + 2 \times 68.3 + 94.0 + 170.9 + 2 \times 104.2 = 397.1 \text{ kcal};\ E_{CH} = 99.3 \text{ kcal}$$

For a hydrocarbon $C_nH_{2n+2}$ we have:

$$E_{total} = n\,Q_C + (n+1)\,Q_{H_2} - Q_{C_nH_{2n+2}} + n\,S_C + (n+1)\,D_{H_2}$$

(*b*) In order to derive the value of the separate bond energies from the total bond energy, it is necessary to introduce the assumption that the total bond energy is composed additively from these separate amounts, thus

$$E_{total} = (2\,n + 2)\,E_{CH} + (n - 1)\,E_{CC}.$$

* At present the most probable value for the heat of sublimation (atomization to carbon atoms) of carbon at 0° K seems to be 169.58 ± 0.45 kcal, or 170.9 kcal at 298° K (BREWER and SEARCY, 1956). Other possible values which have also been used for the calculation of bond energies are about 125 kcal (p. 204) (COATES and SUTTON, 1948) 138 ± 3 kcal (COTTRELL, 1954) and 141.9 (DOEHAERD, GOLDFINGER and WAELBROEK, 1952). For a discussion of this, see SPRINGALL, 1950; COTTRELL, 1954; BREWER and SEARCY, 1956; KERN, 1956. Different values have also been given for the dissociation energy of $N_2$, *e.g.*, 170.26 kcal and 225.04 kcal respectively.

** This heat of dissociation of $H_2$ ($\Delta$ H, 298°K, 1 at), which is also the H—H bond energy, is not identical with the spectroscopic dissociation energy. The latter quantity is the heat of dissociation at 0° K since the kinetic energy is not taken into account. The two values are 104.18 kcal/mole and 103.24 kcal/mole respectively.

In the homologous series of the *n*-alkanes the heat of combustion per $CH_2$ group (thus $E_{CC} + 2\ E_{CH}$) must increase by a constant amount if this assumption is correct. This is indeed the case within 0.3 kcal from $C_3H_8$ on, and within 0.1 kcal from $C_5H_{12}$ on. Between $CH_4$ and $C_2H_6$, the discrepancy is appreciable, namely 3 kcal. The difference in the bond length C—H of 1.095 Å and 1.100 Å for $CH_4$ and $C_2H_6$ respectively, also indicates a difference in bond energy for the C—H bond.

One finds the same constant difference in the series of the alcohols, ethers, alkenes, alkynes, etc., with more than 5 carbon atoms.

The influence of the heat of vaporization of graphite $S_C$ is different for different bonds. It can be verified readily that $E_{CH} - 1/4\ S_C$, and similarly $E_{C-C} - {}^1/_2\ S_C$, $E_{C=C} - S_C$, $E_{C=O} - {}^1/_2\ S_C$ and $E_{C\equiv C} - 3/2\ S_C$ are all constants.

Using $S_C = 124.3$ kcal, we obtain for the bond energy of $C_{al.}$—H, C—C and C=C the values of 86.8, 59.7 and 99.8 kcal respectively. This low value for the heat of sublimation was used in the preparation of tables by PAULING (PAULING, 1950), by SYRKIN (SYRKIN, 1943; SYRKIN and DYATKINA, 1950) and by COATES and SUTTON (COATES and SUTTON, 1948), The very extensive collection of data by COTTRELL (COTTRELL, 1954) is based on a somewhat higher value of 138 kcal. PITZER (PITZER, 1953) used the value of 170.4 kcal and calculated the bond energies for 0° K. The differences from the values in Table 18A are only small.

The direct determination of the heat of hydrogenation gives additional information on the difference between $E_{C=C}$ and $E_{C-C}$; however, in the calculation use is made of $E_{C-H}$ which depends again on the value chosen for $S_C$ (KISTIAKOWSKY *et al.*, 1935, 1936, 1951; WILLIAMS, 1942).

GLOCKLER (GLOCKLER, 1951) has tried to take into account the differences in the C—H bond energy; the values so obtained (Table 18, last column), though valuable as indications, are based on too many assumptions to be of practical use.

Besides the (average) bond energy, some values for the heat

# TABLE 18

## A. AVERAGE BOND ENERGY IN KCAL/MOLE (298.1° K)

| | | | | Glockler 1951 |
|---|---|---|---|---|
| H — H | 104.2 (103.2) | C — H($CH_4$) | 99.3 | |
| F — F | 37.6 | $C_{aliph.}$—H | 98.5 | 96.7 |
| Cl — Cl | 57.9 (57.1) | = C — H | — | 101.6 |
| Br — Br | 46.2 (45.4) | ≡ C — H | — | 103.4 |
| I — I | 36.1 (35.5) | | | |
| Li — Li | (25) | C — C (diam.) | 85 | 84.5 |
| Na — Na | (17.3) | C — C | 83.0 | 83.3 |
| K — K | (11.8) | C = C | 146.4 | 125 |
| O — O | 35 | C ≡ C | 199.8 | 181 |
| \| O ∴ O \| ($^3\Sigma$) | 119.1 (118.0) | C — F | 110 ± 10 | |
| \| O = O \| ($^1\Delta$) | 96.5 (95.4) | C — Cl | 80 | |
| N — N | 40 — 45 | C — Br | 68 | |
| N = N | 90 | C — I | 52 | |
| N ≡ N | 225.9 (225.0) | N — Cl | 46 | |
| B — H | 93.1 | C — O | 85 | |
| N — H | 93.4 | C = O (ald.) | 176 | |
| O — H | 110.5 | C = O (ket.) | 179 | |
| F — H | 135 (134) | C — S | 67 | |
| Cl — H | 103.1 (102.2) | S — S | 67 | |
| Br — H | 87.4 (86.5) | C — N | 68 | |
| I — H | 71.4 (70.5) | C = N | ~145 | |
| Si — H | 76 | C ≡ N | 213 | |
| P — H | 77 | N — O | ~ 50 | |
| S — H | 87.5 | N = O | ~145 | |
| Subl. graphite | 170.9 (298°K) | —N(=O)O (nitro group) | 210 | |

Values in parentheses are dissociation energies at 0° K.

## B. HEAT OF DISSOCIATION IN KCAL

| | | | | | | | |
|---|---|---|---|---|---|---|---|
| $CH_3$—H | 101 | 101 | $C_{aliph.}$—H | 90—98 | $C_{al.}$—$C_{al.}$ | 80 |
| | | | | | ($CH_2$=$CHCH_2$)—$CH_3$ | 61.5 |
| (rad.)$CH_2$—H | 79 | (100) | $C_{ar.}$ —H | 104 | $C_{ar.}$—$C_{ar.}$ | 91 |
| (rad.)CH —H | (84) | (116) | =C — H | ~104 | ($C_6H_5$)$CH_2$—$CH_2$($C_6H_5$) | 47 |
| (rad.)C —H | 80 | 80 | ≡C — H | <121 | $(C_6H_5)_3C$—$C(C_6H_5)_3$ | 11 |
| sum | 349 | 394 | $C_6H_5CH_2$—H | 83 (77) | C—OH | ~90 |
| | | | $CH_2$=$CH_2CH_2$—H | 77 | HO—OH | 54 |
| $C_{prim.}$—H | 97 | | HO—H | 118 | | |
| $C_{sec.}$ —H | 94 | | $H_2N$—H | 104 | C—Cl | 80 |
| $C_{tert.}$ —H | 90 | | N—N | ~60 | C—Br | 65 |
| | | | O—O | 30—35 | C—I | 52 |

of dissociation are collected in Table 18B (SZWARC, 1950, 1951, 1957; COTTRELL, 1954).

The non-equivalence of the two concepts is evident from the fact that the average bond energy of the O—H bond in $H_2O$ amounts to 110.5 kcal, whereas the heat of dissociation of the first hydrogen atom is 119.5 kcal. The dissociation of the second hydrogen atom (the heat of dissociation of the OH radical) is 101.5 kcal. Naturally we must have the sum of the heats of dissociation equal to the total bond energy, or $119.5 + 101.5 = 2 \times 110.5$ kcal.

The heats of dissociation of all steps of methane, in particular of $CH_2$, are not yet known directly or not well known. If this were actually the case this would furnish a method of deciding whether the sum of the bond energies amounts to 344 kcal or 397 kcal and what value, therefore, must be attributed to the heat of sublimation (and of promotion) of carbon.

The heats of dissociation agree best with the bond energies obtained with the high value for the heat of sublimation.

The differences between the heat of dissociation and the bond energy for the C—H bond in propylene and toluene and for the C—C bond in butene-1 and diphenylethane (Table 18B) are interesting. This is not due to a difference between the bonds of the molecules in question, as can be seen from the total binding energy deduced from the heat of combustion (or heat of hydrogenation); it is due rather to the peculiar stability of the allyl and toluyl radicals formed (p. 254).

The differences in the heats of combustion of isomeric hydrocarbons prove that additivity only holds approximately. The differences are, however, only of the order of magnitude of 1 to 2 kcal per side-chain. For example, the difference between *n*-butane and *iso*-butane is 1.6 kcal, between *n*-octane and 2,2,4 trimethyl pentane 3.1 kcal; the branched hydrocarbon always having the lower heat of combustion and thus the lower energy content.

With the alkenes the differences are *e.g.*, between butene-1 and *iso*-butene 4.0 kcal, between *cis*-butene-2 and *trans* 1.0 kcal and between butene-1 and *trans*-butene-2 2.6 kcal; the first-mentioned of each pair having the higher energy content. Thus the equilibrium between these isomers will be displaced towards the side of the less branched and normal isomers at higher temperatures (FARKAS, 1950).

The discrepant behaviour of the C—H bond in acetylene shows itself in the large differences which are apparently found for the C≡C bond energy (when the C—H and C—C bond energies (Table 18) are taken to be the same throughout!) for acetylene, methylacetylene, dimethylacetylene (2-butyne) and 1-butyne of 194.8 kcal, 199.8 kcal, 204.2 kcal and 199.7 kcal respectively.

An increased energy is apparent in the small rings of the cycloparaffins $C_nH_{2n}$, as was to be expected on the basis of BAYER's strain theory. This effect originates in the deviations of the bond angles in the ring from 109° 28′, whereby the overlap cannot be maximal for an unchanged value of the angles of $sp^3$ functions. However, the constitution of cyclopropane is appreciably different from the open chain hydrocarbons (KILPATRICK and PITZER, 1946; COULSON and MOFFITT, 1947).

| Lowering of C—C bond energy | |
|---|---|
| Cyclopropane | 9.3 kcal |
| Cyclobutane | 6.5 ,, |
| Cyclopentane | 1.2 ,, |
| Cyclohexane | 0.2 ,, |
| Cycloheptane | 0.9 ,, |
| Cyclo-octane | 1.2 ,, |
| *cis*-Decahydronaphthalene | 0 ,, |
| *trans*-Decahydronaphthalene | 0 ,, |

| Lowering of total bond energy | |
|---|---|
| 1.1 Dimethylcyclohexane | (0) kcal |
| *cis* 1.2 ,, | 2.1 ,, |
| *trans* 1.2 ,, | 0.2 ,, |
| *cis* 1.3 ,, | −0.9 ,, |
| *trans* 1.3 ,, | 1.0 ,, |
| *cis* 1.4 ,, | 1.0 ,, |
| *trans* 1.4 ,, | −0.9 ,, |

The energy content of the C—C bond is increased above that of the open chain even in the strain-free cyclohexane. This is analogous to the higher energy content of the normal alkanes, compared with the branched alkanes with more $CH_3$ groups which are completely missing in cyclohexane.

A larger number of pairs of neighbouring hydrogen atoms in the branched hydrocarbons results in a lower energy content;

probably the intramolecular VAN DER WAALS-LONDON attraction energy is greater in a more compact molecular structure. To the same extent, the intermolecular attraction energy is smaller for branched hydrocarbons; consequently these have a lower boiling point than the normal alkanes (§ 42).

Information concerning the finer differences in bond energy of various bonds between similar atoms can be obtained from vibration frequencies in the infrared and RAMAN spectrum and from small variations in the bond length; these are connected with each other and with the bond energy through semi-empirical relations (BADGER's rule, etc.).

BADGER's rule is $k\,(r-d_{ij})^3$ in which $k$ is the force constant, $r$ the bond length and $d_{ij}$, a constant depending on the rows in the Periodic System to which the two atoms belong, (BADGER, 1934) while PAULING's rule is: bond energy times bond length is constant for similar bonds (PAULING, 1954; BAUGHAN, 1957).

*Rotation about the C—C bond**

In the older organic chemistry it was assumed that a free rotation was possible about a single C—C bond because, for example, no isomers of 1,2-dichloroethane can be isolated. Accurate measurements of the specific heat of ethane at low temperatures and likewise the difference between determinations and calculations of equilibria of hydrocarbons have, however, shown that there is no question of a *free* rotation; rotation is indeed possible but there is a potential barrier of about 3 kcal/mole which has to be surmounted. The state of lowest energy is that in which the two methyl groups, or the methyl and the $CH_2$ group alternate. The different rotational isomers of molecules which can not be isolated by the usual methods are called conformations. In 1,2-dichloroethane, etc. there appear to be two positions of (relatively) minimum energy, the *trans* position and a *gauche* position with an energy in the vapour of 1.14 kcal higher than the former, separated by a high barrier. In the liquid state the equilibrium is displaced

* *General references:* PITZER and KILPATRICK, 1946; PITZER, 1951; MIZUSHIMA, 1954; SMITH, 1955, MIZUSHIMA and SHIMANOUCHI, 1957.

towards the *gauche* form ($\Delta H = 0.0$ kcal) because the intermolecular interaction and thus the cohesion energy is larger for this conformation with a dipole moment. For $CH_2BrCH_2Br$ the energy difference is 1.70 kcal and 0.73 kcal for the vapour and the liquid respectively. In the solid state only the *trans* conformation is present (MIZUSHIMA *et al.*, 1953).

The spectrum (RAMAN, infrared, microwave) shows two sets of lines or bands; the intensity ratio varies with the temperature. The fact that the dipole moment of this compound is dependent on the temperature also points to a displacement of the equilibrium between the two isomers.

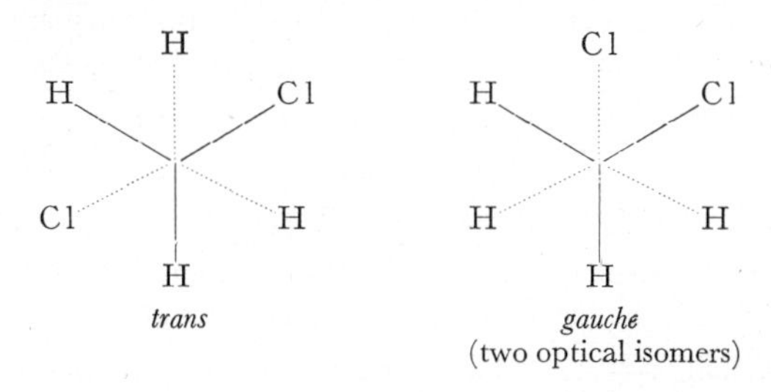


*trans* *gauche* (two optical isomers)

While the height of the potential barrier is about 3 kcal in normal paraffins, one finds only 2 kcal in the olefins for the rotation about the C—C bond, situated next to the C=C bond.

There is completely free rotation about the C—C≡C bond; in toluene and xylene the rotation is also hindered but little (0.5 kcal).

In molecules such as $CH_3NH_2$ and $CH_3OH$, there is a hindrance of the rotation about the C—N and the C—O axis which amounts to about 2 and 1 kcal respectively.

It is not yet quite certain what the explanation of these hindrances is. The mutual BORN repulsion of the hydrogen

BARRIER HEIGHTS FOR $CH_3X$ IN KCAL/MOLE

| X | $CH_3$ | $C_2H_5$ | $CCl_3$ | OH | CHO |
|---|---|---|---|---|---|
| Height | 2.87 | 3.3 | 2.7 | 1.1 | 2.6 |

atoms attached to different carbon atoms certainly plays a role, but this is probably not responsible for the whole amount of energy. Another cause may be the interaction of dipole (and especially quadrupole) moments of the C—H bonds (LASSETTRE and DEAN, 1949; OOSTERHOFF, 1951) and some interaction of the hydrogen atom with the charge cloud of the other carbon atom.

## § 30. RESONANCE BETWEEN VALENCE CONFIGURATIONS OR MESOMERISM

The concept of resonance was developed above as the basis for the atomic bond. In doing so the wave function describing the electrons in $H_2^+$ and $H_2$ was constructed by the combination of functions; these functions describe separate configurations which are distinguished from each other by place exchange ($H_2^+$) or interchange ($H_2$) of electrons.

This multiplicity of electron configuration occurs not only in the bonding between two atoms but also in many cases in which one can compose for the whole molecule more than one electron formula representing different electron configurations.

We use the term configurations to indicate different arrangements of electrons, while the term structure indicates a spatial arrangement of the atomic nuclei. In contrast to the structure, the separate configuration has no real physical meaning.

The stationary state, that is to say the actual state susceptible of physical and also chemical investigation (p. 116), can only be represented by a combination of all configurations, with certain limitations, in contributions of various sizes. Many properties, such as bond lengths and charge distribution, will be intermediate between those expected for the separate configurations. However, the energy will always be lower than that to be expected for one of the separate configurations. The resonance energy (R.E.) is the difference between the energy of the stationary state and that calculated for the configuration of lowest energy.

It may again be emphasized that neither resonance nor the separate configurations possess physical significance (p. 136). It should be remembered that resonance is not a phenomenon but a method (V.B. method, p. 286) to approximate the true wave function. The justification of the method is its success in correlating observations to a coherent theoretical picture of molecular constitution. Thus it is also incorrect to speak here of an equilibrium between two or more forms of molecule, or to imagine that the molecule occurs now in the one, now in the other configuration. This is the distinction with tautomerism where the structure, *i.e.*, the spatial arrangement of the atomic nuclei, is different. In the latter case each molecule undergoes several collisions before conversion takes place and thus the laws of thermodynamic equilibrium are applicable.

*Conditions for resonance*

1. Resonance exists only when a transition from the one electron configuration into the other is possible in principle. According to wave mechanics the condition for this is that the configurations must possess the same symmetry character; in particular that they must possess the same number (usually zero) of unpaired electron spins*. Thus the symmetrical attractive (bonding) and the antisymmetrical repulsive (antibonding) states of $H_2^+$ (p. 132) cannot combine; likewise the singlet (attractive) and the triplet (repulsive) state of $H_2$ (p. 153) or the ionic and the atomic bonding state in the ferrocyanide ion (p. 179) cannot combine.

From the calculations of the energy of $H_2^+$ and $H_2$, it appears that the quantity $\beta = \int \varphi_I \cdot H \varphi_{II} \, dv$ determines the splitting of the energy levels as a consequence of the resonance (p. 141). The Hamiltonian $H$ depends on the charge distribution and is, therefore, symmetrical (in so far as the molecule is symmetrical) and independent of the spin orientation. Now suppose

* With the exception of the negligible probability due to the small spin-spin and spin-orbit coupling (McClure, 1952).

$\varphi_I$ and $\varphi_{II}$ are of different symmetry character; for example, the former symmetrical and the latter antisymmetrical with respect to reflection in a plane (considered vertical, Fig. 12). Thus integration over the left or the right half of the whole space furnishes equal amounts which are, however, of opposite sign on account of the antisymmetrical character of $\varphi_{II}$; consequently the integral over the whole space becomes zero (orthogonal functions, see p. 127). The same is the case with an integral over the product of two different spin functions.

2. Resonance is only possible, or at any rate of significance for the energy, between electron configurations of the same spatial nuclear structure. As shown (p. 135), the splitting of the energy level corresponds as it were with an exchange frequency. As a result of the much greater mass of the nuclei this frequency would be very small (proportional to $1/\sqrt{m}$) for transitions in which displacements of atomic nuclei are also necessary.

However, the real cause for the small splitting of the energy levels in nuclear resonance is found in the short DE BROGLIE wave length (p. 115) in this case. Thus the wave function is concentrated in a small region and the overlap is extremely small if both configurations do not have an identical arrangement of nuclei.

With a splitting $\delta W < kT$, and this always occurs in nuclear resonance, the splitting no longer results in a stabilization (p. 134).

It should, therefore, be remembered that, *e.g.*, in the representation of the electron configurations of the two KEKULÉ forms of benzene by classical structural formulae, the bond lengths and bond angles must be considered equal, thus with all C—C distances and angles equal to those in benzene.

Nuclear resonance in itself is quite possible and occurs in the ammonia molecule and in certain other phenomena in which hydrogen nuclei are concerned (§ 45). The two forms of the ammonia molecule can be represented with the nitrogen atom on the left or the right, respectively, of the plane of the three hydrogen atoms. These forms are indeed different with respect to the coordinate system of the molecule itself. If one looked upon the three hydrogen atoms as different, then the transition between the two forms would correspond with that from one to the other optical antipode.

The potential curve for $NH_3$ is reproduced in Fig. 20; there are two minima separated by a peak of 5.88 kcal. The two positions of the nitrogen atom are at a distance of 0.38 Å with respect to the plane of the hydrogen atoms. The splitting of the levels into two throughout corresponds to combinations of the two wave functions ($\varphi_L$ and $\varphi_R$ for the left and right form) to give $\varphi_L+\varphi_R$ for the symmetrical and $\varphi_L-\varphi_R$ for the antisymmetrical state. The splitting is here also a consequence of the overlap of $\varphi_L$ and $\varphi_R$; these functions decrease exponentially in the intermediate region, so that this splitting is greater for the higher levels where the potential barrier is narrower.

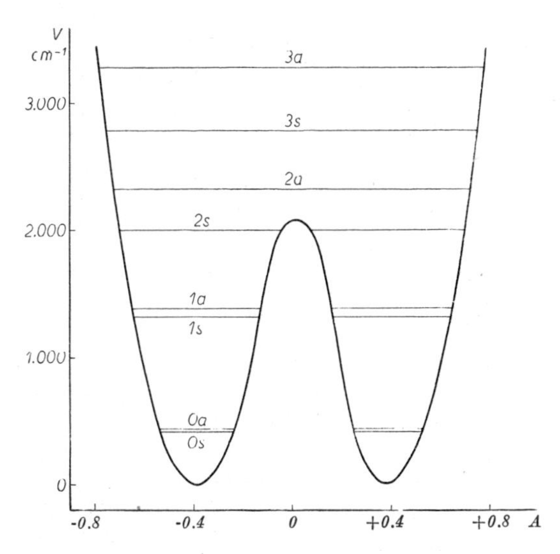


Fig. 20. Potential energy $V$ of $NH_3$ as a function of the distance of the nitrogen atom from the plane of the three hydrogen atoms.

The real measure for the breadth of the potential barrier is the De Broglie wave length; thus the actual "breadth" of the barrier is, for the same geometrical dimensions, larger for deuterons (nuclei of heavy hydrogen) than for protons.

Thus the splitting is much smaller for $ND_3$ than for $NH_3$. It is, furthermore, more correct to say that the pyramid of the hydrogen atoms with the nitrogen atom at the top is turned inside out than to speak of a displacement of the nitrogen atom; in view of the larger mass, the motion of the nitrogen atom will be very small. The splitting of the levels each into a lower symmetrical (s) and a higher antisymmetrical level (a), causes a doubling in the spectrum. While for the infrared absorption spectrum only the transitions from an antisymmetrical to a symmetrical level or vice versa are permissible, the lines in the Raman spectrum correspond to the transitions between levels of the same character.

Energy Levels

| | $NH_3$ | $ND_3$ |
|---|---|---|
| 3 a | 2861 $cm^{-1}$ | 2113 $cm^{-1}$ |
| 3 s | 2380 | 1830 |
| 2 a | 1910 | 1429 |
| 2 s | 1597.4 | 1359 |
| 1 a | 968.08 | 749.0 |
| 1 s | 932.24 | 745.6 |
| 0 a | 0.66 | $<0.2$ |
| 0 s | 0 | 0 |

Infrared: 0 s — 1 a 968.08 $cm^{-1}$

0 a — 1 s 931.58 $cm^{-1}$

$$\Delta \nu = \Delta_1 + \Delta_0 = 36.5 \quad cm^{-1}$$

(for $ND_3$ 749.0 $cm^{-1}$ and 745.6 $cm^{-1}$ resp., $\Delta\nu = 3.4\ cm^{-1}$)
The very small splitting of the ground level of 0.66 $cm^{-1}$ is equal to 1.9 cal/mole, corresponding to 1° K.

The transition 0 s → 0 a is also possible but the corresponding wave length of 1.5 cm is so long that this no longer falls in the region of the infra-red radiation, but in that of the shortest radio waves, the micro waves. This transition was the first observation in 1934 of molecular absorption in this region (CLEETON and WILLIAMS) which is now being studied intensively and in which the pure rotation spectrum of most compounds falls. From observations of microwave spectra of 0.5–10 cm, atomic distances can be derived with amazing accuracy (GORDY, SMITH and TRAMBARULO, 1953; TOWNES and SCHAWLOW, 1955; INGRAM, 1955, *Gen. Disc. Faraday Soc. Nr. 19*, 1955) (for linear non-symmetric molecules $^{16}O^{12}C^{32}S$: C—O: 1.1637 Å, C—S: 1.5586 Å; HCN: C—H: 1.061 Å, C—N: 1.157 Å; FCl: 1.62811 Å).

3. Although the electron configurations must strictly satisfy the two previous conditions for resonance, this is only necessary to a limited extent for conditions 3 and 4.

The resonance energy is a maximum for the case of two (or more) configurations of equal energy. Only configurations with a small difference in energy from the configuration with lowest energy can, therefore, furnish an important contribution to the stationary state; in other words resonance is only possible between configurations with not too great differences in energy.

Fig. 21 shows the resonance energy for two configurations as a function of the energy difference between the two, all expressed in terms of the quantity $\beta = \int \varphi_A \cdot H\varphi_B dv$ as a measure for the energy; for example, $\beta$ is of the order of 40 kcal/mol for benzene*.

* This $\beta$ (see p. 141) must be distinguished from the exchange energy $\beta$ introduced in the M.O. method, on p. 292. The $\beta$ now used corresponds rather with the exchange energy $\alpha$ in the V.B. method (p. 285).

This condition explains the restriction of the configurations to the so-called LEWIS-LANGMUIR configurations in which each atom is surrounded by 8 electrons (hydrogen by 2). There are many exceptions to this, however.

In a chemical reaction the contributions of the various configurations to the (activated) intermediate state, also called the activated complex, will be quite different from their con-

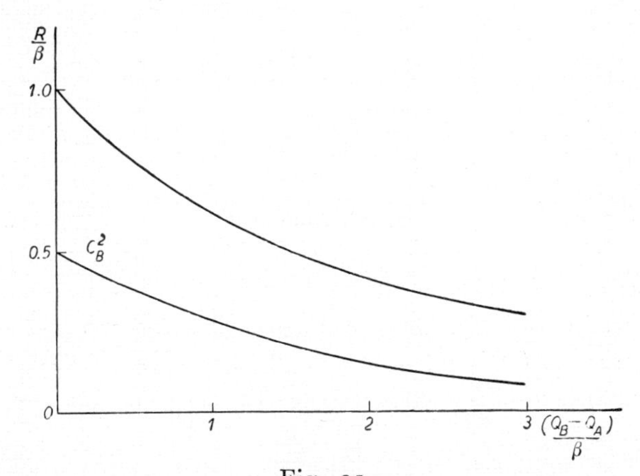


Fig. 21.
Resonance energy R and contribution $C_B^2/(C_A^2 + C_B^2)$ of configuration B as a function of the energy difference between the configurations B and A, expressed in terms of the exchange energy β.

tributions to the ground state since the activated state has a high energy content.

Thus a particular high energy configuration which contributes only a little to the ground state can be by far the most important configuration in the intermediate state (§ 36).

In a derivation, analogous to that on p. 139 but now for two different configurations $A$ and $B$, there arises the determinant:

$$\begin{vmatrix} Q_{AA} - E & \beta - \Delta E \\ \beta - \Delta E & Q_{BB} - E \end{vmatrix} = 0$$

We now put $Q_{BB} \equiv \int \varphi_B \cdot H \varphi_B \, dv$ equal to $Q_{AA} - \delta \beta$. When we neglect $\Delta$, $Q_{AA}-E = +{}^1/_2\,\delta\,\beta \pm \beta\sqrt{1+\frac{1}{4}\delta^2}$. With the negative sign and remembering that $Q_{AA}-E$ represents the resonance energy ($Q_{AA}$, the energy of configuration $A$, is lower than $Q_{BB}$ since $\delta$ is positive and $\beta$ negative) it follows that: $R/\beta = {}^1/_2\,\delta - \sqrt{1+\frac{1}{4}\delta^2}$, which is given in Fig. 21.

$$\text{The ratio } C_B/C_A \text{ is: } -\frac{Q_{AA}-E}{\beta} = -R/\beta.$$

The contribution of configuration $B$ to the charge distribution $C_B^2/(C_A^2 + C_B^2)$ is also plotted in Fig. 21.

It is clear that configurations with higher energy content can still have an important influence on the energy of the stationary state, although their contribution to the charge density is small.

4. The resonance energy is a maximum for a plane structure; thus the electron configurations will be as planar as possible. In most cases it is the electrons in p functions, the so-called $\pi$ electrons (p. 194), that cause the multiplicity of the electron configurations (*cf.* benzene). Now the determinative quantity $\beta$ is very closely connected with the "overlapping" of the wave functions.

As explained with ethylene the wave functions of these $\pi$ electrons are perpendicular to the plane of the group $\begin{matrix}H & & H\\ & C{=}C & \\ R & & R\end{matrix}$. The overlapping is a maximum when two $\pi$ functions are parallel, thus when the whole molecule is plane.

The fact that this overlapping and thus the resonance energy are maximal for a plane structure will result in this plane structure being stabilized compared with other structures. When the realization of a plane structure is hindered by steric factors, this will influence the resonance energy unfavourably (pp. 226 and 263).

The introduction of the resonance concept has led to a satisfactory explanation of numerous experimental facts which were previously inexplicable on the basis of existing theories. This concept of resonance, introduced and developed on the basis of wave mechanical theory, exhibits nevertheless some analogy to earlier ideas such as those of Lowry and Ingold and of Arndt. The term mesomerism, to which some give the preference, is then only used for the resonance, cited here, between valence configurations and thus does not cover the more general concept of resonance. Many examples will illustrate the significance and extent of the resonance concept.

*a. Benzene*

The most important example is the benzene molecule and thus the aromatic molecules in general. Kekulé's hexagon structure, although satisfactory in various respects, suffers from two defects: In the first place the quadrivalency of the carbon gives difficulties as to the way in which the three second bonds

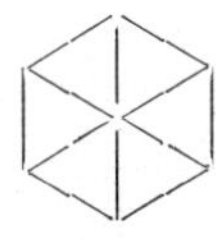

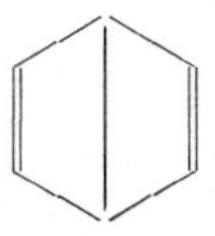

must be arranged. One was compelled either to assume vague or improbable structures such as the Claus-Bayer-Armstrong or the Dewar structure or to assume an oscillation between the two arrangements in Kekulé's formula. Secondly there was no satisfactory explanation why benzene did not react in the way one would expect for a molecule with three double bonds, or, to phrase the problem in another way, what the origin is of the fundamental difference between benzene and cyclohexatriene (the name according to the Geneva nomenclature of a molecule with a structure such as given by one of the Kekulé formulae).

The two Kekulé formulae represent two equivalent electron configurations; thus the actual state will be one of resonance between the two. All six bonds are therefore equal and have a character intermediate between a single and a double bond. At the same time this resonance stabilizes the stationary state in comparison with one of the isolated Kekulé configurations. This lowering of energy will compensate in part the unsaturated character of the double bond (see p. 195).

The resonance concept thus removes both difficulties. In fact, if KEKULÉ had introduced the hypothesis that the oscillation between the two structures might at the same time be the cause of the stabilization, then the resonance concept would have been anticipated in the same way as the tetrahedral carbon atom of VAN 't HOFF and LE BEL anticipated the wave-mechanical theory of mixed wave functions. The resonance concept, like the tetrahedral carbon atom, can be used even without applying explicitly in each case the wave mechanical theories, which lie at the basis of these concepts.

The correct amount of the resonance energy (R.E.) can hardly be deduced from experimental data since the energy content of one separate KEKULÉ configuration is not known (p. 211). However, we can derive fairly well the energy of cyclohexatriene from the bond energies (Table 18), that is to say, for a cyclic molecule with alternate bonds which correspond to those in ethane and ethylene; thus for a cyclic molecule with alternate C—C and C=C bonds with bond lengths of 1.54 Å and 1.34 Å.

According to condition 2 (p. 212) the arrangement of the atoms in the KEKULÉ configuration should be the same as that in the stationary state in benzene, thus a plane structure with six equal C—C distances of 1.39 Å. It has been proved definitely both by electron diffraction and by the interpretation of RAMAN and infra-red spectra that this plane regular hexagon structure is correct.

However, if we neglect the difference in energy between these two different spatial structures then we can calculate for the total bond energy of one KEKULÉ configuration (Table 18):

$$6\,E_{CH} + 3\,E_{CC} + 3\,E_{C=C} = 6 \times 98.5 + 3 \times 83.0 + 3 \times 146.4 = 1279.2 \text{ kcal.}$$

The heat of combustion of benzene (vapour) is 789.1 kcal; thus we find a total bond energy of 1318.1 kcal by the methods used on p. 203. In this way, first used by PAULING, a resonance energy of 38.9 kcal/mole is calculated for benzene.

The R.E. calculated in the same way for various other molecules are given in Table 19.

TABLE 19

RESONANCE ENERGY CALCULATED FROM THE HEAT OF COMBUSTION IN THE GASEOUS STATE IN KCAL/MOLE*

| | | | | | |
|---|---|---|---|---|---|
| Benzene | 39 | 36 | Pyridine | 40 | 23 |
| Toluene | 42 | 35 | Furan | 18 | 16 |
| Naphthalene | 72 | 61 | Pyrrole | 27 | 21 |
| Anthracene | 103 | 84 | Thiophene | 25 | 29 |
| Phenanthrene | 110 | 91 | Quinoline | 61 | 47 |
| Naphthacene | 138 | 110 | Phenol | 41 | 36 |
| Styrene | 44 | 38 | Aniline | 47 | 38 |
| Cycloöctatetraene | 9 | 4 | Benzoquinone | 5 | 4 |
| Biphenyl | 84 | 71 | Acetic acid | 19 | 13 |
| Stilbene (*trans*) | 92 | 77 | Ethyl acetate | 21 | 16 |
| Azulene | 42 | 33 | Acetic anhydride | 30 | 29 |
| Tropolone | 27 | 21 | Acetamide | 17 | 16 |

* 1st column, values calculated from the bond energies in Table 18; 2nd column, values given by WHELAND (WHELAND, 1955, p. 86), calculated by the method of KLAGES (KLAGES, 1949). Almost identical results are obtained by the method of FRANKLIN (FRANKLIN, 1949, 1950). See also p. 202.

In the calculation of the R.E. from the heat of combustion, the difference between two large quantities is calculated. The direct determination of the heat of hydrogenation furnishes a more accurate method (KISTIAKOWSKY *et al.*, 1935, 1936, 1951).

The heat effect in the hydrogenation of benzene to cyclohexane is found to amount to 49.8 kcal. On the addition of a molecule of $H_2$ to a normal (non-conjugated) double bond 28–30 kcal are set free; if we take cyclohexene as comparison substance, we find that this effect amounts to 28.6 kcal. The heat of hydrogenation of benzene is obviously $85.8 - 49.8 = 36.0$ kcal lower than expected for a substance with three normal double bonds. Benzene is thus 36.0 kcal more stable than might be expected for cyclohexatriene; therefore the R.E is 36.0 kcal. Table 20 gives the R.E., calculated from the heat of hydrogenation compared with those of the "normal" hydrocarbons given below; these values were determined by KISTIAKOWSKY and his collaborators. Compounds with the same sub-

TABLE 20

RESONANCE ENERGY FROM THE HEAT OF HYDROGENATION IN KCAL/MOLE

| Substance | Obs. heat of hy-drog. | Calc. | R.E. | Comparison subst. | Obs. heat of hydrog. |
|---|---|---|---|---|---|
| Benzene | 49.8 | 85.8 | 36.0 | Cyclohexene (I) | 28.6 |
| Ethylbenzene | 48.9 | 84.1 | 35.2 | I and Trimethyl ethylene (II) | 26.9 |
| *o*-Xylene | 47.3 | 82.4 | 35.1 | „ „ „ | „ |
| Hydrindene | 45.8 | 82.4 | 36.6 | „ „ „ | „ |
| Styrene | 77.5 | 114.4 | 36.9 | I, II and III | — |
| Indene | 69.9 | 109.3 | 39.4 | II, III and Cyclo-pentene | 26.9 |
| 1,3-Butadiene | 57.1 | 60.6 | 3.5 | 1-Butene (III) | 30.3 |
| 1,3-Cyclohexadiene | 55.4 | 57.2 | 1.8 | Cyclohexene | 28.6 |
| 1,3,5-Cycloheptatriene | 72.8 | 79.5 | 6.7 | Cycloheptene | 26.5 |
| 1,4-Pentadiene | 60.8 | 60.6 | 0 | 1-Butene | 30.3 |
| 1,3-Pentadiene | 54.1 | 58.3 | 4.2 | III and 2-Pentene | 28.0 |
| 1,3-Cyclopentadiene | 50.9 | 53.8 | 2.9 | Cyclopentene | 26.9 |
| 1,5-Hexadiene | 60.5 | 60.6 | 0 | III and 2-Pentene | 28.0 |
| 1,4-Dihydronaphthalene * | 27.6 | 28.6 | 1 | Cyclohexene | 28.6 |
| *cis*-Stilbene * | 26.3 | 28.6 | 2.3 | 2-Butene *cis* | 28.6 |
| *trans*-Stilbene * | 27.6 | 20.6 | 7.0 | „ „ *trans* | 27.6 |

* Only the non-aromatic bond is hydrogenated.

stitution character at the double bond have been chosen as comparison substances.

The stabilization of benzene by the system of three conjugated double bonds in a cyclic system is seen still more clearly if we calculate (from the differences of the heats of hydrogenation as given in the above table) the heat of hydrogenation for the three separate steps: benzene → 1,3-cyclohexadiene → cyclohexene → cyclohexane. In the first step the addition of one molecule of hydrogen is associated with an *increase* of energy of 5.6 kcal. Thus practically the whole R.E. is already lost in the first step. The heat of hydrogenation in the second step, in which $55.4 - 28.6 = 26.8$ kcal are set free, is only 1.8 kcal lower (for this see p. 229) than the heat of hydrogenation of 28.6 kcal for the last step.

The difference between the heat of combustion of the hydrogenated compound and that of the original substance plus that of hydrogen can also be used to calculate the heat of hydrogenation.

The six electrons of the double bonds in benzene, also called electrons of the second kind or $\pi$ electrons, are not localized but can as it were move around the ring; this is shown by the high anisotropic diamagnetism of benzene and other aromatic molecules. If we regard the ring as a superconductor, then the magnetic moment induced by a magnetic field perpendicular to the plane of the ring can be calculated (PAULING, 1936; LONDON, 1937). This was found to agree well with observation (LONSDALE, 1937, 1939).

The results of the investigations on the ozonization of benzene and benzene derivatives, such as *o*-xylene, are in agreement with the equivalence of the bonds; these form, therefore, a chemical proof of the resonance conception of aromatic molecules (LEVINE and COLE, 1932, and especially WIBAUT and his co-workers (WIBAUT, 1950, 1956, 1957); see also p. 281). WIBAUT and HAAYMAN (HAAYMAN and WIBAUT, 1941) found in the ozonization of *o*-xylene that the products of the reaction dimethylglyoxal, methylglyoxal and glyoxal are in the ratio 1 : 2 : 3; this agrees with expectation if it is assumed that both KEKULÉ configurations have an equal chance of reaction with three molecules of ozone.

$CH_3$ $CH_3$

$-CH_3$ $-CH_3$

If we attempt, in accordance with condition 3 (p. 214), to construct all possible LEWIS-LANGMUIR (non-polar) configurations for benzene with electron pair bonds, it appears that there are five of them. Besides the two KEKULÉ configurations there are also three DEWAR configurations.

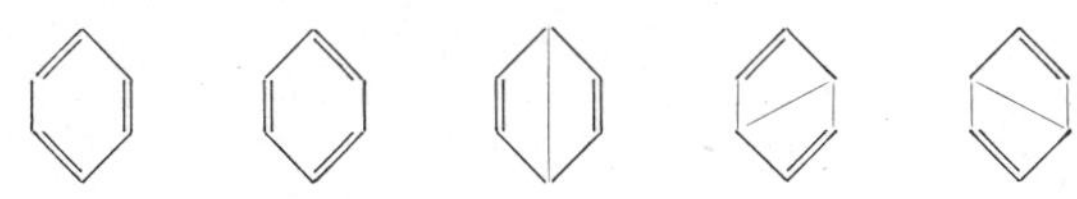

It is true there are still more configurations possible such as the centric formula and three LADENBURG prism formulae projected on to a plane, but it can be shown that these can be regarded as superpositions of the five configurations mentioned above.

The line between atoms in the *para* position in these DEWAR configurations has mainly a formal significance ("long-bond"); it denotes a pair of electrons with opposite spins. At double the normal bond length there is no longer any appreciable overlapping of the wave functions and, therefore, this electron pair does not represent any appreciable bonding energy. The energy content of a DEWAR configuration is, therefore, about 60 kcal, that is to say the amount of one second bond higher than that of a KEKULÉ configuration. In accordance with the propositions on p. 214 the joint contribution of the three DEWAR configurations to the stationary state is small, namely 22% in the charge distribution; the R.E. is increased 15% by their contribution, namely from 0.9 $\alpha$ to 1.11 $\alpha$ (p. 285).

In benzene itself, both KEKULÉ configurations (and also the three DEWAR configurations) will contribute equally to the stationary state; however, this may not be the case with substitution products. In particular it has been thought that the ring strain in the saturated ring of hydrindene would lead to a preference for the configurations with a common single bond since here the necessary deviation of the bond angles from the normal value will be smaller than in the other configuration (MILLS-NIXON effect, MILLS and NIXON, 1930; WHELAND, 1942; BADGER, 1951).

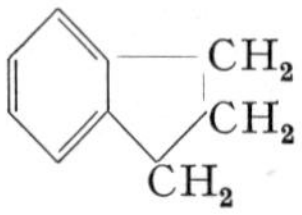

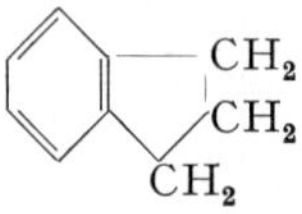

$CH_2$ $CH_2$ $CH_2$ $CH_2$
$CH_2$ $CH_2$

The arguments that were put forward are, however, not convincing. In the meantime it has appeared from accurate calculations (Longuet-Higgins and Coulson, 1946) that the common bond has even a somewhat higher double bond character than the neighbouring bonds. Ozonization likewise furnishes evidence; ozone attacks the common bond for 80% against 20% for the neighbouring bonds (Wibaut and De Jong, 1956).

*b. Other aromatic hydrocarbons and heterocyclic compounds*

*Isocyclic compounds.* All aromatic molecules exhibit resonance between different electron configurations, the number of which becomes rapidly greater for larger molecules. In particular there is an increase in the number of possible so-called excited configurations* in which (analogous to the Dewar structures in benzene) one, two or more formal bonds are present.

There are three unexcited configurations of practically equal energy for naphthalene, one symmetrical (Erlenmeyer) and two asymmetrical (Erdmann); these correspond to the Kekulé configurations.

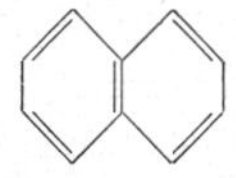
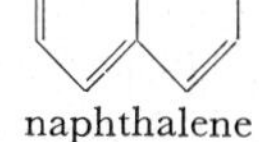
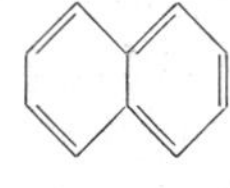

naphthalene

In addition there are sixteen singly excited configurations and also nineteen doubly and four trebly excited configurations to give a total of 42 Lewis-Langmuir configurations.

The three first-mentioned configurations contribute (see p. 286) all (respectively 39.4%, 30.3% and 30.3%**) to the

* These excited *configurations* are to be well distinguished from excited *states* (p. 257).

** These figures are obtained if only the unexcited Kekulé configurations are taken into account. By a more refined calculation we obtain 36.6 % for the symmetrical and 14.4 % for each of the asymmetrical unexcited configurations, 30.5 % for the 16 singly excited configurations taken together, 4.9 % for the 19 doubly excited and 0.04 % for the 4 trebly excited configurations (Sherman, 1934).

stationary state. Thus there is no ground for a discussion on which formula is preferable.

For anthracene and phenanthrene four and five unexcited configurations, respectively, can be written down.

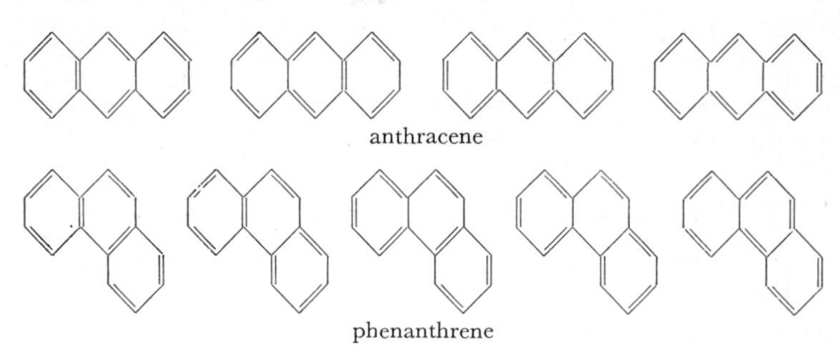


The most important of the excited configurations for anthracene is the symmetrical one , in which the very stable configuration of benzene is retained in two nuclei. This is of importance for the chemical reactions of these hydrocarbons (§ 35) for example, the formation of a 9,10-quinone, *i.e.*, anthraquinone.

The R.E. of anthracene is 103 kcal while that of phenanthrene is 110 kcal (Table 19).

The spatial structure of these three hydrocarbons is completely flat, as seen from the X-ray analysis. This holds likewise for all other condensed aromatic ring systems* (Robertson, 1950, 1953).

We cannot, however, expect that all carbon bonds have the same character and thus are of equal length as is the case in the benzene molecule.

If we conceive the stationary state of these molecules in a

* In "overcrowded" molecules steric hindrance prevents the aromatic molecule from being plane, *e.g.*, in 3:4- 5:6-dibenzanthracene and in triphenylbenzene. In octa-methylnaphtalene only the methyl groups are forced out of the plane (Bell and Waring, 1949; McIntosh, Robertson and Vand, 1954; Donaldson and Robertson, 1953; Bastiansen and Hassel, 1952; Farag, 1954; Harnik, Herbstein, Schmidt and Hirshfeld, 1954).

rough first approximation as a simple superposition with equal contributions of the unexcited configuration (KEKULÉ config.), we will find important differences in the double-bond character of the bonds as defined in this way by PAULING*.

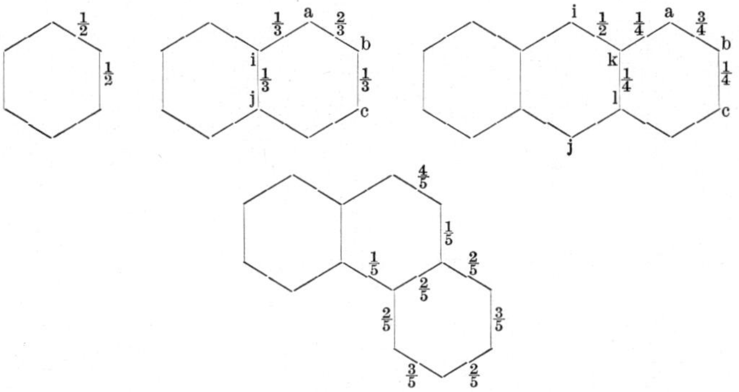

Although very rough, this double-bond character does reproduce the differences fairly well. Thus naphthalene reacts with ozone by preference at the 1, 2 bonds and not at the 2, 3 bond; phenanthrene adds bromine very readily at the 9, 10 bond which has $^4/_5$ double-bond character.

The bond lengths (CRUICKSHANK, 1956, 1957) also exhibit the same *qualitative* picture; the quantitative differences are smaller than might be expected (see p. 301).

| | | | | | |
|---|---|---|---|---|---|
| naphthalene | 1 — 2 $(a — b)$ | 1.361 Å | anthracene | 1 — 2 $(a — b)$ | 1.366 Å |
| | 2 — 3 $(b — c)$ | 1.421 Å | | 2 — 3 $(b — c)$ | 1.419 Å |
| | | | | $i — k$ | 1.399 Å |
| | $a — i$ | 1.425 Å | | $a — k$ | 1.433 Å |
| common bond | $i — j$ | 1.410 Å | | $k — l$ | 1.436 Å |

One can say that the R.E. increases in proportion to the number of valence configurations; phenanthrene does have a higher R.E. than anthracene.

* If the differences in the contributions are taken into account (p. 223), then the bond character for naphthalene through superposition of the KEKULÉ configurations becomes: ab 0.70 (0.63), bc 0.30 (0.29) ai 0.30 (0.27), ij 0.39 (0.41); the bond character given between brackets is obtained if *all* 42 configurations with their respective weights are taken into account. (For other calculations see p. 289 and Table 24.)

When we now proceed to other hydrocarbons then it appears, as is to be expected, that the attachment of alkyl groups as in toluene, xylene, ethylbenzene and hydrindene has no appreciable influence on the R.E. (Tables 19 and 20).

This is, however, not the case, if conjugation exists between multiple bonds in the side chain and those in the aromatic nucleus (compare the R.E. of styrene and stilbene with that of benzene). We shall return to this in the discussion of the conjugation in open chains.

In diphenyl the R.E. is 6 kcal greater than would be expected for two benzene nuclei. This extra R.E. finds its origin in the contributions of excited configurations such as:

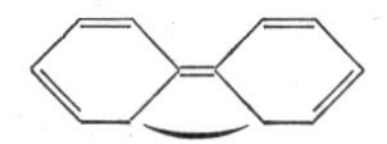

The central bond is also shortened: 1.48 Å (in the crystal). The condition for this is that both phenyl nuclei lie in one plane; this is, in fact, the case for diphenyl and higher polyphenyls.

Since, however, the extra R.E., which stabilizes the coplanarity, is small, it is understandable that the plane structure is lost through steric hindrance (Born repulsion) of groups in the *ortho* positions (2, 2′, 6, 6′) (optically active compounds, absorption spectrum, p. 263).

Stilbene and azobenzene have two isomers. In these cases a plane structure is realized for the *trans*-isomers*; the planar structure is spatially impossible for the *cis*-isomers. The stability of the *trans* forms is a consequence of the extra resonance (extra R.E. *trans*-stilbene 7.0 kcal; energy content of *trans*-azobenzene 10 kcal lower than the *cis* form). This resonance also appears from the interatomic distances; *trans*-stilbene: C—C 1.445 Å, C=C 1.33 Å; azobenzene, *trans* C—N 1.415 Å,

* Strictly speaking this is only the case for half of the molecules in the crystal; the other half has the two phenyl groups in parallel planes. This is certainly a consequence of the opposite influence of stabilization by the extra R.E. and a greater cohesion energy through better packing of the molecules in this particular lattice.

*cis*: C—N 1.46 Å (sum of atomic distances 1.54 Å and 1.47 Å, respectively); in this latter compound the planes of the rings make an angle of 50°.

*trans*- and *cis*-stilbene (azobenzene)

*Heterocyclic compounds*

We can regard benzene as built up of methine groups CH (· Ċ : H) with two electrons which take part in the $\sigma$ bonds and one $\pi$ electron. One or more of these CH groups can be replaced by a nitrogen atom (· Ṅ :). In this way we obtain the heterocyclic compounds with six-membered rings, such as pyridine, quinoline, diazines, triazines, etc. The system of the $\pi$ electrons has remained the same and the same configurations are possible as in the corresponding *iso*cyclic hydrocarbons. They all show the same aromatic character.

One can ask the question why, although the triazines $C_3H_3N_3$ and also the tetrazines $C_2H_2N_4$ are very stable compounds, pentazine $CHN_5$ and hexazine $N_6$ (a polymer of nitrogen) do not exist. This is not due to the instability of these molecules as such but to the special stability of the triple bond in nitrogen and in HCN, compared with the corresponding single and double bonds, while this does not hold to the same extent for the triple carbon-carbon bond (Table 18).

The following relations are determinative here:

$$E\,(\mathrm{N}\equiv\mathrm{N}) > [E\,(\mathrm{N}=\mathrm{N}) + E\,(\mathrm{N}-\mathrm{N})]$$
$$E\,(\mathrm{C}\equiv\mathrm{N}) \approx [E\,(\mathrm{C}=\mathrm{N}) + E\,(\mathrm{C}-\mathrm{N})]$$
$$E\,(\mathrm{C}\equiv\mathrm{C}) < [E\,(\mathrm{C}=\mathrm{C}) + E\,(\mathrm{C}-\mathrm{C})]$$

Thus the triple N≡N and, to a lesser degree, the C≡N bond do not have an unsaturated character as the C≡C bond (p. 196).

Six-membered rings with an oxygen (pyran) or a sulphur atom as the hetero-atom have naturally no aromatic character.

pyran

However, the heterocyclic five-membered ring systems such as pyrrole, furan, thiophene, thiazole, imidazole, etc., deserve special attention.

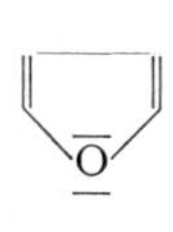


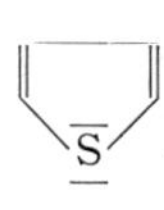


The hetero-atom (N, O or S) has lone electron pairs and thus a system of six $\pi$ electrons can be produced, analogous to that in benzene.

I II III

The same picture holds for furan and thiophene. In configurations II and III the hetero-atom has donated an electron pair and possesses a formal charge of +1. With a more electronegative hetero-atom such as the oxygen in furan, these configurations have an appreciably higher energy and thus contribute little to the resonance. The aromatic character of furan is in fact less pronounced than that of pyrrole and thiophene*. The central C—C bond in all three is longer (1.46, 1.44 and 1.44 Å) than the two others (1) 1.35 Å. Furan also has the smallest resonance energy (Table 19).

* However, it is probable that in thiophene also the d orbitals of the sulphur atom play a role (Longuet-Higgins, 1949a; Evans and De Heer, 1949).

The nitrogen atom in aliphatic amines, pyridine, etc., exhibits basic properties; that is to say, the nitrogen atom can bind a proton through its free electron pair. However, the resonance possibilities II and III in pyrrole are lost on the addition of a proton, so that the positive ion is thus not stabilized by resonance; thus the proton attraction, that is the basicity, is very small for pyrrole. The formation of a negative ion, as in pyrrole-potassium, does not prevent the resonance; consequently pyrrole does show acid properties.

In fact, the loss of a proton will even be stimulated by the formal positive charge on the nitrogen atom; this is similar to the acidic $R_3NH^+$-ion (also the ammonium ion) and to phenol (p. 237). The configuration of the negative pyrrole ion with the negative charge on the nitrogen atom is the most stable one. In tetrazole there are more of these configurations, and this substance is fairly acidic ($K \sim 10^{-5}$), owing to the increased resonance in the ion.

## § 31. CONJUGATION OF DOUBLE BONDS AND FREE ELECTRON PAIRS

*A.* It has long been known that the conjugation of double bonds in open chains has an important influence on the chemical and physical properties. This is illustrated by various values for the heat of hydrogenation in Table 20. From the increment of the refractivity, it is evident that $\pi$ electrons are more mobile in conjugated double bonds than in isolated ones.

Where two *non*-conjugated double bonds occur (as in 1, 4-pentadiene and 1, 5-hexadiene) the heat of hydrogenation is normal, that is to say, equal to twice the value in a corresponding hydrocarbon with one double bond. However, if the two bonds are conjugated in an open or in a closed chain, the heat of hydrogenation is decreased by 2 to 4 kcal/mole. In a conjugated triene this decrease amounts to 6.7 kcal/mole. The same effect is observed whether or not the double bond is conjugated with the phenyl nucleus; compare 1, 4 dihydronaphthalene with styrene and indene (Table 20).

There is again resonance with other configurations; however, these all have a higher energy content than the only "normal" configuration (II).

$$\overset{\ominus}{H_2\overline{C}}-CH{=}CH-\overset{\oplus}{C}H_2 \quad H_2C{=}CH-CH{=}CH_2 \quad H_2\overset{\oplus}{C}-CH{=}CH-\overset{\ominus}{\overline{C}}H_2$$

I II III

$$H_2C-CH{=}CH-CH_2$$

(with a long link connecting the two end carbons)

IV

The long link in IV has again only a formal character and indicates that there are free electrons (that is to say, free valencies) at the ends, the spins of which are oppositely directed.

The corresponding configuration with two parallel spins would actually represent the same energy as IV but according to § 30.1 this configuration is excluded from the resonance.

The contributions of all three of the configurations I, III and IV lend some double-bond character to the 2, 3 bond (20%), as appears from the diminished bond length of only 1.47 Å.

The contributions of the configurations other than II are also seen from the reactive behaviour of the conjugated systems. For example, in the reaction with halogen, we find that 1, 2 and 1, 4 addition take place simultaneously while the reaction with sodium results in polymerization (§ 35).

In butadiyne (biacetylene) HC≡C—C≡CH, the central bond is only 1.38 Å long; here conjugation and the change in the hybridization act in the same direction, since even in propyne or methyl acetylene the length of the C—$CH_3$ bond is already reduced to 1.46 Å.

We have already given several examples of the conjugation of a double bond with an aromatic system. The R.E. are greater here than between two double bonds.

We can give the following configurations for styrene:

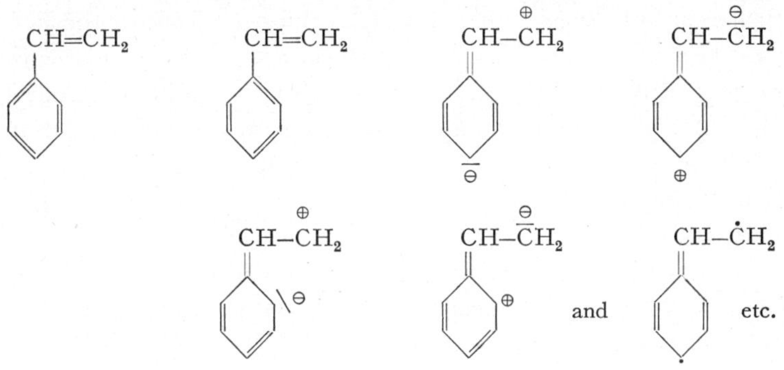

CH=CH$_2$ CH=CH$_2$ $\overset{\oplus}{\text{CH}}$–CH$_2$ $\overset{\ominus}{\text{CH}}$–$\overline{\text{C}}$H$_2$

⊖ ⊕

$\overset{\oplus}{\text{CH}}$–CH$_2$ $\overset{\ominus}{\text{CH}}$–$\overline{\text{C}}$H$_2$ CH–$\dot{\text{C}}$H$_2$

⊖ ⊕ and etc.

and mirror images; in addition the configurations with single electrons with opposite spins at the positions where there is a + and — charge in the above formulae. The number of configurations is, therefore, appreciably greater than in the butadienes.

Conjugation is in no way restricted to that of C=C bonds among themselves; resonance as a consequence of the conjugation of C=C with C=O and of these latter double bonds with one another is also very important.

The first makes its appearance in aromatic ketones, esters of acrylic acid and crotonaldehyde $CH_2$=$CH_2$—CH=O. We meet resonance between two carbonyl bonds in glyoxal and diacetyl where the C—C bond is in fact shortened to 1.47 Å; furthermore, both substances are coloured yellow (§ 34). The calculation of the R.E. is uncertain in this case because the binding energy C=O is variable and because polar interaction also plays a part in the energy content.

*B.* The conjugation of multiple bonds with free electron pairs (lone-pairs) in nitrogen, oxygen, sulphur and halogen atoms is an extension of the historic concept of conjugation, but this is indispensable for a good understanding of the properties of substituted aromatic and unsaturated compounds in general.

When we compare vinyl chloride $CH_2$=CHCl with ethyl chloride $CH_3$—$CH_2$Cl, we find an important difference in the properties of the C—Cl bond. The chlorine atom in the first case can be replaced by hydroxyl (saponification) only with extreme difficulty; this process proceeds very readily with ethyl chloride. Vinyl chloride also appears to be less reactive than ethyl chloride in the reaction with sodium vapour in the dilute flame; that is to say the activation energy for the reaction is higher.

Another illustration is the similar behaviour of the C—Br bond with regard to exchange of bromine by iodine. The velocity constant is:

$$CH_2{=}CH{-}CH_2Br \qquad K = 126$$
$$CH_3{-}CH{=}CHBr \qquad K = 0.00017$$

The R.E. can be calculated at about 20 kcal. This chemical stability runs parallel with a shortening of the bond length in vinyl chloride to 1.69 Å compared with 1.76 Å in ethyl chloride. This stiffening is likewise seen from the increased force constant of the C—Cl bond, *i.e.* the constant $f$ which connects the restoring force with the displacement; this constant is related to the frequency $\nu = \frac{1}{2\pi}\sqrt{\frac{f}{m}}$ of the C—Cl oscillation, which is, therefore, higher in vinyl chloride than in ethyl chloride. The lower dipole moment of vinyl cloride (1.44 D compared with 2.00 D) indicates that the chlorine is less negative with respect to the rest of the molecule in vinyl chloride than in ethyl chloride.

All these experimental facts find a reasonable explanation by considering the electron configuration somewhat further. The molecule is plane; the wave functions of the two $\pi$ electrons of the second C—C bond are perpendicular to this plane and are antisymmetrical with respect to reflection in the plane. The bonding pair of the C—Cl bond is a $\sigma$-pair as in the C—H bonds. One of the non-bonding electron pairs of the chlorine atom is a 2s pair which is symmetrical. When we call the bonding pair in its orbit round the chlorine atom a $2p_x$ pair, the wave function of one of the non-bonding pairs is that of a $2p_y$

pair and also lies in the plane of the molecule, but that of the third pair as a $2p_z$ pair is perpendicular to it. These latter electrons are, therefore, also $\pi$ electrons with the same symmetry character as the pair of $\pi$ electrons from the C=C bond. There are, therefore, two electron configurations which satisfy the LEWIS-LANGMUIR conditions:

$$\begin{matrix} H \\ H \end{matrix} \!\!>\! C{=}C \!<\!\! \begin{matrix} \overline{Cl}| \\ H \end{matrix} \quad \longleftrightarrow \quad \begin{matrix} H \\ H \end{matrix} \!\!>\! \overset{\ominus}{\underline{C}}{-}C \!<\!\! \begin{matrix} {=}\overline{Cl}^{\oplus} \\ H \end{matrix}$$

The energy of the second one is approximately 60 kcal higher. The C—Cl bond has a certain double-bond character of about 15% as deduced from the decrease of the C—Cl distance*; this fact and the changed charge distribution—the chlorine more positive than normal—explain the above-mentioned experimental facts. The diminished double-bond character of the C=C bond also appears clearly from the experimental data, namely a diminished tendency to addition of halogen, etc., and a weaker force constant which is evident from the lowered C=C frequency.

In the series of di-, tri- and tetra-chloroethylenes, the double-bond character of each C—Cl bond becomes smaller but that of the C=C bond decreases further. This appears from the increase of the C—Cl distance to 1.73 Å in $C_2Cl_4$ and the further decrease of the C=C frequency.

It is clear that the same phenomena will occur in the aromatic halogen compounds, for example chlorobenzene, since the same resonance possibilities exist in this case:

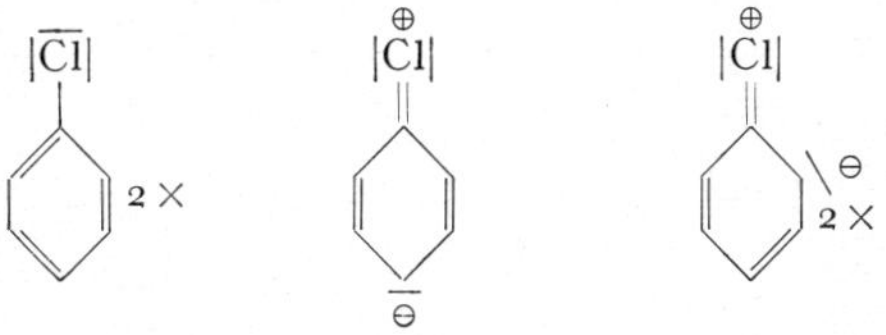

|$\overline{Cl}$| (benzene ring) 2 ×   $\overset{\oplus}{|Cl|}$ (quinoid ring, $\ominus$ para)   $\overset{\oplus}{|Cl|}$ (quinoid ring, $\ominus$ ortho) 2 ×

The small mobility of the halogen atom and the low value

* From quadrupole coupling constants (p. 150) a much lower value of only 6% double bond character has been derived (ref. p. 298).

of the dipole moment are not exclusively characteristic of the aromatic halogen compounds but of a halogen atom bound to an unsaturated carbon atom in general.

The distance C—Cl is also shortened in Cl—C≡N (chlorocyanogen) and Cl—C≡C—H (chloroacetylene) from 1.76 Å even to 1.67 Å and 1.68 Å, respectively.

Quantitative calculations on the character of the C—Cl bond in substituted ethylene and benzene derivatives are in good agreement with the available experimental data (SHERMAN and KETELAAR, 1939; KETELAAR, 1939; however, see also p. 298).

Similar phenomena appear in other atoms with free electron pairs, such as oxygen, sulphur and nitrogen; we shall mainly discuss the basic and acidic properties here.

*C. Base strength*

Let us examine the electron configurations of aniline:

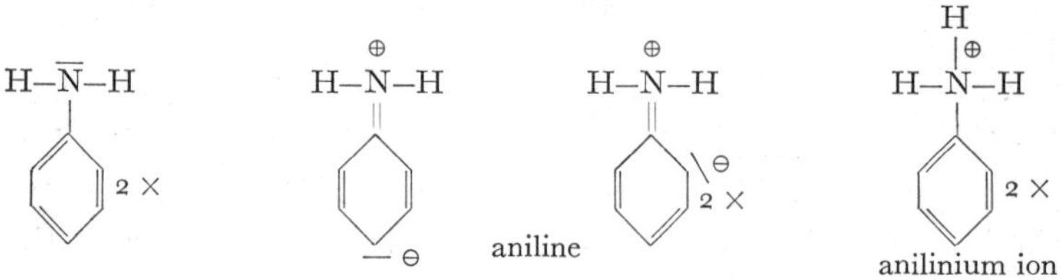

H–N̄–H (2 ×) H–N⊕–H (—⊖) H–N⊕–H (⊖, 2 ×) H–N⊕(H)–H (2 ×)

aniline anilinium ion

There is an extra resonance. However, the basicity of aniline is also smaller than that of an aliphatic primary amine, such as cyclohexylamine. This special resonance in the aniline molecule does not exist any longer in the anilinium ion because the free pair of electrons has now become a bonding pair by proton addition. The base constant $K_b$ is related to the (free) energy $\Delta F$ of the proton addition according to the expression $\Delta F = -RT \ln K_b$.

Now the ratio $K_b$ (for aniline)/$K_b$ (for prim. aliph. amine) amounts to $4.6 \cdot 10^{-10}/3\text{–}5 \cdot 10^{-4} = 1.5$ to $0.9 \cdot 10^{-6}$. This indicates a difference in $\Delta F$ of 8.4 to 7.9 kcal/mole (T=298° K). Since there is no reason to assume any essential difference in $\Delta S$, the proton affinity of aniline, $\Delta U$, will also be 8 kcal lower, which is somewhat larger than the extra R.E. of 2–8 kcal deduced from the heat of combustion.

The above $K_b$ for the equilibrium: amine $+ H^+ \rightleftharpoons$ ammonium ion, bears a simple relation to the more customary but less general basicity constant $K_b'$ of the equilibrium: amine $+ H_2O \rightleftharpoons$ ammonium ion $+ OH^-$. The expression is $K_b = K_b' . [H_2O]/K_W = 55.5 \cdot 10^{14} \cdot K_b'$, while $K_b'' = 55.5\, K_b'$ is always quoted. This has no influence on the above ratio.

The basicity of diphenylamine and triphenylamine is still lower. This last amine forms salts only with the strongest acids such as $HClO_4$. A condition for maximum resonance is a completely plane structure; however, this can not be satisfied in the last-mentioned substance. This is also the case with dimethyl *o*-toluidine, which is a weaker base than dimethylaniline, while *o*-toluidine has practically the same strength as aniline.

The acidic character of cyclopentadienes forms an interesting example of a similar influence. Remarkably enough, this hydrocarbon readily forms a potassium salt. While only one configuration is of interest in cyclopentadiene (we thus neglect conjugation), the cyclopentadienyl-ion has the same electron system as pyrrole and, therefore, also the same appreciable stabilization by resonance.

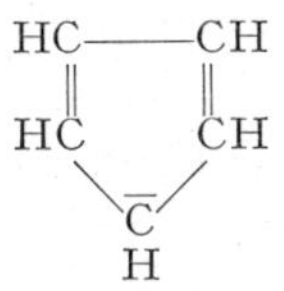

```
                                                  HC═CH
                                                 /     \
                                               HC       CH
HC────CH              HC────CH                 ‖        ‖
‖      ‖              ‖      ‖                 HC       CH
HC     CH             HC     CH                  \     /
  \   /                 \   /                     \   /
   C̄                     C                          C
   H                     H2                         H
[C5 H5]-             hydrocarbon                [C7 H7]+
```

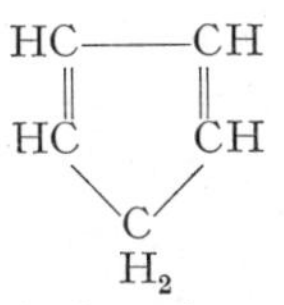

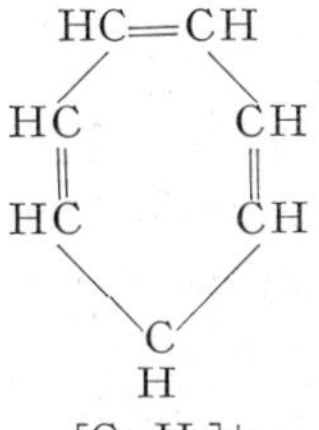

We have already discussed the stable biscyclopentadienyl complex compounds such as ferrocene, $Fe(C_5H_5)_2$ (p. 191). Related to the cyclopentadienyl-anion is the cycloheptatrienyl-cation or tropylium-ion as in $(C_7H_7)Br$. In fact the interatomic distances and force constants are very nearly equal to those of benzene; all three are plane, regular polygons (NELSON, FATELEY and LIPPINCOTT, 1956; FATELEY and LIPPINCOTT, 1957). Thus the constitution is essentially the same for all three 6 $\pi$-electron systems (p. 305) as already predicted by HÜCKEL (HÜCKEL, 1931).

The small basicity of pyridine cannot be explained in such a simple way; the same resonance is possible in the base and in the pyridinium ion. The following can be said: Just as $NH_4^+$ is more strongly acidic than $CH_4$, so $C_5H_5NH^+$, the pyridinium ion, will also be more acidic than benzene $C_6H_6$. Since $C_6H_6$ is more acidic than $CH_4$ (p. 240) the pyridinium ion will also be more acidic than an alkylammonium ion; that is to say pyridine will be a weaker base than the alkyl amine. No quantitative calculation is, however, yet available.

*Acid strength* (KIRKWOOD and WESTHEIMER, 1939, 1947). Two factors are mainly:

1. Electrostatic induction
2. Resonance

The first influence, known for a considerable time, appears from the variation of the acid strength in the following series: 1-chlorobutyric acid $1.45 \cdot 10^{-3}$; 2-chlorobutyric acid $8.8 \cdot 10^{-5}$; 3-chlorobutyric acid $3 \cdot 10^{-5}$; butyric acid $1.5 \cdot 10^{-5}$.

In fact the positive pole of the C—Cl dipole is situated closer to the oxygen atom of the OH group and induces a positive charge in this oxygen atom; as a result, the dissociation energy of the proton is lowered. The strong dependence on the distance and the lack of an alternating effect are indications that a direct electrostatic effect is indeed involved here. The influence of this effect can be calculated readily.

The second influence is the reason that, among other things, phenol is a much stronger acid than an aliphatic alcohol such as cyclohexanol and that, as already stated, cyclopentadiene has acid properties. It also plays a predominant role in the carboxyl group.

With phenol there are two causes which act in the same direction. A positive formal charge is formed in the oxygen atom by the contribution of the other configurations in phenol; further the resonance in the phenolate ion is more important than in phenol itself because the energy differences with the normal configuration are smaller.

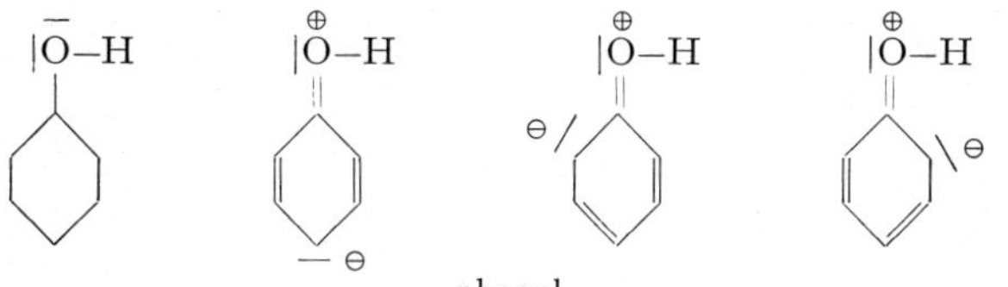

|Ō–H ⊕|O–H ⊕|O–H ⊕|O–H

⊖ ⊖ ⊖

phenol

|Ō|⊖ |O| |O| |O|

⊖ ⊖ ⊖

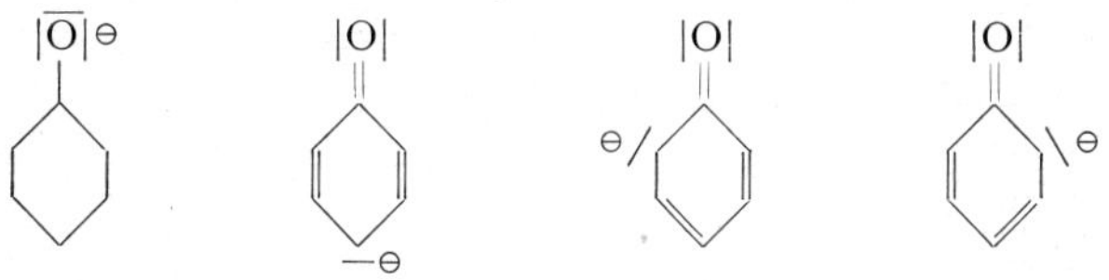

phenolate ion

This result can be extended to the statement that, in general, an enol-group C=C—OH is more strongly acidic than a saturated alcohol. Thus 1, 3-cyclohexadione and glutaconic dialdehyde are clearly acidic ($K_z \sim 10^{-6}$) in the enol form:

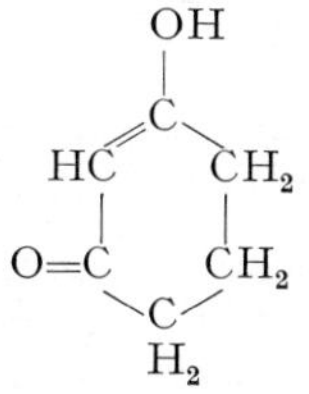

OH

C

HC CH₂

O=C CH₂

C

H₂

HO–CH=CH–CH=CH–CH=O

Vinyl alcohol would be acidic through the contribution of the configuration

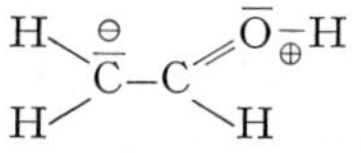

H ⊖ Ō–H

C–C ⊕

H H

As a result this compound readily isomerizes to acetaldehyde before it can be isolated.

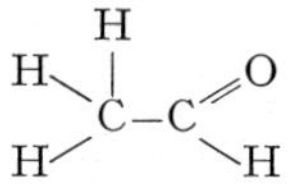

H

H O

C–C

H H

Acetone also has an acidic character as appears from the complete exchange of the hydrogen for deuterium in alkaline media where the equilibrium is displaced towards the side of the acid enol form.

$$CH_2{=}C{-}CH_3$$
$$|\overline{O}{-}H$$

The nitrophenols are still stronger acids than phenol. The nitro group should not, as has been remarked repeatedly, be formulated as $R{-}N{\overset{\overline{O}}{\underset{\overline{O}}{\lessgtr}}}$ with quinquevalent nitrogen; rather it is a resonance hybrid between

$$R{-}\overset{\oplus}{N}(\overline{O}|^{\ominus})(=\overline{O}) \longleftrightarrow R{-}\overset{\oplus}{N}(=\overline{O})(\overline{O}|^{\ominus})$$

This is in agreement with the very high dipole moment of this group 3.3 D, the bond angle of 127° and the N—O distance of 1.21 Å.

There are, however, still further configurations possible with — $NO_2$ as a substituent in aromatic molecules:

$$^{\ominus}|\overline{O}\diagdown\overset{\oplus}{N}\diagup\overline{O} \quad (4\times) \qquad ^{\ominus}|\overline{O}\diagdown\overset{\oplus}{N}\diagup\overline{O}|^{\ominus} \qquad ^{\ominus}|\overline{O}\diagdown\overset{\oplus}{N}\diagup\overline{O}|^{\ominus} \quad (2\times)$$

The dipole moment is increased by this resonance to 3.93 D. If we proceed to the nitrophenols, we have the following configurations:

$$|\overline{O}\diagdown N\diagup\overline{O}| \ \ldots \ ^{\oplus}|\overline{O}{-}H \qquad |\overline{O}\diagdown N\diagup\overline{O}| \ \ldots \ \overset{\oplus}{\overline{O}}{-}H \qquad |\overline{O}\diagdown N\diagup\overline{O}| \ \ldots \ \overset{\oplus}{\overline{O}}{-}H$$

| | *para* | *ortho* | *meta* |
|---|---|---|---|
| *K*: | $6.5 \cdot 10^{-8}$ | $6.8 \cdot 10^{-8}$ | $5.3 \cdot 10^{-9}$ |

The nitrophenols are appreciably stronger acids than phenol itself ($K$ phenol $1.3 \cdot 10^{-10}$). The resonance illustrated above is only possible without a formal bond for *ortho*- and *para*-nitrophenol. These are in fact both stronger acids than the *meta* isomer. However, induction must also play a part since the *meta* isomer is more acidic than phenol. In 2,4,6-trinitrophenol, picric acid, the acidity is still further increased. Similarly the CH-groups become more acidic in polynitrobenzene owing to the positive charges which are induced on the carbon atoms by the nitro groups.

With the nitrophenols, as well as phenol, the resonance is stronger in the ion than in the undissociated molecule; this is evident from the well-known yellow colour of the ions compared with the colourless molecules of undissociated phenol (p. 263).

The best known organic acids are the carboxylic acids. Why has the group $R{-}C{\overset{\diagup\!\!\diagup \overline{O}}{\underset{\diagdown \underline{\overline{O}}{-}H}{}}}$ so pre-eminently the tendency to donate a proton?

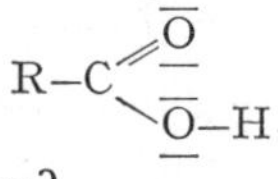

There is also resonance here, both in the undissociated acid and in the ion. For the carboxyl group there are two non-equivalent configurations; however, these are equivalent in the ion. This is confirmed by crystal structure analysis.

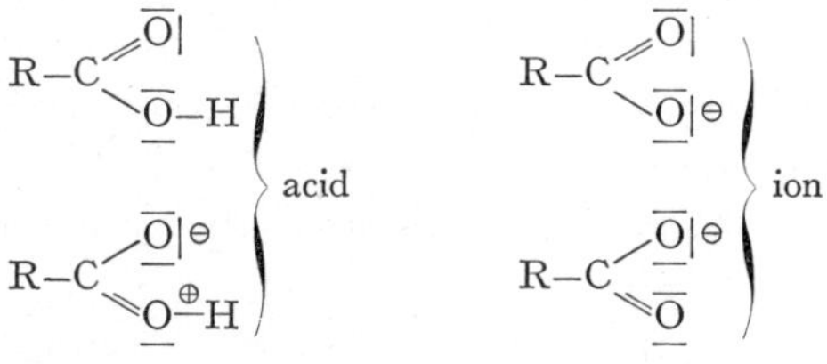

$$\left.\begin{array}{l} R{-}C{\overset{\diagup\!\!\diagup \overline{O}|}{\underset{\diagdown \underline{\overline{O}}{-}H}{}}} \\[2em] R{-}C{\overset{\diagup \overline{O}|^{\ominus}}{\underset{\diagdown\!\!\diagdown \underline{O}\overset{\oplus}{-}H}{}}} \end{array}\right\}\text{acid} \qquad \left.\begin{array}{l} R{-}C{\overset{\diagup\!\!\diagup \overline{O}|}{\underset{\diagdown \underline{\overline{O}}|^{\ominus}}{}}} \\[2em] R{-}C{\overset{\diagup \overline{O}|^{\ominus}}{\underset{\diagdown\!\!\diagdown \underline{\overline{O}}}{}}} \end{array}\right\}\text{ion}$$

The high acid strength of the hydroxyl group must be attributed mainly to this resonance, which confers a formal positive charge to the oxygen atom, and to the stabilization of the ion by complete resonance between two equivalent configurations.

The two C-O distances in the acid are 1.24 Å and 1.36 Å

compared with the normal values of 1.24 Å and 1.43 Å for the C=O and C—OH distances, respectively. Both are equal to 1.28 Å in the ion.

The same possibilities of resonance are present in the esters and in the acid amides as in the acids (Table 19).

The anhydrides have, however, three configurations:

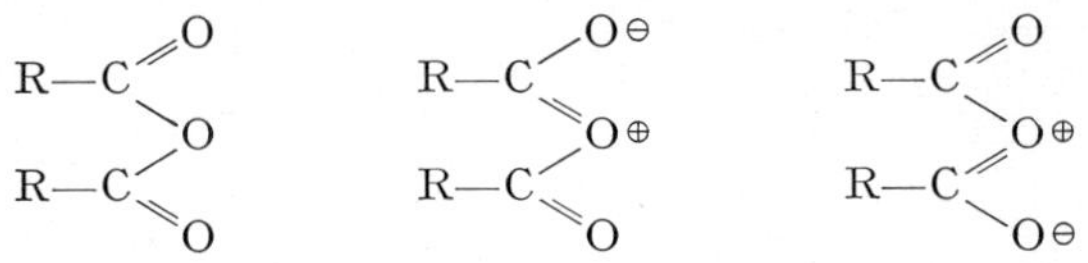

$$\begin{matrix} R{-}C\begin{matrix}\nearrow\!\!\!\!=O\\ \searrow O\\ \end{matrix} \\ R{-}C\begin{matrix}\nearrow\\ \searrow\!\!\!\!=O\end{matrix}\end{matrix} \qquad \begin{matrix} R{-}C\begin{matrix}\nearrow O^{\ominus}\\ \searrow\!\!\!\!= O^{\oplus}\\ \end{matrix} \\ R{-}C\begin{matrix}\nearrow\\ \searrow\!\!\!\!=O\end{matrix}\end{matrix} \qquad \begin{matrix} R{-}C\begin{matrix}\nearrow\!\!\!\!=O\\ \searrow O^{\oplus}\\ \end{matrix} \\ R{-}C\begin{matrix}\nearrow\!\!\!\!=\\ \searrow O^{\ominus}\end{matrix}\end{matrix}$$

The R.E. is approximately 30 kcal in this case.

Another influence on the acid strength has not yet been mentioned; this a change of the charge distribution through change in the hybridization.

If we compare the C—H bond in the series C (aliph.)—H, C(ethylene)—H, C(arom.)—H and C (acetylene)—H, then the character changes from $sp^3$ through $sp^2$ to sp. A calculation shows that the maximum in the charge distribution is displaced towards the carbon atom in this succession. This results, on the one hand, in a shortening of the C—H distance (p. 160) and in increase of the bond energy (p. 160) and, on the other hand, in an alteration in the effective charge of the hydrogen atom in the direction of a more positive charge.

One can also say, therefore, that the electronegativity of the carbon atom increases in this series (p. 150). In spite of the increase in the energy of dissociation to a H atom, the energy of dissociation to a $H^+$ ion decreases in the same direction and the acid strength increases.

This change in the charge density in the series mentioned above is also evident from the partial moments of the C—H bond, though the absolute values are still in doubt. From the intensities of absorption bands in the infrared a change from —0.4 D (H negative) to +0.4 D has been deduced from stretching vibrations (Gent, 1948; Mecke, 1950; Lippert and Mecke, 1951), but also a change was found from +0.2 D (H positive) to +1.0 D as deduced from deformation (bending) vibrations (BELL, THOMPSON and VAGO, 1948; HORNIG and McKEAN, 1955; COULSON and STEPHEN, 1957) for $CH_4$ and $C_2H_2$ respectively.

Important changes in the charge distribution can also occur in the bond C(aliph.)—H. In chloroform, $HCCl_3$, the charge of the hydrogen atom is more positive owing to the influence of the electronegative chlorine atoms (see also p. 372).

Another change in the electronegativity occurs in the series $C_{prim}$—, $C_{sec}$—, $C_{tert}$—; the negative charge of the central carbon atom increases when H is replaced by $CH_3$ (see also p. 282). This results in a decrease of the dissociation energy for the H atom (Table 183) and in a decrease of the (hypothetical) acid strength of the hydrocarbons. For halogenated hydrocarbons this results in an increase of the dipole moment and of the tendency to heterolytic dissociation (into ions) of the C—Cl bond (increasing rate of hydrolysis in going from primary to secondary and to tertiary chlorides).

## § 32. OTHER RESONATING MOLECULES

### BORON HYDRIDES

There are numerous other interesting cases where a clear idea of the constitution is only possible if the concept of resonance is introduced.

The customary formulae of the nitriles (R—C≡N) and the isonitriles (R—N=C) would point to a profound difference in bond character. However, it appears that the distances and the vibrational frequencies are the same in both cases. In other words the carbon-nitrogen bond is the same in both groups and actually bears mainly the character of a triple bond. The configuration $R—\overset{(+)}{N}\equiv\overset{(-)}{C}\,|$ is obviously the predominant one in the isonitriles.

Resonance is also common in inorganic molecules. The three-fold symmetry and the shortened bond length of the nitrate ion (p. 164) and carbonate ion point to resonance between:

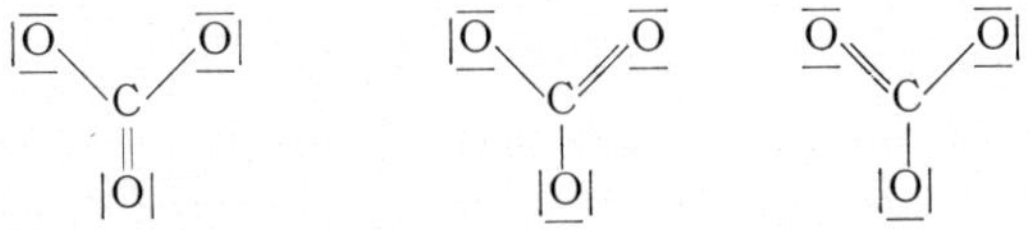

$$|\overline{O}\diagdown C(=|\overline{O}|)\diagup \overline{O}| \qquad |\overline{O}\diagdown C(-|\overline{O}|)\diagup\!\!\!\diagup \overline{O} \qquad \overline{O}\diagdown\!\!\!\diagdown C(-|\overline{O}|)\diagup \overline{O}|$$

The observed distances are C—O: 1.31 Å and N—O: 1.21 Å, while the values from Table 16 with 0.02 A corrections for the charges would give.

$$\begin{array}{llll} C—O^- & 1.45\ \text{Å}, & C{=}O & 1.21\ \text{Å} \\ N^+—O^- & 1.36\ \text{Å}, & N^+{=}O & 1.13\ \text{Å} \end{array}$$

We have already discussed the resonance in $SO_3$ and in $[SO_4]^{2-}$ (p. 168).

In general it is more difficult to make statements on the constitution of the inorganic compounds with any degree of certainty. In the first place, the possibility of comparison with a number of similarly constituted compounds, as in the case of the carbon compounds, is lacking. The values for atomic radii, etc., have, therefore, also a much smaller reliability. The R.E. cannot be calculated at all on account of the lack of values for the contributions of the separate bonds. Furthermore, polar effects and contributions from ionic configurations play a much more important part since much greater differences in electronegativity occur in this case.

The azide ion $N_3^-$ of hydrazoic acid is also remarkable. This was previously formulated as Na–N$\begin{smallmatrix}\diagup\!\!\!\diagup N \\ | \\ \diagdown\!\!\!\diagdown N\end{smallmatrix}$, but crystal structure analysis has shown that the ion is linear; the configurations given below contribute:

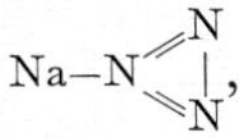

$$\underset{\text{I}}{\overset{\ominus\quad\oplus\quad\ominus}{\overline{\underline{N}}{=}N{=}\overline{\underline{N}}}} \qquad \underset{\text{II}}{\overset{(2-)\ \oplus}{|\overline{\underline{N}}{-}N{\equiv}N|}} \qquad \underset{\text{III}}{\overset{\oplus\ \ (2-)}{|N{\equiv}N{-}\overline{\underline{N}}|}}$$

Since the distance of 1.15 Å is smaller than expected for the first configuration, namely 1.22 Å, the other two configurations must also contribute to a considerable extent. The shortening due to the contribution of the triple bond must be larger than the lengthening due to the contribution of the single bond.

In the organic azides $\underset{R}{\diagup}\overset{1.24}{N \overset{}{\text{—}}} \overset{1.10}{N \text{—}} N$ (R–N: 1.47), the first two configurations contribute:

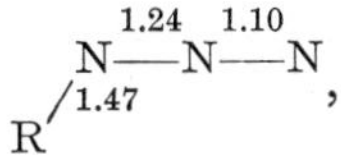

$$R{-}\overline{N}{=}\overset{\oplus}{N}{=}\overset{\ominus}{\underline{N}}| \qquad R{-}\overset{\ominus}{\underline{\overline{N}}}{-}\overset{\oplus}{N}{\equiv}N|$$

The third possibility:

$$R{-}\overset{\oplus}{N}{=}\overset{\oplus}{N}{-}\overset{(2-)}{\underline{\overline{N}}}|$$

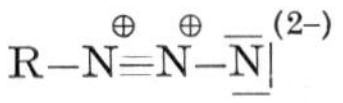

is energetically improbable, since this would produce a like charge on neighbouring atoms ("adjacent charge rule" of PAULING).

There is therefore a smaller possibility for resonance in the organic and non-ionogenic inorganic (B-subgroup and other non-inert gas ions) azides; this is probably one of the factors which leads to instability of compounds like silver and lead azide as compared with ionogenic azides such as $NaN_3$ and $Ba(N_3)_2$.

$CNO^-$, $N_2O(NNO)$, $CO_2$ and $NO_2^+$ are all linear molecules in which resonance between analogous configurations should be considered; these molecules are iso-electronic with $N_3^-$:

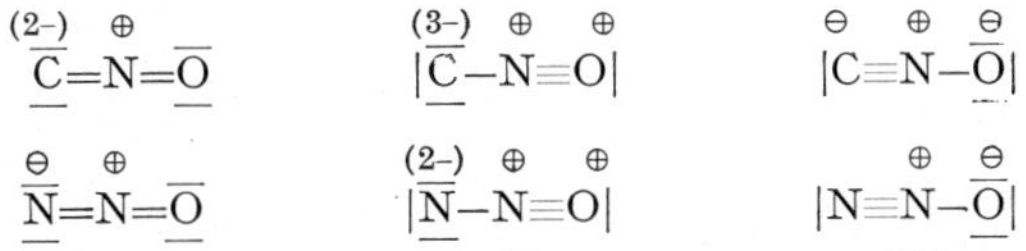

| I | II | III |
|---|---|---|
| $\overset{(2-)}{\underline{\overline{C}}}{=}\overset{\oplus}{N}{=}\underline{\overline{O}}$ | $\vert\overset{(3-)}{\underline{\overline{C}}}{-}\overset{\oplus}{N}{\equiv}\overset{\oplus}{O}\vert$ | $\vert\overset{\ominus}{C}{\equiv}\overset{\oplus}{N}{-}\overset{\ominus}{\underline{\overline{O}}}\vert$ |
| $\overset{\ominus}{\underline{\overline{N}}}{=}\overset{\oplus}{N}{=}\underline{\overline{O}}$ | $\vert\overset{(2-)}{\underline{\overline{N}}}{-}\overset{\oplus}{N}{\equiv}\overset{\oplus}{O}\vert$ | $\vert N{\equiv}\overset{\oplus}{N}{-}\overset{\ominus}{\underline{\overline{O}}}\vert$ |

In both cases configurations II are excluded on account of the unfavourable charge distribution.

All three configurations are possible for $CO_2$, COS and $CS_2$, as in the case of $N_3^-$. If we were to calculate the energy of $CO_2$ from the binding energy of the carbonyl group, then a difference of 33 kcal/mole would appear, which could with important restrictions be considered as the R.E.; PAULING calculates 20 and 11 kcal/mole for COS and $CS_2$. Again the force constant for $CO_2$ is higher than for the carbonyl group, in agreement with the statements above.

For $CO_2$, $\overline{O}=C=\overline{O}$, which is very stable in contrast to allene $H_2C=C=CH_2$ (p. 197), a special type of resonance is present. If the $z$-axis is taken as the molecular axis, the left double bond may be described as a $\sigma_z$ bond and a $\pi_x$ bond with two lone pairs at the oxygen atom, a 2s and 2 $p_y$ pair; the other double bond is then a $\sigma_z$ bond and a $\pi_y$ bond with a 2s and a 2 $p_x$ lone pair on the oxygen atom at the right. Now resonance is possible between the 2 $p_x$ lone pair and the $\pi_x$ bonding pair and between the 2 $p_y$ and $\pi_y$ pairs. The bond distance of 1.16 Å is also very short compared with the value of 1.24 Å calculated for a double bond (Table 16).

In carbon monoxide CO (triple bond 1.12 Å) the bond distance of 1.128 Å is even shorter. Moreover the dipole moment of 0.12 D is very small and the properties of CO are about equal to those of $N_2$ with a triple bond. We have here a $\pi_x$ and $\pi_y$ bond and a $\sigma$ bond: $|C\equiv O|$, just as in $N_2$. The $\sigma$ bonding pair and the lone pair at the carbon atom occupy two non-equivalent sp hybrid orbitals (p. 162); at the oxygen atom the $\sigma$ bond is formed by the $p_z$ orbital, with the lone pair in the 2 s orbital. The difference of electronegativity would give rise to a negative charge on the oxygen atom. However, the lone pair in the sp hybrid orbital at the carbon atom balances this dipole moment almost completely.

The linear nitronium ion $NO_2^+$ (iso-electronic with $CO_2$) occurs in $NO_2PF_6$ and in solid $N_2O_5$ which, according to the crystal structure, is actually nitronium nitrate $NO_2^+.NO_3^-$ (GRISON, ERIKS and DE VRIES, 1950). This ion is also present as the active constituent in nitrating acid, *i.e.*, the mixtures of nitric acid and sulphuric acid (p. 276).

Resonance almost always leads to a shortening of bond lengths. However, the abnormally large N—Cl distance (1.95 Å; calc. 1.69 Å) in nitrosyl chloride NOCl forms a special case. This must also be attributed to resonance; however, the resonance is not with a configuration with a multiple Cl—N bond but with an ionogenic configuration (KETELAAR and PALMER, 1937).

$$\begin{matrix}\overline{N}=\overline{\underline{O}} \\ | \\ |\underline{Cl}|\end{matrix} \qquad \begin{matrix}[|N\equiv O|]^{\oplus} \\ \\ |\overline{\underline{Cl}}|^{\ominus}\end{matrix}$$

Paramagnetic molecules, among which are $O_2$, NO, $NO_2$ and $ClO_2$, form a separate group. The last three have an odd number of electrons and must possess an unpaired electron which is then responsible for the magnetism.

For NO the configurations

$$\overset{\ominus}{\overline{N}}=\overset{\oplus}{\dot{O}}| \quad \text{and} \quad \dot{N}=\overline{O}$$

have to be considered in a ratio of 1 to 2 (DOUSMANIS, 1955). An unpaired π-electron is thus exchanged for an electron pair. This is one of the rare examples of a three-electron bond such as in $He_2^+$ (p. 154). We can indicate this symbolically as | N⋮=O |. The distance is in fact shorter (1.14 Å) than that calculated for N=O (1.18 Å).

The dipole moment of NO is, however, only small (0.2 D) so that a configuration: $\overset{\oplus\cdot}{N}-\overset{\ominus}{\overline{O}}|$ must be also considered. It is doubtful whether the resonance idea is really of much value for simple inorganic molecules such as NO, CO, $CO_2$, etc. On the other hand, it is just as little possible to formulate ionic structures for most of these molecules. It would be better, if possible, to calculate the charge distribution by more accurate wave mechanical methods without attempting to interpret the results by the superposition of valence configurations.

The molecule of $NO_2$ has a V-shape with a NO distance of 1.189 Å and a bond angle of 134° (MOORE, 1950; WESTON, 1957). This structure points to a resonance between

N
|O| |O|

two mirror-image configurations with a three-electron bond analogous to the bond in NO.

NO and $NO_2$ form $N_2O_3$ and each substance dimerizes with the formation of diamagnetic molecules by the pairing of the odd π electrons in all three cases (GRAY and YOFFE, 1955). $(NO_2)_2$ has a planar ethylenic-type structure with a large N-N distance of 1.64 Å (BROADLEY and ROBERTSON 1949, crystal) or 1.74 Å (SMITH and HEDBERG, 1956, gas) with resonance between different configurations of the type

|O| |O̅|⊖
N—N
⊕ ⊕
⊖|O̲| |O|

Between the nitrogen atoms a weak $\pi$-$\pi$ bond is formed (COULSON and DUCHESNE, 1957), which is further weakened under the influence of the adjacent charges; $N_2O_4$ dissociates easily ($\Delta H = +13$ kcal/mole).

Nitric oxide NO only dimerizes at low temperatures with a very weak intermolecular NO bonds (2.38 Å) of a bond character of $\frac{1}{2}$ from the configurations:

$$\begin{array}{ccc} \overline{N}=O & \quad & \overline{N}=\overline{O} \\ \quad | & & | \\ \underline{\overline{O}}=\underline{N} & & \underline{O}=\underline{\overline{N}} \end{array}$$

derived from those given above for NO (DULMAGE, MEYERS and LIPSCOMB, 1953; ORVILLE-THOMAS, 1954).

For the oxygen molecule one would expect $\overline{O}=\overline{O}$ as the valence configuration. However, it would be diamagnetic in this configuration whereas in fact $O_2$ shows a paramagnetism derived from two parallel electron spins. The first-mentioned diamagnetic states $^1\Delta$ and $^1\Sigma$ lie but little (22.6 kcal and 37.4 kcal respectively) above the paramagnetic ground state ($^3\Sigma$). PAULING gives the configuration | O⋮⋮O |; the bond length of 1.207 Å is indeed shorter than that of the corresponding ions (see below). One can regard this configuration of the $O_2$ molecule also as a transition case between HUND's rule, valid for the electrons in one atom, according to which the electron spins are set parallel as much as possible in the lowest energy state (see also p. 156), and the LEWIS-LANGMUIR rule, valid for molecules, according to which the electrons are joined in pairs as much as possible in the lowest energy state. We shall not go further into the question why this solitary transition case appears just in oxygen (COULSON, book, p. 99).

The so-called tetroxides, such as $K_2O_4$, are in reality salts with the hyperoxide ion $O_2^-$ [O⋮—O] with a bond length of 1.28 Å; this ion is paramagnetic, similar to NO. The peroxide ion $O_2^{2-}$ has a normal valence configuration: | $\overline{\underline{O}}$—$\overline{\underline{O}}$ |, with a bond length of 1.49 Å (ABRAHAMS *et al.*, 1954, 1955).

The structure of ozone was uncertain for a long time but it has now definitely been established that the bond length is 1.278 Å and that the bond angle is 116°45′; ozone has a small dipole moment of 0.58 D (SHAND and SPURR, 1943; WILSON and BADGER, 1948; HUGHES, 1952, 1953, 1956). The following four configurations contribute and consequently the O—O distance lies between those of a single and of a double bond (1.46 Å and 1.10 Å).

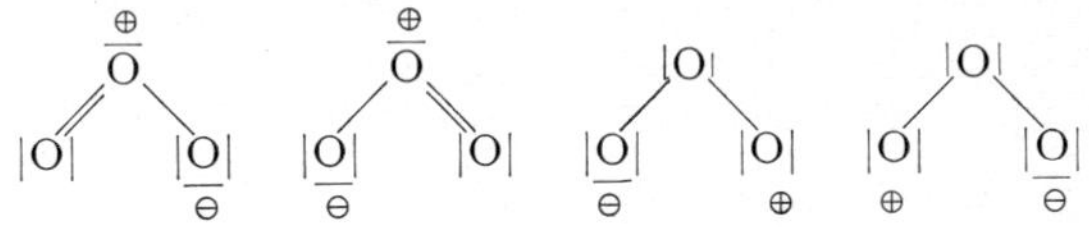

*Boron hydrides*

The boron hydrides form a remarkable group of compounds. (BELL and EMELÉUS, 1948; LIPSCOMB, 1954, 1957; PLATT, 1954a; STONE, 1954; RUNDLE, 1957; MOORE, DICKERSON and LIPSCOMB, 1957; LONGUET-HIGGINS, 1958). A simple compound $BH_3$, does not exist. The electropositivity is too small for a salt-like boride $B^{3+}H_3^-$, while a sextet configuration would be produced with electron pair bonds. An octet configuration is possible for $BH_4^-$; in fact the salts $Li[BH_4]$ and $Na[BH_4]$ do exist; they have a lattice similar to NaCl. The well-known $LiAlH_4$, lithium-aluminohydride is also very similar.

In the very stable compounds like $BH_3.CO$ and $BH_3.N(CH_3)_2$ the boron sextet has been completed with the lone pairs of electrons from the other components. Also $B(CH_3)_3$, though it does exist as such, contrary to $BH_3$, readily adds compounds with lone pairs such as $NH_3$. This also occurs with the boron halides, especially with $BF_3$, *e.g.*, $BF_3.NH_3$ (p. 176). An octet can also be attained in other halides by resonance with configurations such as

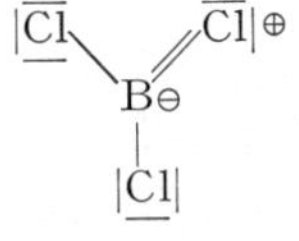

The contribution of these configurations appears from the shortened bond length (1.75 A). However, a sextet configuration on the borium atom will give rise to less repulsion between pairs of bonding electrons, and thus also a shortening of the bond length will result.

In the action of acids on magnesium boride a large number

of complex boron hydrides are produced, in the first place $B_2H_6$ and further $B_4H_{10}$, $B_5H_9$, $B_5H_{11}$, $B_6H_{10}$ and $B_{10}H_{14}$. Many suggestions have been made regarding the constitution of $B_2H_6$, diborane. The principal difficulty arises from the fact that there are less electrons available than are necessary to fill the orbitals on the atoms (electron-deficient compounds). This situation bears some resemblance to that existing in metals, *e.g.*, in the alkali metals, where the number of atomic orbitals is twice the number of electrons.

Originally it was concluded from results of electron diffraction that the structure of $B_2H_6$ ought to be similar to ethane, but with abnormally large B—H (1.27 Å) and B—B distances (1.86 Å instead of 1.76 Å). It was assumed that one-electron bonds (as in $H_2^+$) contribute through resonance between the various configurations such as:

```
     H   H                  H   H
     ..  ..                 ..  .
 H : B : B · H   and   H : B · B : H    etc.
     .   ..                 ..  ..
     H   H                  H   H
```

A true double bond, as previously postulated by WIBERG, is excluded in any case.

```
      H\         /H
  H+    B  =  B     H+
      H/         \H
```

Nevertheless, the correspondence of diborane with ethylene was found from extensive investigations on the infra-red absorption spectrum and the RAMAN spectrum to be greater than the correspondence with ethane. There is also a correspondence in the RAMAN spectrum with $Al_2Cl_6$ which is built up of two tetrahedra with a common edge.

The structure of $B_2H_6$ now generally accepted is a bridge structure (DILTHEY, SYRKIN and DYATKINA, LONGUET-HIGGINS and BELL).

```
 H\    ,H.    /H
    B       B
 H/    `H'    \H
```

The quadrilateral indicated by dotted lines lies in one plane, while the four outer B—H bonds form a plane perpendicular to the first one, analogous to the structure of $Al_2Cl_6$.

A new interpretation of the electron diffraction results (HEDBERG and SCHOMAKER, 1951) is compatible with the structure with a B—B distance of 1.770 Å. This structure has two groups of B—H distances of 1.187 Å and 1.334 Å; this is in agreement with the special bonds in the bridge.

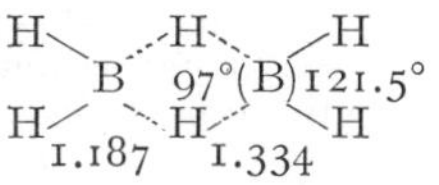

H H H
B 97° B 121.5°
H H H
1.187 1.334

Two hydrogen atoms also appear to be in a special position since it is only possible to introduce four methyl groups to form $B_2H_2(CH_3)_4$. The sodium compound $Na_2[B_2H_6]$ would indeed contain an anion with a normal ethane structure; however, its existence is doubtful. The salt-like ammonia compound $2NH_3.B_2H_6$ is different and has the structure $NH_4^+$ $[BH_3—NH_2—BH_3]^-$ or $BH_4^-[H_2B(NH_3)_2]^+$ (SCHULTZ and PARRY, 1958).

The bonds, indicated by the dotted lines in the bridge structure of $B_2H_6$, are of a special kind. Here we have a bond which could be regarded as a resonance between

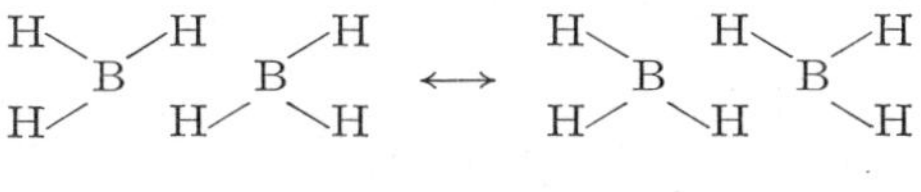

H H H H H H
B B ⟷ B B
H H H H H H

Also it has been thought (SYRKIN and DYATKINA) that ionic configurations would contribute

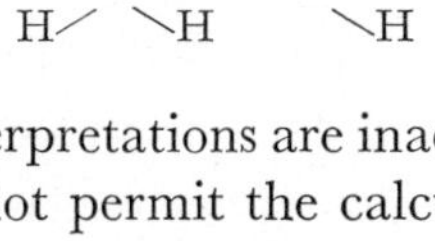

H ⊖ H ⊕ H
B B
H H H

However, these interpretations are inadequate as it has been shown that they do not permit the calculation of a sufficient stability for the molecule of $B_2H_6$.

PITZER suggested a "protonated double bond"

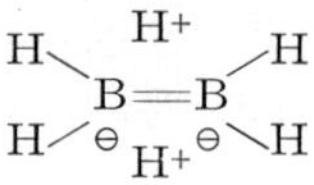

$$\begin{array}{ccc} H\diagdown & H^+ & \diagup H \\ & B{=}B & \\ H\diagup^{\ominus} & H^+ & {}^{\ominus}\diagdown H \end{array}$$

However, it is incorrect to think of a real double bond because of the large B—B distance observed; moreover, $B_2H_6$ does not have the acidic properties which would result from the presence of the two protons.

There is a strong similarity between this picture of the protonated double bond and the conception of the bonding of silver ions to an olefin in complexes such as $AgClO_4$–cyclohexene, –benzene, etc.; the silver ion is embedded in the charge cloud of the $\pi$ electrons in the centre above the plane of RCH = CHR ($\pi$-bond) (WINSTEIN and LUCAS, 1938; ANDREW and KEEFER, 1949, RUNDLE and GORING, 1950).

However, it is more correct to look upon the two bonds in the bridge as two three-center molecular orbitals (p. 291) to each of which belong two electrons (LONGUET-HIGGINS, 1949b). The electrons are non-localized just as *e.g.*, the $\pi$-electrons in benzene. In metals we also have orbitals which embrace many atoms. These molecular orbitals are compounded from tetrahedral $sp^3$ hybridized orbitals at the boron atoms and a 1s orbital at the hydrogen atom in the bridge.

Other electron-deficient compounds (RUNDLE, 1957; LONGUET-HIGGINS, 1949b, 1958) with bridge structures are, *e.g.* $Al(BH_4)_3$, $Ca(CH_3)_2BH_4$, $Be(BH_4)_2$, with the structures:

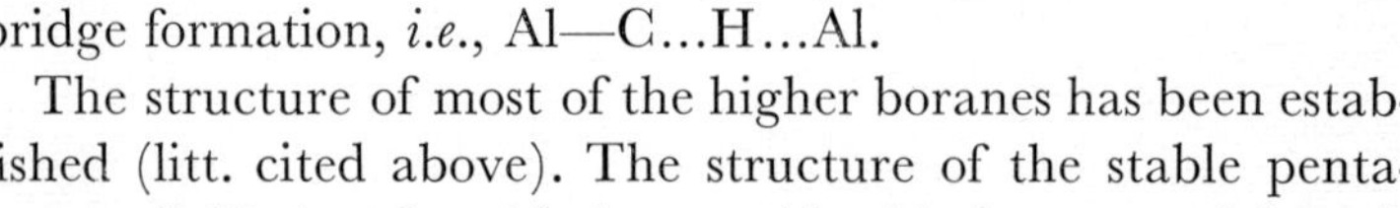

$$Al\left[\begin{array}{c} H\cdots\ \ \diagup H \\ B \\ H\cdots\ \ \diagdown H \end{array}\right]_3 \qquad \begin{array}{c} H\diagdown\ \ \cdots H\cdots\ \ \diagup CH_3 \\ B\qquad Ga \\ H\diagup\ \ \cdots H\cdots\ \ \diagdown CH_3 \end{array} \qquad \begin{array}{c} H\diagdown\ \ \cdots H\cdots\ \ \cdots H\cdots\ \ \diagup H \\ B\qquad Be\qquad B \\ H\diagup\ \ \cdots H\cdots\ \ \cdots H\cdots\ \ \diagdown H \end{array}$$

The constitution of the dimeric form of aluminium trimethyl $[Al(CH_3)_3]_2$ presents a new problem. Here the hydrogen atoms of the methyl groups might be involved in bridge formation, *i.e.*, Al—C...H...Al.

The structure of most of the higher boranes has been established (litt. cited above). The structure of the stable pentaborane $B_5H_9$ is a foursided pyramid with five normal (terminal) B—H bonds (1.22 Å) and four bridge hydrogen atoms B...H...B (1.35 Å) between the boron atoms in the basal plane at a distance of 1.80 Å. The four B—B distances to the boron atom at the top are 1.69 Å. These four B—B bonds are formed by only six electrons in three many-center molecular orbitals. In the related structure of the unstable pentaborane $B_5H_{11}$ one of the B...H...B bridges in the $B_5H_9$ structure is broken and these two boron atoms, and also the boron atom at the top, now each carry two normal B—H bonds.

In $B_4H_{10}$ there are two triangles with a common base (B—B: 1.75 Å) and four B...H...B sides (B—B: 1.85 Å, B—H: 1.33 and 1.43 Å); the six normal terminal B—H bonds are 1.19 Å.

For the very stable $B_{10}H_{14}$ a structure has been found with two five-sided regular pyramids with a common edge. There are ten normal B—H bonds (1.25 Å) and four B...H...B bridges (B—H 1.34 and 1.42 Å); the 19 B—B distances are 1.76 Å (KASPAR, LUCHT and HARKER, 1950; LUCHT, 1951). In $B_6H_{10}$ the boron atoms are arranged in a regular five-sided pyramid (HIRSHFELD *et al.*, 1958).

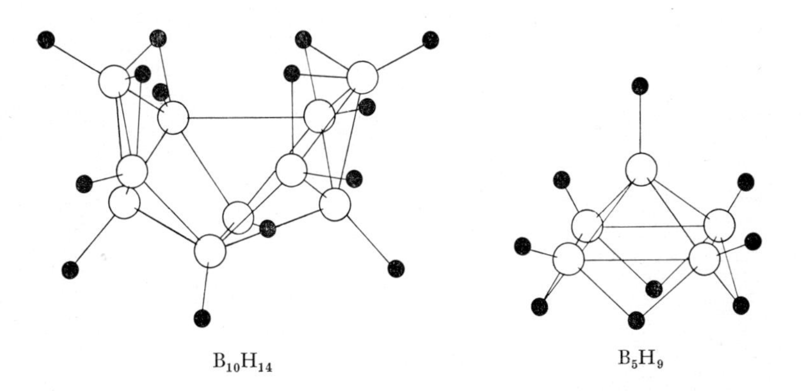

$B_{10}H_{14}$ $B_5H_9$

The stable borazole or triborine-triamine $B_3N_3H_6$ is completely analogous to and iso-electronic with benzene. These two compounds have the same structure, stability, mesomerism and even the same smell. Derivatives analogous to *symm.* trichlorobenzene and *meta*dibromobenzene are also known.

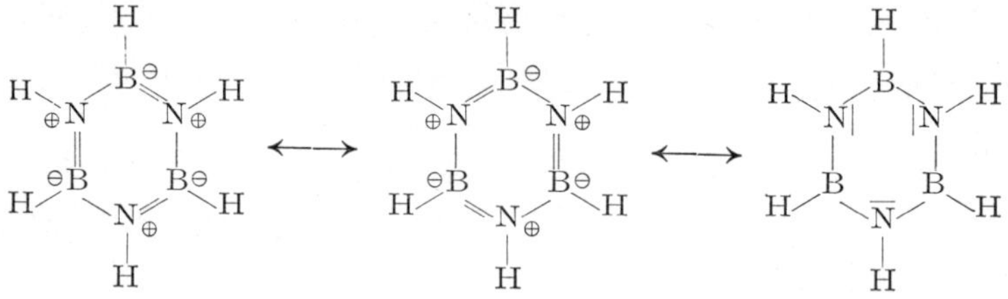

However, owing to the unfavourable charge distribution (nitrogen is more electronegative than boron), the single-bonded structure must also contribute. The observed B—N distance is 1.44 Å (B—N: 1.58 Å, B=N: 1.36 Å). Boroxol $(BO)_3$ is unknown, but $(Cl.BO)_3$ has been prepared. The derivative $(CH_3.BO)_3$ is analogous to paraldehyde $(CH_3.CHO)_3$, and has a flat six-membered ring of BO links with resonance [BO obs. 1.39 Å, calc. B—O 1.54 Å, B=O 1.31 Å]. Boron nitride, BN, has about the same crystal structure as graphite; the B—N distance is 1.45 Å so that the difference between borazol and BN is smaller than between benzene (1.39 Å) and graphite (1.42 Å).

As another inorganic analogue of benzene reference may be made to the constitution of the polymeric phosphorus nitrile chlorides $P_3N_3Cl_3$ and $P_4N_4Cl_8$, in which the PN bonds in the ring also appear to be equivalent (Ketelaar and De Vries, 1939; Brockway and Bright, 1943; also Audrieth *et al.*, 1943; Scott and Audrieth, 1954; Klement and Koch, 1954; Craig and Paddock, 1958). The stability of the ring is particularly striking. This ring is, however, not flat!

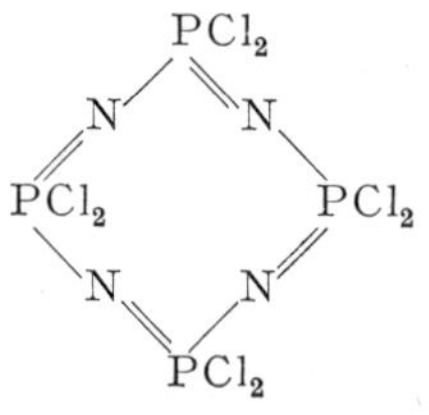

*Cyclo-octatetraene.* The question of the constitution of cyclo-octatetraene $C_8H_8$ is interesting. Although it had already been obtained by WILLSTÄTTER in 1911 in a not quite pure state, this compound has only recently become available for further investigation through its direct synthesis from acetylene (REPPE). It is a yellow-coloured liquid, M.P.—4.7° C, B.P. 142–145° C. The spatial structure has now been rather well established (KARLE, 1952; LIPPINCOTT, LORD and MCDONALD, 1951; PERSON, PIMENTEL and PITZER, 1952; BASTIANSEN, HEDBERG and HEDBERG, 1957). A non-planar structure was found with alternating single and double bonds of length, 1.462 Å and 1.334 Å respectively, and with a bond angle C=C—C of 126.5°. A tub or cradle model with rhombic symmetry ($D_{2d}$) is to be preferred to a crown model with fourfold symmetry. The resonance energy is small, only 4–6 kcal (Table 19), which approaches the R.E. for twice a pair of conjugated double bonds in an open chain. Cyclo-octatraene is about 35 kcal less stable than the isomeric styrene.

In various reactions (ozonolysis, WIBAUT and SIXMA, 1954) it reacts with the formation of a six-membered ring; this may be due to an important contribution of a "DEWAR" configuration below to the active state (compare anthracene, p. 224).

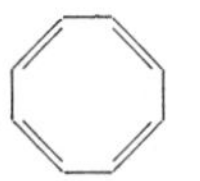

## § 33. FREE RADICALS*

The cause of the ready dissociation of, for example, hexaphenylethane into triphenylmethyl radicals forms an interesting problem. A solution of this substance is dissociated to a considerable extent; the dissociation energy is 11 kcal (Table 18b, p. 205).

However, the dissociation energies of the $C_3$—H bond in propene-1 and the $C_4$—$C_3$ bond in butene-1 are also particularly low (Table 18b; SCHMIDT's rule).

* *Gen. Disc. Faraday Soc.*, No. 3 (1947); COULSON, 1947a; MOFFITT and COULSON, 1948a; WATERS, 1948; STEACIE, 1954; WALLING, 1957; INGRAM, 1958.

In these two cases, the heat of combustion and spectra, show that there is nothing special about the bonds themselves. The low dissociation energy must, therefore, be due to the special stability of the products of dissociation, in these cases the allyl radical. The particular stability of this radical results from the resonance between two equivalent configurations.

$$H_2C{=}CH{-}\dot{C}H_2 \longleftrightarrow H_2\dot{C}{-}CH{=}CH_2$$

The reactivity of the $\alpha$-methylene group in olefins is directly connected with this resonance. According to Table 18 B the same consideration holds for the energy of dissociation of the aliphatic C—H bond in toluene and the C—C bond in diphenylethane whereby the benzyl radical is produced. Not less than five configurations are possible for this radical, although the last three represent a somewhat higher energy. The double-bond character of the C—C bond outside the ring is of the same order as that of the other bonds, according to COULSON's calculations.

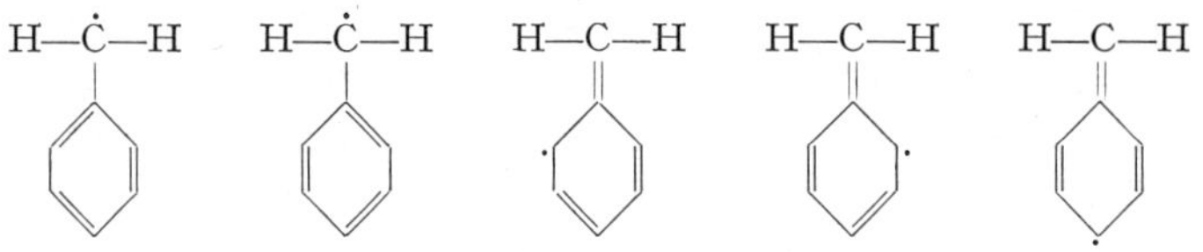

H—Ċ—H H—Ċ—H H—C—H H—C—H H—C—H

benzyl or phenylmethyl radical

Still more configurations can be given for the triphenylmethyl radical, since the unpaired electron can be found in all three of the phenyl groups at the *ortho* and *para* positions. However, paramagnetic resonance measurements seem to indicate that the unpaired electron has a small probability of being on any of the carbon atoms other than the central carbon atom (WEISSMAN and SOWDEN, 1953).

It is clear that the triphenylmethyl radical will possess a high electron affinity (48 kcal) and will also react readily with molecules such as oxygen which contain unpaired electrons.

The radical cannot be completely flat owing to the interaction of the hydrogen atoms in the *ortho* positions, although this would indeed be most favourable for the resonance. Perhaps however the C—C distance is increased.

The heat of dissociation is further lowered when the phenyl groups are replaced by diphenyl and naphthyl groups with still more configurations. Hexa *p*-nitrophenylethane is also wholly dissociated. In this case, configurations such as the following can occur:

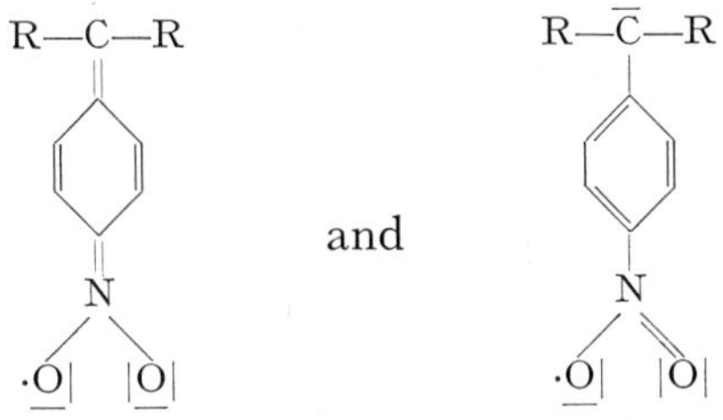

R—C—R and R—C̄—R

N N

·O| |O| ·O| |O|

The radical which is produced by the removal of a hydrogen atom, is actually the stable form in the case of α, α′-diphenyl-β-picryl-hydrazine (DPPH).

Previously the dissociation of hexaphenylethane had been attributed to a "Valenzbeanspruchung" or a steric strain but tri- and tetraphenylmethane are, however, very stable substances.

It is impossible to explain the low heats of dissociation exclusively by steric effects. However, this does play a certain part (about 30 kcal) in producing the extraordinary lowering of the heat of dissociation of the C—C bond from about 80 kcal in ethane to 11.5 kcal in hexaphenyl-ethane. Coops (Coops *et al.*, 1946, 1953) has compared the heats of combustion with that of toluene and shown that a weakening of the ethane bond itself probably occurs to the extent: $CPh_3$—$CHPh_2$: 25.8 kcal, $CPh_3$—$C_2H_2Ph$: 9.4 kcal, $CPh_3$—$CH_3$: 7.9 kcal and $CHPh_2$—$CHPh_2$: 5.3 kcal. The influence of the steric factor also appears from the fact that tetraphenylethane does not dissociate but tetraphenyl di-*t*-butylethane and tetramesitylethane do.

There is still no noticeable weakening of the C—C bond in diphenylethane or dibenzyl; on the contrary, this central C—C distance is 1.48 Å (normal value 1.54 Å); in hexamethylethane a weakening does perhaps appear (C—C: 1.58 Å), probably as a consequence of steric influences; however, the heat of combustion has a normal value.

A possible biradical is TSCHITSCHIBABIN's hydrocarbon:

$$Ph_2\dot{C}-C_6H_4-C_6H_4-\dot{C}Ph_2 \longleftrightarrow Ph_2C{=}C_6H_4{=}C_6H_4{=}CPh_2$$

However, in the ground state the two free electrons are paired in agreement with condition 1. (p. 211), so that the substance in this state is diamagnetic and is a pseudobiradical. The only weak coupling is, however, seen from the circumstance that this substance does actually catalyse the reaction *para* $H_2 \rightarrow$ *ortho* $H_2$ (p. 154) to some extent. The paramagnetic triplet-state with parallel spins has an energy of 2.5 kcal above the singlet ground state; thus at room temperature only 4.5% of the molecules are in the former, biradical, state (HUTCHINSON, KOWALSKY, PASTOR and WHELAND, 1952).

If we substitute in TSCHITSCHIBABIN's hydrocarbon four chlorine atoms in the *ortho* positions with respect to the middle bond, then a plane structure is no longer possible and the substance is paramagnetic due to the absence of coupling. Here a true biradical is realized through the effect of isolation.

SCHLENCK's hydrocarbon is a true biradical in which no quinoid configuration is possible; the triplet state with a spin moment of $S = 1$ is the stable state (SCHWAB and BÄUMEL, 1957).

$$(Ph)_2\dot{C}-C_6H_4-C_6H_4-\dot{C}(Ph)_2 \quad (meta,meta')$$

Pentacene with 5 aromatic rings has still stronger than anthracene (p. 224) the character of a (pseudo-) biradical with free valencies at the two innermost carbon atoms, but again with opposite orientation of the electron spins.

SZWARC discovered the production of *p*-quinodimethane in the pyrolytic decomposition of *para*-xylene; this product can also be formulated as a biradical:

$$H_2C{=}\langle\!\!=\!\!\rangle{=}CH_2 \quad \text{or} \quad H_2\dot{C}{-}\langle\!\!=\!\!\rangle{-}\dot{C}H_2$$

However, the electrons also have opposite spins in the ground state (singlet state).

In the alkyl radicals the stability increases a little in the series $CH_3$, $C_2H_5$, *n*–$C_3H_7$, *sec.*–$C_3H_7$ and *tert.*–$C_4H_9$ as the energy of dissociation of the hydrogen atom from the parent hydrocarbon decreases from 101 kcal to 86 kcal (SZWARC, 1950).

## § 34. THEORY OF COLOUR

The relation between colour and chemical constitution has given rise to much experimental and theoretical work. The colour of a substance, *i.e.*, of dyes and pigments, appears to us in transmitted or incident light and is therefore complementary to the colour of the absorption band (Table 21). Light is absorbed with a wave length such that its elementary quantum $h\nu$ corresponds to the energy difference $E_1$—$E_0$ between the ground level and one of the excited states of the electron system of the molecule. A theory of colour must therefore embrace an investigation of the system of energy levels con-

TABLE 21

ABSORPTION REGION AND COLOUR

| Wave length | Colour abs. band | Compl. colour | Wave length | Colour abs. band | Compl. colour |
|---|---|---|---|---|---|
| 4000–4350 Å | violet | yellow green | 5600–5800 Å | yellow green | violet |
| 4350–4800 | blue | yellow | 5800–5950 | yellow | blue |
| 4800–4900 | green blue | orange | 5950–6050 | orange | green blue |
| 4900–5000 | blue green | red | 6050–7500 | red | blue green |
| 5000–5600 | green | purple | | | |

nected with the various electron configurations of the molecule.

Witt's older theory bore a purely phenomenological character. Chromophors or colour-carriers were distinguished, usually "unsaturated" groups such as C=C, the azo group N=N, the quinoid group =⟨ ⟩=, the $NO_2$ group, etc.

In addition auxochromic groups were recognized; these deepened the intensity of the colour and at the same time changed its hue. A bathochromic effect of the group represented a displacement of the absorption band towards longer wavelengths; the opposite is called a hypsochromic effect. The colour itself is displaced in the first case from yellow via red, purple to violet, blue and finally green (see Table 21). The auxochromic groups included the $NH_2$, $N(CH_3)_2$, OH, $OCH_3$ and COOH groups. However, this theory does not give any real explanation of the observed effects and also leads to contradictions and ambiguities.

The wave-mechanical theory of resonance has now contributed an important insight into the problem (Pauling, 1939; Brooker, 1942, 1945; Maccoll, 1947; Ferguson, 1948; Wahl, 1948). For a molecule with one single valence configuration only, *e.g.*, the saturated hydrocarbons, the first excited state lies at such high energy values that the light absorption occurs in the far ultraviolet part of the spectrum (< 1500 Å). These substances are therefore colourless, irrespective of the size of the molecule.

Other molecules which contain exclusively single bonds but also atoms with free pairs (in particular oxygen, fluorine or nitrogen) similarly absorb only at wave lengths shorter than 2000 Å (water: 1860 Å; ether: 1900 Å; ammonia: 1900 Å). Chlorine, bromine and iodine bound to carbon displace the absorption to longer wave lengths (R—Cl: < 2000 Å; R—Br: 2100 Å; R—I: 2600 Å). A further bathochromic displacement takes place when more halogen atoms are substituted on one carbon atom ($CH_2Br_2$: 2300 Å; $CH_3I$: 2575 Å; $CH_2I_2$: 3000 Å; $CHI_3$: 3490 Å).

One double bond or isolated C=C bonds also give rise to absorption only at wave lengths shorter than 2000 Å. However, the carbonyl group $R_2C=\overline{O}$ has a weak absorption band at a much longer wavelength of 2900 Å. This transition is of a different type (N→A) in which an electron of a lone-pair is promoted. The much more intense transition of the double bond (N→V) is found here at 1600 Å where a $\pi$ electron of the double bond is excited (p. 297). For the azo group (R—$\overline{N}$=$\overline{N}$—R) the weak N→A band is at 3470 Å, but the N→V transition is at much shorter wavelengths.

Displacement of the absorption to appreciably longer wave lengths takes place only if conjugation occurs. When the absorption region has reached the wave lengths of the visible region, coloured substances are produced. Thus the occurrence of colour is very closely associated with the resonance between more than one electron configuration.

The conjugation of two carbonyl groups, as in glyoxal and in dimethylglyoxal or diacetyl (N→A 4200 Å), already gives rise to yellow-coloured substances; glyoxal is the simplest

TABLE 22A

ABSORPTION OF POLYENES AND DIPHENYLPOLYENES
Ph—(CH=CH—)$_n$Ph

| Number of C=C groups | Compound | λ max. | | |
|---|---|---|---|---|
| | | polyenes | diphenylpolyenes | |
| | | | obs. | calc.† |
| 0 | — | — | 2415 Å | (2300 Å) |
| 1 | Ethylene | 1650 Å | 3190 | 3170 |
| 2 | Butadiene | 2100 | 3520 | 3530 |
| 3 | Hexatriene | 2500 | 3770 | 3810 |
| 4 | Octatetraene | 3000 | 4040 | 4040 |
| 5 | Vitamin A | 3280 | 4240 | 4245 |
| 6 | Tetrahexadecaene | 3600 | 4450 | 4430 |
| 8 | Dihydro-β-carotene | 4200 | | |
| 10 | α-Carotene | 4450 | | |
| 11 | γ-Carotene | 4600 | | |
| 15 | Dehydro-lycopene | 5040 | | |

† $\lambda = 870\sqrt{n} + 2300$ (p. 270).; see also DRENTH, 1954.

coloured organic substance. In acrolein, $CH_2=CH-CHO$, the N→A absorption band is only shifted to 3300 A. In mesityloxide, $(CH_3)_2C=CH-CO-CH_3$, where the carbonyl group is also conjugated with the carbon double bond, this absorption band lies at 3270 Å. The N→V transitions in these

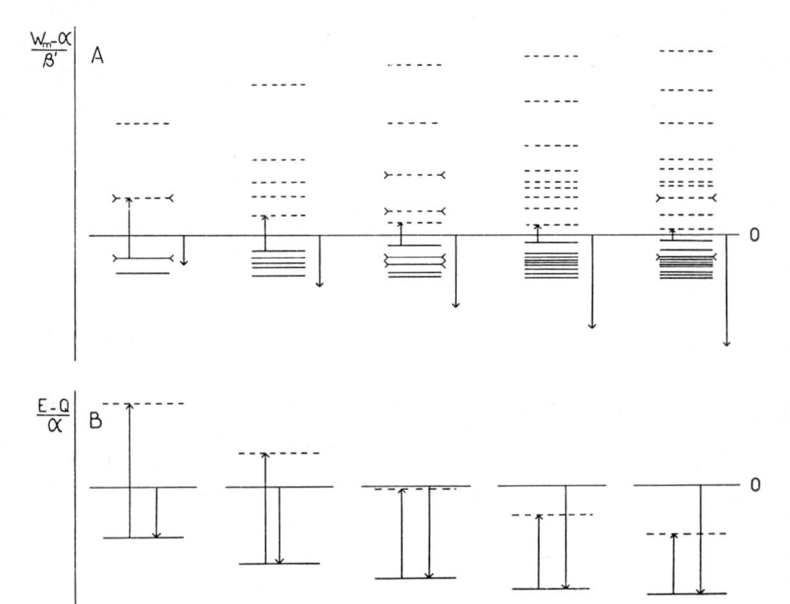


Fig. 22. Energy levels of benzene, naphthalene, anthracene, naphthacene and pentacene.

--- unoccupied levels, — occupied levels;
↑ Long wave length absorption transition;
↓ Resonance energy;
A Molecular orbital method, 1st Approximation (p. 295), >—< double degenerate levels;
B Valence bond method with only KEKULÉ configurations (p. 262, Table 22B).

three substances are also shifted to longer wave lengths; they are found at 1750, 1935 and 2150 Å respectively.

It has already been pointed out in the discussion of the hydrogen molecule ion that resonance between two configurations gives rise to the production of two energy states, one of lower and one of higher energy than that of the isolated configuration. The number of energy levels also increases with increasing number of configurations, while the average separation between the energy levels decreases (Fig. 22). Therefore, an increase of the number of possibilities of resonance for a molecule will be associated with a displacement of the first absorption band towards longer wave lengths. The substance can thus become coloured or undergo a change of colour towards the blue (bathochromic effect). Aromatic nuclei and systems of conjugated double bonds in general, including the azo group —N=N— and the carbonyl group C=O, all possess $\pi$ electrons; the introduction of these groups will increase the number of valence configurations.

On increasing the number of conjugated bonds, *e.g.*, in the series of the polyenes, diphenylpolyenes (Table 22A) and acenes (Table 22B), the number of electron configurations is increased and the maximum of the absorption band is shifted continuously towards longer wave lengths. Since the energy of the ground level decreases in this same sequence owing to the increasing resonance energy, we must conclude that the energy of the first excited level decreases still more rapidly with increasing number of $\pi$ electrons (Fig. 22).

The black graphite which absorbs over the whole visible and infrared region fits in here as the extreme case. The deep red tetraphenylnaphthacene or rubrene is also a well-known coloured hydrocarbon.

Though extension of the $\pi$ electron system in a homologous series has, in general, a bathochromic effect, there are some exceptions. In the series *para*-benzoquinone, naphtha-1,4-quinone and anthra-9,10-quinone, a hypsochromic effect is observed.

Other influences, however, also play a part. Thus the absorption band of the acenes with linear annulization is at a longer wave length than that of the corresponding phenes with angular annulization (comp. anthracene 3790 Å with phenanthrene 3535 Å; naphthacene 4750 Å with 1,2-benzanthra-

TABLE 22B

ABSORPTION AND COLOUR OF ACENES

| Substance | Absorption band | Colour | Calculated* |
|---|---|---|---|
| Benzene | 2630 Å | colourless | 2570 Å |
| Naphthalene | 3125 | colourless | 3130 |
| Anthracene | 3790 | colourless | 3870 |
| (Phenanthrene) | 3535 | colourless | 3150 |
| Naphthacene | 4750 | orange | 4720 |
| Pentacene | 5800 | violet | 5730 |
| Hexacene | ~ 6500 | green | |
| Heptacene | ~ 8300 | greenish black | |

* Calculated according to the (simplified) "Valence Bond" method with $\alpha$ = 46 kcal instead of 30—35 kcal (p. 301).

cene 3850 Å, 3,4-benzphenanthrene 3650 Å, chrysene 3600 Å, triphenylene 3500 Å).

In addition there are the groups or atoms which possess lone pairs of electrons, *e.g.*, the amino group $NH_2$, the dimethylamino group $N(CH_3)_2$ etc., and to a smaller extent the hydroxyl and methoxyl group, since the oxygen atom is more electronegative, and furthermore the halogen atoms, sulphur, etc.

As we have already seen, these lone-pairs can form part of the system of $\pi$ electrons. Thus the difference between chromophoric and auxochromic groups becomes a matter of secondary importance. Similarly the much discussed question whether a benzoid (benzene-like) or a quinoid (quinone-like) structure should be attributed to dyestuffs becomes an incorrectly chosen alternative in the light of the resonance theory. It is the possibility of resonance which is reflected in the multiplicity of the valence structure that forms the true basis for light absorption. An isolated benzoid configuration is no more a coloured substance than a quinoid structure; compare the uncoloured hydroquinone and the very weakly coloured quinone.

Thus the absorption bands of aniline (2870 Å) and of dimethylaniline (2950 Å) are displaced towards longer wave lengths compared to benzene because of the extra possibilities for resonance. These possibilities are again destroyed on the addition of a hydrogen ion in the formation of the anilinium ion (p. 234). Consequently the absorption spectrum of this ion is analogous to that of toluene (2700 Å).

Phenol also absorbs at longer wave length (2750 Å) than benzene but here on ionisation a bathochromic effect is observed (phenolate ion 2910 Å) because the possibilities for resonance are increased (p. 237).

Saturated groups such as the methyl and *t* butyl group exert a small secondary effect which is, in general, bathochromic (some exceptions in methylazulenes). This effect is caused by the electron-donating properties of the alkyl groups which are less electrophilic than hydrogen (see also p. 282). In the series methane, ethane, hexane, the absorption band shifts from 1250 Å to 1350 Å and to 1530 Å. This shift is exclusively due to differences in the resonance possibilities of the molecule in the very highly excited upper level where one electron is nearly ionized.

When the resonance is restricted, for example, when two systems of conjugated electron systems are separated by a —$CH_2$— group, then the spectrum is only the superposition of those of the separate parts (isolation effect). For example, the spectra of diphenylmethane and of dibenzyl are very similar to that of toluene (abs. band around 2700 Å). Steric hindrance of the resonance also leads to a displacement towards shorter wave lengths through this isolation effect.

*trans*-azobenzene 4500 Å (N→A), 3200 Å (N→V); *trans*-stilbene 2950 Å (p. 226)
*cis* ,, 4300 Å (N→A), 2800 Å (N→V); *cis* ,, 2750 Å

A remarkable steric influence on the spectrum has also been observed on the introduction of a *tert.* butyl group (RAMART-LUCAS). Thus $C_6H_5.C[C(CH_3)_3]=CH_2$ gives a spectrum which is the same as that of benzene in contrast to styrene $C_6H_5.CH=CH_2$, because in the first-mentioned compound the vinyl group has been forced out of the plane of the phenyl nucleus. Another example is provided by 2,6-dimethyl-N,N-dimethylaniline

(2600 Å) as compared with N,N-dimethylaniline (2950 Å). Here the *ortho* substituents produce a rotation of the N,N-dimethylamino group and thus prevent the $\pi$ electrons of the nitrogen from partaking in the resonance with the aromatic nucleus.

Other examples are found among *ortho*-substituted diphenyl derivatives. Here the spectrum of 2,4,6,2′,4′,6′-hexamethylbiphenyl or bismesityl has a spectrum comparable to that of trimethylbenzene (mesitylene) without the strong band at 2480 Å of biphenyl (O'Shaughnessy and Rodebush, 1940). The same is true for the spectra of *o,o′*-substituted biphenyl derivatives in contrast to those of *m,m′* and *p,p′*. In the *ortho*-disubstituted biphenyls the band at about 2500 Å is very weak or absent, indicating the absence of conjugation between both phenyl groups whose planes make a large angle of 70° owing to steric hindrance (Braude and Forbes, 1955; Beaven and Hall, 1956).

The nitro group is an important chromophoric group. This group itself already has two configurations; for a nitro group attached to an aromatic nucleus still further configurations can be assigned (p. 238). Nitrobenzene itself is slightly coloured; the colour is a more intense yellow in the polynitro compounds and still stronger in the (poly)nitrophenols, especially in the ionized form (*e.g.*, *p*-nitrophenol 3150 Å, *p*-nitrophenolate 4050 Å; p. 238). Because the resonance of the nitro group gives rise to (formal) positive charges at the *ortho* and *para* positions, this group can oppose the effect of other groups such as the $NH_2$ group (anti-auxochrome).

Although picric acid is already a dye, in general the dyestuffs are more complicated compounds. There are many thousands of dyes; we shall discuss only the triphenylmethane derivatives here.

Let us compare the electron configurations of triphenylmethane (abs. 2690 Å, similar to benzene) with those of triphenylmethylchloride (abs. 4250 Å) and of fuchsone dimethylammonium chloride (abs. 4810 Å), where a dimethylamino group has been introduced.

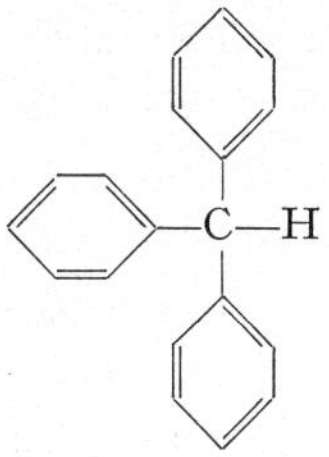

C—H triphenylmethane

There is no resonance in triphenylmethane other than that in benzene itself with the diverse KEKULÉ configurations.

C ⊕

C

⊕

⊕

C

⊕

C

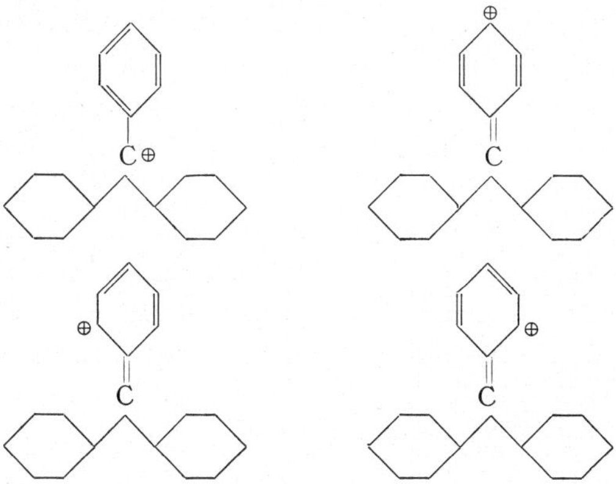

triphenylmethyl ion

In triphenylmethyl chloride, besides the KEKULÉ configurations, there are also nine configurations with the positive charge (sextet) at the *ortho* and *para* positions of the three phenyl groups.

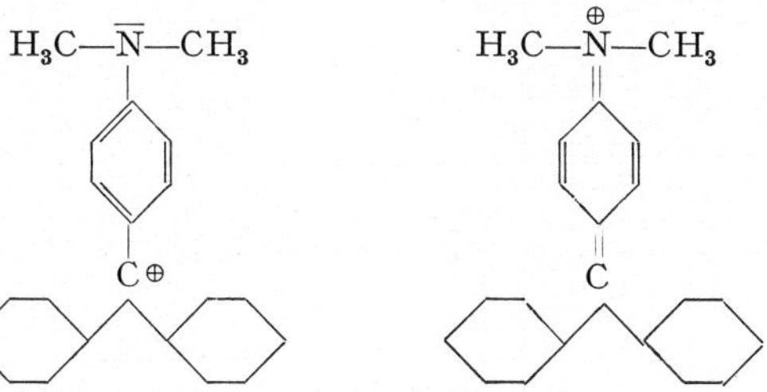

$H_3C—\overline{N}—CH_3$

C ⊕

$H_3C—\overset{\oplus}{N}—CH_3$

C

fuchsone-dimethylammonium ion

Fuchsone-dimethylammonium chloride, or fuchsonimide (yellow), has the configurations above with the positive charge on a carbon atom (carbonium configurations) and also others with a positive charge on the nitrogen atom, which has donated its lone electron pair to the general system of the $\pi$ electrons (imonium configurations). However, only octets occur and consequently these latter configurations are of particular importance because of the low energy (FÖRSTER, 1950; THEILACKER, 1951).

If now a dimethylamino group is introduced into a second phenyl nucleus in the *para* positions, still more possibilities of resonance are produced; this compound, malachite green, has an absorption maximum at 6100 Å. On the introduction of a third dimethylamino group to form crystal violet, the bathochromic effect of this group changes into a hypsochromic effect because the absorption maximum is displaced to 5900 Å. At the same time the intensity of the absorption increases. This is incomprehensible from the standpoint of the old theory. According to the resonance theory, this remarkable effect is a consequence of the high symmetry of the crystal violet ion; thus a number of levels will have the same energy value (degeneracy), although the total number of levels has actually increased. The average separation of the energy levels is increased so that the absorption band is displaced towards shorter wave lengths, while the intensity, which depends on the absorption probability, has increased proportionally with the number of corresponding levels.

$$[(CH_3)_2NC_6H_4]_2\,\overset{H}{\overset{|}{C}}-C_6H_4-N(CH_3)_2 \underset{\text{reduction}}{\overset{\text{oxidation}}{\rightleftharpoons}} [(CH_3)_2NC_6H_4]_2\,C{=}C_6H_4{=}\overset{\oplus}{N}(CH_3)_2\ [Cl^-]$$

leuco base — dye salt

leuco base $\downarrow$ oxidation; carbinol base $\nearrow$ HCl (to dye salt); dye salt $\downarrow$ KOH

$$[(CH_3)_2NC_6H_4]_2\,\overset{OH}{\overset{|}{C}}-C_6H_4-N(CH_3)_2 \underset{\text{isomerization}}{\rightleftharpoons} [(CH_3)_2NC_6H_4]_2\,C{=}C_6H_4{=}\overset{\oplus}{N}(CH_3)_2\ [OH^-]$$

carbinol base — colour base

As is well known, the dye salt itself and the true colour base are coloured, in contrast to the colourless carbinol base and the leuco base. In the latter there is no longer an electron "hole" (one electron missing from a pair of electrons) at the central carbon atom. In addition, these colourless compounds probably have a tetrahedral structure in contrast to the approximately plane structure of the ion.

Salt formation can, in general, give rise to colour (halochromy) since new possibilities of resonance can be produced by ionization. Conversely, however, the attachment of a proton to a nitrogen atom of an amino group hinders resonance since a lone, available electron pair is transformed into a bonding pair. Thus on the addition of a mineral acid to a solution of crystal violet a reversible colour change is produced via green to yellow; the resonance systems of malachite green and of fuchsonimide are successively reached by the effective elimination of one and two dimethylamino groups, respectively. The introduction of a nitro group also has a similar antiauxochromic action.

The semiquinones, *e.g.*, Wurster's red and quinhydrone, form a remarkable class of intensely coloured compounds. There is no question of a molecular compound between one molecule of *as*-dimethyl-*p*-phenylenediamine (I) and one molecule of the completely oxidized (by two Br atoms) form, the dimethylquinone diimonium salt (II). Wurster's red is a true monomeric semiquinone resonating between two electron configurations; hence the colour.

$$\text{I} \xrightarrow{\text{oxidation}} \left[\ldots \longleftrightarrow \ldots\right]^{+} \xrightarrow[\text{[Br}^-]]{\text{oxidation}} \left[\ldots\right]^{2+} [Br^-]_2$$

I Wurster's red II

Like the free radicals the semiquinone is also paramagnetic because of the presence of an unpaired electron. For quinhydrone we have:

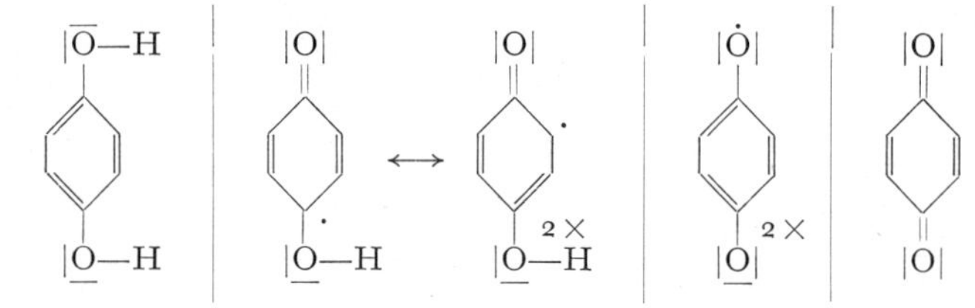

hydroquinone quinhydrone ion quinone

In alkaline solution, the semiquinoid ion is further stabilized by the resonance between two benzoid configurations with the odd electron on one of the two oxygen atoms.

Quinhydrone itself is apparently polymerized in the solid state since it is diamagnetic.

The substances from the tetrapyrrole class are remarkable because of the very deep colour and the extreme stability to chemical and physical agents; both factors naturally go together according to the resonance theory. This class includes the coloured constituent of the blood (haemin) and of plants (chlorophyll), both derivatives of porphyrin and also the artificial pigments discovered by LINSTEAD, the phthalocyanines. The four pyrrole nuclei of the latter compound are joined by four nitrogen atoms instead of four CH groups as in porphyrin. Here we have a very extensive system of continuous conjugated double bonds which is responsible for the colour.

Just as the symmetry of benzene does not follow from one KEKULÉ formula, the particular formula given in Fig. 22 does not indicate that:

1. the metal atom is bound equivalently to all four of the nitrogen atoms;

2. both the sixteen C—N bonds in the large ring and the eight C—C bonds joining the ring with the benzene nuclei are equivalent. The crystal structure analysis (ROBERTSON and WOODWARD, 1937, 1940) has, however, proved this convinc-

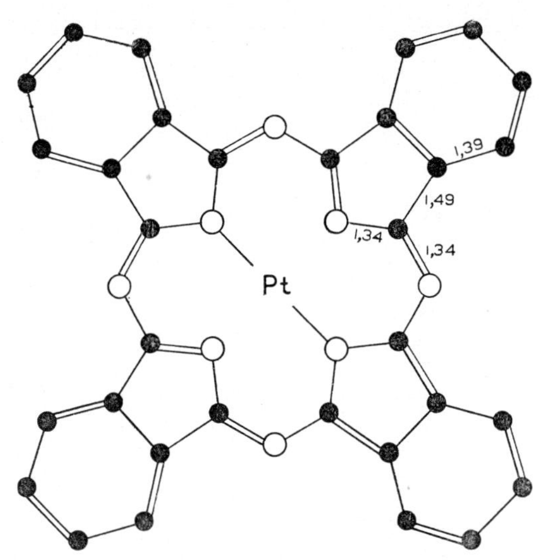


Fig. 23. The molecule of phthalocyanine (platinum complex) according to ROBERTSON (○ = nitrogen atom, ● = carbon atom).

ingly. They found for the C—N bonds 1.34 Å (C—N: 1.47 Å; C=N: 1.28 Å) and for the C—C bonds 1.49 Å (C—C: 1.54 Å; C=C: 1.34 Å). The C—N bond can be expected to possess roughly $^6/_{16}$ = 37.5% double-bond character, the C—C $^2/_8$ = 25%, which agrees approximately with the values of 44% and 10% calculated from the observed distances. The benzene nuclei have the same constitution as in the free molecule.

The absorption bands in the ultraviolet and visible part of the spectrum correspond to changes in the energy of the electrons but simultaneously in the vibrational and rotational energy of the molecule. In this way a system of bands is produced in the gaseous state. In the liquid state there is nothing of the rotational fine structure to be seen, and usually little or nothing of the vibrational structure, as a result of the interaction with the molecules of the solvent. With aromatic compounds in non-polar solvents such as hexane and carbon tetrachloride the vibrational structure is, however, still clearly visible in the ultraviolet absorption spectrum. This vibrational structure is mainly determined by the vibrations of the excited state, which therefore do not occur in the infrared and Raman spectrum of the normal molecule.

Many attempts have already been made to arrive at a quantitative interpretation of the position of the ultraviolet and visible absorption bands.

Purely empirical relations (CLAR, 1952) can indeed be of practical interest for the establishment of the constitution but to obtain a definite insight into the problem a theoretical foundation is necessary.

In his first publications HÜCKEL has already pointed out the possibility of the calculation of the transition frequencies from the calculated energy levels. An objection to this was, however, that in the so-called zeroth approximation (p. 293) the value of the parameters chosen, both in the "valence bond" and in the "molecular orbital" method, had to be quite different in order to calculate either the resonance energy or the transition frequencies in agreement with observation (FÖRSTER, 1940; HERZFELD and SKLAR, 1942).

Indeed in this way there appears to be a fair correlation between the calculated transition frequencies and the observed frequencies of the longest wave absorption bands, for example in the benzene-pentacene series (Table 22B) and in the diphenylpolyenes (DRENTH, 1954).

Agreement can, however, be reached for benzene, with continued improvements in the calculations (VAN DRANEN and KETELAAR, 1949, 1950; ROOTHAAN and PARR, 1949); we cannot, however, deal with this more fully (p. 297).

Another path is taken by introducing a simple model for the common $\pi$ electrons in a conjugated system. These are partially quasi-classical models. Thus LEWIS and CALVIN (LEWIS and CALVIN, 1939) regard a polyene consisting of $n$ conjugated double bonds as a series of coupled oscillators. For each separate oscillator we have: $\nu = \frac{1}{2\pi}\sqrt{f/m}$, in which $f$ is the force constant, $m$ the effective mass.

For $n$ coupled oscillators the lowest frequency produced is: $\nu = \frac{1}{2\pi}\sqrt{f/nm}$, Thus they obtain for the change in the wave length of the absorption band on increasing the length of the chain: $\lambda = k\sqrt{n}$. HENRICI's model of a vibrating electron cloud leads to similar results (HENRICI, 1940). Another small constant $k_2$ must be added (so-called end-group effect), for example $\lambda = k_1\sqrt{n}+k_2$ or also $\lambda^2 = k_1'n + k_2'$.

Such formulae reproduce very well the position of the absorption bands in the polyenes and in the diphenylpolyenes $C_6H_5(—CH=CH)_n—C_6H_5$ (Table 22A).

Such a $\sqrt{n}$ law is not always found. In the ions of the cyanine dyes it is assumed that there is a uniform electron distribution in the polyene chain through the equal contributions of the two configurations:

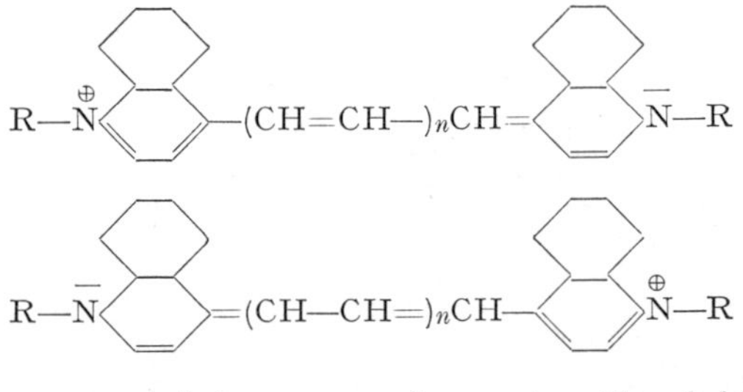

$$R—\overset{\oplus}{N}\langle\ \rangle—(CH=CH—)_nCH=\langle\ \rangle\overline{N}—R$$

$$R—\overline{N}\langle\ \rangle=(CH—CH=)_nCH—\langle\ \rangle\overset{\oplus}{N}—R$$

This homogeneous chain is now equated to a string of length $l$ for which we have $\nu \propto 1/l$ or $\nu = k/n$; $\lambda = kn$. In these dyes the position of the first absorption band is in fact proportional to the length of the polyene chain.

*Free electron model* (KUHN, 1948; SIMPSON, 1948; BAYLISS, 1948, 1952; PLATT, 1949).

Further insight is obtained by employing a simplified model but applying wave-mechanical calculations to it. Such a model is O. SCHMIDT's "Kasten" ("Box") model in which the $\pi$ electrons are treated as being in a box, the dimensions of which vary with the size of the molecule (that is to say, of the region over which the electrons are spread, thus without saturated end and side groups (SCHMIDT, 1938, 1939, 1940; PLATT, 1953, 1954b; even earlier PAULING, 1936; LONSDALE, 1937, in connection with the diamagnetism, p. 211).

For a linear system such as that in the ion of the carbocyanines already mentioned, a very simple model gives interesting results according to H. KUHN. This model is the one-dimensional simplest metal model discussed in § 37.

The general formula for the energy of the levels is (p. 322):

$$W_k = V_0 + \frac{h^2 k^2}{8\, m\, L^2}$$

in which $L$ is the length and $k$ the quantum number with the values, 1, 2 . . . Each level, beginning with the lowest, will be occupied each time by two electrons.

If there are $N$ $\pi$-electrons then the level $k = N/2$ is the highest filled level and $k = N/2 + 1$ the lowest empty level. In the absorption band of longest wave length, an electron goes from the former into the latter band.

$$\Delta E = h\nu_{\text{abs}} = \frac{h^2}{8\, m\, L^2}\left[(N/2 + 1)^2 - (N/2)^2\right] = \frac{h^2}{8\, m\, L^2}(N + 1)$$

Now in these carbocyanines each carbon atom contributes one, the two nitrogen atoms (one at both ends) together three $\pi$ electrons. If there are $Z$ atoms in the chain with $Z = 2n + 9$ for the above chemical formula, then there are $N = Z + 1$ electrons and the length $L$ has to be put equal to $l \cdot (Z + 1)$ where $l$ is the average separation and $2l$ has to be added for the extension of the $\pi$-electron chain beyond the terminal atoms ($l = 1.39$ Å). Thus $L = l \cdot N$ or

$$\Delta E = \frac{h^2}{8\, ml^2} \cdot \frac{N + 1}{N^2} \quad \text{or} \quad \lambda_{\text{max}} = \frac{8\, mcl^2}{h} \frac{N^2}{N + 1}$$

| $N$ | $n$ | $\lambda_{\text{max.}}$ calc. | $\lambda_{\text{max.}}$ obs. |
|---|---|---|---|
| 10 | 0 | 5790 Å | 5900 Å |
| 12 | 1 | 7060 | 7100 |
| 14 | 2 | 8340 | 8200 |
| 16 | 3 | 9590 | 9300 |

This result differs little from the previously mentioned formula for the string since $N$ is large. This model can also be applied successfully to other molecules; the "length" is, however, sometimes chosen rather arbitrarily, while it is also often necessary to assume that the bottom of the "well", that is to say $V_0$, is not constant but, for example, lower at the positions of the more strongly electronegative nitrogen atoms.

In the pure polyenes, the configuration with double bonds displaced one position along the chain is not energetically equivalent to the normal configuration (p. 230). Here the potential for the $\pi$ electrons must be considered as a periodic function and we have to deal with disturbances such as are dealt with in § 37.

LICHTEN (LICHTEN, 1954; WHELAND, 1955, book p. 681) has discussed the removal of the difficulties of the free electron model in connection with the virial theorem (p. 138). The results of the free electron model are essentially identical with those obtained with the molecular orbital method (p. 297) (COULSON, 1953; RÜDENBERG and SCHERR, 1953).

## § 35. CHEMICAL REACTIONS*

Chemistry is on the one hand a knowledge of the chemical compounds as such; on the other hand it is a knowledge of the reactions of the substances. It has even always been the chemical reactions—the formation of other compounds on the interaction with reagents, both chemical and physical (heat etc.)—by which the substances have been characterized, that is by their so-called chemical properties. These chemical properties, however, are in fact more closely related to the activated complex (transition state) than to the molecule in its normal nonactivated state. The physico-chemical properties really characterize the normal molecule, *e.g.*, geometrical structure, thermodynamical, optical (refraction), electrical (dielectric constant and dipole moment) and magnetic properties and infrared spectral data. It is only in more recent times that these properties have become of importance for identification and for the determination of the constitution of a molecule.

Since our knowledge of the stable state is restricted, our insight into the chemical reactions themselves is extremely small. The hydrogen molecule is the only one which we know completely, and consequently the reaction $H_2$ (*para*) + H →H + $H_2$ (*ortho*) is the one about which we know the most.

The chemical reaction is characterized on the one hand by the kinetic mechanism, that is to say the dependence on the concentrations of the participants in the reaction, on the other hand by the reaction (velocity) constant. The velocity constant

* S. GLASSTONE, K. J. LAIDLER and H. EYRING, *Theory of Rate Processes*, New York, 1941. *Gen. Disc. Reaction Kinetics, Trans. Faraday Soc.*, 34 (1938) 1; *ibid.*, 37 (1941) 601, *Mechanism and Chemical Kinetics of Organic Reactions in Liquid Systems.* Simpler: K. J. LAIDLER, *Chemical Kinetics*, New York, 1950; S. GLASSTONE, *Textbook of Physical Chemistry*, 2nd Ed. p. 1087, New York, 1946, or other textbooks.

in the simplest form is $k = Ae^{-E/RT}$ in which $E$ is the energy of activation and $A$ the frequency factor. The latter is equal to $PZ$ in the classical collision theory, where $Z$ is the collision number ( $\approx 10^{11}$) and $P$ the probability factor or steric factor. This factor can be much larger than unity if the activation energy is divided over several internal degrees of freedom (monomolecular reactions) but it can also be as low as $10^{-8}$ in cases where steric hindrance plays a role.

In the theory of absolute reaction rates given by POLANYI and especially by EYRING (transition state theory), the frequency factor $A$ contains the frequency $kt/h$, instead of the collision number, and the probability factor is replaced by $e^{\Delta S/RT}$ where $\Delta S$ is the entropy of activation. This entropy includes the concept of steric hindrance, according to which the probability that partners collide in the correct way is small in certain cases.

The difficulty in obtaining a complete insight into chemical reactions lies in our ignorance regarding the active state, that is to say of the "transition state", also called the "activated complex", which occurs in the course of the reaction. The energy of the transition state lies 20—50 kcal/mole higher than the normal state; therefore the concentration ranges from $10^{-8.6}$ to $10^{-12.5}$ at 500° K. This is so small that normal methods cannot be employed to establish the structure and constitution of these active complexes.

The transition state or the activated complex in bimolecular reactions consists furthermore of two components*. Consequently changes in the structure of both parts must be considered.

The reaction mechanism is the simplest in those atomic reactions where no energy of activation occurs, as in $Na + Cl_2 \rightarrow NaCl + Cl$, and in many reactions involving free radicals. In the corresponding reactions of sodium with or-

* Because of the association the entropy of activation is always negative for bimolecular reactions (—10 to —50 cal/mole degree) with exception of reactions between oppositely charged ions ($\Delta S$ up to +30 cal/mole degree).

ganic chlorides an energy of activation is already present which is dependent on the nature of the C—Cl bond.

Thus the difference between chlorine bound to a saturated carbon atom or bound to one with multiple bonds as in ethylene and benzene derivatives (p. 233) exhibits itself in a higher energy of activation in the second case.

We have seen (p. 215) that $\varphi = C_A \varphi_A + C_B \varphi_B$ when the wave function which represents the stationary state can be regarded as composed of two wave functions corresponding to two configurations $A$ and $B$. The ratio of the coefficients $C_A$ and $C_B$ depends on the energy difference between $A$ and $B$.

If the energy of $A$ is appreciably lower than that of $B$, then for the stationary state of lowest energy we have $C_A \gg C_B$, that is to say, it is mainly the configuration $A$ which contributes to this state. There is, however, a second energy state for which $C_A \ll C_B$; this state, therefore, corresponds mainly to configuration $B$. This consideration is valid for resonance between electron configurations and these two states also appeared in the treatment of the hydrogen molecule. Besides the ground state (singlet) H $\downarrow\uparrow$ H, we have the triplet state H$\uparrow\uparrow$H in which the electrons have parallel spins and, furthermore, the ionic or polar configurations $H^+H^-$ and $H^-H^+$. The same possibilities exist in principle for every electron pair bond.

When in a chemical reaction a molecule goes over from its initial state into the transition state by the absorption of the energy of activation, the radical and polar configurations, which contribute little to the ground state, will contribute mainly to this transition (quantum-mechanically considered, stationary) state. Thus it is justifiable, in reactions of organic molecules, to consider in first approximation that these molecules frequently react in one of these unusual electron configurations (so-called limiting structures).

It is not correct, however, to suppose that the electron distribution of the stable state goes back and forth between the various *configurations* and that the molecule reacts when it is in the configuration in question.

The nature of the molecule and the nature of the other reaction partner or of the catalyst (also of the solvent) all play important roles in determining what sort of configurations predominate in the transition state.

However, there is thermodynamic equilibrium between molecules in the ground *state* and in the activated *state*; the molecules going back and forth between both states by internal energy transfer between different degrees of freedom and by energy transfer through collisions.

In the chemical reaction of a molecule $A$ with $B$, a new bond is formed. If the electron pair of this bond comes only from partner $A$, we speak of a nucleophilic (anionoid) reaction of $A$; if both partners contribute one electron we speak of a radical reaction; and if both electrons come from $B$ we speak of an electrophilic (cationoid) reaction of $A$. It is clear that an electrophilic reaction of $A$ is at the same time a nucleophilic reaction of $B$.

In the first and third type of reaction (also called heterolytic reactions), the polar configurations play the most important role, while the radical configurations are the most important in the second type (homolytic reactions). The energy of activation for the isolated molecule will be higher for heterolytic reactions than for homolytic reactions in most cases. However, the high solvation energy in (polar) solvents will make heterolytic reactions proceed in solution, but not in the gas phase.

In order to understand the mode of reaction of a molecule it will thus be necessary to investigate which will be the most stable (activated) configuration, apart from the normal configuration of the initial state. This particular configuration will provide the largest contribution to the actual transition state; the others would lead to transition states with a still higher activation energy (WHELAND, 1942; BROWN, 1952; GREENWOOD, 1952).

A quantitative theory will also take account of the energy difference between the normal state and the activated state. On the reacting atom is localized either a pair of electrons (electrophilic reaction $S_E$), a sextet (pos. charge, nucleophilic reaction $S_N$) or a single electron (radical reaction $S_R$), or a pair of electrons is localized in a certain bond (true double bond reactions). The remaining possibilities for resonance will determine mainly which of the possible activated states will have the lowest energy and thus which course the reaction will take (localization hypotheses, WHELAND, 1942; KOOYMAN and KETELAAR, 1946).

The orientation of the substituents in reactions to introduce new substituents into the benzene nucleus is a case in which we can understand the experimental results fairly well.

Most reactions such as halogenation, nitration, sulphonation, etc., are reactions with a positive ion, *i.e.*, an electrophilic reagent therefore, where the aromatic molecule reacts nucleophilically. In hydrolysis, alcoholysis and aminolysis of aryl halides, the reagents are nucleophilic. Radical reactions are also possible, especially in the gas phase at high temperatures.

In nitrobenzene the electron configurations with a positive charge on the *ortho* and *para* positions (p. 238) will result in mainly *meta*dinitrobenzene being formed on nitration with the nitronium ion $NO_2^+$ (p. 244). This reaction will proceed more slowly (deactivation) than with benzene itself because the electron density in the ring is smaller in nitrobenzene. $Br^+$ is the active reagent in bromination; this is formed by complex formation of the bromine molecule with the catalyst: $FeBr_3 + Br_2 \rightleftharpoons [FeBr_4]^- Br^+$. This reaction also leads to the *meta* derivative of nitrobenzene.

Bromobenzene has the configurations:

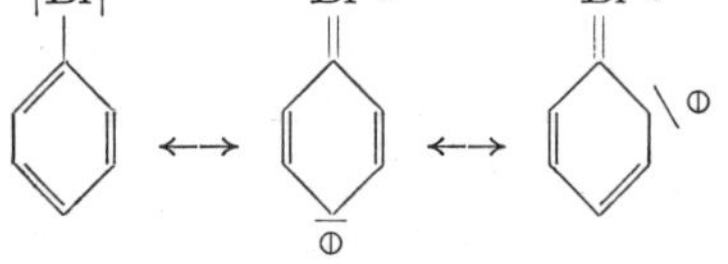

|Br| ⟷ Br⊕ ⟷ Br⊕ (2 ×)

Here, according to expectation, bromination and nitration will mainly lead to the *ortho* and *para* derivatives and, further, these reactions will be associated with a general activation. The reaction type is indeed correct. However, there is in fact a deactivation in bromobenzene because, besides the effect of the resonance (R effect), there is also an electrostatic induction effect (I effect); the strongly electronegative bromine atom will withdraw electrons from the phenyl nucleus. This induction effect decreases with the distance from the key atom and will thus influence the *ortho* positions most.

The nitration of aniline in strongly acid medium involves the reaction of the anilinium ion, without special resonance, with the $NO_2^+$ ion. Electrons are withdrawn from the phenyl nucleus by the $—NH_3^+$ group and consequently *meta* and *para* nitraniline are produced but not *ortho*. If the aniline is first acetylated then mainly *ortho* and *para* nitraniline is produced because of the R effect.

In the reaction of chloronitrobenzene and nitraniline with alkali, the halogen atom or the amino group is only mobile in the *o* and *p* isomers; they are replaced by OH (also by CN, CNS, etc.) much more readily than in chlorobenzene or aniline. This is a reaction of the nucleophilic $OH^-$ ion. *o*-Nitrophenol and some *p*-nitrophenol (but no *meta*) can also be produced from nitrobenzene with alkali, though with difficulty.

HAMMETT (HAMMETT, book, Chapter 7; JAFFÉ, 1953) has introduced an empirical constant $\sigma$ by correlating the effects of *meta* or *para* substituents on rates of reaction or on dissociation equilibria involving a functional group in the side chain:

$$\log k - \log k_0 = \rho\sigma$$

Here $k_0$ and $k$ are the constants (rate or equilibrium) for the unsubstituted and the substituted derivative, respectively; $\rho$ is the reaction constant depending on the type of reaction or equilibrium and $\sigma$ is the characteristic substituent constant. On arbitrarily putting $\rho = 1.000$ for case of the ionization of benzoic acids, tables can be made for the $\sigma$ (and $\rho$) values (ref. above). Without going into details, we may remark that $-\sigma$ measures a positive change in the electron density produced by the substituent (SIXMA, 1953b, 1954). An $NH_2$ group gives rise to a large increase (*para* $\sigma$ = —0.660), the $NO_2$ group (*para* $\sigma$ = +0.778 or + 1.27, the latter for aniline and phenol derivatives) to a decrease of electron density in the aromatic nucleus. The influence on *meta* positions is much smaller, as follows from our former considerations (p. 233, p. 238) [*m* $NH_2$ $\sigma$ = —0.161, *m* $NO_2$ $\sigma$ = +0.710). The $\rho$ value indicates the sensibility of the reaction to changes in electron density, but its signification is complex.

Recently it has been attempted to separate the two contributions of induction and of resonance: $\sigma = \sigma_i + \sigma_r$, by considering that the induction hardly plays a role for the para position (TAFT, 1957).

The HAMMETT $\sigma$ values are related to the $\alpha$, the Coulomb energy in the M.O. theory (p. 298) as both are in some way connected with the electron donor or acceptor properties of the substituents (JAFFÉ, 1952). $\sigma_r = 15.5\ (q_r—1)$, with $q_r$ the charge on the carbon atom (p. 299). For the same reason there is a relation between the $\sigma$ parameter and the quadrupole resonance frequency (p. 150) in substituted chlorobenzenes as both are related to the double-bond character of the C—Cl bond (p. 233) (BRAY and BARNES, 1957).

One can expect many empirical relations to exist between totally different properties of substituted aromatic molecules as all depend on the chemical constitution of the molecule as a whole just as BUTLEROW had proclaimed when he introduced the notion of chemical structure a century ago.

In radical reactions, the radical will enter at the position where a free electron is most readily produced in the molecule. Phenyl radicals (from the reaction with benzoyl peroxide) will enter in nitrobenzene not at *meta* but at *ortho* (or *para*) positions. At high temperatures (275° C—600° C), as in the chlorination and bromination in the gas phase of chloro- or bromobenzene the substitution type is predominantly *meta*. The radical reaction will predominate at high temperatures and in the gas phase because the halogen molecules are then partially dissociated into atoms and solvation, which favors heterolytic dissociation, is absent. The reaction probability for halogen *atoms* is approximately the same for all positions, which means that a priori more *meta* than *para* derivative is produced (WIBAUT, 1949; SIXMA and WIBAUT, 1950). However, it is also possible that this repartition of isomers is due to the establishment of equilibrium as there is very little change with temperature of the *meta-para* ratio (ENGELSMA, KOOYMAN and VAN DER BIJ, 1957). In the liquid state radical reactions between chlorine and benzene (*e.g.*, under the influence of light) lead to addition of halogen to hexachlorocyclohexane $C_6H_6Cl_6$.

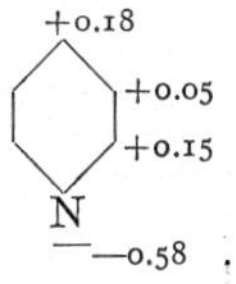

+0.18
+0.05
+0.15
N
−0.58

charge distribution of pyridine

The charge distribution in pyridine leads to deactivation for electrophilic substitution, the least for the position 3 (formation of 3-bromopyridine). At high temperatures, mainly 2-bromopyridine is produced by radical substitution*. With sodium amide, 2-aminopyridine is produced in a nucleophilic substitution reaction.

Another example from an important group of reactions is the polymerization of vinyl derivatives: $R—CH{=}CH_2$, *e.g.*, styrene, acrylic acid esters, etc. The configurations are:

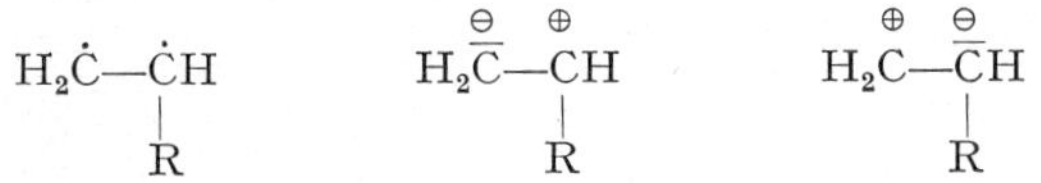

$$\underset{\text{I}}{H_2\dot{C}—\dot{C}H(R)} \qquad \underset{\text{II}}{H_2\overset{\ominus}{\overline{C}}—\overset{\oplus}{C}H(R)} \qquad \underset{\text{III}}{H_2\overset{\oplus}{C}—\overset{\ominus}{\overline{C}}H(R)}$$

The first configuration must be considered in radical reactions. In the polymerization under the influence of phenyl radicals (·Ph) from benzoyl peroxide as "catalyst", the course of the reaction is:

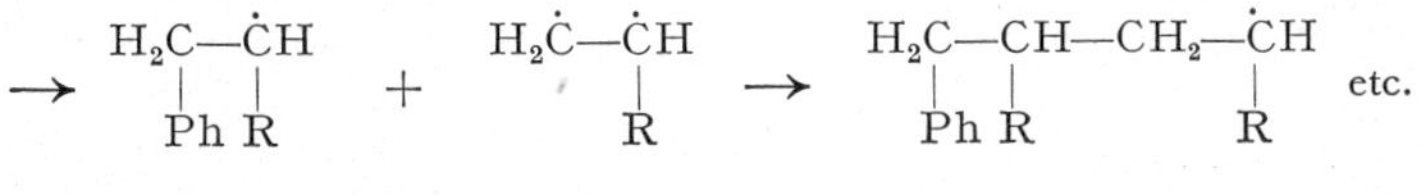

$$\rightarrow H_2C(Ph)—\dot{C}H(R) + H_2\dot{C}—\dot{C}H(R) \rightarrow H_2C(Ph)—CH(R)—CH_2—\dot{C}H(R) \quad \text{etc.}$$

With an electrophilic reagent such as strong sulphuric acid, $BF_3$ (sextet!), $SO_3$, $SnCl_4$ (see p. 370), configuration II will be stabilized by attachment of the catalyst.

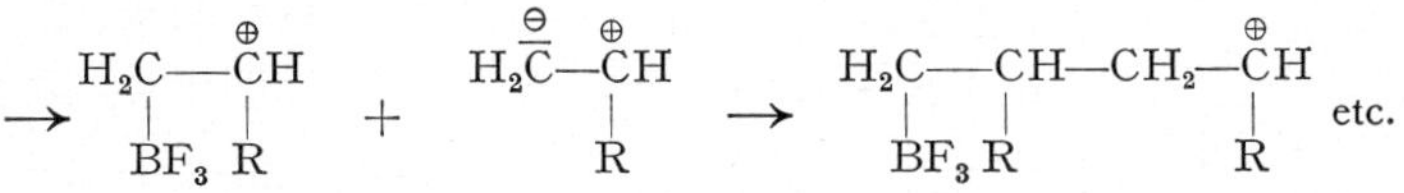

$$\rightarrow H_2C(BF_3)—\overset{\oplus}{C}H(R) + H_2\overset{\ominus}{\overline{C}}—\overset{\oplus}{C}H(R) \rightarrow H_2C(BF_3)—CH(R)—CH_2—\overset{\oplus}{C}H(R) \quad \text{etc.}$$

With a nucleophilic reagent such as the amide ion $NH_2^-$ and

* The 4-bromopyridine, which would be produced, reacts again with pyridine.

the negative triphenylmethyl ion, the same polymerization is produced via configuration III.

The reagent will always react with the end carbon atom because only then does the conjugation of the $\pi$ electrons from R (a phenyl or carbonyl group) with the free electron, the sextet or the free pair on the $\alpha$-carbon atom, remain intact. The predominant "head-to-tail" polymerization is explained in this way.

The electropositive sodium can act as a nucleophilic reagent reagent since it donates electrons. This is responsible for the polymerization of butadiene under the influence of sodium metal to the well-known synthetic Buna rubber (in U.S.A.: GRN). A small amount of disodium butadiene is first produced:

$$Na^+ [H_2\overset{\ominus}{\overline{C}}—CH=CH—\overset{\ominus}{\overline{C}}H_2]^{(2-)} Na^+.$$

This reacts in a chain reaction with the remaining butadiene via configurations I and III (p. 230):

$$[H_2\overset{\ominus}{\overline{C}}—CH=CH—\overset{\ominus}{\overline{C}}H_2]^{(2-)}$$

$$\overset{\ominus}{\overline{C}}H_2—CH=CH—\overset{\oplus}{C}H_2 \qquad \overset{\oplus}{C}H_2—CH=CH—\overset{\ominus}{\overline{C}}H_2$$

$$Na^+ [\overset{\ominus}{\overline{C}}H_2—CH=CH—CH_2—CH_2—CH=CH—CH_2—CH_2—CH=$$
$$=CH—\overset{\ominus}{\overline{C}}H_2]^{(2-)} Na^+ \text{ etc.}$$

As a third example, we will discuss the ozonization (WIBAUT, 1950, 1956, 1957) of aromatic molecules (p. 221), in particular that of naphthalene. KOOYMAN and KETELAAR (KOOYMAN and KETELAAR, 1946; KOOYMAN, 1947; KETELAAR and VAN DRANEN, 1949) assumed that in the first step the ozone molecule reacts with a pair of $\pi$ electrons in a bond. If now one asks whether there will be a difference between the 1—2 and the 2—3 bond, then the energy of the other $\pi$ electrons after the bond localization of the one pair must be considered. It is clear that this is much lower with bond localization at the

1—2 bond since the remaining bonds form a system like that in styrene, *i.e.*, with the very stable "aromatic" configuration in one ring. On localization at the 2—3 bond, there is only an open series of four conjugated bonds (corresponding to the non-existent phthalene or *o*-quinodimethanobenzene).

$O_3$ $O_3$

Naphthalene does react with ozone at the 1—2 bond; the reaction product in the ozonization of 2,3-dimethylnaphthalene is mainly dimethyl glyoxal.

Little is known of the actual mechanism (BROWN, 1950b; BADGER, 1951, 1952; SIXMA and WIBAUT, 1952). A mode of reaction is possible, in which the oxygen atom at the top of the ozone molecule with a formal positive charge (p. 247) reacts with an electron pair, not localized in a bond but on one carbon atom; in this case the ozone would react by an electrophilic mechanism (WIBAUT, SIXMA, KAMPSCHMIDT and BOER, 1950; SIXMA, BOER and WIBAUT, 1951). However, in order to explain the differences between the reaction course for ozonization and for other electrophilic reactions, *e.g.*, bromination and nitration with pyrene, these authors also assume an interaction of one of the other oxygen atoms with the adjacent carbon atom. The net result is, however, about the same as that predicted by the bond localization hypothesis.

Ozonization experiments also demonstrate the contribution of polar configurations for pyrrole (p. 228), at least to the activated complex.

The energy of the configuration with free electrons at the 9,10 positions is still relatively low in anthracene; thus this molecule will readily enter into radical reactions such as oxidation (p. 225) at these places.

In the reaction of halogen with butadiene, both 1,4 and 1,2 addition occur simultaneously. The first step is again the reaction between a positive bromine ion and butadiene in configuration I (or III p. 230) leading to the resonating configurations:

$$H_2\underset{|}{\overset{Br}{C}}\text{—}CH\text{=}CH\text{—}\overset{\oplus}{C}H_2 \longleftrightarrow H_2\underset{|}{\overset{Br}{C}}\text{—}\overset{\oplus}{C}H\text{—}CH\text{=}CH_2$$

In the second step, the negative $Br^-$ ion will be attached either at the 4 or at the 2 position. In long chains of conjugated double bonds, 1,2 addition will occur together with addition at both ends.

The rule of MARKOWNIKOW states that on addition of hydrogen halides to a double bond the hydrogen always goes to the carbon atom already carrying the largest number of hydrogen atoms.

In the series $H > CH_3 > C_2H_5 > i\,C_3H_7 > n\,C_3H_7 > t\,C_4H_7$, the electronegativity (or electrophilic character) decreases (increasing electron-donating properties); this can be deduced *e.g.*, from the first ionization potential (of the chlorine atom):

| | | | |
|---|---|---|---|
| HCl | 12.78 eV. | $i\,C_3H_7Cl$ | (10.8) eV. |
| $CH_3Cl$ | 11.46 ,, | $n\,C_3H_7Cl$ | 10.96 ,, |
| $C_2H_5Cl$ | 11.18 ,, | $t\,C_4H_9Cl$ | 10.2 ,, |

The same sequence is found from the increasing dipole moments of the alkylbenzenes.

Now the proton naturally will react most readily with the most electronegative carbon atom present at the double bond; this corresponds to the rule mentioned above. In the second step, the chlorine is attached to the other carbon atom. Apparent exceptions are in many cases due to a radical mechanism involving oxygen or peroxides present in the reacting system.

Many other problems of reaction kinetics could also be discussed with profit (lit. p. 310: DEWAR, 1949; HERMANS, 1953; INGOLD, 1955).

One of the simplest reactions of a saturated molecule is the exchange between an alkyl bromide and a (radioactive) bromine ion. In this reaction $^*Br^- + RBr \rightarrow {}^*BrR + Br^-$; the (radioactive) bromine atom must be attached at the side opposite to the expelled atom since the reaction with an optically active alkyl bromide is associated with racemization (WALDEN-inversion). The transition state in this case is, therefore, a state with both bromine atoms at equal distances from the carbon atom and the three hydrogen atoms in a plane perpendicular to the line Br C Br.

```
      H H                   H H
       \/                    \/
|Br|   C—|Br|   ←→   |Br—C   |Br|
        |                     |
        H                     H
```

In this nuclear configuration, the energy of the transition state will be further lowered by resonance. In this case the activation energy is due to the energy of repulsion of the atoms not attached to each other, the lengthening of the bond distances, and to the change in the bond angles (INGOLD *et al.*, 1955).

## § 36 A. WAVE-MECHANICAL CALCULATIONS* VALENCE BOND METHOD AND MOLECULAR ORBITAL METHOD

As previously remarked, an exact solution of the wave equation is possible for the $H_2^+$ molecule with two nuclei and one electron but only approximate methods can be applied to the simplest stable molecule, the $H_2$ molecule.

We would like to learn to understand the properties of other molecules from an insight into their constitution, but these molecules are even more complicated.

A qualitative insight is frequently of great value and our insight into the properties and reactions of chemical compounds has often been deepened in this way. Nevertheless a real theoretical chemistry should make it possible to deduce quantitative results from the fundamental laws. The importance of the quantitative aspect of the theory becomes all the more pressing because it frequently happens that a number of effects are present; these all exert their influence on the properties of compounds but may act in opposite directions. It is true that it is then easy to give a qualitative explanation *a posteriori* but it was *a priori* not at all certain that a particular effect is really predominant.

There are two major ways in wave mechanics which can be chosen in order to obtain an approximate solution of the wave equation.

*A. Perturbation method.* The equation is first solved exactly by neglecting some terms in the interaction (unperturbed system). These solutions are the so-called oth order wave functions(s) $\varphi_0$ with the corresponding energy value $W_0$. The

---

* This section can be skipped by readers who are less interested in the theoretical elaborations. Reference may be made to p. 309 at the end of this chapter for further literature.

energy of the perturbed system is $W = W_0 + W'$, in which $W'$ is given by $W' = \int \varphi_0 H' \varphi_0 dv$ and $H'$ is the small perturbing (potential) energy.

This method is in general of little practical significance for molecules because it is usually difficult to define an unperturbed system for which the solutions are known. Moreover, the 1st order perturbation calculation only furnishes results of a poor accuracy, while an excessive amount of calculation is connected with higher approximations.

It has been used for some special problems, *e.g.*, the induction effect of substituents on the energy levels and intermediate states of aromatic molecules (SIXMA, 1951, 1953a; DEWAR, 1952).

*B. The variational method.* This method, which we have already employed (p. 139), is based on the proposition that the expression

$$\frac{\int \phi^* H \phi \, dv}{\int \phi^* \phi \, dv}$$

($\phi^*$ is the conjugated complex of $\phi$) represents an *upper* limit for the energy of the system and $\phi$, the variation function, represents an approximation to the correct wave function*. A minimum value for this expression is sought by variation of the parameters in an appropriately chosen function $\phi$; in this way an approximate solution can be obtained both for the energy of the system and for the wave function itself.

The important question is the choice of the variation function $\phi$ for which a linear combination of other functions is usually taken: $\phi = \Sigma c_K \varphi_K$, with the coefficients $c_K$ as the parameters to be varied.

Now there are two important methods for obtaining these linear combinations.

*I. Valence Bond (V.B.) method*

(HÜCKEL, 1937; PAULING, 1933; PAULING and WHELAND, 1933; SHERMAN, 1934; WHELAND, 1935)

* For the proof see *e.g.*, PAULING and WILSON, EYRING *et al.* or KAUZMANN, books cited on p. 22.

In this method it is postulated that the bonding electrons are united into pairs and one then has to find in how many (independent) ways the $2n$ electrons of $n$ bonds can be arranged in a molecule of given (geometrical) structure. These configurations can be obtained by investigating the possible permutations of the electrons, as we have already done in the case of the $H_2$ molecule. The V.B. method is, in fact, an extension of the method of HEITLER and LONDON to polyatomic molecules.

The number of these (independent) configurations or canonical structures for $2\,n$ electrons amounts to:

$$\frac{(2n)!}{n!\ (n+1)!}$$

| | | |
|---|---|---|
| $n = 3$ | (benzene, 6 $\pi$ electrons) | 5 (see p. 221) |
| $n = 5$ | (naphthalene, 10 $\pi$ electrons) | 42 (see p. 213) |
| $n = 7$ | (anthracene, phenanthrene, 14 $\pi$ electrons) | 429 (see p. 224) |

The variation function is now chosen as a linear combination of the functions $\varphi_K$ which represent these canonical structures. Rules for calculating the quantities which occur in the calculations have been given by PAULING (PAULING, 1933) and EYRING (EYRING and KIMBALL, 1933).

This method, HÜCKEL's 1st method or the H(EITLER) L(ONDON) S(LATER) P(AULING) method or the "valence bond" (V.B.) method, fits directly on to the electron pair theory of valency of LEWIS, LANGMUIR, INGOLD and others. Each configuration can be described by bond lines, each of which signifies an electron pair between the various atoms. It can be proved that these lines never intersect in the canonical structures; configurations with intersecting lines can be regarded as combinations of the former.

The minimum condition produces in a similar way as in the M.O. method, a set of equations which have a solution and thereby a physical significance if the determinant of the coefficients is equal to zero. This determinant forms an equation for benzene of the 5th degree in the energy $E$. The roots are of the form $E_m = Q - m\alpha$ in which $Q$ is the COULOMB energy and $a$ the (single) exchange integral (sometimes also given as $J$), corresponding to the integrals in the case of hydrogen (resp. with $Q$ and $\beta$, pp. 144, 215).

The lowest root for benzene ($\alpha$ negative) is found to be $-m = \sqrt{13} - 1 = 2.61$. The energy of benzene is therefore: $E_B = Q + 2.61\ \alpha$. The energy of a single KEKULÉ configuration is: $E_K = Q + 1.5\ \alpha$ (for a DEWAR configuration $E_D = Q$). The energy lowering as a result of resonance (R.E.) is, therefore, $E_K - E_B = -1.11\ \alpha$ according to the V.B. method.

The stationary state of the molecule is, therefore, a combination of various configurations for which we preferably but not necessarily choose the canonical configurations. The square of the coefficient represents the contribution of the configuration in question to (the charge distribution of) the stationary state. For benzene we have:

$$\phi = c_{K_1} \cdot \varphi_{K_1} + c_{K_2} \cdot \varphi_{K_2} + c_{D_1} \cdot \varphi_{D_1} + c_{D_2} \cdot \varphi_{D_2} + c_{D_3} \cdot \varphi_{D_3} \text{ with } \Sigma c_K^{\,2} = 1$$

(normalization) and for the state of lowest energy:

$$c_{K_1}^{\,2} : c_{K_2}^{\,2} : c_{D_1}^{\,2} : c_{D_2}^{\,2} : c_{D_3}^{\,2} = 0.389 : 0.389 : 0.073 : 0.073 : 0.073$$

so that the DEWAR configurations collectively contribute 22 %.

Besides the KEKULÉ and DEWAR configurations, polar configurations are also possible (CRAIG, 1950):

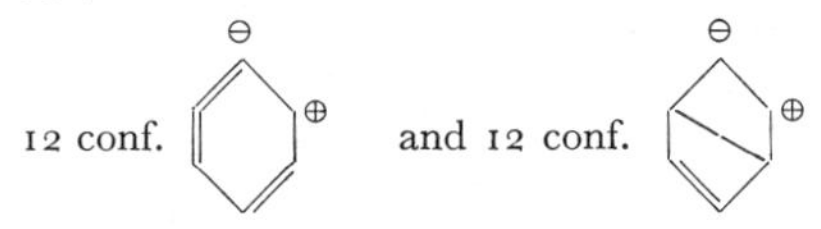


However, the contributions to the ground state are unimportant: 1.1% and 0.2% respectively for both groups. They contribute much more to the excited state.

The idea of resonance of the conjugated bonds is connected typically with this V.B. approximation method and it has in fact, as already stated, (p. 136), no deeper real physical significance. However, the V.B. method can be readily represented in diagrams which correspond to the usual chemical formulae; consequently the resonance idea also has considerable success in its qualitative application to numerous problems, as has been shown in many places in this chapter. Usually the calculations by the "valence bond" method are especially complicated on account of the large number of configurations. The consideration is, therefore, frequently restricted to those configurations in which the "bonds" run exclusively between neighbouring atoms (KEKULÉ or non-excited configurations without "long-bonds"). In the usual approximation it appears that the contributions of the single and multiple excited configurations increase very rapidly (in anthracene 90%, in naphthacene rather more than 99%). However, calculations to higher approximations give lower values for these contributions. The value of calculations in this simple way on the absorption bands (FÖRSTER, 1940) is therefore also somewhat doubtful, although calculations for a series of related compounds can nevertheless be relatively valuable through a corresponding compensation of errors (p. 262, Table 22B).

Account has been taken of the single and double excited configurations in the calculations of DAUDEL and PULLMAN ("Diagrammes moléculaires", molecular diagram method) on the bond character and charge distribution in very complicated aromatic molecules (DAUDEL and PULLMAN, 1946; DAUDEL and DAUDEL, 1948; PULLMAN and PULLMAN, 1949, 1952). In view of the remarks above, it is dubious whether the calculated values of these contributions have any real significance even if we ignore the fundamental difficulty that the canonical configurations are not unique (invariant) for the calculation of the charge distribution (though they are for the energy calculation) and also ignore normalization difficulties on account of non-orthogonality.

The total weight ($c_k^2$) of the configurations in which the bond between atoms $i$ and $j$ is double gives the double-bond character $p_{ij}$ (PAULING, BROCKWAY and BEACH, 1935; PAULING and BROCKWAY, 1937).

In benzene it is found by superposition of the five canonical configurations mentioned that each bond has a double-bond character of $0.389 + 0.073 = 0.462$. In view of the single $\sigma$-bond always present one also speaks of total bond character equal to $1 +$ the double-bond character. This bond character ("indice de liaison double", DAUDEL and PULLMAN) from the calculations based on the Valence Bond method is different from the bond order (PENNEY, COULSON), *e.g.* in the Molecular Orbital Method (p. 29[illegible]); however, both terms are frequently used without discrimination. In PAULING's earlier simple concept (p. 225) the bond character of benzene is just 0.5 since only the KEKULÉ configurations are taken into account.

One can also speak of a free valence (index) or "indice de liaison libre" of 0.07 for each corner of the benzene molecule since the *para-para* bond in the DEWAR-configurations is not a real bond but rather represents two free electrons (with opposite spins) at opposite corners.

This free valence $f_i$ (in the V.B. method) is again found from the total weight of those configurations where this atom $i$ lacks a bond (= carries a formal bond). The sum $f_i + \sum_j p_{ij} = 1$, as can be easily verified (DAUDEL and PULLMANN, ref. above; COULSON, DAUDEL and DAUDEL, 1947; MOFFITT and COULSON 1948a).

Both the bond character and the free valence index (but not the energy) depend in principle on the choice of the canonical configurations. In general, however, it is easy to make a proper choice on the basis of chemical intuition. In naphthalene the results for both quantities are as given below (see also Table 24 and p. 223).

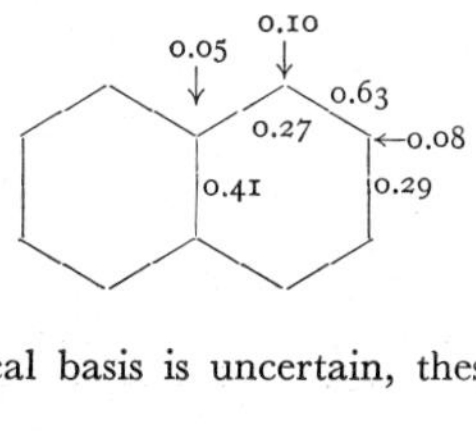

0.05 0.10 0.63 0.27 ←0.08 0.41 0.29

Although the theoretical basis is uncertain, these figures have nevertheless some value for comparative calculations, as appears on comparison with other methods (Table 24). Besides numerous other properties such as substitution reactions, redox potentials etc., there is a very interesting connection between a localized high $\pi$ electron density (two neighbouring atoms with a high free valence index and a high double-bond character for the intermediate bond) and the carcinogenic action in aromatic hydrocarbons (SCHMIDT, 1939a; PULLMAN, 1954; DAUDEL, 1953; BADGER, 1949; KOOYMAN and HERINGA, 1952). In 1,2-benzanthracene the so-called K region of high density is sought in the 3—4 bond.

Substitution of a methyl group (electron donor) at a position of high free valency increases the action (the 10-methyl derivative is active). In 1,2,5, 6-dibenzanthracene, one of the first known carcinogenic hydrocarbons, there are two bonds (3—4 and 7—8) which both possess a high $\pi$-electron density. The difference between the inactive 1,2-benzopyrene and the active 3,4-benzopyrene from coal tar would be due to the fact that the former possesses one K region, the 6—7 bond, while the latter, has also the 1—2 bond as such.

It was even possible to predict the carcinogenic activity of hydrocarbons prior to their synthesis.

The usual V.B. method leads to lengthy calculations (however, see WHELAND, 1955; HEITLER, 1955, 1957) or can only be employed by the introduction of unjustified approximations and doubtful suppositions; but there is also an alternative method, that of the "spin states" (S method, HEITLER, SLATER, PENNEY), which can be applied more easily even to large molecules (HARTMANN, 1947; VROELANT and DAUDEL, 1949; DAUDEL *et al.*, 1950).

Here we consider all arrangements of the spins of the $\pi$ electrons for which the total spin component $S_z = \Sigma s_z = 0$ (the ground state is almost always a singlet state). Now, however, we do not reduce this large number (namely $(2n)!/(n!)^2$ for $2n$ electrons) to a set of canonical configurations. Although the degree of the equations is higher, the solutions are nevertheless easier to find and above all it is now possible to give good general approximate solutions. Furthermore we avoid the difficulty mentioned above, *i.e.*, that the canonical configurations are not unique for the charge distribution, since all configurations are considered in this case.

We shall only give a scheme (VROELANT and DAUDEL, 1949) according to which the energy, the bond order and the free valency of an arbitrary conjugated system can be deduced in a simple approximate way (with open chain or even-membered rings, alternating hydrocarbon, p. 304).

For this purpose we divide the carbon-carbon bonds into four classes, dependent on the number of adjacent C—C bonds belonging to the conjugated system.

| | —C—C | —C—C— or >C—C | >C—C— | >C—C< |
|---|---|---|---|---|
| class | 1 | 2 | 3 | 4 |
| | $f$ 0.618 | 0.414 | 0.302 | 0.236 |

(An isolated double bond is class 0, $f = 1$).

Thus in butadiene the central bond belongs to class 2, in benzene all are of class 2, in naphthalene the division is as indicated.

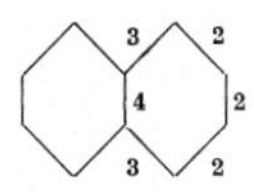


The energy in this approximation depends only on the number of bonds and the classes to which they belong.

$$W = Q + \alpha \Sigma_k n_k f_k,$$

in which again $Q$ is the COULOMB energy and $\alpha$ the exchange integral in the V.B. method, a parameter to be determined experimentally. In addition $n_k$ is the number of bonds in class $k$ and $f_k$ is a factor, the exchange factor characteristic of class $k$.

For naphthalene we thus have:

| | $n_k$ | $f_k$ | $n_k \cdot f_k$ | sym-bol | bond order | distance calc. | distance exp. | |
|---|---|---|---|---|---|---|---|---|
| class 2 | 6 | 0,414 | 2.484 | 22 | 0.612 | 1.398 Å | 1.404 Å | 2–3 |
| | | | | 23 | 0.652 | 1.388 Å | 1.365 Å | 1–2 |
| class 3 | 4 | 0.302 | 1.208 | 234 | 0.508 | 1.420 Å | 1.425 Å | 1–0 |
| class 4 | 1 | 0.236 | 0.236 | 3333 | 0.407 | 1.445 Å | 1.393 Å | 0–0′ |
| | | $\Sigma n_k f_k$ | 3.928 | | | | | |

Thus $W = Q + 3.928\ \alpha$; the correct solution, both by the V.B. method and the spin method without any approximation, is: $W = Q + 4.040\ \alpha$.

For hexatriene we have:

| | $n_k$ | $f_k$ | $n_k \cdot f_k$ |
|---|---|---|---|
| class 1 | 2 | 0.618 | 1.236 |
| class 2 | 3 | 0.414 | 1.242 |
| | | $\Sigma n_k f_k$ | 2.478 |

$W = Q + 2.478\ \alpha$ instead of $W = Q + 2.482\ \alpha$.

For the calculation of the R.E., we also need to know the energy of the isolated configuration. This is $W_i = Q + b\alpha - c \cdot {}^1/_2\ \alpha$ in which $b$ is the number of double bonds and $c$ the number of single bonds in the system of conjugated C—C bonds.

For naphthalene $W_i = Q + 2\alpha$, R.E. 1.928 $\alpha$; for hexatriene $W_i = Q + 2\alpha$, R.E. 0.478 $\alpha$ according to this simplified spin method (Table 24).

While thus the energy depends only on the class of the bonds in question, the bond order is also determined by the classes of the adjacent bonds*. Here a table can be made for all possibilities. In this the symbol 3333 denotes a bond such as the central bond in naphthalene which is bounded by four bonds of class 3; the bond itself is thus of the 4th class. From the relation between this V.B. bond order and bond length (compare M.O. bond order and C—C distance, Fig. 19) the calculated length can also be given for each bond.

This treatment is an approximation** since the central bonds in coronene, symbol 4444, are in reality not identical with those in graphite; the former is 1.43 Å long, the latter 1.42 Å (see also Table 24).

TABLE 23

| Symbol | Bond order $p$ | Length in Å |
|---|---|---|
| 1st class | | |
| 2 | 0.827 | 1.362 |
| 3 | 0.873 | 1.353 |
| 2nd class | | |
| 11 | 0.437 | 1.438 |
| 12 | 0.524 | 1.416 |
| 13 | 0.566 | 1.408 |
| 22 | 0.612 | 1.398 |
| 23 | 0.652 | 1.388 |
| 24 | 0.676 | 1.385 |
| 33 | 0.692 | 1.380 |
| 34 | 0.714 | 1.377 |
| 44 | 0.735 | 1.373 |

| Symbol | Bond order $p$ | length in Å |
|---|---|---|
| 3rd class | | |
| 123 | 0.367 | 1.455 |
| 124 | 0.387 | 1.450 |
| 133 | 0.407 | 1.445 |
| 134 | 0.428 | 1.440 |
| 144 | 0.440 | 1.436 |
| 222 | 0.412 | 1.443 |
| 223 | 0.452 | 1.433 |
| 224 | 0.472 | 1.428 |
| 233 | 0.493 | 1.423 |
| 234 | 0.508 | 1.420 |
| 244 | 0.537 | 1.414 |
| 333 | 0.537 | 1.414 |
| 334 | 0.556 | 1.410 |
| 344 | 0.578 | 1.405 |

| Symbol | Bond order $p$ | Length in Å |
|---|---|---|
| 4th class | | |
| 2233 | 0.324 | 1.465 |
| 2234 | 0.346 | 1.460 |
| 2244 | 0.367 | 1.455 |
| 2333 | 0.367 | 1.455 |
| 2334 | 0.387 | 1.450 |
| 2344 | 0.407 | 1.445 |
| 2444 | 0.428 | 1.440 |
| 3333 | 0.407 | 1.445 |
| 3334 | 0.428 | 1.440 |
| 3344 | 0.440 | 1.436 |
| 3444 | 0.469 | 1.430 |
| 4444 | 0.489 | 1.425 |

By applying this calculation to the system which remains after localization, it is possible to calculate the localization energy (p. 276) even for complicated molecules, or, better, differences in localization energy for various positions.

We can also give a free valence number (quite different from the free valence index in V.B.) for atom $i$ in this method of approximation (see also pp. 287 and 300) in the form $I_i = C - \sum_j P_{ij}$, that is to say, by taking the sum of the bond orders of all bonds starting from atom $k$. The constant $C$ is unimportant for comparisons; it is taken as 1.682 to ensure that no negative numbers are produced (see however p. 300).

* This V.B. bond order related to the energy corresponds to the "bond order" introduced by PENNEY (PENNEY, 1937) and is thus quite different from the bond character of PAULING (p. 225), but differs little numerically from the M.O. bond order according to COULSON (p. 299 and Table 24).

** A further refinement has been introduced (CHALVET, 1955, 1956).

For naphthalene this free valence has the following values for the 1, 2 and 0 positions, respectively:

$$I_1 : 1.682 - 0.652 - 0.508 = 0.522$$
$$I_2 : 1.682 - 0.652 - 0.612 = 0.418$$
$$I_0 : 1.682 - 2 \cdot 0.508 - 0.407 = 0.165$$

These free valence numbers in the S method run parallel to the self-polarizability from the M.O. description which still has to be discussed. A larger free valence therefore also means a smaller activation energy for (electrophilic) substitution and probably for radical substitution (p. 302). A high bond order runs parallel to a low bond localization energy of a $\pi$ electron pair in this bond and thus with a low activation energy for molecular addition and ozonization.

The agreement of these results according to the S method with those of the M.O. method is very satisfactory, which gives confidence in their reliability. The ready illustration of the usual V.B. method by the structural formulae of the canonical configurations is, however, no longer present.

## *II. Molecular Orbital (M.O.) method*

(HÜCKEL, 1937; WHELAND, 1934, 1941; COULSON, 1939, 1947b; LONGUET-HIGGINS and COULSON, 1947b; MULLIKEN, 1949)

HÜCKEL's second method is also known as the HMH method (HUND-MULLIKEN-HÜCKEL) and corresponds with the treatment of the electrons in an atom and in a metal (Chapter IV). Each electron is assumed to be moving in a field due to the nuclei and the other electrons. The total wave function of the electrons is then a product of these one-electron functions.

We now compose a wave function for each $\pi$ electron in a conjugated system which describes its behaviour in the whole system; thus there is no restriction of the electron to particular bonds (molecular orbital, M.O.). It is now customary to compose these M.O. by the method of LENNARD-JONES as a linear combination of "atomic orbitals" (A.O.) provided with coefficients (L.C.A.O. approximation). These atomic orbitals are the $p_z$ functions of the carbon atoms in a molecule with double bonds. The square of a particular coefficient indicates the contribution of the electron in question to the charge around this particular atom.

Thus we have an approximate wave function $\phi = \sum_{k=1}^{k=r} c_k \varphi_k$ in which $k = 1 \ldots r$ is the index of atom $k$. Since all the electrons are equal, this same variation function $\phi$ holds for all the electrons $j$. In benzene $k$ runs from 1 to 6, $j$ likewise from 1 to 6, but they need not always be the same; compare vinyl chloride (p. 233) $k$ 1 to 3, $j$ 1 to 4, and the positive triphenylmethyl ion (p. 265) $k$ 1 to 19, $j$ 1 to 18.

The energy expression given above can again be calculated for one electron ($\phi$ is real):

$$W = \frac{\int \phi \,.\, H\phi \, dv}{\int \phi^2 \, dv}$$

After substitution of the expression for $\phi$ and the introduction of the abbreviations:

$\int \varphi_k \,.\, H\,\varphi_k \, dv = \alpha_k$ (COULOMB integral)
$\int \varphi_i \,.\, H\,\varphi_k \, dv = \varphi_k \,.\, H\,\varphi_i \,.\, dv = \beta_{ik}$ (resonance integral).
$\int \varphi^2_k \, dv = 1$ (A.O. are normalized)
$\int \varphi_i \,.\, \varphi_k \, dv = s_{ik}$ (overlap integral)

we have:

$$W = \frac{\sum_k c_k^2 \,\alpha_k + \sum_i' \sum_k c_i \, c_k \, \beta_{ik}}{\sum_k c_k^2 + \sum_i' \sum_k c_i \, c_k \, s_{ik}}$$

($\sum_i'$ signifies summation over $1 \ldots r$ with the exception of $i = k$).

According to the principle of the variation method $W$ must now be minimized with respect to variations of the $r$ parameters $c_k$; this furnishes $r$ conditions $\dfrac{\partial W}{\partial c_k} = 0$.

We thus obtain a set of $r$ linear homogeneous equations with $c_1 \ldots c_r$ as unknowns.

$$(\alpha_k - W)\; c_k + \sum_i' (\beta_{ik} - s_{ik}\, W)\; c_i = 0$$

This set of equations only has a non-trivial solution (*i.e.*, other than $c_1 = \ldots = c_r = 0$) when the determinant of the coefficients is equal to zero.

$$\begin{vmatrix} \alpha_1 - W & \beta_{12} - s_{12} W & \beta_{13} - s_{13} W \ldots\ldots\ldots \\ \beta_{21} - s_{21} W & \alpha_2 - W & \beta_{23} - s_{23} W \ldots\ldots\ldots \end{vmatrix} = 0 \quad (1)$$

This determinant of $r$ rows and columns forms an equation of the $r$th degree for the energy $W$ and there are, therefore, $r$ roots for $W$.

We find these same roots $W_m$ for each electron $j$ and obtain the total energy of the ground state by putting two electrons with opposite spins in each energy level, beginning with the lowest root. We find the wave functions by determining the coefficients $c_1 \ldots c_r$ for each value $W_m$ of $W$. This is done by the substitution of $W_m$ in the $r$ linear equations. One of the unknown $c$'s is then arbitrarily set equal to 1, and the correct values are established by the normalizing condition (in the oth approximation method $\sum_k c_k^2 = 1$ for each M.O. wave function).

If, as is frequently the case, we have an equal number of atoms ($r$) and of $\pi$ electrons ($j$), half of the roots $W_m$ are occupied.

It is now necessary to limit the number of unknown parameters $\alpha$, $\beta$ and $s$ in our determinant by further approximation.

*Zeroth Approximation method*

We neglect all interaction integrals $\beta_{ik}$ between atoms which are not bound to each other and we put the other $\beta$'s equal to each other in molecules where the conjugated system consists of one kind of atom, *e.g.*, in the isocyclic hydrocarbons and polyenes. We also assume that the $a_k$ is equal for all the atoms in this case; this is strictly correct for a molecule such as benzene, but is no longer obvious even for naphthalene. In this approximation we also assume that the $s_{ik}$ is always zero.

This may seem somewhat strange since the interaction integral $\beta_{ik}$ is closely related to the overlap and thus connected with $s_{ik}$. This procedure is similar to the perturbation calculations where the perturbation $H'$ is used together with the unperturbed wave function for the energy calculation. The value of the energy is thus known more accurately than the wave functions (or charge distribution). This is in general true for wave-mechanical calculations.

For benzene, therefore, we have as the (secular) determinant

$$\begin{vmatrix} \alpha - W & \beta & 0 & 0 & 0 & \beta \\ \beta & \alpha - W & \beta & 0 & 0 & 0 \\ 0 & \beta & \alpha - W & \beta & 0 & 0 \\ 0 & 0 & \beta & \alpha - W & \beta & 0 \\ 0 & 0 & 0 & \beta & \alpha - W & \beta \\ \beta & 0 & 0 & 0 & \beta & \alpha - W \end{vmatrix} = 0 = \begin{vmatrix} x & 1 & 0 & 0 & . \\ 1 & x & 1 & 0 & . \\ 0 & 1 & x & 1 & . \\ . & . & . & . & . \\ . & . & . & . & . \end{vmatrix} \quad (2)$$

with $(\alpha - W) / \beta = x$.

This equation of the 6th degree can be factorized. It is, however, easier to derive these factors directly with the aid of the symmetry of the charge distribution of the molecule.

Let us consider the two symmetry planes I and II. It is clear that since the charge on atoms left and right of a reflection plane must be equal, this also holds for the squares of the coefficients in the M.O. wave functions $\phi$, thus $c_2{}^2 = c_6{}^2$ etc. This means, however, that the wave functions fall into two groups according as they are symmetrical ($s$) or antisymmetrical ($a$) with respect to the reflection plane, that is to say $c_2 = c_6$ or $c_2 = -c_6$ (p. 132); wave functions of different symmetry character do not combine and so the following groups of four variation functions are produced. (The coefficient in the antisymmetrical case of an atom in the reflection plane is equal to zero because we then have: $c_1 = -c_1$ from which follows $c_1 = 0$.)

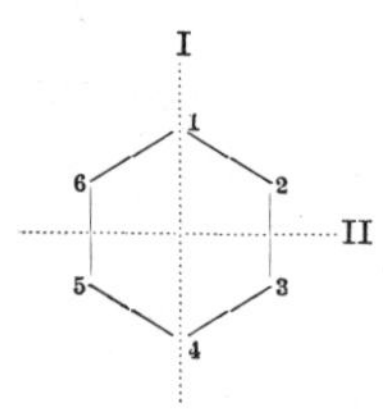


*aa* $c_1 = c_4 = 0 \quad c_2 = -c_6 = -c_3 = c_5$

$$\phi_{aa} = c_2 (\varphi_2 - \varphi_3 + \varphi_5 - \varphi_6) \equiv c_2 \phi_a$$

*as* $c_1 = c_4 = 0 \quad c_2 = -c_6 = c_3 = -c_5$

$$\phi_{as} = c_2 (\varphi_2 + \varphi_3 - \varphi_5 - \varphi_6) \equiv c_2 \phi'_a$$

*sa* $c_1 = -c_4 \quad c_2 = c_6 = -c_3 = -c_5$

$$\phi_{sa} = c_1 (\varphi_1 - \varphi_4) + c_2 (\varphi_2 - \varphi_3 - \varphi_5 + \varphi_6) \equiv c_1 \phi_A + c_2 \phi_B$$

*ss* $c_1 = c_4 \quad c_2 = c_6 = c_3 = c_5$

$$\phi_{ss} = c_1 (\varphi_1 + \varphi_4) + c_2 (\varphi_2 + \varphi_3 + \varphi_5 + \varphi_6) \equiv c_1 \phi'_A + c_2 \phi'_B$$

The variation principle can also be applied to these reduced variation functions separately and then four equations for $W$ in determinantal form are produced, two of the 1st degree and two of the 2nd degree which again give six roots altogether but now in a simpler way than by the solution of an equation of the 6th degree.

Example: *sa*

$$\begin{vmatrix} Q_{AA} - \Delta_{AA} W & Q_{AB} - \Delta_{AB} W \\ Q_{BA} - \Delta_{BA} W & Q_{BB} - \Delta_{BB} W \end{vmatrix} = 0$$

$$Q_{AA} = \int(\varphi_1 - \varphi_4)\, H\, (\varphi_1 - \varphi_4)\, dv = 2\,\alpha$$
$$Q_{BA} = Q_{AB} = \int(\varphi_1 - \varphi_4)\, H\, (\varphi_2 - \varphi_3 - \varphi_5 + \varphi_6)\, dv = 4\beta$$
$$Q_{BB} = \int(\varphi_2 - \varphi_3 - \varphi_5 + \varphi_6)\, H\, (\varphi_2 - \varphi_3 - \varphi_5 + \varphi_6)\, dv = 4\alpha - 4\beta$$

$$\Delta_{AA} = 2 \quad \Delta_{BB} = 4 \quad \Delta_{BA} = \Delta_{AB} = 0$$

$$\begin{vmatrix} 2\,\alpha - 2\,W & 4\,\beta \\ 4\,\beta & 4\,\alpha - 4\,\beta - 4\,W \end{vmatrix} = \begin{vmatrix} \alpha - W & 2\,\beta \\ \beta & \alpha - \beta - W \end{vmatrix} = 0$$

or $\alpha - W = 2\,\beta$ and $\alpha - W = -\beta$

The solutions for $W$ (in general form $W_m = \alpha - m\beta$) are as follows with the lowest value below ($\beta$ is a negative quantity):

| | | $c_1$ | $c_2$ | $c_3$ | $c_4$ | $c_5$ | $c_6$ | $\Sigma c_k^2$ | |
|---|---|---|---|---|---|---|---|---|---|
| *sa* | $W = \alpha - 2\beta$ | 0.408 | −0.408 | 0.408 | −0.408 | 0.408 | −0.408 | 1 | unoccupied |
| *ss* | $\alpha - \beta$ | 0.578 | −0.289 | −0.289 | −0.578 | −0.289 | −0.289 | 1 | ,, |
| *aa* | $\alpha - \beta$ | 0 | −0.500 | 0.500 | 0 | −0.500 | 0.500 | 1 | ,, |
| *sa* | $\alpha + \beta$ | 0.578 | 0.289 | −0.289 | −0.578 | −0.289 | 0.289 | 1 | occupied |
| *as* | $\alpha + \beta$ | 0 | 0.500 | 0.500 | 0 | −0.500 | −0.500 | 1 | ,, |
| *ss* | $\alpha + 2\beta$ | 0.408 | 0.408 | 0.408 | 0.408 | 0.408 | 0.408 | 1 | ,, |
| | $\Sigma c_m^2$ | 0.5 | 0.5 | 0.5 | 0.5 | 0.5 | 0.5 | | |

With two electrons in each of the three lowest roots one obtains for the total energy $E$ of the $\pi$ electrons:

$$E = 6\,\alpha + 8\,\beta$$

With the $\pi$ electrons localized in three double bonds one calculates simply $E = 6\alpha + 6\beta$; a lowering of energy of $2\beta$ is thus produced by the delocalization. This is thus the "resonance energy" in the M.O. method, actually better called the "delocalization energy" (p. 323).

*First Approximation*

In the next approximation $s_{ik}$ is no longer put equal to zero, but equal to 0.25 as the best value. The solution can then be derived from that of the zeroth approximation without fresh arithmetic (WHELAND, 1941).

It is easy to verify that the determinant (1) with the approximation given above can be reformed to:

$$\begin{vmatrix} \alpha - W & \beta - sW & 0 & . \\ \beta - sW & \alpha - W & \beta - sW & . \\ 0 & \beta - sW & \alpha - W & . \\ . & . & . & . \end{vmatrix} = \begin{vmatrix} y & 1 & 0 & . \\ 1 & y & 1 & . \\ 0 & 1 & y & . \\ . & . & . & . \end{vmatrix} \tag{3}$$

which is of exactly the same form as (2), only with $y$ instead of $x$. Instead of the solutions $x_m = m = (\alpha - W_m)/\beta$ or $\alpha - W_m = m\beta$ we will now have $y_m = m = (\alpha - W_m)/(\beta - sW_m)$ or $\alpha - W_m = m(\beta - sW_m)$.

With the substitution*

$$\beta' = \beta - s\alpha$$

we obtain after rearrangement:

$$\alpha - W_m = \frac{m}{1 - ms}\beta' \text{ or } W_m = \alpha - \frac{m}{1 - ms}\beta'$$

Previously in the 0th approximation $W_m = \alpha - m\beta$.

In the first approximation the energy values for benzene are thus:

$W = \alpha + 1.333\ \beta'$, $W = \alpha + 0.800\ \beta'$ (twice), $W = \alpha - 1.333\ \beta'$ (twice) and $W = \alpha - 4.000\ \beta'$.

The energy of a configuration with localized bonds can also be expressed in terms of the new parameter $\beta'$.

To obtain this we can apply our calculations to the $\pi$ electron of a single double bond as in ethylene. From the secular determinant:

$$\begin{vmatrix} \alpha - W & \beta - sW \\ \beta - sW & \alpha - W \end{vmatrix} = 0$$

we obtain ($m = \pm 1$, the lower sign is the bonding state):

$$\alpha - W_i = -(\beta - sW) = -\frac{1}{1+s}\beta'$$

or $W_i = \alpha + \frac{1}{1+s}\beta'$ ($= \alpha + 0.80\ \beta'$, against $W_i = \alpha + \beta$ in 0th appr.).

Now $\beta'$ is negative just as $\beta$, and again the negative roots of $m$ ($m = -2, -1, -1$) correspond to the lowest energy levels. With $s = 0.25$ we have for the total energy of the six electrons $E = 6\alpha + 5.867\ \beta'$ compared to $E_i = 6\alpha + 4.800\ \beta'$ for the completely localized configuration. The resonance energy is thus now $1.067\ \beta'$, compared to $2.00\ \beta$.

It appears that the R.E. in a series of compounds according to this 1st approximation method with "overlap" have practically the same ratios to each other as in the zeroth approximation (Table 24, p. 301).

*Further approximations, absorption bands*

As we have remarked (p. 218), the "experimental" values of the resonance energies are based on a molecule with alternating "normal" C—C and C=C bonds with bond lengths of 1.54 Å and 1.34 Å, whereas the calculated values are based on a KEKULÉ configuration with bonds of equal lengths 1.39 Å. To obtain this latter structure from the first, the bonds have to be compressed and expanded, which will take a considerable energy (about 30 kcal for benzene). The experi-

* Instead of $\beta'$ some authors (COULSON, PULLMAN) use $\gamma$; MULLIKEN on the other hand designates with $\gamma$ the quantity most authors (and we) call $\beta$ in the M.O. method, whereas he uses $\beta$ for our $\beta'$. Instead of $\alpha$ in the M.O. method, $q$ (WHELAND) and $E_0$ (COULSON, PULLMAN) are also used.

mental R.E. would have to be increased with this amount. Other changes, however, have then also to be discussed, such as changes in the C—H bond energy and in hybridization; these probably counterbalance the first correction. We will not discuss these refinements which cannot be evaluated with any accuracy. Moreover the importance of our considerations lies especially in relative calculations and there these corrections are of little influence: they only change the absolute values of our parameters $\alpha$, $\beta$ and $\beta'$.

When, however, we calculate the position of the first absorption band (p. 260), that is to say, the difference $\Delta E$ for the highest occupied and the lowest unoccupied level, we find in the two approximations $\Delta E = 2\beta$ and $\Delta E = 2.13\beta'$ respectively. With the experimental value of 36 kcal for the R.E. we then calculate for $\beta$ and $\beta'$ 18 and 34 kcal, respectively, thus for $\Delta E$ 7900 Å and 3920 Å, respectively, whereas 2630 Å is the observed value. The first approximation is thus clearly much better for the $\Delta E$. In a still better approximation, it is no longer necessary to put $\beta$ equal to zero for non-adjacent atoms. It is also possible to calculate the parameters $\alpha$ and $\beta$ absolutely, but it is more useful in practice to use a semi-empirical relation: $\beta_{ik} = \frac{s_{ik}}{s_{ab}} \cdot \beta_{ab}$; using the readily calculated overlap integrals $s$, the values of $\beta_{ik}$ for all combinations and distances can then be related to a "normal" value $\beta_{ab}$ for one particular bond between the atoms $a$ and $b$. If in a molecule such as naphthalene the difference in length between non-equivalent bonds is known, $\beta$ can also be assumed different for these bonds (VAN DRANEN and KETELAAR, 1949, 1950). Now we have in the 2nd approximation for benzene R.E. $= 0.76\,\beta'$ or with $\beta' = 47.3$ kcal a position of the absorption band of 2790 Å. In other words, the values of the constant $\beta$ or $\beta'$ calculated from thermal data (R.E.) and from spectroscopic data (abs. band) are practically equal in the 2nd approximation.

With the variation of the exchange integral with the distance (0.95 $\beta$ and 0.65 $\beta$ for both C—C bonds, respectively) we obtain for butadiene a R.E. of 0.218 $\beta$ and of 0.079 $\beta'$, respectively. The values of 16 kcal and 44 kcal now deduced for $\beta$ and $\beta'$ from the experimental R.E. of 3.5 cal are in much better accordance with the others (comp. Table 24). The COULOMB integral $\alpha$ also varies. According to MULLIKEN it changes from 8.14 eV in ethylene to 7.42 eV in butadiene and to 7.18 eV in benzene.

According to MULLIKEN, the orbitals are divided into bonding and non-bonding or anti-bonding orbitals. In the 0th approximation M.O. these levels for the $\pi$ electrons are distributed symmetrically around the zero; however, this is not so in the 1st approximation (Fig. 22). In benzene and other aromatic molecules the bonding orbitals with $m$ negative are all filled. The transition of an electron of the highest bonding ($N$) to the lowest anti-bonding level $V_1$ (the $N \rightarrow V_1$ transition) corresponds to the absorption band at longest wave length (p. 259). The ground state is a singlet state with all electron spins paired.

For the first excited state there are, however, two possible spin states: the singlet state with both spins antiparallel and the triplet state with both spins parallel. The singlet state is $\delta$ higher, the triplet state the same amount lower than the theoretical $V_1$ level. As only the singlet-singlet transitions are allowed (the triplet-singlet transition may be observed in phosphorescence), the observed absorption band corresponds to $\Delta E_{NV_1} = E_{V_1} + \delta - E_N$ (neglecting differences in $\alpha$ and the spin interaction in the ground level). For a more refined discussion of the absorption spectra the singlet-triplet separation 2 $\delta$ (which is about 11,000—14,000 cm$^{-1}$ in the acenes) has to be taken into account (Platt *et al.*, 1949).

| | $\lambda$ obs. | $\Delta E_{NV_1}$ obs. | $2\,\delta$ | $E_{V_1}$–$E_N$ exp. | $E_{V_1}$–$E_N$ calc. | $\beta'$ calc. spect. |
|---|---|---|---|---|---|---|
| naphthalene | 2860 Å | 35000 $cm^{-1}$ | 13700 $cm^{-1}$ | 28200 $cm^{-1}$ | 1.26 $\beta'$ | 63 kcal |
| anthracene | 3750 | 26700 | 12000 | 20700 | 0.84 | 70 |
| naphthacene | 4770 | 21000 | 11000 | 15500 | 0.64 | 69 |
| pentacene | 5780 | 17300 | 11000 | 11800 | 0.44 | 76 |

Semi-empirical methods of calculation are of practical importance (comp. p. 289). Thus CARTER (CARTER, 1949) puts for the resonance energy $R$:

$$R/\beta = 0.6\,D + 1.5 \ln (N - 1)$$

Where $D$ = number of double bonds, $N$ = number of KEKULÉ configurations (see also BROWN, 1949, 1950a; HARTMANN, 1947).

A theoretically more attractive approximation has been given by ROUX and DAUDEL (ROUX and DAUDEL, 1950):

$$R/\beta = a_0 n_0 + a_1 n_1 + a_2 n_2 + a_3 n_3 + a_4 n_4.$$

Here $n_0$, $n_1$, $n_2$, $n_3$ and $n_4$ are the numbers of bonds of the 0th, 1st, 2nd, 3rd and 4th classes (p. 289), while the $a$'s are semi-empirical factors. The exact values of $R/\beta$ for some simple substances indicate that $a_0 = 2$, $a_1 = 1.568$, $a_2 = 1.333$, $a_3 = 1.177$ (better $= 1.158$) and $a_4 = 1.050$.

The calculations based on these formulae yield values for the R.E. which are in close agreement with those obtained by exact calculation, even for very large molecules.

*Hetero-atoms, bond order*

It is particularly easy in the M.O. method to take into account the difference in electronegativity compared with carbon; for molecules in which other atoms than carbon are included in the conjugated system, we substitute $\alpha_c + \delta_k \cdot \beta$ for $\alpha_k$ of atom $k$. (Frequently a small change is also made in the COULOMB integral of the carbon atom situated next to the hetero-atom, for example next to a nitrogen atom: $\alpha_c + {}^1/_4\,\beta$, on account of the induction.) Thus for chlorine $\delta = 1.5$ and for nitrogen $\delta = 2$ (ORGEL *et al.*, 1951). In this way, the constitution of the polychloroethylene and chlorobenzene derivatives could be calculated with these values in good agreement with the (scarce) experimental data (p. 233) (KETELAAR, 1939; SHERMAN and KETELAAR, 1939). However, more elaborate calculations have been made with more parameters, *e.g.*, with different values of $\beta$ for different bonds.

As a starting point lower values were now used for the double character (p. 233) (BERSOHN, 1954; KNIPE, 1955; GOLDSTEIN, 1956; ANNO and SADO, 1956; HOWE and GOLDSTEIN, 1957).

COULSON and his co-workers have applied the M.O. method to numerous fairly complicated compounds, such as even coronene $C_{28}H_{12}$ and ovalene $C_{40}H_{14}$ (COULSON, 1947b; LONGUET-HIGGINS and COULSON, 1947; MOFFITT and COULSON, 1948b; BUZEMAN, 1950; COULSON, DAUDEL and ROBERTSON, 1951). A good method of calculating the changes in the charge distribution on the introduction of substituents, starting from the calculation of the unsubstituted hydrocarbon, has been given by LONGUET-HIGGINS (LONGUET-HIGGINS 1950).

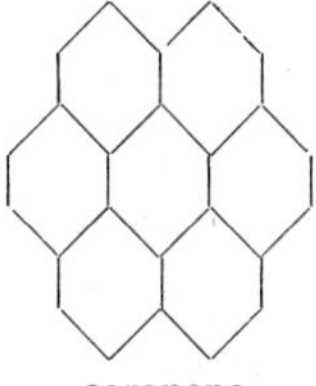

coronene

Two important quantities $q_k$ and $p_{ij}$ can be deduced from the results of the M.O. calculation. The electron distribution, expressed in units of the elementary charge, is found by calculating the quantity $q_k = \Sigma_m c_{mk}^2$ for each atom, that is to say by totalling the squares of the (normalized) coefficients $c_k$ for each of the electrons in the occupied wave functions $m$. The net charge is $1—q_k$.

It is found that this charge distribution is qualitatively correct but quantitatively the differences in charge are always much smaller than the calculated values.

Instead of the bond character of the V.B. method we have in this case the "mobile bond order" or double bond order as defined by COULSON (COULSON, 1939, 1947b, 1951): $p_{ij} = \Sigma_m c_{mi} c_{mj}$ of the bond between the atoms $i$ and $j$ summated over all electrons in the occupied levels $m$. The double bond order runs from 0 for the pure single bond to 1 for a pure double bond. For benzene we find 0.667. With a factor 2 on account of the occupation of each level by two electrons (p. 295): $\Sigma_m c_1 c_2 = 2(0.578 \cdot 0.289 + 0 \cdot 0.500 + 0.408 \cdot 0.408) = 0.667$ for naphthalene, see p. 301. (By total bond order is again meant the above double bond order + 1.)

It was possible to construct a curve with the experimental values of the bond lengths for C—C, benzene and C=C (Fig. 19) that gives the relation between the bond character according to PAULING and this length; the same can also be done for the relation to the bond order (COULSON, 1939, 1947b, 1951) (Fig. 19). These curves also have a theoretical basis.

As noted, the bond order in benzene is found to be not $^1/_2$ but $^2/_3$; this is connected with the lowering of the energy of the system by the resonance energy, that is to say, because benzene is not merely a superposition of the two KEKULÉ configurations (energy per bond in benzene $8\,\beta/6 = 1.33\,\beta$, for the normal double bond 2 β; thus the "bond order" is also energetically equal to $^2/_3$). The bond length in benzene is also smaller than the mean of the single and double C—C length owing to this fact (Fig. 19). The curve showing the bond length as a function of the bond order is much less curved and, moreover, is continuous from single to the triple bond in contrast to the curve as a function of the bond character.

There is a very good quantitative agreement between the theoretical lengths calculated in this way from the curve and the experimental values for many aromatic hydrocarbons as derived from accurate crystal structure determinations (see Table 24).

We can also speak of a figure for the free valency in the M.O. method (COULSON, 1946, 1947b; DAUDEL *et al.*, 1946, 1948), namely for atom $i$: $F_i = A_i - \Sigma_j p_{ij}$, that is to say the sum is taken of the (total) bond orders of all bonds of atom $i$ with its neighbours $j$. For benzene this is 2 · 1.667 + 1 = 4.33. The constant $A_i$ is chosen to obtain reasonable numbers ($A_i$ is 4 for a primary, $3 + \sqrt{2} = 4.41$ for a secondary carbon atom as in benzene and $3 + \sqrt{3} = 4.73$ for a tertiary carbon atom, all in a conjugated system).

The theoretically exact relations are important:

$$q_k = \frac{\partial E}{\partial \alpha_k} \text{ and } p_{ij} = {}^1/_2 \frac{\partial E}{\partial \beta_{ij}}$$

in which $E$ is the total energy for the π electrons. These equations show the great significance of the quantities $q$ and $p$. These relations are also of practical importance because the change in the energy on the transition to heterocyclic and substituted systems thus follows directly from the calculated values of the $p$'s and $q$'s of the isocyclic, unsubstituted molecule.

These relations are also of great importance for the calculation of the difference in activation energy for a chemical reaction which involves an attack accompanied by polarization at various points in the molecule (WHELAND and PAULING, 1935; WHELAND, 1942; COULSON and LONGUET-HIGGINS, 1947). These quantities $p$ and $q$ retain their significance unchanged in the oth and first approximation (CHIRGWIN and COULSON, 1950; LÖWDIN, 1950).

† See p. 225.

* Approximate method (VROELANT and DAUDEL, 1949).

** COULSON, 1939, 1941; LENNARD-JONES and COULSON, 1939. Later slightly different values were obtained from a different bond order-length curve (COULSON, DAUDEL and ROBERTSON, 1951).

*** Benzene X-ray crystal structure: 1.393 Å (COX, CRUICKSHANK and SMITH, 1955; CRUICKSHANK, 1956); Raman-spectrum 1.397 Å (STOICHEFF, 1954, LANGSETH and STOICHEFF, 1956). Naphthalene (AHMED and CRUICKSHANK, 1952; CRUICKSHANK and ROBERTSON, 1953). Anthracene (CRUICKSHANK, 1956, 1957). Coronene (ROBERTSON and WHITE 1945).

TABLE 24

RESONANCE ENERGY

| | V. B. | Spin * | M. O. | | Experimental in kcal | | | |
|---|---|---|---|---|---|---|---|---|
| | | | 0th approx. | 1st approx. | α V.B. | β M.O. | β′ M.O. | R. E. exp. |
| Butadiene | 0.23 | 0.15 | 0.47β | 0.17β′ | 15 | 7.5 | 20 | 3.5 |
| Benzene | 1.11 | 0.98 | 2.00 | 1.07 | 32 | 18 | 34 | 36 |
| Styrene | 1.31* | 1.18 | 2.42 | 1.21 | 29 | 16 | 31 | 38 |
| Naphthalene | 2.04 | 1.93 | 3.68 | 1.86 | 30 | 17 | 33 | 61 |
| Anthracene | 2.95 | 2.87 | 5.31 | 2.61 | 29 | 16 | 33 | 86 |
| Phenanthrene | 3.02* | 2.92 | 5.45 | 2.74 | 33 | 19 | 36 | 99 |

TOTAL BOND CHARACTER AND BOND LENGTH

| | Character PAULING † | Total bond order | | | Length | | |
|---|---|---|---|---|---|---|---|
| | | V.B. Diagr. mol. | Spin* | M.O. COULSON | calc. * Spin | calc.** COULSON | expt.*** |
| Butadiene | | | | | | | |
| 1–2 | 1.90 | 1.88 | 1.827 | 1.894 | 1.362 Å | 1.35 Å | 1.35 Å |
| 2–3 | 1.20 | 1.12 | 1.437 | 1.447 | 1.438 | 1.43 | 1.46 |
| Graphite | 1.33 | — | 1.489 | 1.535 | 1.425 | 1.417 | 1.421 |
| Benzene | 1.50 | 1.463 | 1.612 | 1.667 | 1.398 | (1.390) | 1.393 |
| Naphthalene | | | | | | | |
| 1–2 | 1.67 | 1.63 | 1.652 | 1.725 | 1.388 | 1.378 | 1.365 |
| 2–3 | 1.33 | 1.29 | 1.612 | 1.603 | 1.398 | 1.400 | 1.404 |
| 1–0 | 1.33 | 1.27 | 1.508 | 1.555 | 1.420 | 1.409 | 1.425 |
| 0–0′ | 1.33 | 1.41 | 1.407 | 1.518 | 1.445 | 1.416 | 1.393 |
| Anthracene | | | | | | | |
| 1–2 | 1.75 | 1.45 | 1.652 | 1.738 | 1.388 | 1.376 | 1.366 |
| 2–3 | 1.25 | 1.38[5] | 1.612 | 1.586 | 1.398 | 1.403 | 1.419 |
| 1–0 | 1.25 | 1.36 | 1.508 | 1.535 | 1.420 | 1.413 | 1.433 |
| 9–0 | 1.50 | 1.37 | 1.556 | 1.606 | 1.410 | 1.399 | 1.399 |
| 0–0′ | 1.25 | 1.15 | 1.407 | 1.485 | 1.445 | 1.424 | 1.436 |
| Coronene | | | | | | | |
| internal | 1.30 | — | 1.489 | 1.522 | 1.425 | 1.415 | 1.430 |
| radial | 1.40 | — | 1.440 | 1.538 | 1.436 | 1.411 | 1.430 |
| ext. $C_{sec}$-$C_{sec}$ | 1.70 | — | 1.692 | 1.757 | 1.380 | 1.372 | 1.385 |
| ext. $C_{sec}$-$C_{tert}$ | 1.30 | — | 1.508 | 1.538 | 1.420 | 1.411 | 1.415 |

*See notes p. 300.*

When atom $k$ of a hydrocarbon is approached by a nucleophilic, negative (or an electrophilic, positive) reagent (p. 275), the change $\partial\alpha_k$ will be in opposite directions, namely an increase (or a decrease) of the COULOMB energy $\alpha_k$. Therefore the lowest energy $E$ is produced and so a reaction occurs where the electron density $q_k$ is low (or high respectively) or the net charge $1-q_k$ is positive (or negative); this was always postulated intuitively (p. 276).

In general we have:

$$dE = \frac{\partial E}{\partial \alpha_k} d\alpha_k + \tfrac{1}{2} \frac{\partial^2 E}{\partial \alpha^2_k} d\alpha^2_k + \ldots$$

In most isocyclic hydrocarbons (alternating hydrocarbons, see p. 304) the charge distribution is uniform, so that $q_k = 1$ for all atoms. Then these quantities are replaced by the so-called self-polarizability:

$$\pi_{kk} = \frac{\partial q_k}{\partial \alpha_k} = \frac{\partial^2 E}{\partial \alpha^2_k}$$

and the mutual polarizability:

$$\pi_{ik} = \frac{\partial q_i}{\partial \alpha_k} = \pi_{ki} = \frac{\partial^2 E}{\partial \alpha_i \, \partial \alpha_k}$$

These are important (negative!) quantities. While the charge density on atoms 1 and 2 is the same in naphthalene this is not the case with the selfpolarizability $\pi_{11}$ and $\pi_{22}$. The first is appreciably larger, so that in electrophilic substitution (chlorination, bromination and nitration), but also with nucleophilic reagents the activation energy is smallest for the 1-position, in agreement with experiment. At higher temperatures a transition to radical substitution via halogen atoms also occurs here, whereby positions 1 and 2 react the same (SIXMA and WIBAUT, p. 278).

The mutual polarizability is important because, through the alternating positive and negative sign of $\pi_{ik}$ depending on whether there is an even or an odd number of bonds present between $i$ and $k$, the well-known alternating polarity on introduction of a substituent is explained theoretically and can also be calculated quantitatively in a simple way.

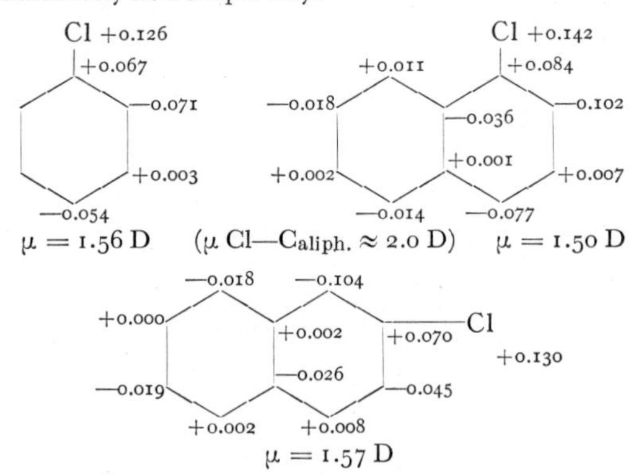


Difference 2 Cl- and 1 Cl-naphthalene $\Delta\mu = 0.07$ D, calculated $\Delta\mu = 0.08$ D (KETELAAR and OOSTERHOUT, 1946).

## § 36 B. DIPOLE MOMENT, NON-ALTERNATING HYDROCARBONS, COMPARISON OF V.B. AND M.O. METHODS, HYPERCONJUGATION

### *Dipole moment*

The electric dipole moment of a molecule is a valuable characteristic of its structure and also the value of the dipole moment is an important factor determining the cohesion energy. However, the relation between the dipole moment and the constitution is complicated even for a diatomic molecule or for one bond (COULSON, book, p. 210); MULLIKEN, 1950; SMYTH, 1955; BURNELLE and COULSON, 1957).

We have to discern:

*a. the primary dipole.* The molecular orbital for a molecule $AB$ is: $\varphi = \varphi_A + \lambda\varphi_B$. The value of the parameter $\lambda$ depends on the difference in electronegativity. If $B$ is more electronegative the charge cloud will be displaced towards $B$, even if both $\varphi_A$ and $\varphi_B$ are spherical. Only for $\lambda = 1$ will the dipole moment be zero.

A more detailed discussion would show that for $\lambda = 2$ the relative moment will be $\mu/e.R_{AB} = 0.56$. For HF, HCl, HBr and HI it is calculated that $\lambda = 1.88$, 1.28, 1.19 and 1.06.

In the valence bond method the primary dipole has its origin in the contribution of ionic terms (p. 147).

*b. homopolar dipole.* Even if $\lambda = 1$ or if there are no ionic terms, a small dipole moment may arise from the difference in size of both atoms.

The charge is: $(\varphi_A + \varphi_B)^2 = \varphi_A{}^2 + 2\varphi_A\varphi_B + \varphi_B{}^2$. Even if $\varphi_A{}^2$ and $\varphi_B{}^2$ are both spherical and equal, the charge from the term $2\varphi_A\varphi_B$ will not lie half way between $A$ and $B$ if one of the functions $\varphi_A$ and $\varphi_B$ extends further in space than the other.

*c. atomic dipole.* The charge clouds corresponding to s, p, d, etc. atomic wave functions are symmetric with respect to the centre. However, this is no longer the case for hybrid functions like sp, $sp^2$ and $sp^3$. Thus bonds arising from these functions will also have a dipole moment, irrespective of the other causes.

*d. inductive dipole.* The dipole moment will be influenced by the polarization of non-bonding electron pairs. Owing to this effect the dipole moment increases somewhat in the series of the alkyl chlorides from methyl chloride ($\mu = 1.92$ D) to *n*-butyl chloride ($\mu = 2.12$ D). The difference between the moment of methyl chloride ($\mu = 1.92$ D) and chloroform ($\mu = 1.02$ D) must also be ascribed to polarization rather than to the unimportant change of bond angles (p. 161). The vector addition of bond moments is approximately allowed only for cases where these bonds have no common atom.

*e. lone pair.* Lone pairs of electrons in hybrid orbitals will also contribute to the total dipole moment by their atomic dipole (see *c*). In some cases this contribution will be quite large, of the order of 1–2 D, *e.g.*, in water and ammonia. $NH_3$ (107°) and $NF_3$ (102°) have about the same bond angles and one would expect the N–F bond to be just as polar as the N–H bond because of the equal difference in electronegativity. Since $NF_3$ has a very small moment of 0.2 D there must be a compensating contribution from the moment of the lone pair of electrons. In $NH_3$ the bond moment will have the opposite sign ($\sim$ 0.7 D with H positive) and the lone-pair contribution ($\sim$ 0.7 D) has to be added; consequently the dipole moment is rather larger (1.47 D) (McKean and Schatz, 1956).

*Non-alternating hydrocarbons*

It is useful to divide the hydrocarbons with a conjugated system of bonds into the common, alternating hydrocarbons which have exclusively open chains or rings with an even number of bonds in which the double and single bonds alternate with each other, and the non-alternating hydrocarbons. The non-alternating hydrocarbons include compounds such as azulene (Gordon, 1952) and fulvene (Day, 1953) with ten and six "aromatic" electrons respectively; these are isomers of naphthalene and benzene.

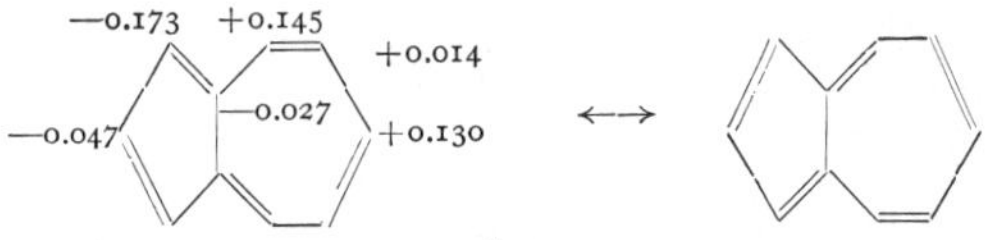

−0.173 +0.145 +0.014 −0.047 −0.027 +0.130 ⟷

azulene

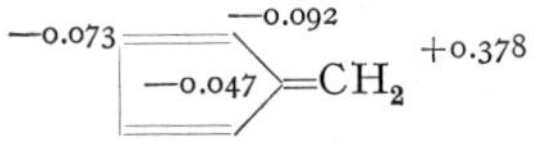

−0.073 −0.092 −0.047 $=CH_2$ +0.378 and excited configurations such as $-CH_2$

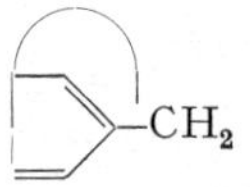

fulvene

Here the charges as indicated (Coulson, Graig and Maccoll, 1948; Berthier, 1953) are no longer the same for each carbon atom as in the alternating hydrocarbons. Consequently the hydrocarbons have rather large dipole moments (azulene 1.0 D, dimethylfulvene 1.48 D, Wheland and Mann, 1949; fulvene 1.1 D, Thiec and Wiemann, 1956). The hydrocarbons are also remarkable because they are coloured, fulvene being the simplest coloured hydrocarbon.

Tropolone, discovered by Dewar (Dewar, 1945), and tropone or cycloheptatrienone (Cook and London, 1951; Pauson, 1955a; Nozoe, 1956) resemble azulene.

O= HO− ⟷ ⊖ |O− HO− ⊕

From an electron-diffraction study of tropolone (Heilbronner and Hedberg, 1951; Kimura and Kubo, 1953) and from X-ray investigations of tropolone derivatives (Robertson, 1951; Sasada, Osaki and Nitta, 1954) and tropone (Kimura *et al.*, 1957) it has been found that the seven-membered ring is flat and that all bonds are about equal in length (1.40 Å); it is thus a true aromatic system.

To express this equivalence according to the V.B. method by electron configurations, it is necessary to consider ionic configurations such as those above. The dipole moments of tropolone (3.53 D) and tropone (4.17 D) are larger than might be expected.

However, in sodium tropolonate resonance between the equivalent configurations makes the bond between both oxygen-carrying carbon atoms much longer (1.47 Å) than the others (1.42—1.38 Å) (SASADA and NITTA, 1956).

The positive tropylium-ion (cycloheptatrienylium-ion) might be recognized as the aromatic kernel; it is iso-electronic with the cyclopentadienyl-anion and with benzene (p. 191).

The sydnones (BAKER, OLLIS and POOLE, 1949; HILL and SUTTON, 1949; BAKER and OLLIS, 1957) are also remarkable, the configuration which best represents the stationary charge distribution being that given below. Here *only* ionic configurations can be written down (meso-ionic compounds). The substances also have very high dipole moments of about 6.7 D.

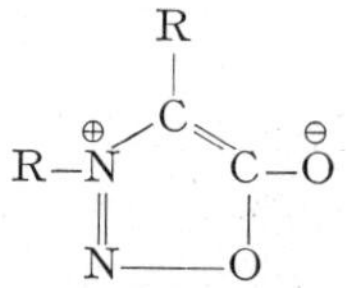

The M.O. representation, which foregoes the setting up of special chemical formulae and gives only bond orders and charge distribution for the various bonds, is greatly preferable to the very artificial V.B. interpretation in the case of these non-alternating compounds. It is the number of "aromatic" electrons which is characteristic.

### *Comparison of V.B. and M.O. methods*

Summarizing, we can interpret the advantages and disadvantages of the V.B. and M.O. methods as follows: The V.B. method can be interpreted on the basis of the chemical structural formulae by the introduction of the resonance idea. Here the formation of electron pairs is introduced *a priori* in agreement with experience in practically all compounds. It appears, however, that the charge density between two atoms, for example in $H_2$, is found too low according to this method. In addition, it is not easy to apply the method to more complicated molecules without introducing further simplifying assumptions; it is also difficult to take account of the difference in electronegativity in an appropriate way with hetero-atoms in the molecule. The calculations are much simpler with the M.O. method both for hydrocarbons and for compounds with hetero-atoms; moreover, it is not difficult to carry out the calculation to better approximations by taking into account the non-equivalence of similar atoms and the interaction between non-adjacent atoms. Since the formation of pairs is only introduced at a later stage, the M.O. method does not make sufficient allowance for the interaction between the electrons themselves (correlation energy). Because of this, the calculated charge density between the atoms in $H_2$ is found too high and calculated variations in the charge density are too large. For the calculation of the activation energies in chemical reactions, there is also the difficulty that the usual construction from "atomic orbitals" always results in a stability for complexes such as $H_3$ and $H_4$ etc.

At present, the M.O. method (with refinements) is used throughout for reliable quantitative calculations. In the interpretation of the results one operates, however, with concepts such as bond order and free valency which actually correspond to ideas of the V.B. method. Again for qualitative interpretations the V.B. method is generally used, as has often been the case in this book. One calculates by the M.O. method but speaks the V.B. language!

The V.B. and M.O. methods become equivalent if we carry the approximations further; this can be shown from a discussion of the $H_2$ molecule by both methods. We have improved the HEITLER-LONDON treatment (V.B. method) by including ionic terms (p. 146):

$$\varphi_{V.B.} = [\varphi_A(1)\,\varphi_B(2) + \varphi_B(1)\,\varphi_A(2)] + c[\varphi_A(1)\,\varphi_A(2) + \varphi_B(1)\,\varphi_B(2)]$$

In the M.O. method, the wave function in the L.C.A.O. approximation for both electrons is:

$$\varphi_{M.O.} = \varphi_{M.O.}(1) \cdot \varphi_{M.O.}(2) = [\varphi_A(1) + \varphi_B(1)]\,[\varphi_A(2) + \varphi_B(2)] =$$
$$= \varphi_A(1)\,\varphi_B(2) + \varphi_B(1)\,\varphi_A(2) + \varphi_A(1)\,\varphi_A(2) + \varphi_B(1)\,\varphi_B(2)\,.$$

To this function for the configuration with both electrons in the bonding orbital $\varphi_A + \varphi_B$, we can add a contribution from a configuration with both electrons in the anti-bonding orbital $\varphi_A - \varphi_B$ in order to improve the variation function:

$$+\,k[\varphi_A(1) - \varphi_B(1)]\,[(\varphi_A(2) - \varphi_B(2)]\,.$$

(The configuration with one electron in both the bonding and the anti-bonding orbital does not contribute because of different symmetry, p. 211.)

The wave functions according to the two methods are now in principle equal.

On dividing by $(1 - k)$, the second function can be brought into exactly the same form as the first, only with $(1 + k)\,/\,(1 - k)$ instead of $c$. If we now choose the parameters in the variation function so as to make the energy a minimum, the same solution will be obtained with both methods. The equivalence of both methods in further approximations is quite generally true (LONGUET-HIGGINS, 1948).

Several more refined methods (LÖWDIN, 1957) have been used which give good results (PARR and ELLISON, 1955). However, rather elaborate calculations are necessary in most cases. A discussion of such methods is outside the scope of this book, *e.g.*, the antisymmetrised M.O. method or ASMO (GOEPPERT-MAYER and SKLAR, 1938; PARISER and PARR, 1953), the self-consistent field, SCF, treatment (ROOTHAAN, 1951), configuration interaction, C. I., (PARR, CRAIG and ROSS, 1950), atoms in molecules (A.I.M.) method (MOFFITT, 1951).

The success of the wave-mechanical ideas lies especially in the province of the conjugated systems*. The influence of saturated groups, for example the changes in the properties on the replacement of a hydrogen atom by a methyl group, can be interpreted partly in the same way as was done in the older electron theory of the bond, namely as an electro-inductive effect in which the methyl group is less electrophilic than the hydrogen atom, so that in toluene, xylene, etc., the methyl group is positive with respect to the ring (pp. 240, 282). There is, however, another possible explanation.

*Hyperconjugation*

The heat of hydrogenation of *trans*-dimethylethylene or bu-

* Other subjects to which the methods of quantum chemistry have been applied with success are, *e.g.*, redox potentials of quinones (EVANS and DE HEER, 1950; FRITZ and HARTMANN, 1951; MAGNUS, 1956) and polarographic reduction (MACCOLL, 1949; WATSON and MATSEN, 1950; HOYTINK *et al.*, 1953, 1955; BERGMANN, 1954; MATSEN, 1956; GIVEN, 1958).

There is a relation between the value of the half-wave potential $E_{\frac{1}{2}}$ and the energy $h\nu$ corresponding to the long wave U.V. absorption band; $h\nu = 2\,E_{\frac{1}{2}} +$ constant, the energies expressed in eV/mole.

We have seen that in the oth approximation (p. 293) the highest occupied level has an energy equal to $\alpha + m\beta$ and the lowest unoccupied level is $\alpha - m\beta$. Thus $h\nu = -2\,m\beta$, whereas $E_{\frac{1}{2}} = \alpha - m\beta$ as one electron is added in the lowest unoccupied level on polarographic reduction.

Basicity or proton affinity of aromatic hydrocarbons (MACKOR, HOFSTRA and VAN DER WAALS, 1958).

tene 2 is 5.2 kcal lower than that of ethylene, etc.; the former molecule is, therefore, more stable. We have seen already that branched aliphatic hydrocarbons are more stable than the normal hydrocarbons (p. 206). MULLIKEN introduced the hypothesis of hyperconjugation (DEASY, 1945; CRAWFORD, 1949; BAKER, 1952; BECKER, 1953) drawing a formal parallel between acrylonitrile (or vinylacetylene) and propene.

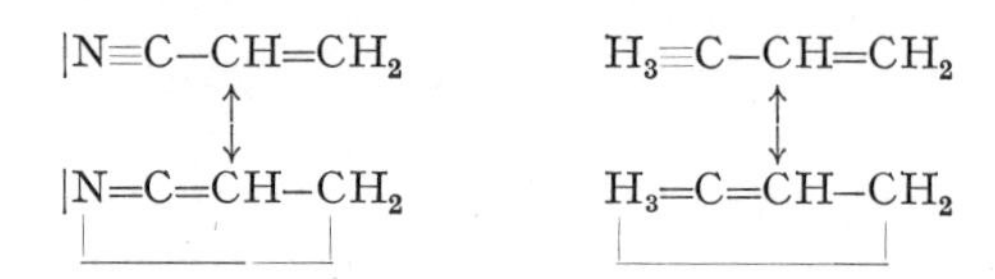


Although this hyperconjugation of the 1st order (that of the 2nd order is a hyperconjugation between two $CH_3$-groups, as in ethane, similar to cyanogen or to diacetylene CH≡C—C≡CH) is possible in many cases, it is difficult to see how this hyperconjugation would be the most important among the numerous effects of the second order which occur besides ordinary resonance in a conjugated system. On the contrary we have seen (p. 160) that the change in the hybridization on the transition from H—$CH_2$—C to H—CH=C and to H—C≡C has a very important influence on the length of the H—C bond, although there is no question of hyperconjugation in acetylene. A similar change in the hybridization will certainly also occur for the C—$CH_3$ bond, explaining thus at least partially the observed C—$CH_3$ distance of 1.46 Å in methyl acetylene.

We believe thus that, although the idea of hyperconjugation is correct in principle, there are nevertheless no sufficient grounds for attributing so much value to this effect rather than to the influence of changes in hybridization and differences in electronegativity for an explanation of the properties of organic compounds.

Our understanding is incomplete on many points; the correlation energy and the interaction between $\sigma$ and $\pi$ electrons are important problems in this respect.

## CONCLUSION

We have seen that wave mechanics is able to produce a satisfactory picture of the atomic bond. In particular the application of the resonance concept brings understanding of countless phenomena.

Resonance, strictly speaking, is *not* a real physical phenomenon but only an interpretation, as a consequence of the way in which in the valence bond method the wave function of the stationary state, for example of the benzene molecule, can be constructed approximately by linear combination of other wave functions. This construction is possible in a way which fits in well with the interpretation of these systems based on the theory of chemical structure.

The method of molecular orbitals is of great value for quantitative discussions, especially of molecules containing hetero-atoms.

Much may still be expected in the future from the elaboration of the modern ideas, also in the quantitative sense, and their application to the extensive experimental data on the countless organic compounds. For this purpose it will, however, be necessary to prepare many of these compounds, although they have long been known, in a pure state and to determine their heats of combustion, spectra, bond lengths, dipole moments, etc.

## GENERAL LITERATURE

*Wave Mechanical Theory of the Chemical Bond.* See p. 22 and also:

C. A. Coulson, *Quart. Revs. (London)*, 1 (1947) 144.

C. A. Coulson, *Valence*, Oxford, 1952, a very recommendable book on the fundamental concepts of the theory of valence.

P. and R. Daudel, *Les Apports de la Mécanique Ondulatoire à l'Etude de la Molécule,* Paris, 1950.

H. Hartmann, *Theorie der Chemischen Bindung*, Berlin, 1954.

H. C. Longuet-Higgins and G. W. Wheland, in *Ann. Rev. Phys. Chem.*, 1 (1950) 133.

W. G. Penney, *The Quantum Theory of Valency*, London, 1935.

A. and B. Pullman, *Les Théories Electroniques de la Chimie Organique*, Paris, 1952.

J. H. Van Vleck and A. Sherman, *Revs. Modern Phys.*, 7 (1935) 174.

Interesting symposium on bond energies and bond lengths: *Proc. Roy. Soc., (London)*, 207 (1951) 1–136. Symposia on the chemical bond: *J. chim. phys.*, 46 (1949) 185–306; *Z. Electrochem.*, 61 (1957) 857–1110; *J. Phys. Chem.*, 61 (1957) 1–68.

*Theoretical (Organic) Chemistry*

G. E. K. BRANCH and M. CALVIN, *The Theory of Organic Chemistry*, New York, 1945.
L. B. CLAPP, *Chemistry of the Covalent Bond*, San Francisco, 1957.
M. J. S. DEWAR, *The Electronic Theory of Organic Chemistry*, Oxford, 1949, 1953.
B. EISTERT, *Tautomerie und Mesomerie*, Stuttgart, 1938; *Chemismus und Konstitution*, I, Stuttgart, 1948.
L. P. HAMMETT, *Physical Organic Chemistry*, New York, 1940.
P. H. HERMANS, *Introduction to Theoretical Organic Chemistry*, Amsterdam, New York, 1953.
J. HINE, *Physical Organic Chemistry*, New York, 1956.
W. HÜCKEL, *Theoretische Organische Chemie*, Weinheim, 1953; *Theoretical Principles of Organic Chemistry*, Amsterdam, 1955.
C. K. INGOLD, *Structure and Mechanism in Organic Chemistry*, Ithaca, 1955.
E. MÜLLER, *Neuere Anschauungen auf dem Gebiete der organischen Chemie*, 2nd Ed., Berlin, 1957.
L. PAULING, *The Nature of the Chemical Bond*, Ithaca, 1950.
A. E. REMICK, *Electronic Interpretations of Organic Chemistry*, 2nd Ed., New York, 1949. Older electron theory also C. K. INGOLD, *Chem. Revs.*, *15* (1934) 225.
W. A. WATERS, *The Physical Aspects of Organic Chemistry*, 4th Ed., Oxford, 1950.
G. W. WHELAND, *The Theory of Resonance and its Applications to Organic Chemistry*, New York, 1945; *Resonance in Organic Chemistry*, New York, 1955.

## REFERENCES


ABRAHAMS, S. C. and KALNAP, J., *Acta Cryst.*, *7* (1954) 838; *8* (1955) 503.
AHMED, F. R. and CRUICKSHANK, D. W. J., *Acta Cryst.*, *5* (1952) 852.
AHRENS, L. H., *Nature*, *169* (1952) 463.
ANDERSON, J. S., *Quart. Revs. (London)*, *1* (1947) 331.
ANDREWS, L. J. and KEEFER, R. M., *J. Am. Chem. Soc.*, *71* (1949) 3644.
ANNO, T. and SADO, A., *J. Chem. Phys.*, *25* (1956) 176.
AUDRIETH, L., STEINMAN, R. and TOY, A., *Chem. Revs.*, *32* (1943) 109.

BACON, G. E., *Neutron Diffraction*, London, 1955.
BADGER, G. M., *J. Chem. Soc.*, (1949) 456.
BADGER, G. M., *Quart. Revs., (London)*, *5* (1951) 147; *Rec. trav. chim.* *71* (1952) 468.
BADGER, R. M., *J. Chem. Phys.*, *2* (1934) 128.
BAILAR, J. C., *Chemistry of Coordination Compounds*, New York, 1956.
BAKER, J. W., *Hyperconjugation*, Oxford, 1952.
BAKER, W. and OLLIS, W. D., *Quart. Revs. (London)*, *11* (1957) 15.
BAKER, W., OLLIS, W. D. and POOLE, V. D., *J. Chem. Soc.*, (1949) 307.
BASTIANSEN, O. and HASSEL, O., *Acta Chem. Scand.*, *6* (1952) 205.
BASTIANSEN, O., HEDBERG, L. and HEDBERG, K., *J. Chem. Phys.*, *27* (1957) 1311.
BAUGHAN, E. C., *Trans. Faraday Soc.*, *53* (1957) 1046.
BAYLISS, N. S., *J. Chem. Phys.*, *16* (1948) 287.
BAYLISS, N. S., *Quart. Revs. (London)*, *6* (1952) 319.
BEAVEN, H. G. and HALL, D. M., *J. Chem. Soc.*, (1956) 4637.
BECKER, F., *Angew. Chem.*, *65* (1953) 97.
BELL, F. and WARING, D. H., *J. Chem. Soc.*, (1949) 2689.
BELL, R. P. and EMELEUS, H. J., *Quart. Revs. (London)*, *2* (1948) 132.

BELL, R. P., THOMPSON, H. W. and VAGO, E.E., *Proc. Roy. Soc. (London), A 192* (1948) 498.
BERGMANN, I., *Trans. Faraday Soc., 50* (1954) 829.
BERSOHN, H., *J. Chem. Phys., 22* (1954) 2078.
BERTHIER, G., *J. Chem. Phys., 21* (1953) 953; *J. chim. phys., 50* (1953) 344.
BETHELL, D. E. and SHEPPARD, N., *J. chim. phys., 50* (1953) C 72.
BJERRUM, J., *Chem. Revs., 46* (1950) 381.
BJERRUM, J., BALLHAUSEN, C. J. and KLIXBÜLL JÖRGENSEN, C., *Acta Chem. Scand., 8* (1954) 1275; *Rec. trav. chim., 75* (1956) 658.
BOESEKEN, M., *Bull. soc. chim. France, 53* (1933) 1332.
BORN, M., *Science, 122* (1955) 675.
BRAUDE, E. A. and FORBES, W. F., *J. Chem. Soc.*, (1955) 776.
BRAY, P. J. and BARNES, R. G., *J. Chem. Phys., 27* (1957) 551.
BREWER, L. and SEARCY, A. W., *Ann. Rev. Phys. Chem., 7* (1956) 259.
BROADLEY, J. S. and ROBERTSON, J. M., *Nature, 164* (1949) 915.
BROCKWAY, L. O. and BRIGHT, W. M., *J. Am. Chem. Soc., 65* (1943) 1551.
BROOKER, L. J. S., *Revs. Modern Phys., 14* (1942) 275; *Frontiers of Chemistry, 3, Advances in Nuclear Chemistry and Theoretical Chemistry*, New York, 1945.
BROWN, R. D., *Trans. Faraday Soc., 45* (1949) 296; *46* (1950a) 146, 1013.
BROWN, R. D., *J. Chem. Soc.*, (1950b) 3249.
BROWN, R. D., *Quart. Revs. (London), 6* (1952) 63.
BURKIN, A. R., *Quart. Revs. (London), 5* (1951) 1.
BURNELLE, L. and COULSON, C. A., *Trans. Faraday Soc., 53* (1957) 403.
BUZEMAN, A., *Proc. Phys. Soc. (London), 63* (1950) 827.
BIJVOET, J. M., *Koninkl. Ned. Akad. Wetenschap. Proc., 52* (1949) 313.
BIJVOET, J. M., PEERDEMANS, A. F. and VAN BOMMEL, A. J., *Nature, 168* (1951) 271.

CABLE, J. W. and SHELINE, R. K., *Chem. Revs., 56* (1956) 1.
CARTER, P. G., *Trans. Faraday Soc., 45* (1949) 597.
CHALVET, O., *Rec. trav. chim., 75* (1956) 385; *Compt. rend., 240* (1955) 871.
CHIRGWIN, B. H. and COULSON, C. A., *Proc. Roy. Soc. (London), A201* (1950) 196.
CLAR, E., *Aromatische Kohlenwasserstoffe*, Berlin, 1941, 1952.
COATES, G. E. and SUTTON, L. E., *J. Chem. Soc.*, (1948) 1117.
CONWAY, B. E., BOCKRIS, J. O'M. and LINTON, H., *J. Chem. Phys., 24* (1956) 835.
COOK, J. W. and LONDON, J. D., *Quart. Revs. (London), 5* (1951) 99.
COOPS, J. *et al., Rec. trav. chim., 65* (1946) 128; *72* (1953) 785.
COTTON, F. A., *Chem. Revs., 55* (1955) 563.
COTTON, F. A. and WILKINSON, G., *Z. Naturforsch., 9b* (1954) 453.
COTTRELL, T. L., *The Strength of Chemical Bonds*, London, 1954.
COULSON, C. A., *Proc. Roy. Soc.* (*London*), *A 169* (1939) 413; *Proc. Roy. Soc.* (*Edinburgh*), *A 61* (1941) 115.
COULSON, C. A., *Trans. Faraday Soc., 42* (1946) 106, 265.
COULSON, C. A., *Discussions Faraday Soc., Nr. 2* (1947a) 9.
COULSON, C. A., *Quart. Revs.* (*London*), *1* (1947b) 144.
COULSON, C. A., *Proc. Roy. Soc.* (*London*), *A 207* (1951) 91.
COULSON, C. A., *Valence*, Oxford, 1952.
COULSON, C. A., *Proc. Phys. Soc.* (*London*), *66A* (1953) 652.
COULSON, C. A., CRAIG, D. P. and MACCOLL, A., *Proc. Phys. Soc.* (*London*), *61* (1948) 22.
COULSON, C. A., DAUDEL, P. and DAUDEL, R., *Rev. sci., 85* (1947) 29.
COULSON, C. A., DAUDEL, R. and ROBERTSON, J. M., *Proc. Roy. Soc.* (*London*), *A 207* (1951) 306.

Coulson, C. A. and Duchesne, J., *Bull. classe sci. Acad. roy. Belg.*, *43* (1957) 522.
Coulson, C. A. and Longuet-Higgins, H. C., *Proc. Roy. Soc. (London)*, *A 192* (1947) 16.
Coulson, C. A. and Moffitt, W. E., *J. Chem. Phys.*, *15* (1947) 151.
Coulson, C. A. and Stephen, M. J., *Trans. Faraday Soc.*, *53* (1957) 272.
Cox, E. G., Cruickshank, D. W. J. and Smith, J. A. S., *Nature*, *175* (1955) 766.
Craig, D. P., *Proc. Roy. Soc. (London) A 200* (1950) 401.
Craig, D. P. *et al.*, *J. Chem. Soc.*, (1954) 352.
Craig, D. P. and Paddock, N. L., *Nature*, *181* (1958) 1052.
Crawford, V. A., *Quart. Revs. (London)*, *3* (1949) 226.
Cruickshank, D. W. J., *Acta Cryst.*, *9* (1956) 757, 915; *10* (1957) 470.
Cruickshank, D. W. J. and Robertson, A. P., *Acta Cryst.*, *6* (1953) 698.

Daudel, P. and R., *J. Chem. Phys.*, *16* (1948) 639.
Daudel, P. and R. *et al.*, *Rev. sci.*, *84* (1946) 849; *Compt. rend.*, *223* (1946) 223.
Daudel, R., *Cahiers phys.*, *44* (1953) 1.
Daudel, R., Brion, H. and Odiot, S., *J. chim. phys.*, *51* (1954) 74, 358, 553; *J. Chem. Phys.*, *23* (1955) 2080.
Daudel, R. and Pullman, A., *J. chim. phys.*, *43* (1946) 77; *J. phys.*, *7* (1946) 59, 74, 106.
Daudel, R. *et al.*, *Bull. soc. chim. France*, (1950) 66.
Day, J. H., *Chem. Revs.*, *53* (1953) 167.
Deasy, C. L., *Chem. Revs.*, *36* (1945) 145.
Dewar, M. J. S., *Nature*, *155* (1945) 50; *J. Chem. Soc.*, (1952) 3532.
Doehaerd, T., Goldfinger, P. and Waelbroek, F., *J. Chem. Phys.*, *20* (1952) 757.
Donaldson, D. M. and Robertson, J. M., *J. Chem. Soc.*, (1953) 17.
Dousmanis, G. C., *Phys. Rev.*, *97* (1955) 967.
Drenth, W., *Rec. trav. chim.*, *73* (1954) 249.
Dulmage, W. J., Meyers, E. A. and Lipscomb, W. N., *Acta Cryst.*, *6* (1953) 760.
Dunitz, J. D. and Orgel, L. E., *Nature*, *171* (1953) 121.
Dunitz, J. D., Orgel, L. E. and Rich, A., *Acta Cryst.*, *9* (1956) 373.

Engelsma, J. W., Kooyman, E. C. and Van der Bij, J. R., *Rec. trav. chim.*, *76* (1957) 325.
Evans, M. G. and De Heer, J., *Acta Cryst.*, *2* (1949) 263.
Evans, M. G. and De Heer, J., *Quart. Revs. (London)*, *4* (1950) 94.
Eyring, H. and Kimball, G. E., *J. Chem. Phys.*, *1* (1933) 239, 626.

Falk, M. and Giguère, P. A., *Can. J. Chem.*, *35* (1957) 1195.
Farag, M. S., *Acta Cryst.*, *7* (1954) 117.
Farkas, A., *Physical Chemistry of Hydrocarbons*, Vol. I, New York, 1950.
Fateley, W. G. and Lippincott, E. R., *J. Chem. Phys.*, *26* (1957) 1471.
Ferguson, L. N., *Chem. Revs.*, *43* (1948) 385.
Ferriso, C. C. and Hornig, D. F., *J. Am. Chem. Soc.*, *75* (1953) 4113; *J. Chem. Phys.*, *23* (1955) 1464.
Fischer, E. O. and Hafner, W., *Z. Naturforsch.*, *10b* (1955) 665; *Z. anorg. u. allgem. Chem.*, *286* (1956) 146.
Fischer, E. O. and Pfab, W., *Z. Naturforsch.*, *7b* (1952) 377.
Förster, Th., *Z. physik. Chem. (Leipzig)*, *B 47* (1940) 245.
Förster, Th., *Angew. Chem.*, *62* (1950) 336.
Franklin, J. L., *Ind. Eng. Chem.*, *41* (1949) 1070; *J. Am. Chem. Soc.*, *72* (1950) 4278.
Fritz, G. and Hartmann, H., *Z. Elektrochem.*, *55* (1951) 181.
Furberg, S., *Acta Chem. Scand.*, *9* (1955) 1557.

GEHLEN, H., *Z. physik. Chem. (Leipzig)*, *203* (1954) 124.
GENT, W. L. G., *Quart. Revs. (London)*, *2* (1948) 383.
GERDING, H., NIJVELD, W. J. and MULLER, G. J., *Z. physik. Chem. (Leipzig)*, *B 35* (1937) 193.
GILLESPIE, R. J. and NYHOLM, R. S., *Quart. Revs. (London)*, *11* (1957) 339.
GIVEN, P. H., *Nature*, *181* (1958) 1001.
GLOCKLER, G., *J. Chem. Phys.*, *19* (1951) 124.
GOEPPERT-MAYER, M. and SKLAR, A. L., *J. Chem. Phys.*, *6* (1938) 645.
GOLDSTEIN, J. H., *J. Chem. Phys.*, *24* (1956) 507.
GORDON, M., *Chem. Revs.*, *50* (1952) 127.
GORDY, W., *Phys. Rev.*, *69* (1946) 604.
GORDY, W., *J. Chem. Phys.*, *19* (1951) 792.
GORDY, W. and ORVILLE THOMAS, W. J., *J. Chem. Phys.*, *24* (1956) 439.
GORDY, W., SMITH, W. V. and TRAMBARULO, R. F., *Microwave Spectroscopy*, New York, 1953.
GRAY, P. and YOFFE, A. D., *Chem. Revs.*, *55* (1955) 1069.
GREENWOOD, N. N., *Trans. Faraday Soc.*, *48* (1952) 585.
GREENWOOD, N. N., *J. Inorg. & Nuclear Chem.*, *5* (1958) 224, 229.
GREENWOOD, N. N., and MARTIN, R. L., *J. Chem. Soc.*, (1951) 1915.
GRIFFITH, J. S. and ORGEL, L. E., *Quart. Revs. (London)*, 11 (1957) 381.
GRISON, E., ERIKS, K. and DE VRIES, J. L., *Acta Cryst.*, *3* (1950) 290.

HAAYMAN, P. W. and WIBAUT, J. P., *Rec. trav. chim.*, *60* (1941) 842.
HAISSINSKY, M., *J. chim. phys.*, *46* (1949) 298.
HARNIK, E., HERBSTEIN, F. H., SCHMIDT, G. M. J. and HIRSHFELD, F. J., *J. Chem. Soc.*, (1954) 3288, 3295, 3302, 3314.
HARTMANN, H., *Z. Naturforsch.*, *2A* (1947) 259, 263.
HARTMANN, H., *Z. physik. Chem. (Frankfurt)*, *4* (1955) 376.
HARTMANN, H. and ILSE, F. E. or SCHLÄFER, H. L., *Z. physik. Chem. (Leipzig)*, *197* (1951) 116, 239; *Z. Naturforsch.*, *6a* (1951) 751, 754, 760.
HEDBERG, K. and SCHOMAKER, V., *J. Am. Chem. Soc.*, *73* (1951) 1482.
HEILBRONNER, E. and HEDBERG, K., *J. Am. Chem. Soc.*, *73* (1951) 1386.
HEIN, F., *Chemische Koordinationslehre*, Zürich, 1950.
HEITLER, W., *Helv. Chim. Acta*, *38* (1955) 5; *J. chim. phys.*, *54* (1957) 265.
HENRICI, A., *Z. physik. Chem. (Leipzig)*, *B47* (1940) 93, 111.
HERMANS, P. H., *Z. anorg. Chem.*, *142* (1925) 83.
HERZBERG, G. and STOICHEFF, B. P., *Nature*, *175* (1955) 79.
HERZFELD, K. L. and SKLAR, A. L., *Revs. Modern Phys.*, *14* (1942) 294.
HILL, R. W. and SUTTON, L. E., *J. chim. phys.*, *46* (1949) 244.
HIRSHFELD, E. L., ERIKS, K., DICKERSON, R. E., LIPPERT, E. L. and LIPSCOMB, W. N., *J. Chem. Phys.*, *28* (1958) 56.
HOARD, J. L., *Acta Cryst.*, *4* (1951) 396, 399, 405.
HONIG, A., MANDEL, M. STITCH, M. L. and TOWNES, C. H., *Phys. Rev.* *96* (1954) 629.
HORNIG, D. F. and MCKEAN, D. C., *J. Phys. Chem.*, *59* (1955) 1133.
HOYTINK, G. J., *Rec. trav. chim.*, *74* (1955) 1525.
HOYTINK, G. J. and VAN SCHOOTEN, J., *Rec. trav. chim.*, *72* (1953) 903.
HOWE, J. A. and GOLDSTEIN, J. H., *J. Chem. Phys.*, *26* (1957) 7.
HÜCKEL, E., *Z. Physik*, *70* (1931) 204.
HÜCKEL, E., *Z. Elektrochem.*, *43* (1937) 752, 827 (review).
HUGGINS, M. L., *J. Am. Chem. Soc.*, *75* (1953) 4123, 4126.
HUGHES, R. H., *Phys. Rev.*, *85* (1952) 717; *J. Chem. Phys.*, *21* (1953) 959; *24* (1956) 131.
HUTCHINSON, C. A., KOWALSKY, A., PASTOR, R. C. and WHELAND, G. W., *J. Chem. Phys.*, *20* (1952) 1485.

INGRAM, D. J. E., *Spectroscopy at Radio and Microwave Frequencies*, London, 1955.
INGRAM, D. J. E., *Free Radicals-As studied by Microwave Methods*, London, 1958.
INGOLD, C. K. *et al.*, *J. Chem. Soc.*, (1955) 3200.
IRVING, H. and WILLIAMS, R. J. P., *Nature*, *162* (1948) 746; *J. Chem. Soc.*, (1953) 3192.

JAFFÉ, H. H., *J. Chem. Phys.*, *20* (1952) 279, 778.
JAFFÉ, H. H., *Chem. Revs.*, *53* (1953) 191.

KARLE, I. L., *J. Chem. Phys.*, *20* (1952) 65.
KASPAR, J. S., LUCHT, C. M. and HARKER, D., *Acta Cryst.*, *3* (1950) 436.
KAUZMANN, P., *Quantum Chemistry*, New York, 1957.
KERN, D. M. H., *J. Chem. Educ.*, *33* (1956) 272.
KETELAAR, J. A. A., *Rec. trav. chim.*, *58* (1939) 266.
KETELAAR, J. A. A. and DE VRIES, T. A., *Rec. trav. chim.*, *58* (1939) 1081.
KETELAAR, J. A. A. and PALMER, K. J., *J. Am. Chem. Soc.*, *59* (1937) 2629.
KETELAAR, J. A. A. and VAN DRANEN, J., *Rec. trav. chim.*, *69* (1949) 477.
KETELAAR, J. A. A. and VAN OOSTERHOUT, G. W., *Rec. trav. chim.*, *65* (1946) 448.
KILPATRICK, J. E. and PITZER, K. S., *J. Chem. Phys.*, *14* (1946) 463.
KIMURA, M. and KUBO, M., *Bull. Chem. Soc. Japan*, *26* (1953) 250.
KIMURA, K. *et al.*, *J. Chem. Phys.*, *27* (1957) 320.
KIRKWOOD, J. G. and WESTHEIMER, F. H., *J. Chem. Phys.*, *6* (1939) 506, 513; *Trans. Faraday Soc.*, *43* (1947) 77.
KISTIAKOWSKY, H. *et al.*, *J. Am. Chem. Soc.*, *57* (1935) 876; *58* (1936) 137; *73* (1951) 2972.
KLAGES, F., *Chem. Ber.*, *82* (1949) 358.
KLEMENT, R. and KOCH, O., *Chem. Ber.*, *87* (1954) 9253.
KLINKENBERG, L. J. and KETELAAR, J. A. A., *Rec. trav. chim.*, *54* (1935) 157.
KNIPE, R. H., *J. Chem. Phys.*, *23* (1955) 2089.
KOOYMAN, E. C., *Rec. trav. chim.*, *66* (1947) 477.
KOOYMAN, E. C. and HERINGA, J. W., *Nature*, *170* (1952) 661.
KOOYMAN, E. C., and KETELAAR, J. A. A., *Rec. trav. chim.*, *65* (1946) 859.
KUHN, H., *Helv. Chim. Acta.*, *31* (1948) 1441.

LANGSETH, A. and STOICHEFF, B. P., *Can. J. Phys.*, *34* (1956) 350.
LASSETTRE, E. N. and DEAN, L. B., *J. Chem. Phys.*, *17* (1949) 317.
LENNARD-JONES, J. E., *Adv. Sci.*, *51* (1954) 136.
LENNARD-JONES, J. E. and COULSON, C. A., *Trans. Faraday Soc.*, *35* (1939) 811.
LEVINE, A. A. and COLE, A. G., *J. Am. Chem. Soc.*, *54* (1932) 338.
LEWIS, G. N. and CALVIN, M., *Chem. Revs.*, *25* (1939) 273.
LICHTEN, W., *J. Chem. Phys.*, *22* (1954) 1278.
LINNETT, J. W., *Trans. Faraday Soc.*, *52* (1956) 904.
LIPPERT, E. and MECKE, R., *Z. Elektrochem.*, *55* (1951) 366.
LIPPINCOTT, E. R., LORD, R. C. and MCDONALD, R. S., *J. Am. Chem. Soc.*, *73* (1951) 3370.
LIPPINCOTT, E. R. and NELSON, R. D., *Spectrochim. Acta*, *10* (1958) 307.
LIPSCOMB, W. N., *J. Chem. Phys.*, *22* (1954) 985, 989.
LIPSCOMB, W. N., *J. Phys. Chem.*, *61* (1957) 23.
LONDON, F., *J. Chem. Phys.*, *5* (1937) 837; *J. chim. phys.*, *8* (1937) 397.
LONGUET-HIGGINS, H. C., *Proc. Phys. Soc. (London)*, *60* (1948) 270.
LONGUET-HIGGINS, H. C., *Trans. Faraday Soc.*, *45* (1949a) 173.
LONGUET-HIGGINS, H. C., *J. chim. phys.*, *46* (1949b) 275.
LONGUET-HIGGINS, H. C., *J. Chem. Phys.*, *18* (1950) 275.
LONGUET-HIGGINS, H. C., *Quart. Revs. (London)*, *11* (1958) 121.

LONGUET-HIGGINS, H. C. and COULSON, C. A., *Trans. Faraday Soc.*, *42* (1946) 756.
LONGUET-HIGGINS, H. C. and COULSON, C. A., *Trans. Faraday Soc.*, *43* (1947) 87.
LONSDALE, K., *Proc. Roy. Soc.* (*London*), *A 159* (1937) 149; *A 171* (1939) 541.
LONSDALE, K., *Science Progress*, *39* (1951) 209.
LÖWDIN, P-O., *J. Chem. Phys.*, *18* (1950) 365.
LÖWDIN, P-O., *J. Phys. Chem.*, *61* (1957) 55.
LUCHT, C. M., *J. Am. Chem. Soc.*, *73* (1951) 2373.

McCLURE, D. S., *J. Chem. Phys.*, *20* (1952) 682.
MACCOLL, A., *Quart. Revs.* (*London*), *1* (1947) 16.
MACCOLL, A., *Nature*, *163* (1949) 178.
MACCOLL, A., *Trans. Faraday Soc.*, *46* (1950) 369.
McINTOSH, A. O., ROBERTSON, J. M. and VAND, V., *J. Chem. Soc.*, (1954) 1061.
McKEAN, D. and SCHATZ, P. N., *J. Chem. Phys.*, *24* (1956) 316.
MACKOR, E. L., HOFSTRA, A. and VAN DER WAALS, J. H., *Trans. Faraday Soc.*, *54* (1958) 66, 186.
MAGNUS, A., *Z. phys. Chem.* (*Frankfurt*), *9* (1956) 241.
MARTELL, A. E. and CALVIN, M., *Chemistry of the Metal Chelate Compounds*, New York, 1952.
MATSEN, F. A., *J. Chem. Phys.*, *24* (1956) 602.
MECKE, R., *Trans. Faraday Soc.*, *Discussions Nr. 9* (1950) 161.
MILLS, W. H. and NIXON, I. G., *J. Chem. Soc.*, (1930) 2510.
MIZUSHIMA, S., *Structure of Molecules and Internal Rotation*, New York, 1954.
MIZUSHIMA, S. and SHIMANOUCHI, T., *Ann. Rev. Phys. Chem.* *7* (1957) 445.
MIZUSHIMA, S. *et al.*, *J. Chem. Phys.*, *21* (1953) 1411.
MOFFITT, W. E., *Proc. Roy. Soc.* (*London*), *A 202* (1950) 534, 538.
MOFFITT, W. E., *Proc. Roy. Soc.* (*London*), *A 210* (1951) 224, 245.
MOFFITT, W. E., *J. Am. Chem. Soc.*, *76* (1954) 3386.
MOFFITT, W. E. and COULSON, C. A., *Trans. Faraday Soc.*, *44* (1948 a) 81.
MOFFITT, W. E. and COULSON, C. A., *Proc. Phys. Soc.* (*London*), *60* (1948 b) 309.
MOORE, E. M., DICKERSON, R. E. and LIPSCOMB, W. N., *J. Chem. Phys.*, *27* (1957) 209.
MOORE, G. E., *J. Chem. Phys.*, *43* (1950) 1045.
MULLHAUPT, J. T. and HORNIG, D. F., *J. Chem. Phys.*, *24* (1956) 169.
MULLIKEN, R. S., *J. chim. phys.*, *46* (1949) 497, 675.
MULLIKEN, R. S., *J. Am. Chem. Soc.*, *72* (1950) 4493.

NELSON, R. D., FATELEY, W. G. and LIPPINCOTT, E. R., *J. Am. Chem. Soc.*, *78* (1956) 4870.
NOZOE, T., *Fortschr. Chem. org. Naturstoffe*, *13* (1956) 232.

OOSTERHOFF, L. J., *Trans. Faraday Soc.*, *Discussions, Nr. 10* (1951) 79.
ORGEL, L. E., *J. Chem. Soc.*, (1952) 4756; *J. Chem. Phys.*, *23* (1955) 1004, 1824, 1958.
ORGEL, L. E., *J. Inorg. & Nuclear Chem.*, *2* (1956) 315.
ORGEL, L. E., and SUTTON, L. E., *Proc. Symposium on Coordination Chemistry*, Copenhagen, 1954 p. 17.
ORGEL, L. E. *et al.*, *Trans. Faraday Soc.*, *47* (1951) 113.
ORVILLE-THOMAS ,W. J., *J. Chem. Phys.*, *22* (1954) 1267.
O'SHAUGHNESSY, M. T. and RODEBUSH, W. H., *J. Am. Chem. Soc.*, *62* (1940) 2906.

PARISER, R. and PARR, R. G., *J. Chem. Phys.*, *21* (1953) 466.

PARR, R. G., CRAIG, D. P. and ROSS, I. G., *J. Chem. Phys.*, *18* (1950) 1560.
PARR, R. G. and ELLISON, F. O., *Ann. Rev. Phys. Chem.*, *6* (1955) 171.
PAULING, L., *J. Chem. Phys.*, *1* (1933) 280.
PAULING, L., *J. Chem. Phys.*, *4* (1936) 673.
PAULING, L., *Proc. Natl. Acad. Sci. U.S.*, *25* (1939) 577.
PAULING, L., *Proc. Natl. Acad. Sci. U.S.*, *35* (1949) 229.
PAULING, L., *The Nature of the Chemical Bond*, 2nd Ed., 2nd Impr., Ithaca, 1950.
PAULING, L., *J. Am. Chem. Soc.*, *58* (1954) 663.
PAULING, L. and BROCKWAY, L. O., *J. Am. Chem. Soc.*, *59* (1937) 1223.
PAULING, L. BROCKWAY, L. O. and BEACH, J. Y., *J. Am. Chem. Soc.*, *57* (1935) 2705.
PAULING, L. and WHELAND, G. W., *J. Chem. Phys.*, *1* (1933) 362.
PAUSON, P. L., *Chem. Revs.*, *55* (1955a) 9.
PAUSON, P. L., *Quart. Revs. (London)*, *9* (1955b) 391.
PENNEY, W. G., *Proc. Roy. Soc. (London)*, *A 158* (1937) 306.
PERSON, W. B., PIMENTAL, G. C. and PITZER, K. S., *J. Am. Chem. Soc.*, *74* (1952) 3437.
PETERSON, S. W. and LEVY, H. A., *J. Chem. Phys.*, *19* (1951) 1416.
PITZER, K. S., *J. Am. Chem. Soc.*, *70* (1948) 2140.
PITZER, K. S., *Trans. Faraday Soc., Discussions, Nr. 10* (1951) 66.
PITZER, K. S. *Quantum Chemistry*, London, 1953.
PITZER, K. S., and KILPATRICK, J. E., *Chem. Revs.*, *39* (1946) 435.
PLATT, J. R., *J. Chem. Phys.*, *17* (1949) 484; *et al.*, 470.
PLATT, J. R., *J. Chem. Phys.*, *22* (1954a) 1033.
PLATT, J. R., *J. Chem. Phys.*, *21* (1953) 1597; *22* (1954b) 1448.
PRITCHARD, H. O., and SKINNER, H. A., *Chem. Revs.*, *55* (1955) 745.
PULLMAN, A., *Bull. soc. chim. France*, (1954) 595.
PULLMANN, A. and PULLMAN, B., *J. chim. phys.*, *46* (1949) 212.
PULLMAN, B. and PULLMAN, A., *Les Théories Electroniques de la Chimie Organique*, Paris, 1952.

QUAGLIANO, J. V. and SCHUBERT, L., *Chem. Revs.*, *50* (1952) 201.

RICHARDS, R. E. and SMITH, J. A. S., *Trans. Faraday Soc.*, *47* (1951) 1261.
ROBERTSON, J. M., *J. Chem. Soc.*, (1951) 1222.
ROBERTSON, J. M., *Organic Crystals and Molecules*, Ithaca, 1953.
ROBERTSON, J. M. and WHITE, J. G., *J. Chem. Soc.*, (1945) 603.
ROBERTSON, J. M. and WOODWARD, I., *J. Chem. Soc.*, (1937) 219; (1940) 36.
ROBERTSON, J. M. *et al.*, *Acta Cryst.*, *3* (1950) 245.
ROOTHAAN, C. C. J., *Revs. Modern Phys.*, *23* (1951) 69.
ROOTHAAN, C. C. J., and PARR, R. G., *J. Chem. Phys.*, *17* (1949) 1001.
ROUX, M. and DAUDEL, R., *Bull. soc. chim. France*, *17* (1950) 260.
RUCH, E. and FISCHER, E. O., *Z. Naturforsch.*, *7b* (1952) 676.
RUCH, E., *Rec. trav. chim.*, *75* (1956) 638; *Z. physik. Chem. (Frankfurt)*, *6* (1956) 356.
RÜDENBERG, K. and SCHERR, C. W., *J. Chem. Phys.*, *21* (1953) 1565, 1583.
RUNDLE, R. E., *Ann. Rev. Phys. Chem.*, *2* (1951) 235.
RUNDLE, R. E., *J. Phys. Chem.*, *61* (1957) 45.
RUNDLE, R. E. and GORING, J. H., *J. Am. Chem. Soc.*, *72*( 1950) 5337.

SASADA, Y. and NITTA, I., *Acta Cryst.*, *9* (1956) 205.
SASADA, Y., OSAKI, K. and NITTA, I., *Acta Cryst.*, *7* (1954) 113.
SCHMIDT, O., *Z. physik. Chem. (Leipzig)*, *B 39* (1938) 59; *B 42* (1939a) 83; *B 44* (1939a) 185, 194; *B 47* (1940) 1.

SCHOMAKER, V. and STEVENSON, D. P., *J. Am. Chem. Soc.*, *63* (1941) 37.
SCHULTZ, D. R. and PARRY, R. W., *J. Am. Chem. Soc.*, *80* (1958) 4.
SCHWAB, G. M. and BÄUMEL, A., *Z. physik. Chem. (Frankfurt)*, *10* (1957) 347.
SCOTT, E. S. and AUDRIETH, L. F., *J. Chem. Educ.*, *31* (1954) 173.
SELWOOD, P. W., *Magnetochemistry*, 2nd Ed., New York, 1956.
SHAND, W. and SPURR, R. A., *J. Am. Chem. Soc.*, *65* (1943) 179.
SHERMAN, J., *J. Chem. Phys.*, *2* (1934) 488.
SHERMAN, J. and KETELAAR, J. A. A., *Physica*, *6* (1939) 572.
SIDGWICK, N. V. and POWELL, H. M., *Proc. Roy. Soc. (London)*, *A 176* (1940) 153.
SIMPSON, W. T., *J. Chem. Phys.*, *16* (1948) 1124.
SIXMA, F. L. J., *J. Chem. Phys.*, *19* (1951) 1209; *Rec. trav. chim.*, *72* (1953a) 273; (1953b) 538, 543, 673; *73* (1954) 235, 243.
SIXMA, F. L. J., BOER, H. and WIBAUT, J. P., *Rec. trav. chim.*, *70* (1951) 1005.
SIXMA, F. L. J. and WIBAUT, J. P., *Rec. trav. chim.*, *69* (1950) 577.
SIXMA, F. L. J. and WIBAUT, J. P., *Rec. trav. chim.*, *71* (1952) 473.
SMITH, D. W. and HEDBERG, K., *J. Chem. Phys.*, *25* (1956) 1283.
SMITH, J. W., *Science Progress*, *43* (1955) 660.
SMYTH, Ch. P., *J. Phys. Chem.*, *59* (1955) 1121.
SPRINGALL, H. D., *Research (London)*, *3* (1950) 260.
STEACIE, E. W. R., *Atomic and Free Radical Reactions*, I and II, New York, 1954.
STOICHEFF, B. P., *Can. J. Phys.*, *32* (1954) 339.
STONE, F. G. A., *Quart. Revs. (London)*, *9* (1954) 174.
SYRKIN, Y., *J. Phys. Chem. U.S.S.R.*, *17* (1943) 347.
SYRKIN, Y. and DYATKINA, M. E., *Structure of Molecules and the Chemical Bond*, London, 1950.
SZWARC, M., *Chem. Revs.*, *47* (1950) 75; *Quart. Revs. (London)*, *5* (1951) 22; *Ann. Rev. Phys. Chem.*, *8* (1957) 439.
SZWARC, M. and EVANS, M. G., *J. Chem. Phys.*, *18* (1950) 618.

TAFT, R. W., *J. Am. Chem. Soc.*, *79* (1957) 1045; *J. Chem. Phys.*, *26* (1957) 93.
TAYLOR, R.C. and VIDALE, G. L., *J. Am. Chem. Soc.*, *78* (1956) 5999.
THEILACKER, W., *Chem. Ber.*, *84* (1951) 204.
THIEC, J. and WIEMANN, J., *Bull. soc. chim. France*, (1956) 177.
TOWNES, C. H. and DAILEY, B. P., *J. Chem. Phys.*, *17* (1949) 782.
TOWNES, C. H. and SCHAWLOW, A. L., *Microwave Spectroscopy*, New York, 1955.

VAN DRANEN, J. and KETELAAR, J. A. A., *J. Chem. Phys.*, *17* (1949) 1338; *18* (1950) 151, 1225.
VAN PANTHALEON VAN ECK, C. L., *Rec. trav. chim.*, *72* (1953) 50, 529.
VROELANT, C. and DAUDEL, R., *Bull. soc. chim. France*, *16* (1949) 37, 217; *Compt. rend.*, *228* (1949) 399.

WAHL, H., *Bull. soc. chim. France.*, *15* (1948) 726.
WALLING, C., *Free Radicals in Solution*, New York, 1957.
WALSH, A. D., *Trans. Faraday Soc.*, *43* (1947) 60.
WATERS, W. A., *The Chemistry of Free Radicals*, Oxford, 1948.
WATSON, A. I. and MATSEN, F. A., *J. Chem. Phys.*, *18* (1950) 1305.
WEISSMAN, S. I. and SOWDEN, J. C., *J. Am. Chem. Soc.*, *75* (1953) 503.
WENTORF, R. H., *J. Chem. Phys.*, *26* (1957) 956.
WESTON, R. E., *J. Chem. Phys.*, *26* (1957) 1248.
WESTRIK, R. and MACGILLAVRY, C. H., *Rec. trav. chim.*, *60* (1941) 7941; *Acta Cryst.*, *7* (1954) 764.
WHELAND, G. W., *J. Chem. Phys.*, *2* (1934) 474;
WHELAND, G. W., *J. Chem. Phys.*, *3* (1935) 356.

Wheland, G. W., *J. Am. Chem. Soc.*, *63* (1941) 2025.
Wheland, G. W., *J. Am. Chem. Soc.*, *64* (1942) 900.
Wheland, G. W., *Resonance in Organic Chemistry*, New York, 1955; also: *The Theory of Resonance and its Applications to Organic Chemistry*, New York, 1945.
Wheland, G. W., *J. Chem. Phys.*, *23* (1955) 79.
Wheland, G. W. and Mann, D. E., *J. Chem. Phys.*, *17* (1949) 264.
Wheland, G. W. and Pauling, L., *J. Am. Chem. Soc.*, *57* (1935), 2086.
Wibaut, J. P., *Experientia*, *5* (1949) 337.
Wibaut, J. P., *Bull. soc. chim. France*, (1950) 998; *J. chim. phys.*, *53* (1956) 111; *54* (1956) 143; *Festschrift A. Stoll*, p. 227, Basel, 1957.
Wibaut, J. P. and De Jong, F. P. K., *Koninkl. Ned. Akad. Wetenschap. Proc.*, *B 59* (1956) 285.
Wibaut, J. P. and Sixma, F. L. J., *Rec. trav. chim.*, *73* (1954) 796.
Wibaut, J. P., Sixma, F. L. J., Kampschmidt, L. W. F. and Boer, H., *Rec. trav. chim.*, *69* (1950) 1355.
Wilkinson, G., Pauson, P. L. and Cotton, F. A., *J. Am. Chem. Soc.*, *76* (1954) 1970, 4281.
Williams, R. B., *J. Am. Chem. Soc.*, *64* (1942) 1395.
Wilson, E. B. and Badger, R. M., *J. Chem. Phys.*, *16* (1948) 741.
Winstein, S. and Lucas, H. J., *J. Am. Chem. Soc.*, *60* (1938) 836.

## IV. THE METALLIC BOND

The characteristic properties of the metals are the high conductivity for electricity and heat and the metallic lustre. This latter property is a direct consequence of the very strong absorption for light of all wave lengths. In the finely divided state the metals are in fact black.

Formerly these metallic properties were already attributed to the presence of free electrons. The classical theory of this electron gas (LORENTZ) leads, however, to absurdities; for instance, a specific heat of $3/2\ R$ would be expected for this monatomic gas, contrary to the observation that DULONG and PETIT's rule (atomic specific heat $\approx 6/2\ R$) holds for both conductors and non-conductors. The calculated ratio of heat conductivity to electrical conductivity (WIEDEMANN-FRANZ constant) also failed to agree with observation.

However, since the electrons possess a spin $^1/_2\ h/2\pi$, this gas behaves quite differently (FERMI-DIRAC statistics) from a system of spinless particles (BOSE-EINSTEIN statistics), such as ordinary gas molecules.

In FERMI-DIRAC statistics, each state can accommodate at most only two particles with opposed spins. In BOSE-EINSTEIN statistics, just as in the classical MAXWELL-BOLTZMANN statistics, there is no limitation to the number of particles in a given state. In classical statistics the particles in the same state were assumed to be distinguishable one from the other. As this assumption has been shown to be incorrect in quantum theory, the particles in the same state in BOSE-EINSTEIN quantum statistics are indistinguishable. Interchanges of two particles in identical states are not significant in quantum statistics, contrary to classical statistics. If the distance between the energy levels is large compared with the thermal energy $kT$, then in FERMI-DIRAC statistics all the levels, beginning from the lowest, will be occupied by two electrons as far as their number suffices; the remaining levels remain unoccupied. According to classical statistics as well as to BOSE-EINSTEIN statistics all the particles would naturally occupy the lowest level at very low temperatures. At high temperatures, however, when the level separation has become relatively small compared with $kT$, a distribution over numerous levels arises. The distinction between the FERMI-DIRAC, BOSE-EINSTEIN and MAXWELL-BOLTZMANN distributions disappears then because the prohibition of more than two particles per level ceases to be effective, since even in the classical statistics it becomes extremely improbable that one level would be occupied by more than two particles. (The total number of levels is very large compared with the number of electrons).

The number of particles $n_i$ which will be present in the state with energy $\varepsilon_i$ and statistical weight $g_i$ (the number of states $i$) in the most probable distribution is given by the following expressions for the three forms of statistics mentioned*.

MAXWELL-BOLTZMANN (classical)

$$n_i = \frac{g_i}{B\,e^{\varepsilon_i/kT}}$$

FERMI-DIRAC (particles with odd (half integral) spin)

$$n_i = \frac{g_i}{B\,e^{\varepsilon_i/kT} + 1}$$

BOSE-EINSTEIN (particles with even (integral) spin including zero)

$$n_i = \frac{g_i}{B\,e^{\varepsilon_i/kT} - 1}$$

$B$ is a constant of proportionality, to be determined from the condition $\Sigma\, n_i = N$ with $N$ the total number of particles.

* See also textbooks such as: W. J. MOORE, *Physical Chemistry*, New York, 1957; S. GLASSTONE, *Theoretical Chemistry*, New York, 1944; J. C. SLATER, *Introduction to Chemical Physics*, New York, 1939; E. A. MOELWYN-HUGHES, *Physical Chemistry*, Cambridge, 1957; H. EYRING, J. WALTER and G. E. KIMBALL, *Quantum Chemistry*, New York, 1944.

If $g_i$, the number of available states, is very large compared with $n_i$, so that $g_i/n_i = Be^{\varepsilon_i/kT} + a$ ($a = 0$ or $\pm 1$ for the three cases above) is large compared to 1, then the difference between these three forms disappears, that is to say the classical statistics holds. This is the case for the translational energy of gases at temperatures above 1° K. In this case $B \cdot N = \sum_i g_i \cdot e^{-E/kT} \equiv Z$ or $B = Z/N$, with $Z$ the (molecular) partition function ("Zustandssumme").

For a mono-atomic gas (only translational energy)

$$B = \frac{(2\pi m kT)^{3/2}}{h^3} \cdot \frac{V}{N}$$

We see that $B$ will always be much smaller for electrons than for atoms because $m_e \ll m_H$ and also because the particle density $N/V$ is almost always much higher for electrons than for gases. Thus the classical statistical laws, such as the law of equipartition from which the above-mentioned extra specific heat was derived, do not hold for electrons; this will only be the case at very much higher temperatures. Thus 1° K for He atoms (1 at) corresponds to a temperature of 25,200 °K for electrons (V = 13.0 cm³, Liat 298° K), both with $\varepsilon = kT$.

Although the theory of metals, and thus also that of the metallic bond, is essentially of wave-mechanical nature, a rough classical consideration nevertheless furnishes a good approximation for the total bonding energy from positive ions and electrons, *i.e.*, of the lattice energy. In this the negative charge is thought of as uniformly distributed over space with the positive ions arranged in a regular lattice. This model gives rather good results when we have a large separation of the ions in relation to their size, as in lithium (distance 3.03 Å, $r^+$: 0.68 Å). The formula for the lattice energy of a metal (WILSON, 1936, 1953) is closely related to that for an ionic lattice; we obtain:

$$U = -1.581 \frac{Ne^2}{r} \text{ (body-centred metal).}$$

$$U = -1.628 \frac{Ne^2}{r} \text{ (face-centred metal).}$$

The correspondence between calculated and observed values is better than we could expect (Table 25).

With the monovalent metals both lattice types do occur; the alkali metals are body-centred cubic, those of the copper group are face-centred.

TABLE 25

LATTICE ENERGY AT 0° K IN KCAL/G ATOM

| | $S$ | $I_1$ | $U$ obs. | $U$ calc. | | $S$ | $I_2$ | $U$ obs. |
|---|---|---|---|---|---|---|---|---|
| Li | 37.1 | 124.4 | 161.5 | 175 | Be | 78 | 634 | 712 |
| Na | 26.0 | 118.5 | 144.5 | 143 | Mg | 36 | 522 | 558 |
| K | 21.5 | 100.0 | 121.5 | 113 | Ca | 42 | 415 | 467 |
| Rb | 20.5 | 96.1 | 116.6 | 107.5 | Sr | 39 | 385 | 424 |
| Cs | 18.8 | 89.7 | 108.5 | 100 | Ba | 42 | 350 | 392 |
| Cu | 82 | 178.0 | 260 | 211 | Zn | 31.2 | 631 | 662 |
| Ag | 69 | 174.7 | 244 | 187 | Cd | 26.8 | 597 | 624 |
| Au | 91 | 212.8 | 304 | 187.5 | Hg | 14.5 | 674 | 689 |

The experimental value of the lattice energy $U$ is found from the sum of the heat of sublimation of the metals $S$ and the ionization energy of the atom $I$: $U = S + I$.

## § 37. ELECTRONS IN A METAL

A simple treatment of the wave-mechanical model (SOMMERFELD) is, however, more important. The electrons in a piece of metal are situated as it were in a potential box with reflecting walls. In fact they cannot in general leave the metal because a high excitation (work function, photoelectric threshold energy) is necessary for this. Let us now consider more particularly a one-dimensional strip of metal of length $l$. Here the electrons are as it were in a channel closed at both sides. The possible stationary energy states are given in Fig. 24. The stationary wave motion must always have nodes at the extremities, since the wave function must be zero outside the box; the probability of finding an electron there is zero as the electrons cannot get out. The wave lengths are $2\,l/1$, $2\,l/2$, ... $2\,l/k$; $k = 1, 2, 3, \ldots$ The energy of each state is: $W = V_0 + \frac{h^2}{2\,m}\frac{1}{\lambda^2} = V_0 + \frac{h^2 k^2}{8\,m\,l^2}$; the first term corresponds to the potential energy at the bottom of the box, the second to the kinetic energy $^1/_2 mv^2 = \frac{h^2}{2\,m}\frac{1}{\lambda^2}$, because $\lambda = h/mv$ (DE BROGLIE's relation § 18).

Each level will be occupied by two electrons with opposite spins. If there are $n$ atoms in the metal strip with $n$ conduction electrons altogether (as in the alkali metals, copper group), then $^1/_2\, n$ levels are occupied. The energy is a quadratic function of the wave number $1/\lambda$; this relation is given by half a parabola, the right half of Fig. 25. The picture of the electron in the box is also important in other respects for our insight into the chemical bond.

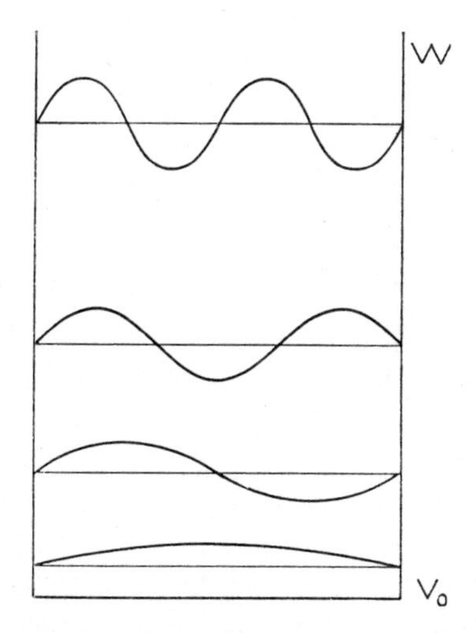


Fig. 24. Energy levels and wave functions for an electron in a box.

Let us imagine another similar box placed next to the box of Fig. 24; in both the lowest level contains two electrons; the others are unoccupied.

When we remove the separating wall and place the four electrons in the twice enlarged box, a new level $k' = 1$ has become available below the lowest level $k = 1$ in the original boxes, which now has become the level $k' = 2$ in the large box with $l' = 2l$. The total energy of the four electrons, previously $4\left(V_0 + \frac{h^2}{8\,m\,l^2}\right)$ has become:

$$2\left(V_0 + \frac{h^2}{32\,m\,l^2}\right) + 2\left(V_0 + \frac{4\,h^2}{32 m l^2}\right) = 4\,V_0 + \frac{5}{2}\,\frac{h^2}{8\,m\,l^2}$$

Thus the kinetic energy is now $\frac{3}{2}\,\frac{h^2}{8\,m\,l^2}$ lower.

This lowering of energy by increase of the space in which the electrons can move is just what we also noticed in the transition of one single isolated KEKULÉ configuration, in which each pair of $\pi$ electrons is restricted to one C = C bond, to benzene, in which a ring-shaped potential gutter of the double length is now available to the six $\pi$ electrons together. This picture of the stability of benzene as a consequence of the "enlargement" or "delocalization" energy appears completely different from the resonance concept. Nevertheless, the two are related and as the resonance idea corresponds most closely with the "valence bond" method, so the above-mentioned picture fits better the "molecular orbital" method (§ 36).

In the example of the box the lowering of the energy is exclusively due to a decrease of kinetic energy. In the formation of molecules like $H_2^+$ and $H_2$, however, it is the decrease of the potential energy that is the important factor; the kinetic energy even increases as demanded by the virial theorem (p. 138).

The same model of a metal has been applied by O. SCHMIDT, H. KUHN and others for the calculation of the light absorption of coloured substances (p. 270).

In place of the above "intuitive" solution the result can also be deduced from SCHRÖDINGER's wave equation.

It was proved on p. 121 that a solution of this equation, for $V$ = const. = $V_0$, is: $\varphi = A \sin 2\,\pi\,x/\lambda$ (or the corresponding cos) with $(2\,\pi/\lambda)^2 = \frac{8\,\pi^2 m}{h^2}\,(W - V_0)$, in which $W$ is the total energy.

The complete solution is, however:

$$\varphi = A \sin 2\,\pi\,x/\lambda + B \cos 2\,\pi\,x/\lambda \;\; (\text{or} = A' \cos (2\,\pi\,x/\lambda + \delta).$$

Thus every value of $W$ (provided $W > V_0$) and therefore of $\lambda$ is possible, that is to say, the translational energy of a free electron is not quantized. For the electron in the box there are, however, boundary conditions that must be fulfilled

$$(1)\ \varphi = 0 \text{ for } x = 0 \text{ and } (2)\ \varphi = 0 \text{ for } x = l.$$

It thereby becomes an eigenvalue problem, since only a few values of $W$ are eigenvalues for which corresponding eigenfunctions $\varphi$ exist which satisfy the equation and the boundary conditions.

The conditions mentioned above furnish: (1) $B = 0$; (2) $2\pi/\lambda = \pi k/l$ in which $k$ must be an integer with the exception of zero, for then $\varphi$ would become zero everywhere, which is without physical signification. We thus have $\varphi = A \sin \pi kx/l$, as in Fig. 24 and

$$W = V_0 + \frac{h^2k^2}{8\,ml^2} \quad (k \text{ integer but } \neq 0).$$

(Apart from being obtained directly from DE BROGLIE's relation, as above, $W$ can also be calculated according to the general method of p. 130).

The quantization arises in this problem again, resulting directly from the boundary conditions, without *ad hoc* hypotheses being necessary, as in BOHR's theory. Furthermore, the existence of a zero point energy also finds its natural basis; no solution is possible which satisfies the boundary conditions and in which the energy is equal to $V_0$ at the bottom of the box.

The depth of the box $V_0$ can be calculated or found from the experiments mentioned on p. 122 in which the refraction of electron beams is determined. The box is indeed very deep, *e.g.*, 10 eV/mole = 230 kcal/mole, which is very large in comparison with the thermal energy $RT$ = 0.6 kcal/mole.

The energy $W_i$ of the highest filled level above the bottom of the box is also called the level of the FERMI sea.

It is of interest to note that the minimum electron wave length corresponding to this maximum energy is of the order of the distance between the atoms.

For a one-dimensional strip of metal with a length of $l$ = 1 cm with the atoms at a distance of 3.0 Å (lithium), we have $n = 0.33 \cdot 10^8$ atoms with the same number of free valence electrons. These $n$ electrons occupy $^1/_2\, n$ levels. The highest level thus corresponds to $k = {}^1/_2\, n = 0.165 \cdot 10^8$ (or $\lambda_{min}$ = 12 Å) and so we calculate for its energy $W_{max} = V_0 + W_i = V_0 + 1.65 \cdot 10^{-12}$ erg/atom or $= V_0 + 1.0$ eV. Thus $W_i = 1.0$ eV for this one-dimensional example.

The general formula for $W_i$ in the one-dimensional case is

$$W_i = \frac{h^2}{8\,m}\left(\frac{n}{2\,l}\right)^2.$$

The formula for the highest FERMI energy per atom for the three-dimensional box is:

$$W_i = \frac{h^2}{8\,m}\left(\frac{3N}{\pi V}\right)^{2/3}$$

with $V$ the atomic volume.

For a simple cubic lattice with the interatomic distance $a$ we have $1/a = n/l = (N/V)^{1/3}$, thus both formulae differ only in the numerical factor. Values for $W_i$ are given in Table 26.

The energy to remove an electron from the highest filled level to the edge of the potential hole is $|V_0| - W_i$. This energy is equal to the photoelectric threshold energy of a metal.

The same energy, then called work function $\Phi$, enters the formula for the thermal emission of metals (thermionic current $i \propto e^{-\Phi/kT}$) such as happens in heated filaments (direct heated cathodes) of radio valves (thermionic emission). The average thermal energy of the electrons is still very small but it has to be taken into account for this phenomenon, since only those rare electrons with a kinetic energy equal to $\Phi = |V_0| - W_i$ can escape. In Table 26 we have used the experimental values of this quantity to calculate $V_0$, which is very difficult to determine directly.

The PAULI-SOMMERFELD theory of metals is the extension of this simple wave-mechanical picture to three dimensions, and it already enables us to calculate some properties reasonably well.

TABLE 26

FERMI ENERGY AND WORK FUNCTION

| Valence | $W_i$ calc. | $-V_0$ calc. | $(\lvert V_0 \rvert - W_i)$ obs. | | $\lvert V_0 \rvert^* = U + {}^3/_5 NW_i$ |
|---|---|---|---|---|---|
| | | | photoelectric | therm. emiss. | |
| Li 1 | 4.72 e.V | 6.9 e.V | 2.2 e.V | — e.V | 9.86 e.V |
| Na 1 | 3.12 | 5.0 | 1.9 | — | 7.91 |
| K 1 | 2.14 | 3.9 | 1.8 | — | 6.54 |
| Cu 1 | 7.04 | 11.1 | 4.1 | 4.3 | 15.45 |
| Ag 1 | 5.51 | 10.2 | 4.7 | 4.1 | 13.83 |
| Ca 2 | 4.67 | 7.9 | 3.2 | 3.0 | — |
| Al 3 | 11.7 | 14.7 | 3.0 | — | — |

* The *mean* FERMI energy per electron is $\overline{W} = {}^3/_5\, W_i$ [total FERMI energy: ${}^3/_5\, NW_i$] and the quantity $|V_0| - \overline{W}$ is the (average) binding energy of an electron. This would be equal to the lattice energy $U$ [p. 322, *cf.* the relation between potential of a negative ion and the COULOMB energy of an ionic lattice p. 35], if we neglect the contributions of the repulsion energy, the VAN DER WAALS attraction energy of the cores, the exchange energy of the electrons, etc.

Now the electrons in a real metal, however, are situated as if they were in a potential box in which the value of the distance from the highest level to the edge is again equal to the energy of a light quantum of the threshold wave length of the

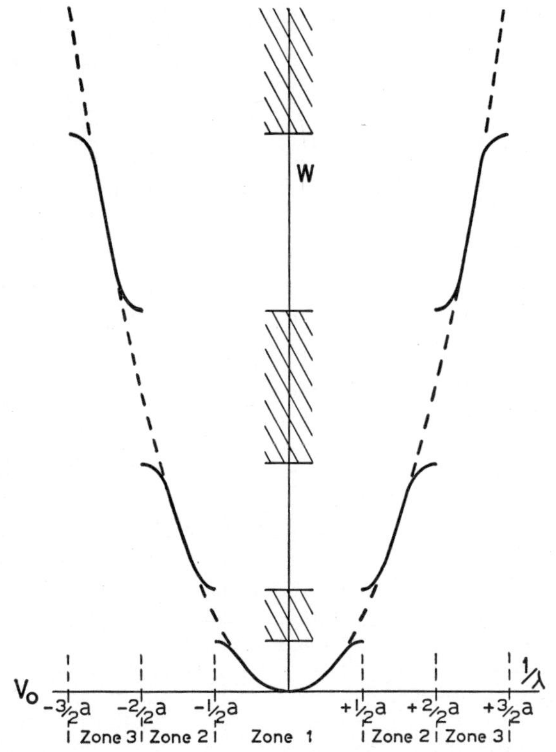


Fig. 25. Energy $W = V_0 + W_i$ as a function of the reciprocal wave length. - - - in a constant potential field; — in a periodic potential field of a lattice with period $a$. Discontinuities at $1/\lambda = \pm m/2a$. The forbidden energy zones are shaded.

photoelectric effect, but where the bottom of the potential box is not flat. The potential in a metal lattice is naturally periodic with the period of the lattice. It appears, as is immediately plausible, that, as long as there is no phase relation between electron wave and perturbing periodic potential, only the average value of the latter is of influence, just as the constant potential $V_0$ above. However, this becomes different, if such a relation does exist accidentally, that is to say, for those waves with wave lengths which are a rational fraction of the lattice period in the direction of propagation. This strong influencing of the electron motion by the periodic lattice potential occurs each time for $\lambda = 2a/m$ or $2/\lambda = m/a$ in which $m$ is an integer and $a$ the lattice spacing. Now the energy levels in the unperturbed case of the box with a flat bottom were doubly degenerate: actually there were always two equal energy values for $1/\lambda$ positive or negative. This degeneracy is removed by the perturbation and two levels are produced, one higher and the other lower than the levels in the unperturbed problem.

This is completely analogous to the removal of the double degeneracy in the $H_2^+$ problem and in the $H_2$ problem (p. 132 *et seq.*), when the two nuclei approach one another. The course of the $W \cdot 1/\lambda$ curve is now like the drawn line in Fig. 25. Forbidden zones of energy values appear.

The existence of these bands of permitted and forbidden energy values is now extremely important for the explanation of metallic properties and for the formation of intermetallic compounds.

We can also demonstrate the correctness of the above results simply. The solution of the wave equation for $V$ constant was:

$$\varphi = A \sin 2 \pi x/\lambda.$$

The actual periodic lattice potential can now be written as

$$V = V_0 + V_1 \cos 2 \pi x/a + V_2 \cos 2 \pi \cdot 2 x/a + \ldots.$$

or the perturbing potential as

$$V' = \sum_{m=1}^{m=\infty} V_m \cos 2 \pi m x/a.$$

The lattice potential is expanded here in a so-called FOURIER series, in which $m$ is an integer, $a$ the lattice period and $V_m$ the amplitude coefficient of the term with the period $a/m$.

The energy becomes $W = W_0 + W'$, with $W_0$ the unperturbed energy for $V = V_0$ = constant and $W'$ the perturbation.

The (first order) perturbation $W'$ is now according to the wave-mechanical perturbation calculation* (p. 284) $W' = \int_0^l V' \varphi^2 \, dx$ ($\varphi$ is real).

* This is not a strict derivation, since actually degeneracy must be taken into account, see literature on quantum mechanics, p. 22.

After substitution we have

$$W' = A^2 \Sigma V_m \int_0^l \sin^2 2\,\pi\, x/\lambda \cdot \cos 2\,\pi m\, x/a \cdot dx].$$

The expression under the integral sign can be transformed by changing to double angles into:

$$({}^1/_2 - {}^1/_2 \cos 4\,\pi\, x/\lambda) \cos 2\,\pi\, mx/a,$$

and then into:

$$ {}^1/_2 \cos 2\,\pi\, mx/a - {}^1/_4\,[\cos 2\,\pi\, x(2/\lambda + m/a) + $$
$$ + \cos 2\,\pi\, x\,(2/\lambda - m/a)].$$

Now integration over an odd power of a sine or cosine over a range of integration large compared with the period ($l \gg a$) always gives zero; in fact the function is as often negative as positive in that region. The perturbation $W'$ is, therefore, also zero in general, except naturally for the cases in which the argument of the cosine is zero, since $\cos 0 = 1$. This integration thus only furnishes a perturbation different from zero if the following conditions are satisfied:

$$2/\lambda + m/a = 0 \text{ or } 2/\lambda - m/a = 0 \text{ or } \lambda = \pm\, 2\, a/m.$$

Whether the perturbation is important for a particular value of $m$, and consequently also whether the splitting and the breadth of the corresponding forbidden zone are large, is determined by the magnitude of the amplitude $V_m$ in the expansion of the potential.

At the position of the perturbation, characterized by the number $m$, the energy $W = W_0 \pm V_m$, the breadth of the forbidden zone is therefore $2V_m$.

A similar deduction furnishes a similar condition for the three-dimensional problem, in which $1/\lambda$ and $m/a$ are now vectors in a reciprocal space, well known in crystallography (BIJVOET, KOLKMEYER and MACGILLAVRY 1951; BUERGER, 1942).

Instead of $2/\lambda = \pm\, m/a$ we now have for a cubic crystal:

$$(2 \sin \theta)/\lambda = \sqrt{h^2 + k^2 + l^2}/a \qquad (1)$$

This condition is, however, identical with BRAGG's law:

$$2\, d \sin\, \theta = \lambda, \text{ since } d = \frac{a}{\sqrt{h^2 + k^2 + l^2}}$$

This is not so strange as it may seem; actually BRAGG's law, which determines the reflection of X-rays, is also valid for electron beams of the same wave length $\lambda$.

A forbidden energy state, that is to say, an electron wave (defined as to direction and wave length) which is perturbed by the lattice, signifies an electron wave which is reflected by the lattice on penetration from the outside.

Thus the diffraction directions of X-rays give direct information on the energy zones; the intensity of the reflections likewise gives an indication regarding the breadth of the forbidden zone, that is to say, regarding $V_m$.

In Fig. 25 the positions of the perturbations are indicated on the $1/\lambda$ axis. The ranges of forbidden energy values are to be found in the shaded portions or forbidden zones. The first allowed zone $m = 1$ has a width of $1/a$ cm$^{-1}$.

There remains the question of the number of states in the first zone. In this zone $1/\lambda$ runs from the minimum value determined by the boundary condition: $\lambda_{max} = 2l = 2Na$, when we consider $N$ atoms with a separation $a$, to $1/\lambda = 1/2a$, the zone limit.

Now $1/\lambda = k/2Na$ in which $k$ must be a positive integer, which obviously runs from $1 \ldots . N$. This corresponds to the right half of Fig. 25. There are therefore on $N$ atoms $N$ states in the first zone. This result holds generally, also for three dimensions. Negative numbers for $k$ here have no physical significance, since only the absolute sign of the wave function is changed thereby.

We have so far considered a large but finite piece of metal and we have used the boundary conditions which belong to this case. For a general and more rigorous treatment, in particular of the conduction, it is, however, simpler and more customary to consider an infinitely large metal, or still better, parts of it of length $L = Na$, which all have the same properties, arranged, *e.g.*, in a ring. The wave function must then be periodic in the large period $L$. This then furnishes as conditions $\lambda_{max} = L = Na$ and $1/\lambda = k/L = k/Na$, but now we consider both the negative and positive values of $1/\lambda$ or of $k$, as already indicated in Fig. 25, for there are now no stationary waves but progressive ones.

The first zone now runs from $1/\lambda = -1/2a$ to $1/\lambda = 1/2a$ and $k$ will traverse the values $-{}^1/_2N, -{}^1/_2N + 1, \ldots {}^1/_2N - 1, +{}^1/_2N$ (excluding 0), that is to say, $k$ can take on $N$ values, thus also one value per atom. Thus in both methods there is one level per atom in the first allowed band, in which two electrons can be accommodated with opposite spins. It is also clear that the nature of both essentially equal boundary conditions should have no essential influence on the result.

In a strip of a monovalent element, only half of the levels therefore are occupied, it will thus be a conductor (p. 334). However, a completely filled band results for a divalent element, and this element will be an insulator, corresponding to a linear molecule M–M–M–M with electron pair bonds.

This latter case is realized in the elements sulphur, selenium and tellurium. On the other hand a linear *infinite* polyene $-C=C-C=C-$ with one $\pi$ electron per atom corresponds to the first case. The first case is also realized in the linear chain of a carbocyanine dye (p. 270) and in the rings of benzene and other acenes with always one $\pi$ electron per atom (p. 293).

Since $1/\lambda = k/L$, we can also say that when we consider one cm of metal, there is one state per unit step (in $cm^{-1}$) on the reciprocal scale of $1/\lambda$. The density of the states in the reciprocal space is, therefore, 1; thus 2 electrons can be placed per unit if account is taken of the electron spin.

In the reciprocal space in three dimensions, instead of line sections, zones become geometrical bodies determined by the values of the three integers *h*, *k*, and *l*, instead of by *m*. These bodies are polyhedra (BRILLOUIN zones) in the reciprocal lattice of the same kind as the faces of a crystal in ordinary space which correspond to the same *hkl* (*e.g.*, 100 is the cube, 111 the octahedron, etc. in the cubic system).

For a simple cubic metal the first zone is given by $hkl = 100$ (and equivalent values 010, 001, $\bar{1}00$, $0\bar{1}0$ and $00\bar{1}$). In the reciprocal lattice 100 is the point on the (reciprocal) *x* axis at a distance $1/a$ from the origin. The BRILLOUIN zone is now produced as the locus of the general condition (1) (Fig. 26a, drawn there for 110):

$$(2 \sin \theta)/\lambda - \sqrt{h^2 + k^2 + l^2}/a = 0;$$

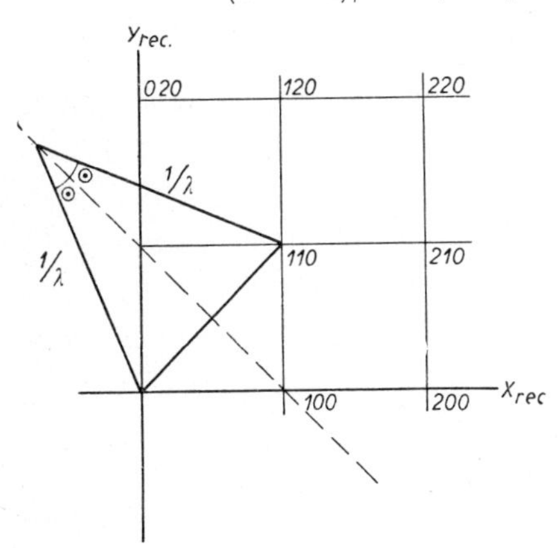


Fig. 26a. Construction of BRILLOUIN zone 110 as the locus (- - -) of $(2 \sin \theta)/\lambda = \sqrt{2}/a$.

here the special case is:

$$(2 \sin \theta)/\lambda - 1/a = 0.$$

A plane is thus produced perpendicular to the *x* axis at a distance $1/2a$ from the origin.

The six equivalent points 100 thus give rise to six planes which enclose a cube of side $1/a$ and volume $(1/a)^3$. The density of the states is also 1 per (reciprocal) unit volume. This cube thus encloses $(1/a)^3$ states. A crystal with dimensions 1 × 1 × 1 cm with a simple cubic lattice contains $(1/a)^3$ atoms so that there is also 1 state available per atom in this zone, or there is space for 2 electrons per atom. If, for example, the reflection from the octahedral planes 111 is, as in copper, the first strong X-ray reflection, then this means that an octahedron in the reciprocal lattice encloses the states below the first important forbidden energy zone (Fig. 26b). The corners of the octahedron are truncated by the planes of the cube forming the next important zone 200 (Fig. 26c).

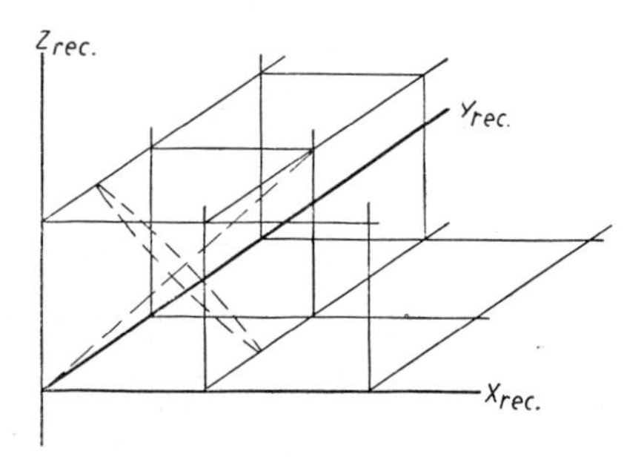


Fig. 26b. Reciprocal lattice and one plane of the 111 BRILLOUIN zone (octahedron) - - - -.

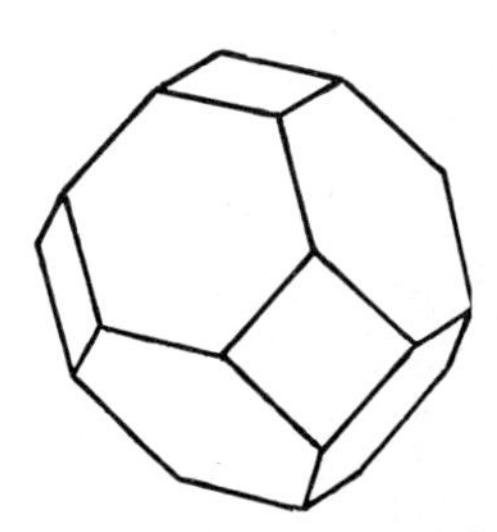

Fig. 26c. Truncated octahedron; 111, 200 zone

The surface of states of equal energy remains approximately spherical with increasing energy until the inscribed sphere is reached.

In order to find the number of states up to a practically equal maximum energy in a zone, we draw the inscribed sphere in the reciprocal space, in this case the inscribed sphere of the octahedron (Fig. 27).

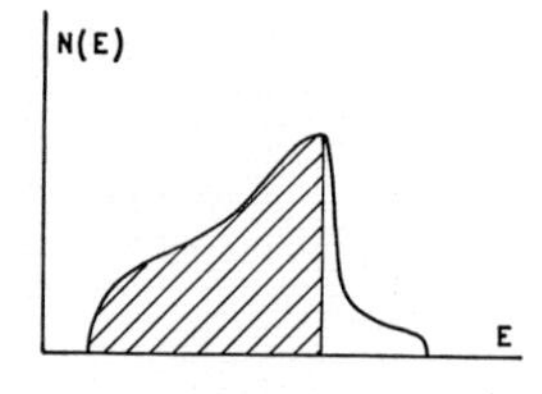


Fig. 27. Number $N(E)$ of states with energy between $E$ and $E + dE$ as a function of $E$ in a zone. The shaded part indicates the total number of states within the inscribed sphere of the zone.

The volume of this sphere is $4/3\ \pi\ \left(\frac{1}{2a}\sqrt{3}\right)^3 = 2.72/a^3$. With two electrons per state, twice as many electrons, *i.e.*, $5.44/a^3$, can therefore be placed. With a face-centred lattice, as in copper, we have four atoms per elementary cell of volume $a^3$ and with a monovalent metal there are also four electrons present.

There are thus $4/a^3$ atoms and electrons for 1 cm³ metal. So only 4/5.44 of the states are occupied, in other words: 5.44/4 = 1.36 electrons per atom are possible in this zone. As we shall see, this means that in the replacement of copper atoms by zinc atoms, which each bring with them two electrons per atom, we can go to 36 % zinc since there are then just

$$\frac{0.36 \times 2 + 0.64}{1} = 1.36 \text{ electrons per atom.}$$

Naturally instead of 36 % only 18 % of an element such as aluminium, which brings with it three electrons per atom, can be dissolved (p. 348).

The BRILLOUIN zones also play an important part in intermetallic compounds (p. 348). In the alloy γ-brass, for example, the coincident reflection 330 and 411 is seen in the X-ray diagram to be extraordinarily strong. The inscribed sphere in these polyhedra in the reciprocal space has a radius of $\frac{1}{2a}\sqrt{18}$; the density in reciprocal space is 2, and $80/a^3$ electrons can be placed in it per cm³ metal. The cubic elementary cell of γ-brass contains 52 atoms or $52/a^3$ per cm³ metal, so that 80/52 = 1.54 electrons per atom are possible, while the composition $Cu_5Zn_8$ (see below) corresponds to 21/13 = 1.62.

The states situated in the corners of the polyhedron outside the inscribed sphere must also be taken into account, as is indeed to be expected; the actual volume of the polyhedron corresponds to 90/52 = 1.73 electrons per atom. In view of the course of the $N(E)$ versus $E$ curve (Fig. 27), close to the boundary, the last few electrons added represent a considerable increase in energy. By preference the zone will be almost, but not completely, filled.

If the number of electrons in the lattice is just sufficient to occupy all the levels with electron pairs up to a broad forbidden zone, the substance will be an insulator (Fig. 28C). Indeed, if the breadth of the forbidden zone of energy values is large compared with the thermal energy, there are practically no electrons to be expected in the free permitted levels above this forbidden zone. An electron can nevertheless be brought into a free band by absorption of an appropriate light quantum so that so-called photoconductivity then occurs. The electrons in a completely filled band cannot contribute to the conduction. The substance can only be a conductor if a band is only partially filled.

No current flows in the stationary state of a metal crystal, that is to say, equal numbers of electrons move in both directions. If now a potential difference is applied, the energy of the electrons will become higher for the one direction compared with that for the other direction and thus the distribution is changed; then there will no longer be the same number moving in both directions and there is a current. However, this is only possible when unoccupied levels are still available. If, however, all the levels in the band are filled, each with 2 electrons, no change can occur in the distribution and therefore no current can flow.

In the one-dimensional case (Fig. 25) the permitted bands do not overlap on the energy scale; this is, however, possible with the three-dimensional BRILLOUIN zones.

The surface of states of equal energy in the reciprocal ($1/\lambda$) space is only approximately spherical (see above). Before a zone is completely filled up to the corners, electrons with the same energy will already find a place in the next higher zone (Fig. 28 B). With the alkaline earth metals Ca, Sr (face-centred) and Ba (body-centred) the first zone can contain 2 electrons per atom so that the two valence electrons would just fill this zone. These metals, as a consequence of the overlap, are nevertheless conductors, in contrast to the above-mentioned linear molecule, though appreciably worse than the alkali metals (body-centred) and the metals of the copper group (face-centred) with the same structure but with only one conduction electron per atom (Fig. 28 A).

The conductivity of the pure stoechiometric compound, the intrinsic conductivity, is proportional to $e^{-E_g/2kT}$; $E_g$ is the energy gap between the (filled)

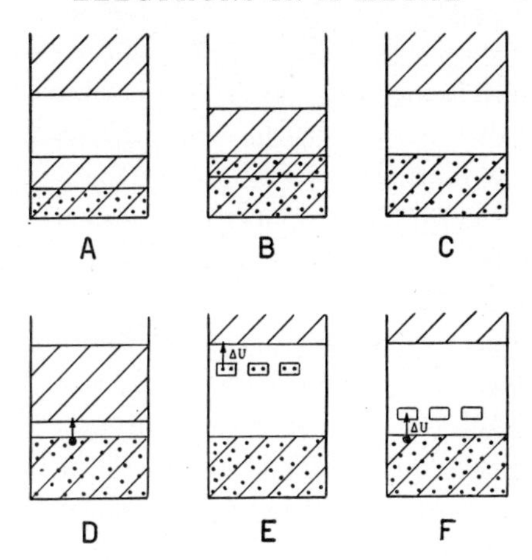


Fig. 28. Shaded parts = allowed zones, . . . electrons, □ electron levels at impurity atoms:

A Metal, first zone half filled (lithium, copper);
B Metal, first zone filled, but overlap between first and second zone (calcium);
C Insulator (diamond);
D Semiconductor (pure compound) intrinsic conductivity (graphite ⊥ C axis, bismuth-tin alloy);
E Semiconductor (impurity) excess conductivity, n-type (germanium and silicium with a pentavalent impurity, *e.g.*, As);
F Semiconductor (impurity) defect conductivity, p-type (Ge and Si with a trivalent impurity, *e.g.*, B, In).

valence band and the (empty) conduction band in Fig. 28. Values of the energy gap are:

| | | | |
|---|---|---|---|
| Diamond | 6 e.V | ZnO | 2.2 e.V |
| Si | 1.10 | $Cu_2O$ | 2.1 |
| Ge | 0.70 | CdS | 2.42 |
| Sn(gray) | 0.08 | CdSe | 1.74 |
| InP | 1.25 | CdTe | 1.45 |
| InAs | 0.33 | PbS | 0.35 |
| InSb | 0.18 | AgI | 2.8 |

The distance of the donor impurity levels (P, As, Sb) to the conduction band (Fig. 28 E) is 0.04 e.V and 0.012 e.V for silicium and germanium (n-type) respectively. The distance of the acceptor (B, In) levels to the valence band in the p-type conductors (Fig. 28F) is 0.045 e.V (B), 0.16 e.V (In) and 0.010 e.V (B, In) again for silicium and germanium respectively.

It is possible to produce in a silicium or germanium crystal both p-type and n-type regions; the interface between both regions is called an n-p junction. Such junctions have very important electrical properties, *e.g.*, rectification and transistor action (KITTEL, book p. 389).

When a substance exhibits an appreciable electron conduction, this is an indication that there are numerous free levels at various small distances from the occupied states. Light of all wave lengths will, therefore, be strongly absorbed; the substance is almost completely opaque and reflects nearly all light in the massive state. In the finely divided state the substance is black. Conversely, it can be said that black substances, at any rate when they do not consist of separate molecules such as the organic dyes, are also electron conductors (many metallic oxides and sulphides). In dyes and in aromatic rings (see p. 270 and p. 221) one could speak of an intramolecular conduction in the system of the $\pi$ electrons of the conjugated double bonds.

In the so-called semiconductors, such as ZnO, $Cu_2O$, etc., the bands are just filled for the perfectly pure substance at low temperatures. Conduction can only occur if the number of electrons is increased (excess conduction or n-type semiconductors, Fig. 28E), which extra electrons find a place in a free band, or if the number of electrons is decreased, whereby a hole is produced in the filled band (defect conduction or p-type semiconductors, Fig. 28F). Such a deficit is displaced in an electric field like an electron with a positive charge. Such a change in the number of electrons, more correctly in the number of electrons per lattice unit, is produced by deviations from the stoichiometric composition.

If the composition is, for example, $Cu_{1.99}O$, the resistance decreases to one millionth of that of pure $Cu_2O$. The copper content of such a sample is 99.5% of the theoretical values for $Cu_2O$ or the sample contains 0.55% CuO. For each 1000 oxygen ions there are 1980 $Cu^+$ ions, together with 10 $Cu^{2+}$ ions and also 10 empty places in the lattice of the metal ions. These $Cu^{2+}$ ions represent as many electrons which are missing from the originally completely filled band (defect conduction), and conduction takes place by an electron passing from a $Cu^+$ ion to a $Cu^{2+}$ ion; the defect goes in the reverse direction. The conductivity increases with the oxygen pressure $P_{O_2}$ because an increase of the deficit occurs hereby (oxidation semiconductor). If a molecule of oxygen is added, then two oxygen ions are formed with absorption of four electrons. These electrons are removed from four $Cu^+$ions, while for the enlargement of the lattice with two $O^{2-}$ions four $Cu^+$ ions are necessary. That is to say, the deficit of $Cu^+$ ions and the number of empty places (and of $Cu^{2+}$ ions), increases by four. WAGNER (WAGNER and DÜNWALD, 1932) has applied the mass action law to this reaction:

$$O_2 + 4e + 4Cu^+ \rightleftharpoons 2\,Cu_2O + 4\,\square e + 4\,\square\,Cu^+$$

$$K = \frac{[\square e]^4\,[\square\,Cu^+]^4}{P_{O_2}} \qquad (\square = \text{empty place})$$

since the other components are present in large quantity. Furthermore, since $\square\, e = \square\, Cu^+$ (that is to say, one electron short always means also one empty place), we have $K = \frac{[\square e]^8}{Po_2}$. If we assume that the conductivity $\varkappa$ is proportional to the electron defect, then we have the proportionality $\varkappa \propto [\square\, e] \propto P_{O_2}^{1/8}$. Experimentally such a law is indeed found with an exponent of 1/7.

The same phenomenon appears in CuI, which almost always contains an excess of iodine, or, stated otherwise, contains some $CuI_2$ and thus likewise exhibits a defect conduction. On heating in vacuum, the conductivity decreases strongly owing to the removal of the excess iodine.

There is excess conduction in ZnO because a small excess of zinc is present in the form of $Zn^{2+}$ ions at inter-lattice positions, against which there are two extra electrons. The equilibrium is here:

$$O_2 + 2\, Zn^{2+}\, (i) + 4\, e\; (extra) \rightleftharpoons 2\, ZnO\; (normal)$$

It follows that $\varkappa \propto e\, (extra) \propto Po_2^{-1/6}$ (experimental: $-1/4.3$) (reduction semiconductor).

In all these cases it is more correct to speak of a deficit or an excess of cations, since the large anions actually form the lattice. The deviations in the stoichiometric composition are produced by empty places in the lattice of the small metal ions or in the other direction by metal ions at interstices between the closely packed anions which are not normally occupied (interlattice positions).

Compounds in which cations already occur in more than one valency in the normal compositions are always strongly coloured and are frequently electron conductors ($Fe_3O_4$, $K_2SbCl_6$ with $Sb^{3+}$ and $Sb^{5+}$, as with $Sb^{4+}$ it would be paramagnetic).

It is characteristic of many semiconductors, in contrast with the true metallic conductors, that the conductivity increases with increasing temperature. This is due to the fact that the number of conduction electrons in a forbidden state of higher energy increases considerably with increasing temperature (exponential increase according to a BOLTZMANN formula $\propto e^{-\varepsilon/kT}$), although the conduction itself through the lattice for one electron( mobility) is hindered by the increasing lattice vibrations.

We always meet this alternation of allowed and forbidden zones. Consequently the possibility of propagation of an electron wave through the lattice is strongly dependent on the direction; so that the complete theory is less simple.

In the very good conductors, such as the monatomic metals, the band is only half-filled, both in the alkali metals of the A-subgroups and in those of the B-subgroups (copper, silver and gold). The elements at the limit of the metals and metalloids show the transition to the insulators. Here there are elements such as bismuth, tellurium and others. Either the principal band in these elements is not completely filled, or there is a small excess of electrons (about 0.001 per atom) which are to be found in the next band. Not only is the conductivity small but, furthermore, it is very much dependent on small amounts of impurities. If, for example, in the lattice of bismuth, a small number of these atoms with five valence electrons are replaced by atoms which each donate fewer electrons, such as tin or lead, then the conductivity decreases very strongly. Apparently there is in bismuth a small excess of electrons, which excess decreases strongly by the above-mentioned addition of tin or lead. The conductivity of these alloys even increases with increasing temperature, as in the semiconductors, showing that the excess in the free band is wholly removed by the addition. On the other hand the conductivity of bismuth increases on the addition of selenium or tellurium from the 6th column, each of which contributes one valence electron more than bismuth. The influence of a magnetic field on the conductivity of bismuth is due to a small change in the energy relations brought about by the magnetic interaction.

In tellurium there is apparently a small deficit (p-type conductor); in fact small impurities, for example of silver, increase the conductivity very greatly in this case. It should be expected that, since tellurium occurs in the 6th column of the periodic table, all impurities give rise to a reduction of the average number of valence electrons per atom. Actually the conductivity of tellurium is found to decrease continuously with increasing degree of purity*. In view of the great influence of traces of admixtures it is not surprising that the data in the literature on the specific resistance of this element differ from each other

* With normal metals it is just the reverse (for example, copper). Foreign atoms in the lattice, just as thermal vibrations, disturb the regularity of the periodic potential in the lattice and decrease the mobility (drift velocity) of the electron (waves) through the lattice because these are scattered. Substances with a low conductivity which, however, decreases with increasing temperature, such as some alloys, carbides and nitrides of titanium, vanadium etc., may be called semi-metals.

For the same reason the conductivity of an alloy with an ordered distribution of the atoms over the lattice sites (compound) will be higher than the conductivity of a disordered solid solution.

by a factor of ten. Addition of 0.5 % antimony, for example, causes the resistance to decrease to one fiftieth of the original value. The purest tellurium prepared by repeated vacuum distillation (BOTTOM, 1952), possessed a specific resistance which is 10–100 times higher than the resistance of other "pure" preparations.

The characteristic behaviour of the resistance of selenium on illumination is also connected with the zone structure. Indeed the calculation of the content of the most important zone shows that there is a small excess in bismuth but a deficit of electrons for complete filling in selenium and tellurium.

In the above paragraphs we started from free electrons but it is also possible with BLOCH to approach the problem from another angle.

In a free sodium atom the 11 electrons occupy sharply determined energy levels, respectively, 2 in the K shell, 8 in the L shell and 1, the valence electron, in the M shell. When now we let two atoms approach one another an interaction occurs, as a result of which symmetrical and antisymmetrical combinations result each time from the wave functions for each state in the separate atom (compare $H_2$), that is to say, splitting occurs. For *m* atoms an *m*-fold splitting of each originally single atomic level occurs. This splitting will be very small for the K electrons, and also only small for the L electrons since the overlap of the corresponding wave functions from different atoms is small. The wave functions of the *m* valence electrons, however, give rise to a broad band corresponding to the abovementioned first allowed zone with, therefore, likewise one state per atom. Owing to the electron spin, this band is only half-filled (Fig. 29).

The methods that we applied here to describe the electrons in a metal are closely related to the *molecular orbital* method in the molecules (p. 291). PAULING has shown that it is also possible to apply the *valence bond* method.

It is, indeed, striking that the so-called 8-*n* rule holds for a large number of elements, *e.g.*, the elements of the 2, 3, 4, 5, 6 and 7th B subgroups and in addition the elements of the same groups in the short periods like carbon, silicon, phosphorus and sulphur. Here 8-*n* is the number of nearest neighbours for an element from the *n*th column. This rule is immediately clear for the atomic electron pair bond and the octet rule. An atom of iodine from the 7th column has one nearest neighbour, because both atoms can thus form an octet. In the elements sulphur, selenium and tellurium, this rule requires that each atom has two neighbours; indeed sulphur forms $S_8$ rings, and the others form infinite spirals in the solid state. Antimony and bismuth ($n = 5$) have three neighbours

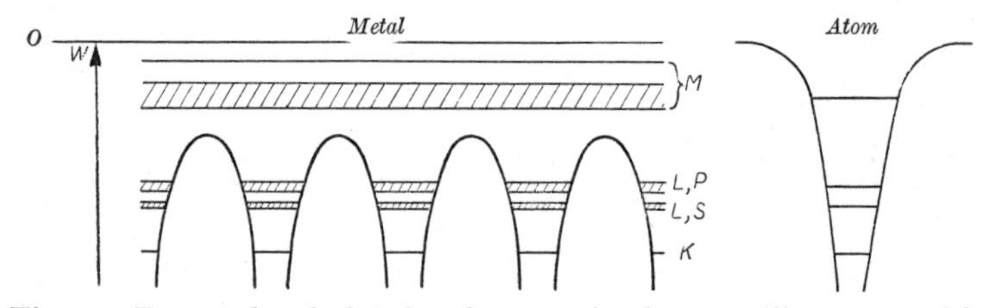


Fig. 29. Energy levels for the electrons in the metallic state and in the free atom (sodium).

at short distances, three others at greater distances. In the 4th group, the diamond structure of C, Si, Ge and Sn is also an example of this rule; each atom forms four electron pair bonds with its neighbours to complete all electron octets. Thus all these elements can be regarded not as metals with free electrons and ions but as structures with atomic bonds. However, it may be remarked that the theory of the Brillouin zones also yields the result that diamond is not a metal and that only a very small number of electrons is present in bismuth outside a completely filled zone.

It is noteworthy that each atom in solid mercury has six nearest neighbours in formal agreement with the 8-*n* rule. This is also the case with zinc and cadmium owing to the fact that the hexagonal closest packing is strongly deformed in these elements. However, there can be no question of the formation of an octet, since there are only two valence electrons available per atom. For the elements before the 4th (B) group it is no longer possible to fill an octet by sharing valence electrons with their neighbours.

These elements, as well as some in the 4B group itself, are typical metals. In the lower part of the Periodic System the transition from insulators to metals takes place in the 5B group (Sb, Bi).

PAULING (PAULING, 1938, 1947, 1949; EWING and PAULING, 1948) assumes in his *resonating-valence-bond-theory* of metals that between a lithium atom with one valence electron and its eight nearest neighbours there is resonance between a very large number ($3.14^N$ for $2N$ atoms according to PAULING) of configurations like:

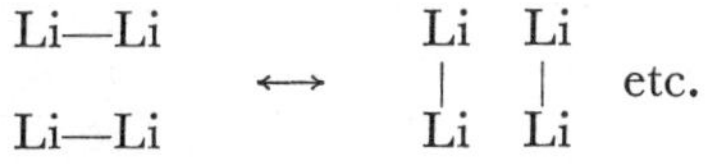

```
Li—Li          Li  Li
       <-->    |   |   etc.
Li—Li          Li  Li
```

This resonance is of the same "synchronized" type as that, *e.g.*, in benzene. However, an even larger number of polar (ionic) configurations also play an important role; PAULING calculates ($2.32 \times 3.14^N$).

```
Li—Li          Li  Li+
       <-->    |
Li—Li         -Li—Li
```

Here the configuration of one bond does not depend on the configuration of the other bonds. This type of resonance through electron transfer has been called "pivotal". It is only possible where unoccupied low-energy levels are available ("metallic" orbitals), like in metals. The electric conduction is only possible through the intermediary of these metallic orbitals. The lattice energy is due to the bond energy and the resonance energy. The first contribution is only small for lithium which has one valence electron per atom (comp. energy $Li_2$: diss. energy 13.4 kcal/g atom; Li metal: subl. energy 37.1 kcal/g atom).

In lithium and the other alkali metals three p levels lie at a small distance above the s level of the valence electron (Li: 42.5 kcal; Na: 46.5 kcal; Cs: 38.5 kcal). Hybridization certainly plays an important role in the formation of stronger bonds than would be possible with pure s orbitals.

For the relation between the bond order $n$ and the interatomic distance or more specifically the atomic radius PAULING (PAULING, 1947) uses the formula: $r_1 - r_n = 0.300 \log n$ ($r_1$ bond radius for a pure single bond, equal to the radius *e.g.*, in diatomic hydrides). Such an expression is found to be also valid for the C—C bond with a coefficient of 0.353.

He has derived a table of metallic radii of the elements giving $r_1$ and $r$ (CN 12), the latter corresponding to the closely packed structure with coordination number 12; here the bond order $n = v/12$ if $v$ is the valence.

Lithium has a body-centred cubic structure (CN 8) with 8 nearest neighbours at 3.032 Å and 6 more at a slightly larger distance of 3.502 Å. For a total bond order of 1, the bond order is calculated to be $n = 0.111$ and $n = 0.018$ for both categories of bonds, with $r_1 = 1.220$ Å (comp. $Li_2$: $r = 1.33$ Å, but for a nearly pure s bond).

In the transition metals of the first long period from scandium to nickel, nine orbitals (five 3d, one 4s and three 4d orbitals) are available for the three to ten electrons present, outside the argon configuration.

The number of unpaired electrons is obtained from the magnetic moment expressed as the number of magnetons per atom as derived from the saturation magnetization at absolute zero (BOZORTH, 1951, see also KITTEL, book, 1953, 1956). The numbers of unpaired electrons are V 0.0, Cr 0.22, Mn 1.22, Fe 2.22, Co 1.66, Ni 0.66 and Cu 0.0. If the magnetization of alloys of these elements is also taken into account we find a maximum value of 2.44 unpaired electrons for a Fe-Co alloy with 22 % Co, which thus has 8.22 electrons per atom (Fig. 30).

PAULING now assumed that there is a constant number of 5.78 (paired) bonding electrons; the other electrons (Cr

6—5.78 = 0.22; Mn 7—5.78 = 1.22; etc.) are present in atomic non-bonding 3d orbitals in which they are unpaired as far as possible (HUND's rule, p. 156). Apparently there are 8.22—5.78 = 2.44 of these non-bonding 3d orbitals available. In cobalt and nickel the number of non-bonding electrons over the 5.78 bonding electrons of 9—5.78 = 3.22 and 10—5.78 = 4.22 respectively can be accommodated in the 2.44 non-bonding orbitals if some pairing takes place, leaving 2 × 2.44—3.22 = 1.66 and 2 × 2.44—4.22 = 0.66 electrons respectively unpaired. In general, small additions to nickel of metals with 10 + $z$ electrons outside an inert gas

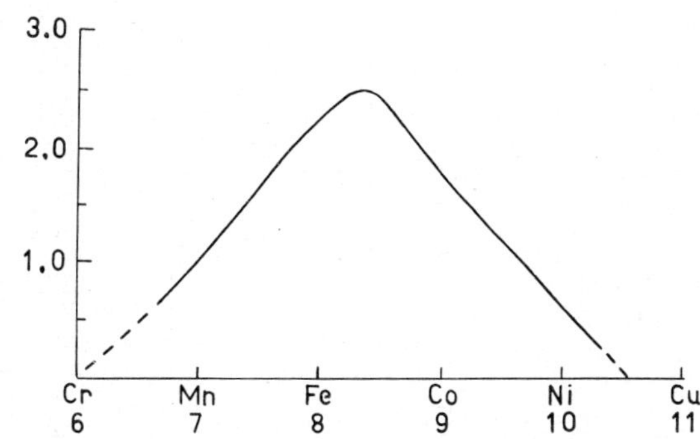


Fig. 30. Atomic magnetic moments of transition metals.

configuration give rise to a decrease of $z$ Bohr magnetons per atom. ($z$ has the values Sn 4, Al 3, Zn 2, Cu 1, Pd 0, Co —1, Fe —2, Mn —3.) An atomic moment equal to zero is obtained for a Ni-Cu alloy with 62% Cu or 10.62 electrons per atom. Addition of hydrogen in solution in metallic palladium (NORBERG, 1952) reduces the magnetic moment in the same way; at a ratio H/Pd 0.66 and higher the susceptibility is zero. There are just 5.78 bonding (paired) electrons and 4.88 non-bonding (paired) electrons present, in total 10.66 electrons.

From the total of nine orbitals available there are only used 5.78 + 2.44 = 8·22, leaving 0.78 orbital unused.

In PAULING's valence bond theory this unused 0.78 orbital

is essential for the "pivotal" resonance and for the conduction (metallic orbital)*.

In the band model the sequence of the saturation magnetic moments of the transition metals is interpreted by assuming that there are about 0.7 electrons in the wide 4 sp-band with opposite spin directions. This leaves 9.3 and 8.3 electrons in the 3d-band for Ni and Co respectively. As the 3d-band comprises five levels this leads to 0.7 and 1.7 unpaired electrons as found from the magnetization. The zero moment of the Ni-Cu alloy with 62 % Cu is explained by a completely filled 3d band with 10 electrons and 0.62 paired electrons in the 4sp-band. For iron a number of 7.3 electrons in the 3d-band would lead to a maximum of 2.7 unpaired electrons whereas there are only 2.22 unpaired electrons. We are also forced to assume that not all 3d-levels are used in iron and the lower transition elements.

In a later version PAULING describes essentially the same concepts in a different way. For example he explains the observed magnetic moment in nickel of 0.61 B.M. by a repartition of two kinds of atoms, both with a valence 6:

| | | 3d | | | | | 4s | 4p | | |
|---|---|---|---|---|---|---|---|---|---|---|
| Ni A | 30 % | ↑↓ | ↑ | ↑ | • | • | • | • | • | • |
| Ni B | 70 % | ↑↓ | ↑↓ | • | • | • | • | • | • | o |

• bond forming orbital, occupied by two electrons;
o metallic, non-occupied orbital;
↑ non-bonding electrons.

Only in iron does he still assume a lower valence of 5.78 from a mixture of atoms in 6-, and 5-valent states.

In the structure of β-manganese two different kinds of atoms in the crystallographic sense are indeed present; 8 atoms with a small radius ($v \approx 6$) and 12 with a larger radius ($v \approx 4$). In α-manganese the unit cell of 58 atoms contains 24 of the high valence and 34 of the lower valence type. The latter valence is represented exclusively in the simple structure of the third γ-modification.

In copper he assumes 5-valent copper atoms B (75 %) to be present together with 7-valent copper atoms A (25 %), leading to a valence of 5.5, derived from the observed distances.

---

* In another theory (GRIFFITH, 1956; ORGEL, 1957; GRIFFITH and ORGEL, 1958) of the electronic distribution in the transition metals two groups of orbitals are also recognized with up to about 6 electrons in bonding orbitals and the others in localized non-bonding orbitals.

| | 3d | 4s | 4p |
|---|---|---|---|
| Cu A | ↑↓ ↑↓ • • • | • | • • • |
| Cu B | ↑↓ ↑↓ ↑↓ • • | • | • • o |

For tin PAULING distinguishes, besides the 4-valent state (SnA), a divalent state (SnB)

| | 4d | 5s | 5p |
|---|---|---|---|
| Sn A | ↑↓ ↑↓ ↑↓ ↑↓ ↑↓ | • | • • • |
| Sn B | ↑↓ ↑↓ ↑↓ ↑↓ ↑↓ | ↑↓ | • • o |

The first kind, forming four $sp^3$ bonds, is a non-metal with a diamond lattice (grey tin). In white tin, with coordination number six, the Sn B atoms form two bonds among six neighbours. The "observed" valency of 2.44 would be caused again by 75 % Sn B with 25 % Sn A in white tin.

Much has still to be clarified in the resonating-valence-bond theory of the metals. It is not yet clear how the various valences and properties of atoms in different states could ever be derived in an independent way.

However, it is certain that the 3d electrons contribute to an important extent to the cohesion of the transition metals with their very low volatility. In contrast MOTT and JONES, on the basis of the band theory, assumed that the bonding is determined essentially by the 4s electrons and even by less than one electron. This would make the transition metals comparable to the alkali metals in lattice energy and volatility, which is completely wrong.

With copper, the 3d shell is completely filled in the free atom and there is only one 4s valence electron. Nevertheless, copper is by no means comparable in lattice energy with the alkali metals. Indeed one can expect that, in analogy to the picture of Fig. 29, the band of the 3d electrons in copper is much broader than that of the 2p electrons in sodium because of the greater overlap between neighbouring atoms. The 3d and 4s band will even overlap and thus hybridization certainly takes place.

The band picture of metals developed by physicists accounts very well for conduction and other electric magnetic properties. The valence bond description of the bonds in metals related to the concepts of chemistry offers a better explanation than the former theory for such properties as lattice energies and bond distances. On the other hand, the V.B. picture does not lend itself well to *a priori* quantitative calculations of these properties and it seems doubtful to what extent a bond in solid lithium with a bond order of 0.11 (with respect to the bond order one in a gas molecule) has any fundamental meaning. There is no doubt, however, that PAULING's theory is valuable as a counterpart to the band picture in less typical metals and compounds, just as the V.B. and the M.O. methods are both of great importance for the description of the constitution of organic molecules.

## § 38. ALLOYS

The metals crystallize mainly in a small number of structures, in which the cubic and hexagonal variants of closest packing of spheres and the body-centred cube type of lattice occur most frequently. Provided the lattice constant does not differ too much, mixed crystal formation frequently occurs, although not always over the whole concentration range. The numerous compounds which occur in most systems are characteristic of the metal systems or alloys. Their existence is proved not only from the phase diagram obtained from thermal analysis but, among other things, from an investigation of the conductivity as a function of the composition. Compounds show up as peaks (see footnote p. 338). The compounds are not always stable up to the melting point. Thus a continuous series of mixed crystals crystallizes from the melt of the system copper-gold, and they can also exist at room temperature after rapid cooling. With slow cooling (tempering), however, an ordering process occurs at about 350° in the arbitrary distribution of the copper and the gold atoms over the positions of the face-centred cubic lattice; as a result the three copper atoms per elementary cell occupy the mid-points of the sides, while the gold atom occupies the corners of the cube. The correct composition of this compound is therefore $AuCu_3$.

An ordering process as described leads to the formation of a "super-structure", which is indicated by the appearance of new diffraction lines in the X-ray diagram and by an increase in conductivity.

A compound may exist over a smaller or larger range of composition through the formation of mixed crystals with both components. In the phase diagram this range of existence is separated from that of other compounds by a heterogeneous part of mixtures of both compounds. In some cases, *e.g.*, CuZn or β-brass, with a CsCl-structure, the typical ordering composition at which the ordering is maximal (here 1 : 1) may be outside the range of existence (46 to 48.5 % Zn).

We will define a chemical compound as a composite homogeneous substance whose properties cannot be transformed continuously into those of its constituent elements or of other compounds by changes in the composition.

The composition of many metallic compounds proved to be an unsurmountable difficulty for the older ideas about fixed and characteristic valencies. These compositions can indeed in no wise be reduced to simple stoichiometric compositions; two elements frequently appear to combine in a very great number of ratios with one another, as for example potassium and mercury: $KHg_{12}$, $KHg_9$, $KHg_4$, $KHg_3$, KHg.

TABLE 27

HUME-ROTHERY COMPOUNDS

| Type | β-brass | γ-brass | ε-brass |
|---|---|---|---|
| $\frac{\text{electrons}}{\text{atoms}}$ | $^3/_2$ | $^{21}/_{13}$ | $^7/_4$ |
| | CuZn<br>AgCd<br>$Cu_3Al$<br>$Cu_5Sn$<br>NiAl etc. | $Cu_5Zn_8$<br>$Ag_5Hg_8$<br>$Cu_9Al_4$<br>$Cu_{31}Sn_8$<br>$Fe_5Zn_{21}$ etc. | $CuZn_3$<br>$AgCd_3$<br>$Ag_5Al_3$<br>$Cu_3Sn$ etc. |

It is equally as incomprehensible that compounds of completely different composition, such as $Cu_5Zn_8$, $Cu_9Al_4$, $Cu_{31}Sn_8$, $Fe_5Zn_{21}$, nevertheless crystallize in the same type of lattice (Table 27). HUME-ROTHERY pointed out that in these cases it is not the atom ratio which is characteristic but rather the ratio of the total number of electrons to the total number of atoms. Thus for $Cu_5Zn_8$ we have

$$(5 \times 1 + 8 \times 2) : 13 = 21 : 13$$

The metals from the eighth group must then be supposed to contribute no electrons.

The ratio $^{21}/_{13}$ is characteristic of compounds of the $\gamma$-brass type (CuZn) and $^{7}/_{4}$ for the $\varepsilon$-brass type ($CuZn_3$) (HUME-ROTHERY compounds).

The characteristic composition of the $\gamma$-phase is in fact $Cu_5Zn_8$ (composition of maximal order) and does not lie at the simpler ratios 3 : 5 or 2 : 3. This follows from the crystal structure in which the elementary cell contains $4 \times 13 = 52$ atoms.

This ratio of atoms to electrons is indeed determinative of the properties in many metallic systems, *e.g.*, the solubility in the melt and in the solid state. Zinc dissolves in the solid state in copper up to 38.4 % as a homogeneous mixed crystal ($\alpha$-brass, the normal brass contains about 35 % zinc); almost the same limit of about 40 % holds for the combinations of the elements copper, silver and gold with zinc and cadmium.

By comparison with zinc or cadmium, elements such as aluminium, gallium and indium from the third column, silicon, germanium and tin from the fourth column and antimony from the fifth column, dissolve to the extent $1 : {}^{1}/_{2} : {}^{1}/_{3} : {}^{1}/_{4}$. Each replacement of a copper or silver atom by zinc or cadmium involves an increase of the number of electrons by one; this is two for aluminium, three for silicon and four for antimony (p. 333).

The product of dissolved amount (in atom fractions) $\times$ (valence $-$ 1) gives the increase of the electron concentration per atom. This is constant for elements from the various columns.

TABLE 28

MAX. SOLUBILITY IN SOLID COPPER AT ROOM TEMPERATURE

| In copper | Atom % | Electron concentration |
|---|---|---|
| Zinc | 38.4 % | 1.384 |
| Aluminium | 20.4 % | 1.408 |
| Gallium | 20.3 % | 1.406 |
| Silicium | 14.0 % | 1.420 |
| Germanium | 12.0 % | 1.360 |

The lowering of the melting point is also the same for these metals when the electron concentration instead of the atomic concentration is plotted against the temperature in the melting diagram.

The system Cu—Zn (the brass alloys) shows a great similarity to the system Cu—Sn (the bronze alloys) with the understanding that the corresponding compounds occur at equal ratios of atoms to electrons and not at equal atomic compositions (Table 27).

An explanation of these HUME-ROTHERY numbers, so strange at first sight, has been given by JONES on the basis of the energy zones. The allowed zone below a broad forbidden band is only half occupied by electrons in copper. JONES calculated that only at a number of electrons per lattice point greater than 1.36, that is at 36 % zinc, do the additional electrons have to find a place in an energy band above the forbidden region (p. 333). Up to this limit mixed crystal formation will thus be possible with polyvalent elements in the above given ratios, provided the dimensions of the atoms do not differ greatly (< 14 %). It is thus also the filling of the band which plays the principal part in the formation of compounds. If the number of electrons is too great, then this is energetically unfavourable. However, this is also the case with too incomplete a filling because then (certainly with alloys) there will be a possibility of the mixed crystal breaking up into a conglomerate of two other lattices, each possessing a better filling of the zones. Thus JONES was able to show that the lattice of the γ-brass type reaches a good filling when the ratio electrons/atoms is between 1.54 and 1.73; this is close to the rational fraction $^{21}/_{13} = 1{\cdot}61$ of HUME-ROTHERY. An alloy, such as γ-brass, must indeed possess a very good filling of the energy zones; this is evident both from the small conductivity and, for example, from the diamagnetism of these alloys, corresponding to the diamagnetism of practically all insulators (whereas metals always possess some paramagnetic contribution from the free conduction electrons).

With larger differences in atomic radius, the composition and the crystal structure of the compounds are mainly determined by the possibility of forming a favourable packing. This is the case, for example, in the so-called LAVES compounds: $MgCu_2$, $KBi_2$, $AgBe_2$ (cubic); $MgZn_2$, $CaMg_2$, $MgNi_2$, $TiCo_2$ (hexagonal) (LAVES and WALLBAUM, 1942). The structure can be described as consisting of two lattices of contacting spheres, which can be just placed one inside the other if the radius ratio is $\sqrt{3} : \sqrt{2}$.

A large group of compounds of transition metals, *e.g.*, Cr, Mn, Fe, Co, Ni, Cu, Pd and Pt with more electro-negative metalloids, *e.g.*, S, Se, Te, As, Sb, Bi, all crystallize in the NiAs structure.

Combinations of two metals which differ greatly in electronegativity result in salt-like compounds, according to the ionic valence. These are often characterized by a high melting point and a large heat of formation. As examples we may cite:

| melting point | heat of formation | melting point | heat of formation |
|---|---|---|---|
| $Mg_2Si$ 1085° | 59 kcal/mole | $Ca_2Pb$ 1100° | 47 kcal/mole |
| $Mg_2Ge$ 915° | — ,, | $Mg_3Sb_2$ 1228° | 68 ,, |
| $Mg_2Sn$ 778° | 17.2 ,, | $Ca_3Sb_2$ — | 160 ,, |
| $Mg_2Pb$ 550° | 12.6 ,, | $Li_3Bi$ 1145° | — |

PAULING's valence bond theory, when it has been further developed, may elucidate the details of many intermetallic compounds. It is, however, quite certain that the atomic (metallic) radius, as PAULING has pointed out, is not at all a constant but varies with the bonding. Thus the apparent radius of sodium is 13 % smaller in NaTl than that derived from the element itself; the radius of the thallium atom in NaTl is only 2 % smaller. The same holds true for the analogous compounds like LiAl, LiGa, NaIn, etc. Certainly the bond order ($n \approx 0.6$) of the Na-Na bonds in this compound is much higher than in metallic sodium. The four electrons which are easily available per unit NaTl would be adequate to form bonds of the order 0.5 in the two penetrating diamond lattices of the sodium and thallium atoms. With d-electrons coming into play, as is probable in the red coloured analogous alloys LiZn and LiCd, still stronger bonds are possible.

The interstitial compounds form a special group. These are the compounds of the transition metals (Sc—Ni, Y—Pd, La—Pt and Ac—Pu) with the smallest metalloids (hydrogen, boron, carbon and nitrogen). The atomic radii of these latter elements are so small that they are accommodated in the interstices; the smallest, hydrogen, is accommodated in the tetrahedral holes in a closest packing of metal atoms with four closest neighbours, the others in the octahedral holes where there are six closest neighbours. The composition is usually variable within wide limits (Pd—H) and determined only by the number of equivalent interstices. Many of these systems (Fe—C, Fe—N) are extremely important technically. These compounds, usually $M_2X$ or MX, are distinguished by very great hardness (WC, so-called Widia metal, p. 96) and high melting point (above 3000°; TaC and HfC have the highest known melting points at 4150° K and 4160° K) as well as a metallic appearance.

## § 39. MECHANICAL PROPERTIES

The mechanical properties of metals and alloys are of the greatest practical importance, more so than in other groups.

It is generally known that metals in a very pure state, especially in the form of single crystals, are almost all extremely soft and have a low yield point *. If, for example, technical beryllium is known as a very hard metal, this actually indicates a still inadequate purity. To increase the hardness and the tensile strength, use can be made either of mechanical working such as hammering for the deformation of the lattice (iron, copper) or of an atomic lattice deformation by the inclusion of foreign atoms. Thus silver and gold are practically never used in the pure state, but always alloyed (with copper for example). With iron it is especially the carbon in steel and cast iron which is important and in aluminium a little copper (duralumin). On heating (annealing of copper or iron), the hardness resulting from mechanical working disappears again completely; this is sometimes the case with alloy hardness (steel, duralumin) and sometimes not (gold-copper).

How can this influence now be understood? We observe that the stretching of a metal crystal (plastic deformation) occurs through gliding of parts of the lattice taking place along certain crystallographic planes. Obviously gliding is not at all equally easy along all crystallographically equivalent planes since gliding first occurs along one plane, then only with higher tension along another plane, etc. The strength increases with increasing deformation since a higher tension is always necessary to cause a further gliding *.

Gliding first takes place along a plane which is but little deformed; naturally many of these planes will occur in an unworked, pure and monocrystalline material. Less ideal planes only glide at higher applied tensions. Obviously the gliding process along a particular plane stops at a certain point, but the crystal does not yet break. It is supposed that along each plane some mechanical or chemical disturbance of the lattice

* With a rod consisting of one single crystal of tin, for example, bending once is sufficient to increase the hardness considerably. Likewise a wire becomes stronger on stretching although the thickness has decreased in the initial stretching.

is present. These disturbances act as points of anchorage. The gliding along a plane ends when the disturbances come together and when deformations are produced by the gliding at the edges of the lattice blocks.

The deformation of the lattice as a result of the mechanical working is seen from the broadening of the lines in the X-ray diffraction picture, which are narrow under normal circumstances (DEBYE-SCHERRER or powder diagram).

Renewed crystal growth becomes possible on heating, whereby undeformed crystals are again produced at the expense of the deformed lattice which has higher energy content (recrystallization). The broadening of the X-ray lines disappears completely thereby.

The influence of heat treatment on iron which contains carbon is fairly complicated, as a consequence of the complications of the iron-carbon system. Broadly speaking, it can be said that the carbon is dissolved homogeneously at high temperatures (above 880°) in $\gamma$-iron as a mixed crystal (austenite) in which the carbon atoms occupy inter-lattice positions (p. 351). With rapid cooling (hardening) the carbon remains homogeneously distributed, but this mixed crystal is no longer stable at low temperatures. An unstable tetragonal deformed crystal (martensite) is produced and consequently a great hardness results. A transition into the stable state (tempering) takes place slowly, more rapidly at higher temperatures — 200–300° — (a chisel already at 100°, do not leave it in the sun!); the carbon is deposited as cementite ($Fe_3C$) and the internal strains disappear partially. Steel owes its ease of working combined with the possibility of attaining a great hardness and tensile strength just to these phenomena. Materials which remain hard under all circumstances can be worked to some extent only by grinding.

In duralumin (with 4 % copper and 0.5 % magnesium), important in modern constructions, the greater strength is produced by the separation of crystals of the compound $CuAl_2$. At temperatures above 500° the copper is dissolved homogeneously in the solid aluminium phase. At lower temperatures the solubility becomes very small, although with rapid cooling no separation of the copper in the form of $CuAl_2$ takes place. In the absence of magnesium this occurs only on tempering at 100–150°; with 0.5 % magnesium, however, it takes place in a few days even at room temperature. The precipitation hardness that is produced must be attributed to the deformation of the crystallites by lattice disturbances, as a result of the accumulation of copper atoms in small lattice regions in the form of $CuAl_2$. The hardness disappears again on the subsequent production of larger crystals. This latter process, which becomes noticeable only at higher temperatures, is undesirable. Therefore duralumin is superior to copper-aluminium alloys without magnesium since it has a low hardening temperature so that softening is not to be feared.

The tensile strength of this self-hardened duralumin is twice as great as that in the soft state and five times as great as pure aluminium.

Annealed duralumin can, therefore, be worked in the soft state at room temperature; it then becomes hard spontaneously after a few days, while steel must be worked at high temperatures.

In modern technical alloys, most of which consist of a large number of components, the presence or absence of traces of some elements plays an extraordinarily great role in determining the mechanical properties. We have previously seen how such a great influence of traces can become manifest just in metals. The individual chemical properties of the admixed elements usually play a minor role in this respect (compare on the other hand de-oxidation of steel by aluminium or sodium).

LITERATURE

C. S. Barrett, *Structure of Metals*, New York, 1952.
C. E. Beynon, *The Physical Structure of Alloys*, London, 1945.
W. Hume-Rothery, *The Structure of Metals and Alloys*, London, 2nd edition, 1950; *Atomic Theory for Students of Metallurgy*, London, 1948.

CH. KITTEL, *Introduction to Solid State Physics*, New York, 1953, 1956.
F. SEITZ, *The Physics of Metals*, New York, 1943.
A. H. WILSON, *Semi-conductors and Metals*, Cambridge, 1939.

The following are more difficult:

N. F. MOTT and H. JONES, *The Theory of the Properties of Metals and Alloys*, Oxford, 1936.
A. H. WILSON, *The Theory of Metals*, Cambridge, 1936, 1953.

REFERENCES

BOTTOM, V. E., *Science, 115* (1952) 570.
BOZORTH, R. M., *Ferromagnetism*, New York, 1951.
BUERGER, M. J., *X-ray Crystallography*, New York, 1942.
BIJVOET, J. M., KOLKMEYER, N. H. and MACGILLAVRY, C.H., *X-ray Analysis of Crystals*, London, 1951.
EWING. F. J. and PAULING, L., *Revs. Modern Physics, 20* (1948) 112.
GRIFFITH, J. S., *J. Inorg. & Nucl. Chem., 3* (1956) 15.
GRIFFITH, J. S. and ORGEL, L. E., *Nature, 181* (1958) 170.
LAVES, F. and WALLBAUM, H. J., *Z. anorg. Chem., 250* (1942) 110.
NORBERG, R. E. *Phys. Rev., 86* (1952) 745.
ORGEL, L. E., *J. Phys. Chem., 3* (1957) 50.
PAULING, L., *Phys. Rev., 54* (1938) 899.
PAULING, L., *J. Am. Chem. Soc., 69* (1947) 542; *Proc. Roy. Soc. London, A 196* (1949) 300, 343.
WAGNER, C. and DÜNWALD, H., *Z. physik. Chem. Leipzig, B 17* (1932) 467.
WILSON, A. H., *The Theory of Metals*, Cambridge, 1936, 1953.

# V. VAN DER WAALS BONDING

## § 40. THE THREE TYPES OF VAN DER WAALS INTERACTION

The three types of bonding discussed in the preceding chapters do not give a complete description of all possible interaction forces. There is *e.g.*, also a mutual attraction between the uncharged atoms of the inert gases, the charge distribution of which is strictly spherically symmetrical. This attraction manifests itself in the possibility of liquefying these gases. As early as 1873, VAN DER WAALS postulated the existence of a general attractive force acting between all molecules and atoms and leading to the term $a/V^2$ in his equation of state. However, the nature of these forces remained obscure for the time being. KEESOM calculated the average interaction energy between particles at a distance $r$ with a permanent electric dipole moment $\mu$ to be:

$$\varepsilon_K = -\frac{2}{3}\frac{1}{r^6}\frac{\mu^4}{kT}.$$

The interaction of two permanent dipoles is given by $\mu^2/r^3$ multiplied by a function $f$ of the mutual orientation; for two dipoles in line this is $\pm$ 2, according as they are directed oppositely (repulsion) or the same way (attraction); for two moments directed parallel to one another this is $\pm$ 1, likewise according as they are directed the same way (repulsion) or oppositely (attraction). Now the energetically favourable orientations will predominate over the energetically unfavourable ones as a result of which an attraction will result on the average. This orientation will be governed by the BOLTZMANN distribution law, that is to say, there is a factor $e^{-\Delta E/kT}$ in which $\Delta E = \mu^2/r^3 f$; since $\Delta E \ll kT$ this factor is equal to $1 - \Delta E/kT$. The second term gives the deviation from the uniform distribution over attractive and repulsive configurations which results in attraction. It can be seen readily that the KEESOM or orientation energy will be proportional to $-(\mu^2/r^3)\cdot(\Delta E/kT)$, therefore to $\mu^4/r^6 \cdot kT$. The numerical factor $^2/_3$ only appears on accurate averaging by integration over all orientations.

It is furthermore understandable that all orientations are equally probable at very high temperatures; thus repulsion and attraction occur equally, and the attraction energy becomes zero.

DEBYE added to this the interaction energy resulting from the attraction between a permanent dipole and the moments induced by this dipole in the neighbouring molecules:

$$\varepsilon_D = -2\,\frac{\alpha\mu^2}{r^6}.$$

This expression can easily be made plausible. The permanent dipole $\mu$ gives rise to a field strength $F \propto \mu/r^3$ at a distance $r$. In a molecule of polarizability $\alpha$ an induced dipole $\mu_i = \alpha F$ is produced by a field $F$. The energy becomes $\varepsilon = -{}^1/_2\alpha F^2$ (p. 73) or this is proportional to $-{}^1/_2\,\alpha\,\mu^2/r^6$.
The temperature has no influence on the interaction energy, since in this case there is always attraction and no influence of the mutual orientation, if at least the polarizability is independent of the direction.
The numerical factor is obtained by taking into account the fact that molecule 1 acts on 2 but likewise 2 on 1 (factor 2) and by averaging the value of $F^2$ over the angle $\gamma$ between the permanent dipole moment and the line joining two molecules. On resolving into components along and perpendicular to this line, $F^2 = \frac{\mu^2}{r^6}(4\cos^2\gamma + \sin^2\gamma) = \frac{\mu^2}{r^6}(1 + 3\cos^2\gamma)$. Since the mean value $\overline{\cos^2\gamma} = {}^1/_3$ it follows that $\overline{F^2} = \frac{2\mu^2}{r^6}$, thus adding another factor 2 to the result.
These formulae can easily be checked by verifying the dimensions. An energy has the dimension $e^2/L$ (charge²/length) and since $\alpha$ has the dimension $L^3$ and $\mu$ that of $e.L$, both formulae for the interaction energy have the right dimensions as $kT$ is already an energy itself.

Neither explanation has any significance in the case of the inert gases which have no dipole moment. Moreover there is absolutely no agreement between the calculated and the experimental values for the attraction energy in most cases.

KEESOM's formula is also not satisfactory since the term *a* from VAN DER WAALS equation, which is proportional to $\varepsilon$, should be strongly dependent on temperature, which is not the case. The DEBYE energy is indeed independent of temperature but is always very small (Table 29).

In 1930 LONDON (1930, 1937) made a more accurate calculation of the interaction of two hydrogen atoms at large distances on the basis of the wave mechanics. This calculation furnished a third form of the VAN DER WAALS attraction energy, besides the KEESOM or orientation energy and the DEBYE or induction energy, namely the LONDON or dispersion energy (Table 29).

This last wave-mechanical type of interaction can be illustrated qualitatively in the following classical way.

If we could take instantaneous photographs of a molecule or atom at certain instants, we should usually find an arrangement of nuclei and electrons such that the whole exhibits an electric dipole moment. This holds also for an atom with a spherically symmetrical charge distribution as in the inert gases and in the hydrogen atom in the ground state (see p. 123). One might, on the basis of BOHR's atom model, think of an electron describing an orbit round the nucleus. The average of very many exposures would show no preferred direction and so no moment.

This rapidly varying dipole, produced by the zero-point motion, gives rise to an electric field and this polarizes the other atom in which a dipole is induced in phase with the first; this interacts with the instantaneous dipole. The zero-point motion is thus, as it were, accompanied by a synchronized electric field. There is no radiation because the atom is in the ground state and the zero-point energy cannot be transformed into radiation.

The theoretical treatment furnishes an attraction energy

$$\varepsilon_L = -\frac{3}{4}\frac{h\nu_0\alpha^2}{r^6}$$

in which $\nu_0$ is the frequency of the above-mentioned zero-point motion and $\alpha$ the polarizability. The ionization energy $I$ can also be taken instead of $h\nu_0$:

$$\varepsilon_L = -\frac{3}{4}\frac{I\alpha^2}{r^6}$$

The formula can be deduced, as LONDON (1930) has shown, by considering the hydrogen atoms semi-classically as oscillators with frequency $\nu_0$.

A coupling between these oscillators arises from the interaction of the oscillating dipoles. The two coupled three-dimensional oscillators can be described by a set of six independent, normal, vibrations, with changed frequencies. We then calculate the total zero-point energy of these six compared with the original amount for the uncoupled oscillators at a large distance. A lowering of the zero-point energy by $^3/_4 \frac{\alpha^2}{r^6} h\nu_0$ occurs as a result of the interaction.

The wave-mechanical calculation of the 2nd order perturbation energy (the 1st order perturbation energy is zero) gives the same result, but it then appears at the same time that $h\nu_0$ for these fictitious oscillators is the ionization energy, that is, the energy of the electron in the lowest energy state, so that $\nu_0$ is also equal to $^4/_3$ of the frequency of the spectral transition of the electron from this state to the first higher state (1st line of the LYMAN series).

In addition this term, proportional to $1/r^6$, is only the first of a series; the next terms with $1/r^8$ and $1/r^{10}$ can be called dipole-quadrupole and quadrupole-quadrupole interactions, just as the first term is a dipole-dipole interaction.

TABLE 29

DISTRIBUTION OF VAN DER WAALS ATTRACTION ENERGY OVER THE THREE TYPES

| | Dipole moment | Polarizability | Lattice energy in kcal/mole divided according to its origin: KEESOM | DEBYE | LONDON | Total |
|---|---|---|---|---|---|---|
| A | 0 D | $1.63 \times 10^{-24}$ cm³ | 0.000 | 0.000 | 2.03 | 2.03 |
| CO | 0.12 ,, | 1.99 ,, | 0.0001 | 0.002 | 2.09 | 2.09 |
| HI | 0.38 ,, | 5.40 ,, | 0.006 | 0.027 | 6.18 | 6.21 |
| HBr | 0.78 ,, | 3.58 ,, | 0.164 | 0.120 | 5.24 | 5.52 |
| HCl | 1.03 ,, | 2.63 ,, | 0.79 | 0.24 | 4.02 | 5.05 |
| $NH_3$ | 1.50 ,, | 2.21 ,, | 3.18 | 0.37 | 3.52 | 7.07 |
| $H_2O$ | 1.84 ,, | 1.48 ,, | 8.69 | 0.46 | 2.15 | 11.30 |

With dissimilar particles the expressions for the VAN DER WAALS-LONDON energy become:

$$\varepsilon_L = -3/2 \frac{\alpha_1 \alpha_2}{r^6} h \frac{\nu_1 \nu_2}{\nu_1 + \nu_2}, \text{ and}$$

$$\varepsilon_L = -3/2 \frac{\alpha_1 \alpha_2}{r^6} \frac{I_1 I_2}{I_1 + I_2}$$

These formulae have only a restricted validity for atoms other than hydrogen when one uses the experimental value of the ionization potential.

These ionization potentials for that matter vary but little

for organic molecules, 200–250 kcal. One can also calculate the frequency $\nu$ from the variation of the refractive index (actually the molar refraction) with wave length, that is to say, from the dispersion, hence the name mentioned above for this type of interaction.

A third expression is sometimes also useful:

$$\varepsilon_L = -3/4 \frac{\alpha^2}{r^6} \frac{he}{2\pi\sqrt{m}} \sqrt{\frac{n}{\alpha}}$$

This was deduced by SLATER and KIRKWOOD (1931); $n$ is the number of electrons in the outermost shell.

The VAN DER WAALS-LONDON attraction is always present, even when there is a bond belonging to one of the other main types of the chemical bond between the particles. This interaction is always attractive, non-directional (apart from the anisotropy of the polarizability) and non-specific. It does not lead to saturation, it acts only over distances of the order of magnitude of the radius of the particle and is dependent on the degree of polarizability of *both* particles.

The contribution of the LONDON energy to the lattice energy (p. 38, 43) of the alkali halides is indeed small in comparison with the electrostatic interaction; however, the transition from NaCl- to CsCl-type of lattice nevertheless depends on it. The geometrical condition, $r_+/r_- > 0.71$, is not sufficient for this transition; in fact, KF with $r_+/r_- = 1.00$ has the NaCl lattice (p. 32).

The electrostatic attraction for the NaCl-type will in fact be greater than for CsCl since the small difference in the MADELUNG constant (1.74756 against 1.76267) is more than compensated by the about 3% greater distance $r$ in the case of 8 nearest neighbours (p. 39). Now the VAN DER WAALS-LONDON interaction, since it is proportional to $1/r^6$, is practically restricted to the nearest neighbours. On summation over the whole lattice we can therefore be satisfied with multiplication by the coordination number. Thus the contribution is greater for the CsCl structure with coordination number 8 than for the NaCl structure with 6, but this is only of importance for counterbalancing the unfavourable influence of the difference in the COULOMB energy if the factor $\alpha_1 \alpha_2$ is large, that is to say, when both particles are readily polarizable. This is indeed the case in CsCl, CsBr, CsI and the corresponding thallium halides which crystallize in the CsCl structure, but is not the case in KF, CsF and TlF* (see also Table 6).

At higher pressures the corresponding rubidium halides also attain the CsCl lattice which corresponds to a smaller molar volume. At 445° CsCl goes over into a modification with the NaCl lattice.

The crystal structure of the ammonium halides, which, with the exception of $NH_4F$, each have modifications with the CsCl- and the NaCl lattice, cannot be explained on this basis; the structure of the $NH_4^+$ ion plays an important part.

It is of importance for a knowledge of the forces acting between colloidal particles that the greatest distance at which the LONDON forces are still important is not the radius of the atom but in fact of the order of magnitude of the radius of the particle itself, since the interaction between all the atoms in each of the colloidal particles must be summed, and this interaction, therefore, will increase with increasing size of the particles. This is quite different from the interaction between particles with a crystal lattice in which only purely electrostatic forces would act; in this case the radius of action remains of the order of the lattice constant and there is only a surface action. The effect of the more deeply situated parts of the lattice does not appear on account of the mutual compensation of the action of the oppositely charged ions.

DE BOER (1936) and HAMAKER (1937) found for the energy of interaction of two infinite plates at distance $h$ per unit of surface $U \propto -1/h^2$ and for spheres with radius $r$ at a small distance $h$: $U \propto -1/h$ $(h < r)$.

However, for distances which are much larger than the characteristic wave length $\lambda$ (corresponding to the frequency $\nu$ in the LONDON formula) the LONDON law $\varepsilon = -C/r^6$ has to be replaced by $\varepsilon = -C'/r^7$ (CASIMIR and POLDER, 1948).

---

* It is then necessary to suppose here that the numerical factor, instead of being $^3/_4$ as calculated for two hydrogen atoms, is about twice as large (see ref. p. 381).

The energy of interaction of infinite plates has then also to be replaced by $U \propto -1/h^3$ for $h \gg \lambda$ or a force $f$ acting between the two bodies $f \propto 1/h^4$. This interaction has indeed been measured directly with very accurate balances (PROSSER and KITCHENER, 1956, 1957; DERYAGUIN and ABRIKOSSOVA, 1958, after earlier experiments by OVERBEEK and SPARNAAY, 1952, which were marred by the overwhelming influence of electrostatic charges).

Macroscopic phenomena can expected to be amenable to an explanation based on classical physics. Indeed LIFSCHITZ (1955, cited by DERYAGUIN and ABRIKOSSOVA, 1958) succeeded in deriving a formula for this general macroscopic interaction by considering the fluctuations of the electromagnetic field; the dependance on distance is the same as given above for the two limiting cases of the ratio of the distance to the wavelength of light absorption.

The role of the VAN DER WAALS-LONDON forces in coagulation was recognized by KALLMANN and WILLSTÄTTER (1932) and later considered in a quantitative theory of the stability of colloids together with the repulsive forces of the diffuse ionic double layers of the colloidal particles (DERYAGUIN,, 1940; VERWEY and OVERBEEK, 1948; see also KRUYT *et al.*, 1952).

The KEESOM energy is an interaction of permanent dipoles and has a purely electrostatic nature. However, both the size of the dipole moment and its position are of essential importance for the strength of the interaction (VAN ARKEL).

The description of the electric field of a polar molecule, as resulting from a dipole situated at a point in this molecule, is only significant for distances which are large compared with the distances between the separate charges.

This can still be defended for a C—Cl bond since another C—Cl dipole can never approach to a short distance. Let us imagine the charges $\varepsilon$ of the dipole at the positions of the nuclei of the atoms such that $\varepsilon \cdot d = \mu$. The minimum distance for the negative pole of the C—Cl dipole is then determined by the VAN DER WAALS radius of the chlorine atom (Table 17); this is 1.8 Å. With the OH group, the VAN DER WAALS radius measured from the nucleus of the oxygen atom is 1.40 Å. Since the O—H distance is 0.97 Å, however, the shortest distance for the (positive) pole to the edge of the VAN DER WAALS sphere is now 0.43 Å.

The charge distribution in groups such as OH, NH and FH is very eccentric as far as the positive pole is concerned; that is to say, the positive pole of the dipole lies externally owing to the small size of the hydrogen atom bound as an ion (no electron cloud!). This gives rise to much stronger interaction than in other molecules with the same or even larger dipole moment. The complex of phenomena related to the interaction of the XH dipole is discussed separately as the "hydrogen bond" (§ 45).

## § 41. MOLECULAR COMPOUNDS

The interaction energy resulting from the VAN DER WAALS forces is actually ten to twenty times smaller than the energy of most atomic or ionic bonds. It is, therefore, not surprising that this type of bonding does not give rise to the formation of chemical compounds with stable molecules.

However, there is still another reason why the LONDON interaction does not lead to the formation of compounds. The attraction between two particles 1 and 2 with polarizibility $\alpha_1$ and $\alpha_2$ is proportional to $\alpha_1\alpha_2$, the geometrical mean of $\alpha_1^2$ and $\alpha_2^2$. The energy that is set free if the particles 1 and the particles 2 each form pairs with their own kind is, however, proportional to $(\alpha_1^2 + \alpha_2^2)/2$, the arithmetical mean, which is always larger than the former. If the differences in radius and in ionization energy are taken into account, the LONDON attraction in general still favours the accumulation of similar particles.

Nevertheless the number of compounds formed under the influence of the VAN DER WAALS bonding in *general* is not inconsiderable. These include numerous so-called molecular compounds which have been shown to occur by the thermal analysis of binary systems, in particular of organic compounds (when cases with major changes in the electron configuration *e.g.*, formation of atomic bonds, salt formation, atom exchange etc. are excluded). We may mention, for example, the numerous organic hydrates and alcoholates and compounds with ether. (The many systems of unsaturated molecules and amines with nitro compounds, etc., are discussed on p. 371.)

In the first group of molecular compounds, both partners possess a dipole moment and the compound is produced by the possibility of attaining a favourable mutual orientation of the dipoles (KEESOM forces). The numerous cases of association can also be considered to belong to this group. However, in most cases of association hydrogen dipoles, such as FH, OH, NH and (CH), play a part; these are discussed under the "hydrogen bond".

The association of nitrobenzene and nitronaphthalene in non-polar solvents, such as hexane and carbon tetrachloride, forms an exception. Here the association depends in the first place on an interaction of the KEESOM type due to the very large moment (4.20 D). The stronger association of the last-mentioned compound also points, however, to an interaction due to complex resonance as observed between nitro compounds and aromatic hydrocarbons in general. It is plausible that when dissolved in benzene this association gives way to a solvation. This interaction between solute and solvent molecules is closely related to the association between like molecules. In, *e.g.*, benzene itself no stoichiometric association is observed but, owing to the anisotropy of the polarizability, a more or less parallel orientation of the plane molecules statistically dominates in the liquid, as shown by X-ray analysis.

Conclusions that association should occur in many other cases on the ground of a departure from the simple additive DEBYE formula for the electrical molecular polarization are invalid, since this formula has been proved to be inapplicable to concentrated solutions (ONSAGER, BÖTTCHER). With the improved formulae of these authors practically the same dipole moments as in dilute solution are found even for the pure polar liquids, in as far as they are not truly associated through the formation of hydrogen bonds.

### *Inclusion compounds*

A first group of molecular compounds is formed by the inclusion compounds (CRAMER, 1952, 1954; BARRER, 1956), such as the clathrates, the gas hydrates and certain compounds of urea, of carbohydrates, etc. Here the compound formation is based on the tendency to form a phase of highest possible density by the inclusion of foreign molecules as far as such a structure is reconcilable with the size of the molecules, in order to reach a state of lowest energy content.

*a. Clathrates.* These are compounds, *e.g.*, of quinol (hydroquinone) with many gaseous substances, *e.g.*, $SO_2$, HCl and the inert gases. POWELL (1948, 1950) has investigated the crystal structure and other properties of the clathrate compounds, a name meaning cage compounds. The quinol forms a lattice (β-quinol) in which the molecules are bound together by hydrogen bonds (§ 45). Completely enclosed holes are present in this lattice with a diameter of 4.2 Å in which there is room for molecules such as $SO_2$, $CO$, $CO_2$, $H_2S$, $HCl$, $N_2$, $O_2$, $C_2H_2$, $HCOOH$ and $CH_3OH$, but also for atoms of the inert gases Ar, Kr and Xe. Larger molecules, *e.g.*, ethanol, hydrocarbons, cannot be accommodated. However, molecules like $H_2$, $H_2O$, He or Ne, which are too small, are also not bound. There is one hole present on three molecules of quinol but the actual composition is somewhat lower than 1 : 3, *e.g.*, $SO_2$ 0.88, Kr 0.74, Xe 0.88 mole per 3 mole quinol.

The heat of formation ($\Delta H$) of the compound is composed of the energy which has to be supplied to compress the gas from 1 atm to the volume it has in the clathrate and the energy liberated by the interaction due to VAN DER WAALS-LONDON attraction and the repulsive forces. There is also a small difference in energy between the unstable (without trapped molecules) $\beta$-quinol and the ordinary stable $\alpha$-modification. The heat of formation for the argon clathrate is $\Delta H = -6.0$ kcal/mole argon; for oxygen $\Delta H = -5.5$ kcal/mole, for HCl $\Delta H = -9.2$ kcal/mole gas (EVANS and RICHARDS, 1954). A calculation of these energies has been made by VAN DER WAALS (1956; VAN DER WAALS and PLATTEEUW, 1956).

The apparent stability in the atmosphere of the clathrates of, *e.g.*, the inert gases, is due to the high energy of activitation of the decomposition reaction and not to bonding in the normal sense (positive free enthalpy of formation, $\Delta G > 0$). The equilibrium pressure is very high (argon, 3.4 atm) but the actual pressure observed is practically zero as the velocity of escape of the gas molecules is so low.

One can say that the existence of these compounds at 1 atm is related to the stability of ordinary stable compounds, *e.g.*, hydrates, as prisoners are to free labourers; the latter are bound to their work by the pay, the (free energy) gain. The prisoners only remain at work because the prison bars prevent them going elsewhere.

*b. Gas hydrates* (VON STACKELBERG *et al.*, 1949, 1951, 1952, 1954; CRAMER, 1954). The gas hydrates, such as $Cl_2.6H_2O$, which had already been discovered by DAVY and FARADAY, also belong to the molecular inclusion compounds. BAKHUIS ROOZEBOOM and later VILLARD and DE FORCRAND investigated these remarkable compounds. Gas hydrates are known for $CO_2$, $SO_2$, $N_2O$, $NH_3$, $PH_3$, $H_2S$, $CH_4$, $C_2H_6$, $C_2H_4$, $C_2H_2$ and for the inert gases argon, krypton and xenon, with about six molecules of water throughout. Associated with these are the hydrates of some very volatile liquids, such as $CH_3Br$ and $Br_2$ both with $8H_2O$, and $C_2H_5Cl$, $CHCl_3$, $CH_3I$, $CH_2Cl_2$, etc., with $17H_2O$.

VON STACKELBERG, (VON STACKELBERG, *et al.*, 1949, 1951, 1952, 1954) has shown that these hydrates have two ice-like cubic structures with a density of 0.79 (compare 0.92 for normal ice which has already an open structure) when the foreign molecules are not taken into account; these foreign molecules are, however, necessary for the stability of these structures. In structure I, in the elementary cell with 46 water molecules, there are 2 small holes of diameter 5.2 Å, and 6 slightly larger ones with a diameter of 5.9 Å; each hole is surrounded by 20 and 24 water molecules respectively. Thus the ideal composition of the gas hydrates with small molecules will be M. $5\frac{3}{4}$ $H_2O$, in agreement with the observations. If only the larger holes are occupied, the mole ratio is $46/6 = 7.67$ as in, *e.g.*, the bromine hydrate. In structure II with 136 water molecules in the cell there are 8 holes with a diameter of 6.9 Å leading to a composition M. $17H_2O$ for the hydrates of volatile liquids. Because there are also sixteen smaller holes (diameter 4.8 Å) available in structure II, double hydrates are formed, *e.g.*, $CHCl_3 . 2H_2S . 17H_2O$. These complicated structures had already been foreseen by CLAUSEN (1951) on the basis of bond distances, and bond angles of the water molecule.

PLATTEEUW and VAN DER WAALS (1958) calculated the dissociation pressures and the heats of formation of the gas hydrates in very good correspondence with the observed values. Contrary to the corresponding quinol clathrates the xenon hydrate (1 atm at $-3.4°$ C, 1.15 atm at $0°$ C) is much more stable than the hydrate of the smaller argon atom (1 atm at —42.8° C, 95.5 atm at 0° C). This indicates that the influence of the attraction (LONDON) energy predominates in the hydrates with the larger holes whereas the differences in repulsion energy have more influence in the quinol clathrates with the smaller holes.

There is a binding energy, though a small one, of about 15, 19 and 31 kcal/mole of substance *M* for most of the 6, 8 and 17 $H_2O$ compounds, respectively, based on gaseous *M* and liquid water; when calculated with respect to ice, these figures are approximately equal to 6–10 kcal/mole of substance *M* for all three groups.

The stability runs parallel to the polarizability but this can indicate both LONDON and DEBYE interaction. When the polarizability is very high, the hydrate becomes unstable through the large cohesion energy of the organic liquid which should be less than 7 kcal/mole or a boiling point below 70° C.

The high coordination number in the gas hydrates makes a rather appreciable contribution from the DEBYE forces improbable; this is, however, favourable for the LONDON interaction. In other compounds, such as those of the inert gases with hydrochloric acid and phenol, the first-mentioned interaction is perhaps of greater importance.

*c. Urea compounds* (SCHLENK, 1949, 1951; ZIMMERSCHMIED, 1949; REDLICH *et al.*, 1950; CRAMER, 1952, 1954, 1956; SMITH, 1952). A group of substances which are closely associated with the gas hydrates are the compounds of urea (and thiourea) with a large number of organic substances with long-chain molecules, such as normal saturated hydrocarbons and olefins, alcohols, acids, esters, ketones, halogenated hydrocarbons, etc. These were discovered accidentally by BENGEN in 1940. These compounds are only produced with unbranched, noncyclic molecules*. This reaction is so specific that it forms the basis

* Dioxan forms an exception in various respects; it is also not certain whether the structure of the complexes is the same in this case. With thiourea, complexes are also produced with branched and cyclic hydrocarbons; here the channels are wider.

for a method of separation of normal and *iso* hydrocarbons in mixtures.

The investigation of the crystal structure has shown that, precisely as ice in the gas hydrates, urea occurs in a special crystal structure which in this case contains long channels with a diameter of 5.2 Å. The organic molecules are now placed in these channels. The binding energy increases by the same constant amount per carbon atom ($CH_2$ group); this points to a LONDON-interaction. The heat of formation is higher for ketones, acids and esters in which dipole action and hydrogen bond formation are probable.

The heat of formation is $\Delta H = +2.9 - 1.55n$ kcal/mole of hydrocarbon with $n$ carbon atoms (at 25° C $\Delta F = -RT \ln K = 2.15 - 0.364\, n$ kcal).

We find that 9.7 kcal is set free in the formation of the complex with *n*-octane, whereas this is 21.0 kcal for hexadecane. Molecules smaller than heptane no longer give stable complexes; $\Delta H$ then becomes too small since too large a part of the channel remains unoccupied between successive molecules. With hydrocarbons such as $C_{55}H_{112}$ complexes are no longer formed because the cohesion energy of the hydrocarbon $Q_1$ (see below) then becomes too large; however, $C_{28}H_{58}$ can form complexes.

There is no rational molecular ratio between urea and hydrocarbon; the ratio urea/hydrocarbon is found to be $0.67\, n + 1.50$. Thus for one molecule of octane there are 6.96 molecules of urea.

One molecule of octane will occupy a channel length of $1.256\,(n-1) + 4.0 = 12.8$ Å. The projection of the C—C distance of 1.54 Å on the molecules axis is 1.256 Å, whereas 4.0 Å is the distance between the carbon atoms of two adjacent molecules, equal to twice the VAN DER WAALS radius of the methyl group. As the *c*-dimension of the elementary cell containing 6 molecules of urea is 11.01 Å, there is channel length of 1.835 Å per molecule of urea. Thus we calculate for the ratio of urea to octane $12.8/1.835 = 6.98$ or in general $0.685\, n + 1.493$, corresponding closely to the experimental relation given above.

The heat of formation of 9.7 kcal for octane and 21.0 kcal for hexadecane $C_{16}H_{34}$ can be divided into three parts:

1. The cohesion energy of the organic molecules; this is the internal latent heat of evaporation (or the heat of sublimation) $Q - RT = 9.3$ kcal or 18.8 kcal : $Q_1$.

2. Binding energy between $m$ molecules of urea and the organic molecule: $Q_2$.
3. Difference in lattice energy between the unstable hexagonal urea lattice and the normal tetragonal lattice for $m$ molecules of urea: $mQ_3$.

We therefore have: $\Delta H = Q_1 - Q_2 + mQ_3$.

By putting $Q_2 = nQ'_2$ proportional to the number of carbon atoms $n$, whereby thus the difference between $CH_2$ and $CH_3$ groups is neglected, $Q'_2$ and $Q_3$ can be calculated from the values of $\Delta H$ for both substances. One then finds $Q_3 = 1.5$ kcal (per mol urea) and $Q'_2 = 3.65$ kcal (per C atom).

The formation of the clathrates and the urea compounds is restricted to the solid state. Contrary to former evidence there is no difference in the behaviour of normal and iso-valeric and butyric acids towards a urea solution, though only the normal acids form compounds with urea in the solid state (KETELAAR and LOOPSTRA, 1955).

The well known blue colour which iodine gives with a starch solution is also due to the formation of an inclusion compound in which the iodine molecules are linearly arranged in the channel formed inside the spirals of the glucose residues forming the carbohydrate molecule (STEIN and RUNDLE, 1948; MURAKAMI, 1954; CRAMER and HERBST, 1952; CRAMER, 1956). The molecule of tobacco mosaic virus also seems to be a kind of a leadpencil-like inclusion compound of two non-pathogenic compounds.

*Electron donor-acceptor complexes.* Compounds may be formed from molecules by the exchange of atoms, *e.g.*, onium compounds (p. 171): $NH_3 + HCl = NH_4Cl$ or $SO_3 + NH_3 = H_2NSO_3H$ (p. 176); such compounds are not molecular complexes. However, a large number of typical molecular complexes are formed through the exchange of electrons, electron donor-acceptor complexes. Two types may be distinguished according to whether the free electron pair of the donor and the incomplete electron configuration (mostly a sextet) of the acceptor are already present in the normal ground state of the components (*a*), or not, (*b*).

*a.* Numerous compounds are formed of $BF_3$ (as acceptor with an electron sextet) with organic molecules which contain free electron pairs, *e.g.*, amines and others but also with the inert gases as donors. Here a normal electron pair bond is formed and though both electrons of the bond are furnished by one of the compounds there is no reason to distinguish this bond as a semi-polar bond (p. 171).

The bonding energy is very appreciable:

| | | | |
|---|---|---|---|
| $BF_3.NH_3$ | 42 kcal | $AlCl_3.NH_3$ | 40 kcal |
| $BF_3$.pyridine | 51 | $AlBr_3.NH_3$ | 38 |
| $BF_3$.ether | 14 | $AlI_3.NH_3$ | 30 |

It has been found (HOARD, 1951) that in the compounds of $BF_3$ with amines the borium atom is tetrahedrally surrounded by the three fluorine atoms and the nitrogen atom with a slight increase in the B—F distance (1.39 Å instead of 1.30 Å) and a B—N distance of 1.57–1.60 Å which is only slightly larger than the sum of the atomic radii 1.58 Å.

These complexes have high dipole moments due both to the transfer of electronic charge and to the pyramidal configuration of molecules, *e.g.*, $BF_3$, $BCl_3$, etc. which are planar in the free state.

| | | | | |
|---|---|---|---|---|
| $BF_3.(CH_3)_2O$ | 4.33 D; | ether | 1.29 D; | diff. 3.04 D |
| $BCl_3$.dioxan | 4.86 ; | dioxan | 0 ; | diff. 4.86 |
| $AlCl_3$.benzene | 5 ; | benzene | 0 ; | diff. 5 |
| $AlCl_3.(C_2H_5)_2O$ | 6.54 ; | ether | 1.14 ; | diff. 5.40 |
| $SnCl_4.(C_2H_5)_2O$ | 3.60 ; | ether | 1.14 ; | diff. 2.46 |

(KLEMM *et al.*, 1931; ULICH *et al.*, 1931, 1932, 1933; BRIEGLEB, 1949). Besides the boron halides, molecular complexes are also formed by $BeCl_2$, $ZnCl_2$, $AlCl_3$, $FeCl_3$, $SbCl_3$, $TiCl_4$, $SnCl_4$, $SbCl_5$, etc. as acceptors and with organic molecules containing oxygen, sulphur or nitrogen atoms. With the tetra- and pentahalides of the higher periods it is no longer a sextet of sp electrons but an incomplete d-shell which is completed by the addition of an electron donor molecule, accompanied by the transformation into a pyramidal structure. The bonding of these latter halides and also $SO_2$ may be considered as a case of the second type of donor-acceptor complexes discussed below. The donor and acceptor molecules discussed could also have been considered as LEWIS bases and LEWIS acids (p. 87) and the complex formation as an acid-base reaction.

This interaction with a free electron pair will have the consequence that in various cases of unsaturated organic molecules certain configurations, which contribute little to the stationary state of the free molecule, are of much greater importance in the complex formed. Consequently many reactions can proceed under the catalytic action of these sextet substances (§ 36). With the proton, thus in $OH_3^+$ and HF, the interaction with the organic molecules is entirely electrostatic (§ 45, 46). However, since the presence of a free electron pair in a configuration gives rise to a greater polarizability, a strong similarity can exist, in particular in the catalytic action, between $BF_3$, HF, and strong acids through changes in the contributions of the various electron configurations.

*b.* Compounds may be formed between a molecule as a potential electron acceptor in which the acceptor configuration (or the free pair) is only present in an excited configuration (p. 223) and a molecule with a free pair (or acceptor configuration) in the normal ground state or between molecules which can only undergo an acceptor-donor reaction when both are in excited configurations (ANDREWS, 1954).

The largest group of organic molecular compounds, in which hydrogen bond formation plays no part, are the compounds (usually in the ratio 1 : 1) between aliphatic or aromatic nitro compounds (nitromethane, tetranitromethane, chloropicrin $CCl_3NO_2$, nitrobenzene, *s*-trinitrobenzene, picric acid), quinones, anhydrides (phthalic acid- and maleic acid anhydride) and ketones with aliphatic and aromatic amines (aniline, pyridine), unsaturated aliphatic and aromatic hydrocarbons, ethers, etc.

This association is frequently accompanied by striking colour reactions. In many cases crystallized compounds have been obtained, among others, the picrates of aromatic hydrocarbons.

A nitrophenol, such as picric acid, forms strongly coloured

complexes of the type discussed here with the weaker basic aromatic amines. With amines having greater proton affinity, however, weakly coloured anilinium picrates are produced by proton exchange. Picric acid even forms two isomeric molecular compounds of both types with bromo aniline, coloured orange red and light yellow, respectively (complex isomerism).

It is natural to think of an interaction of the DEBYE type between the appreciable moment of the nitro or carbonyl group and the readily polarizable unsaturated $C = C$ bond in the unsaturated hydrocarbons or the readily polarizable free electron pair in the amines, etc. Actually the stability increases with increasing polarizability; compare for example, the heat of formation of the compounds of *s*-trinitrobenzene with benzene, naphthalene and anthracene ($\Delta H$: 0.6, 3.4 and 4.4 kcal). In the series mono-, di- and tri-nitrobenzene with acenaphthene $\Delta H$ also increases with increasing number of partial moments ($\Delta H = 0$, 1.35 and 2.45 kcal). Nevertheless this explanation is inadequate. Nitromethane with a moment $\mu = 3.54$ D gives very much less stable compounds than nitrobenzene with $\mu = 4.22$ D, while nitrosobenzene with $\mu = 3.2$ D gives stronger colour effects than nitrobenzene.

The colour reactions often signify a very considerable red shift of the absorption band compared with the components. This indicates a deep-seated effect on the $\pi$ electrons of both components, since the colour is closely related to the $\pi$ electron states of both molecules. Polarization, with a small interaction energy, is not able to explain the important changes in the electron system which correspond to important energy changes; a more specific interaction must be involved.

It seems not improbable that the formation of the bond between these molecules is similar to that between molecules with a sextet configuration (such as $BF_3$) and molecules with a free electron pair. In the molecules of the first group, *e.g.*, nitro compounds, the sextet configuration contributes only to a limited extent to the stationary state of the free molecule. If the energy of this sextet configuration compared with that of the normal octet configuration is lowered sufficiently by complex formation with a suitable partner, complex formation is possible.

BRACKMAN (1949) (WEISS, 1942, has published analogous conceptions) formed the conception of "complex resonance" in which the stationary state is pictured as one of resonance between a "no-bond" and a bonded configuration.

With a nitro compound and an amine:

$$R-\overset{\oplus}{N}(\overset{\ominus}{O})=O \quad |NH_2-R \longleftrightarrow R-\overset{\oplus}{N}(\overset{\ominus}{O})(\overset{\ominus}{O})-\overset{\oplus}{N}H_2-R$$

(The second configuration, however, is unfavourable according to the "adjacent charge rule").

With ketones we have:

$$R_1R_2C=\overline{O} \quad HN(H)-R \longleftrightarrow R_1R_2\overset{\ominus}{C}-\overline{O}-\overset{\oplus}{N}H_2-R \quad \text{or}$$

$$\overline{O}=C(R_1)(R_2) \quad |NH_2-R \longleftrightarrow |\overset{\ominus}{O}-C(R_1)(R_2)-\overset{\oplus}{N}H_2-R;$$

the latter is more probable.

Attaining the sextet configuration costs much energy; the small observed heat of formation is the difference between this promotion energy on one side and the bond- and resonance-energy on the other. Nevertheless an appreciable change in the electron distribution and thus in the spectrum has taken place.

MULLIKEN (1952) has given a more general quantum mechanical theory of the bonding in these molecular complexes. He also considers resonance between no-bond configurations AD with "dative" configurations $A^- D^+$. These latter configurations are equivalent to the configurations of BRACKMAN, which also arise from electron transfer from the N-compound or donor (LEWIS base) to the "sextet"-compound or acceptor (LEWIS acid, p. 87).

Whereas the no-bond configuration contributes most to the ground state, the stationary state in the upper level will have the largest contribution from the dative configurations. Owing to the complex formation this upper level will in general be lowered more than the ground level; thus this complex formation will have a bathochromic effect. The absorption of a light quantum will thus be accompanied by an electron transfer, hence the great intensity of the characteristic absorption bands which have no counterpart in the spectra of either one of the components of the molecular complex.

It has long been noticed that iodine gives violet solutions with some solvents such as $CS_2$, saturated aliphatic hydrocarbons and halogen-substituted hydrocarbons (among them also the unsaturated ones such as di-, tri- and tetra-chloroethylene, see also p. 376) and on the other hand red to brown solutions with other solvents, as happens to be the case in increasing degree in the series benzene, toluene, mesitylene. Brown solutions are also produced with ethers, dioxan, alcohols, water, pyridine; however, di*iso*butylene (2,4,4-trimethylpentene —1 and —2) also gives a brown solution (BENESI and HILDEBRAND, 1948, 1949; KLEINBERG and DAVIDSON, 1948; KORTÜM and KORTÜM-SEILER, 1950; KORTÜM and VOGEL, 1955; ANDREWS and KEEFER, 1950, 1951, 1952, 1955; CROMWELL and SCOTT, 1950; KETELAAR, VAN DE STOLPE *et al.*, 1951, 1952).

In the brown solutions a 1 : 1 complex is present which apparently gives rise to a shift of the absorption band of iodine in the visible region of the spectrum to shorter wave lengths but also a new absorption band is observed in the U.V. at about 3000 Å. From the change of the extinction of either band on dilution of, *e.g.*, the iodine-benzene solution with an "inactive" solvent such as $CCl_4$ or hexane, the dissociation equilibrium constant $K_x$ can be determined. The heat of formation $\Delta H$ is obtained from the temperature dependence of

$K_x$ (Benesi and Hildebrand, 1948, 1949, Ketelaar and Van de Stolpe *et al.*, 1951, 1952, Scott, 1956).

The constitution of the $I_2$-benzene and $I_2$-pyridine complex respectively can be formulated as complex resonance with the two configurations:

| no bond | bond (dative) |
|---|---|
| $\|\bar{\underline{I}}—\bar{\underline{I}}\|$ [benzene ring] | $\|\bar{\underline{I}}\|$ $\|\bar{\underline{I}}$ — [benzene ring] |
| $\|\bar{\underline{I}}—\bar{\underline{I}}\|$ $\|$N[pyridine ring] | $\|\bar{\underline{I}}\|$ $\|\bar{\underline{I}}$ —N[pyridine ring] |

A good conducting solution is even produced with pyridine ($\Delta H = -8.0$ kcal/mole). With other molecules such as dioxan ($\Delta H = -3.5$ kcal/mole), no dissociation occurs but the complex possesses a dipole moment of 1.27 D, although neither of the components exhibits an electric moment (Fairbrother, 1947, 1948). X-ray diffraction has shown that one atom of the iodine molecule has a shortest distance of 3.93 Å to one of the carbon atoms of the benzene ring, whereas the position of the second atom is not well defined (Dallinga, 1954).

It has been found (Collin and D'Or, 1955) from the infrared spectrum of the corresponding chlorine-benzene complex that the charge distribution of the Cl—Cl molecule is no longer symmetric (infrared active Cl—Cl absorption band) and that the bond is weakened (shift from 557 $cm^{-1}$ to 526 $cm^{-1}$), as expected if the bond (dative) configuration contributes.

The course of complex formation in the series of benzene homologues agrees with that of increasing tendency to donate electrons, connected with the less electronegative character of the $—CH_3$ group (see p. 282). With di*iso*butylene the association is much stronger than with cyclohexene, for the same reasons. The table contains some values obtained for the equilibrium constant at 25° C (in mole fractions) and for the heat effect (Andrews and Keefer; Ketelaar, Van de Stolpe *et al.*). The "inert" solvent was *n*-hexane.

| | $K_x$ | $-\Delta H$ | | $K_x$ |
|---|---|---|---|---|
| benzene | 1.21 | 1.3 kcal | mesitylene | 5.3 |
| toluene | 2.24 | 1.8 | di*iso*butylene | 3.3 |
| xylene | 2.96 | 2.0 | cyclohexene | 0.53 |
| naphthalene | 2.31 | 1.8 | *cis*-dichloroethylene | 0.32 |
| 1-methyl naphthalene | 2.78 | 2.1 | *trans* ,, | 0.24 |
| 2-methyl naphthalene | 3.71 | 2.1 | trichloroethylene | 0.19 |
| dioxan | 9.3 | 3.5 | tetrachloroethylene | 0.11 |

Careful measurements of the U.V. absorption spectrum show that complex compounds are also present to a minor degree in the violet solutions of the substituted chloroethylenes, decreasing with decreasing double bond character (KETELAAR and VAN DE STOLPE, 1952).

A molecule like *s*-trinitrobenzene can act as acceptor to form complexes, *e.g.*, with amines as donor (BIER, 1956). Many configurations can be given with a sextet either on the para and ortho carbon atoms, at the nitrogen atom and also at the oxygen atom. In *s*-trinitrobenzene-*p*-iodoaniline a short distance of 3.1 Å is observed between one oxygen atom and the nitrogen atom, whereas in *p*- nitroaniline which forms complexes with itself the shortest distance is found again between an oxygen atom but now to a carbon atom of another molecule (POWELL *et al.*, 1939, 1943; WALLWORK and HARDING, 1953).

With *s*-trinitrobenzene the results obtained were (BIER 1956).

| | $K_x$ | $-\Delta H$ | | $K_x$ | $-\Delta H$ |
|---|---|---|---|---|---|
| benzene | 0.82 | 0.45 | anthracene | 39.8 | 2.74 |
| toluene | 1.82 | 0.86 | phenanthrene | 38.5 | 2.63 |
| xylene | 2.08 | 1.12 | aniline | 5.1 | 1.35 |
| naphthalene | 17.0 | 2.20 | N, N-dimethyl-aniline | 94 | 1.82 |
| 1-methyl naphthalene | 19.0 | 2.41 | 1-naphthylamine | 47.9 | 2.98 |
| 2-methyl naphthalene | 25.8 | 2.56 | 2-naphthylamine | 49.1 | 3.00 |

The entropy of formation from $\Delta S = (\Delta G - \Delta H)/T$ with $-RT \ln K_x = \Delta G$ is a constant of about 4.5 and 2.0. E.U. within both series of complex compounds respectively.

MULLIKEN (1950, 1952) gives for the wave function representing the ground state $N$ of the complex

$$\varphi_N = a\varphi_0 + b\varphi_1$$

in which $\varphi_0$ and $\varphi_1$ are the wave functions representing the no-bond and the dative bound configuration. Here $a \gg b$ because of the difference in energy (p. 215).

However, there will be also an excited state $E$ with

$$\varphi_E = a^* \varphi_1 - b^* \varphi_0 \qquad a^* \gg b^* \text{ and } a \approx a^*$$

Only when the energy difference is very high can the states $N$ and $E$ be identified with the single configurations 0 and 1.

The energy difference between the two states $N$ and $E$ corresponds to the absorption band: $h\nu = W_E - W_N$, where $W_N$ is the heat of formation $\Delta H$. Calculations have given a value of $b^2/(a^2 + b^2) = 0.018$ which indicates that the dative bound configuration contributes only 2% to the charge distribution of the ground state of the $I_2$-benzene complex; a corresponding value is derived from the dipole moment. With $I_2$-pyridine the contribution is much higher, being about 25% (KETELAAR, 1954).

The difference in the far U.V. absorption of iodine dissolved in aliphatic, saturated, hydrocarbons with that of iodine in the vapour state or dissolved in fluorocarbons, is explained by MULLIKEN (1956) (ORGEL and MULLIKEN, 1957) as an extreme case of complex resonance where the charge transfer complex formation is restricted to the upper state of the absorption transition where overlapping of orbits of electrons of both partners will only occur (contact charge-transfer).

Recently it has been found that if oxygen (or another paramagnetic molecule NO) is dissolved in benzene and other aromatic hydrocarbons, light absorption is observed in the range 3000–3500 Å where the singlet triplet transition (p. 297) is to be expected (EVANS, 1957). A kind of complex is formed with an equilibrium constant $K_x = 0.6$ comparable with that of the weakest iodine complexes (DIJKGRAAF, 1957). Probably the magnetic field of the oxygen molecule makes the otherwise forbidden transition allowed in the surrounding benzene molecules.

The rare compounds that are not molecular compounds and that must perhaps be regarded as being due to an interaction of the LONDON type include some very unstable molecules which are encountered only in gaseous discharges, for example HgKr, HgAr and perhaps also $Hg_2$. These compounds have only a very small heat of dissociation (HgKr 0.8 kcal/mol), and the mercury atom is in an excited state so that a one-electron bond is not excluded.

It can be expected that an inert gas atom in an excited state can form an atomic bond when one of the electrons is in a higher level; however, there is no longer any question of an inert gas configuration then ($He_2$, HeNe).

The infrared absorption spectra of mixtures of $CO_2$ with $H_2$, $O_2$ or $N_2$ exhibit an absorption band at a frequency equal to the sum of frequencies of both components (simultaneous transitions). These bands arise from electrostatic polarization when the two molecules are very near (collision complexes) (FAHRENFORT and KETELAAR, 1954, KETELAAR, 1956). However, these are not compound molecules because their lifetime is much shorter than the time between collisions.

## § 42. COHESION ENERGY AND BOILING POINTS

Although VAN DER WAALS forces do not play a great part in the production of stable chemical compounds, they are important for the cohesion energy of solid and liquid phases which are composed of separate molecules as units. This means that many physico-chemical properties such as volatility, solubility, miscibility, viscosity, plasticity and surface tension, which all depend on the intermolecular interaction, and therefore on the cohesion, are determined by the VAN DER WAALS forces. This is true for most organic compounds, for mixtures and for many inorganic substances composed of molecules, *e.g.*, water, ammonia, etc.

The cohesion energy $U$ is equal (with opposite sign) to the heat of evaporation at constant *volume* $\Delta U$, as the potential energy of the vapour is negligible at moderate pressures. The more usual latent heat of evaporation $\Delta H$ also includes the external work done, $\Delta U = \Delta H - RT$.

The molecular interaction is characterized by the specific cohesion or cohesion density $U/V$, where $V$ is the molar volume (Table 33). Another closely related quantity is the so-called internal pressure of a liquid.

According to thermodynamics, since $dU = dA + TdS = -pdV + TdS$ (combination of 1st and 2nd law),

$$\left(\frac{\partial U}{\partial V}\right)_T = -p + T\left(\frac{\partial S}{\partial V}\right)_T = -p + T\left(\frac{\partial p}{\partial T}\right)_V$$

Now for a liquid the pressure coefficient

$\left(\frac{\partial p}{\partial T}\right)_V = \alpha_T/\beta$ ($\alpha_T =$ thermal expans. coeff., $\beta =$ compressibility)

is so large that the second term, the actual internal pressure, amounts to 2000–8000 atm. Thus $\left(\frac{\partial U}{\partial V}\right)_T$ is about equal to the internal pressure $p_i$, neglecting the external pressure $p$.

For a substance which obeys the VAN DER WAALS equation of state $(p + a/V^2)(V - b) = RT$, the internal pressure $\left(\frac{\partial U}{\partial V}\right)_T = p_i = \frac{a}{V^2}$. Since the energy $\frac{U}{V} = -\frac{a}{V^2}$, in this case the internal pressure is equal to the cohesion density $U/V$. This holds for all non-associated liquids, to a good approximation.

The specific cohesion, or the internal pressure, plays a part especially in mixtures. For the case of an exclusive LONDON interaction we have (see p. 381):

$$U = -\frac{a}{V} \propto \frac{\alpha^2}{Vd^3} \propto \frac{\alpha^2}{v^2} \left[\text{or } U/V = -\frac{a}{V^2} \propto \frac{\alpha^2}{v^3}\right]$$

The molar volume $V$ of a liquid is proportional to the actual volume of the molecules $v$ or to $b$ (p. 381) or $d^3$, with $d$ the diameter of the molecule.

We will first study the molecules without, or almost without, dipole moment, in which, therefore, the cohesion is entirely due to LONDON forces.

In the series of the inert gases, the heat of evaporation (and the boiling point) increases steadily with increasing atomic weight. This agrees with the variation of the polarizability divided by the volume $\alpha/v \propto \alpha/d^3$, the characteristic quantity in LONDON's formula. To be able to make a quantitative comparison, it would be necessary to calculate the heat of sublimation, which in this case is equal to the lattice energy. Starting from the LONDON formula for the interaction of two similar particles, the effect must here, as in the ionic lattices, be summed over the whole lattice. In view of the small radius of action of the LONDON forces, the result of this summation is practically equal to a multiplication by the number of nearest neighbours (12 in closest packing) divided by two, lest each atom be counted twice. The data on polarizability (from the molar refractivity $R = 4\pi N\alpha/3$), the ionization potential (from the spectra) and the distance $r$ (from crystal structure and density) are known. Nevertheless another term must be added to the lattice energy before this can be compared with the experimental heat of sublimation. The repulsion energy must be taken into account as in the calculation in Chapter II, p. 36. If the same assumption is introduced ,then we see readily that instead of $1 - \frac{1}{n}$ we now have $1 - \frac{6}{n}$. When $n$ is again about 10–12, the correction for the repulsion energy becomes not 10% as with ionic lattices, but about 50%. In view of the uncertainty of this correction only the attraction energy is given in Table 30. The variation and the order of magnitude, however, are in agreement with experiment.

The fact that the calculated attraction energy is practically equal to the observed total energy, in spite of the undoubtedly important contribution of the repulsion energy, points again

TABLE 30

THE CONSTANT $a$ FROM THE VAN DER WAALS EQUATION AND THE LATTICE ENERGY CALCULATED ACCORDING TO LONDON (1937)

| | $a$ in $10^{-2}$ at·lt²/mole | | Lattice energy in kcal/mole | | |
|---|---|---|---|---|---|
| | calc. | expt. | calc. | expt. | boiling point |
| He | 4.8 | 3.5 | — | — | 4° K |
| Ne | 26 | 21 | 0.47 | 0.59 | 27° ,, |
| Ar | 163 | 135 | 1.92 | 2.03 | 76° ,, |
| Kr | 253 | 240 | 3.17 | 2.80 | 121° ,, |
| Xe | 430 | 410 | — | — | 174° ,, |
| $N_2$ | 147 | 135 | 1.64 | 1.86 | 77° ,, |
| $O_2$ | 135 | 136 | 1.69 | 2.06 | 90° ,, |
| $CH_4$ | 256 | 224 | 2.92 | 2.70 | 112° ,, |
| $Cl_2$ | 680 | 632 | 7.18 | 7.43 | 239° ,, |

to an approximately double factor of proportionality of the VAN DER WAALS energy at short distances (p. 361). The calculation of the constant $a$ of VAN DER WAALS for the gaseous state, in which the average distance is large, comes out very satisfactorily (Table 30).

According to LENNARD-JONES the interaction between non-polar particles can be represented by

$$\varepsilon = j/r^{12} - k/r^6$$

The choice of the figure 12 as exponent for the repulsion energy is mainly determined by the simplification in the calculations for this case.

If we introduce the depth of the hole $\varepsilon_0$ and the distance $d'$ at which the energy is just zero (the intersection of the curve for the potential energy with the line $V = 0$, (see Fig. 2); $d'$ is the effective collision diameter of the molecule.

We then have: $\varepsilon = 4\,\varepsilon_0\,[(d'/r)^{12} - (d'/r)^6]$ (LENNARD-JONES potential).

It is indeed possible to base on this formula a general law of corresponding states which is obeyed very exactly by the inert gases in all three states of aggregation.

The relation between the constant $a$ of VAN DER WAALS and the interaction energy $\varepsilon = C/r^6$ for two molecules is given by:

$$a = -2\,\pi\,N^2 \int_{d_0}^{\infty} \varepsilon\, r^2\, dr$$

in which $d_0$ is the molecular diameter, the shortest distance to which two molecules (hard spheres) can approach one another. According to VAN DER WAALS the constant $b$ is equal to four times the actual volume:

$$b = 2/3\,\pi\,N\,d_0^{\,3}$$

We then have:

$$a = \frac{4\,\pi^2\,N^3}{9\,b}\,C \text{ thus } \alpha \propto \frac{\alpha^2\,I}{d^3}$$

In this, $b$ is taken from the equation of state. The values of $a$ in Table 30 were calculated with this formula.

In a calculation of $C$ according to the three methods, namely from $h\nu_0$, from $I$ and according to SLATER-KIRKWOOD, differences of minor importance appear and the last method always furnishes somewhat higher values.

Many organic compounds, such as the hydrocarbons and their completely halogenated derivatives, have no or small dipole moments. In the latter group on replacing F successively by Cl, Br and I, the increase of the polarizability predominates over that of the volume so that the LONDON attraction also increases in this order ($\alpha \propto d^5$). Thanks to the additive property of these forces, the total cohesion energy can be regarded as the sum of atomic contributions; thus each halogen atom furnishes its fixed contribution to the cohesion energy and to the boiling point (VAN LAAR; VAN ARKEL and DE BOER, book, see lit. p. 106).

If one is only concerned with the replacement of one halogen by another in other groups of compounds, then the dipole moment undergoes little change thereby. One can therefore calculate a fixed change of boiling points (fluorine replaced by chlorine 50°, chlorine by bromine 28.5°, and bromine by iodine 40°).

On the replacement of a hydrogen atom by a halogen atom, however, a dipole moment generally appears. Consequently a contribution to the cohesion by the KEESOM energy of the dipole interaction will show itself as an extra increase of the boiling point (monohalogen derivatives: +77°, dihalogen derivatives (1,1): +82° and trihalogen derivatives (1,1,1): 43°).

In this case it is not so much the total moment of the molecule which plays a part but the moments of the separate groups. In view of the small radius of action of the KEESOM forces ($\propto 1/r^6$), the interaction will only extend to the immediate neighbourhood. Therefore the interaction of the three isomeric dibromobenzene derivatives will be practically equal. The action of one C-Br group is only influenced to a small extent by that of the other C-Br group, which acts either against the first as in the *para* isomer or with it as in the *ortho* isomer. The LONDON contribution is naturally the same for all three. These isomeric derivatives do have practically the same boiling point. The large difference in the total dipole moments (*ortho*: 1.86 D; *meta*: 1.88 D; *para*: 0) produces only a very small difference; as expected, the *ortho* isomer boils at a somewhat higher temperature (221°) than the *meta* (219°) and this again boils higher than the *para* compound (218°—219°). One finds the same thing with the boiling points of *cis*- and *trans*-dichloroethylene and similar compounds (b.pt. *cis*: 60.5°, moment $\mu = 1.89$ D; b.pt. *trans*: 47.7°, moment $\mu = 0$). The 1,1-dichloroethylene boils at 35° although the dipole moment amounts to 1.18 D; here, however, there is only one dipole group, $CCl_2$, in the molecule, compared with two in the two other isomers.

VAN LAAR has postulated that for a molecule we have $\sqrt{a} = \sum_i \sqrt{a_i}$, that is to say, that $\sqrt{a}$ is composed additively from the atomic contributions $\sqrt{a_i}$. According to VAN ARKEL and DE GROOT (1932) this can be derived theoretically.

From TROUTON's rule, $\Delta H/T_b = 22$ or $\Delta U/T_b = 20$ and $U = a/V$ we have now for the boiling point $T_b \propto a/V = \frac{(\sum_i \sqrt{a_i})^2}{V}$

The cohesion energy and the boiling point of the hydrocarbons are interesting from the technical point of view also. The contribution of each $CH_2$ group to the molar refraction and thus to the polarizability is additive to a very good approximation like the contribution to the volume. In the formula $T_b \propto \frac{(\sum_i \sqrt{a_i})^2}{V}$ the contributions $\sqrt{a_i}$ for each $CH_2$ group are therefore equal, and likewise those to $V$, so that $T_b \propto \frac{n^2}{n} = n$ is proportional to the number of carbon atoms $n$ in which $CH_2$ and $CH_3$ groups have been regarded as the same. This is, however, certainly not the case (Table 31). The cause of this must be sought in the fact that the hydrocarbons are present in the liquid mainly in a coiled conformation (p. 208) (these are more probable on account of their greater number than the straight conformation). Consequently the inwardly directed parts of the chain will not contribute to the *inter*molecular interaction.

TABLE 31

BOILING POINT AND MELTING POINT OF THE NORMAL ALKANES

| | Boiling point | Melting point | | Boiling point | Melting point |
|---|---|---|---|---|---|
| *n*-pentane | 36.07 | −129.7 | *n*-undecane | 195.88 | −25.6 |
| *n*-hexane | 68.74 | − 95.3 | *n*-dodecane | 216.28 | − 9.6 |
| *n*-heptane | 98.43 | − 90.6 | *n*-tridecane | 235.47 | − 5.3 |
| *n*-octane | 125.66 | − 59.8 | *n*-tetradecane | 253.59 | + 6.2 |
| *n*-nonane | 150.79 | − 53.5 | *n*-pentadecane | 270.74 | + 9.9 |
| *n*-decane | 174.12 | − 29.7 | *n*-hexadecane | 287.05 | +18.15 |

ATEN Jr. (1937) therefore took the cohesion energy to be proportional to the approximately spherical surface of such a clew or coil, which will increase as $n^{2/3}$ with the number of $CH_2$ groups*. Since now the evaporation entropy, or the TROUTON "constant", also increases somewhat with increasing temperature, that is to say with the number of $CH_2$ groups, ATEN could make plausible an empirical

* The same formula has been tested by KLAGES (1943). Other empirical formulae, see VAN NES and VAN WESTEN (1951).

formula, $T_b \propto n^{1/2}$ or still better $T_b^2 = nA + B$ (WALKER, BOGGIA-LERA, VARSHNI) which has long been known. In this $A = 20{,}500$ is a general constant for open chains while $B$ depends on the nature of the end group; for the paraffins (alkanes) $B$ is equal to $-7{,}000$, for the olefins (alkenes -1) $B$ is $-10{,}000$.

An explanation of the general rule that the boiling point falls with increasing degree of branching follows directly from this consideration, in that the clew becomes denser so that the boiling point of the normal compound is always the highest (Table 35). In the above formula, $B$ is equal to $-12{,}500$ for 2-methylalkanes.

Other details in the structure also exert an influence on the boiling point; a complete explanation of the relation between boiling point and structure is, however, not yet possible.

VAN ARKEL (1932, 1933, 1934) has made an extensive analysis of the boiling point in its dependence on the molecular structure. It sometimes appeared possible to show, on the basis of the boiling point, that the compound in question could not be the isomer which it had been assumed to be.

It should, however, be borne in mind that the theoretical argument can tell us something about the heat of evaporation but not about the boiling point itself, except when the entropy of evaporation ($\Delta H/T$ = TROUTON constant, p. 88) shows no differences for related compounds. This is almost correct in the above-mentioned case of *cis*- and *trans*-dichloroethylene (21.64 and 21.52 cal/mol. deg., respectively).

In the inorganic compounds which are built up of molecules both in the liquid and the solid state, little or nothing of electrostatic forces appears in the cohesion energy. One speaks in this case of shielded compounds (p. 95).

In the tetrahalides of Si, Ti and Ge and in the halides of B, P, Al (with the exception of $AlF_3$ and $TiF_4$), the rise of the boiling point proceeding from the fluoride to the iodide is a direct consequence of the increase of the LONDON attraction which is a result of the increase of the quantity $\alpha/d^3$ from fluorine to iodine. The boiling point of $AlF_3$ (above 1260°) is high compared with that of the volatile chloride, bromide and iodide of aluminium. This is explained by the fact that the first substance possesses a normal coordination lattice built up of ions, while the other halides are composed of molecules $Al_2X_6$, at least in the liquid and vapour states (see p. 95).

The VAN DER WAALS attractive forces also determine other properties of normal molecular (non-conducting) liquids. The viscosity or the resistance to flow, for example, is closely con-

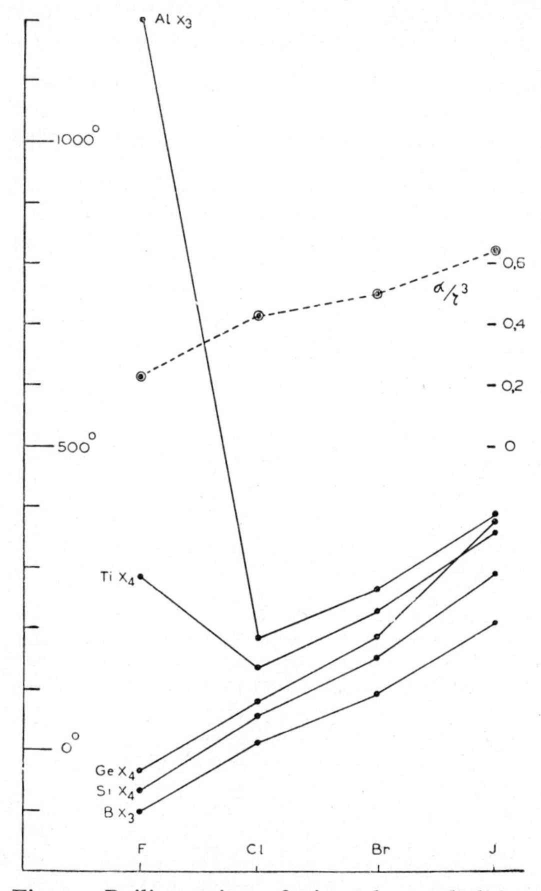


Fig. 30. Boiling points of tri- and tetra-halides.

nected with the interaction between the molecules. In the hydrocarbons, the viscosity increases at the same rate as the volatility decreases with increasing size of molecule. This is also a consequence of the increase in the VAN DER WAALS-LONDON attraction per molecule. Again the shape of the molecule and the degree of branching influence both the viscosity and the volatility. A greater degree of branching, whereby the molecule approaches further to a spherical shape, reduces the interaction and thus leads to greater volatility and smaller viscosity. The very volatile inert gases are also extremely mobile in the liquid state. With stronger attraction, as a result of the presence of dipoles in the molecule, the viscosity increases with decreasing volatility. In this respect the OH dipole is particularly active on account of its eccentric situation and the resulting formation of hydrogen bonds. One may be reminded of the high viscosity of low molecular liquids such as glycerol $C_3H_5(OH)_3$, glycol $C_2H_4(OH)_2$ and of concentrated sugar solutions. Water and alcohol are also very much more viscous than corresponding compounds without OH group but with the same polarizability, *e.g.*, $C_2H_5F$.

The viscosity $\eta$ of liquids is well reproduced over a large temperature range by the originally purely empirical formula of GUZMAN (or ANDRADE):

$$1/\eta = A\,e^{-B/RT}.$$

Theoretical arguments have confirmed this formula; EYRING (GLASSTONE, LAIDLER and EYRING, 1941) showed that the energy $B$, the activation energy of the fluid flow, the energy necessary to loosen partially the bonds of a molecule with its surroundings, is proportional to the evaporation energy and indeed approximately equal to 25–40% of it. This relation results in the viscosities of the saturated hydrocarbons at the boiling point being equal at 0.2 cp since at this temperature $\Delta H/T$ is constant according to TROUTON's rule and this is, therefore, also the above case for $B/T$ in the formula for the viscosity.

Surface tension is likewise based on intermolecular interaction and a strengthening of the latter will lead to an increase of the surface tension. It is, therefore, understandable that the parachor (SUGDEN, 1930; QUAYLE, 1953) $P = \frac{M}{d}\gamma^{1/4}$ shows a better additivity from atomic and group values than the molar volume $M/d$ itself. At a higher value of the cohesion energy, showing itself in a higher surface tension $\gamma$, a small correction is thus applied for the contraction. However, according to KOPP's rule the molar volume at the boiling point is also additive.

The phenomena at the surface of solutions likewise clearly illustrate the influence of the nature of the interaction. In the monomolecular layer in which a higher fatty acid, for example, can be spread on a water surface (LANGMUIR, HARKINS), the polar carboxyl groups are all directed towards the water, while the hydrocarbon tails assume a parallel orientation through the mutual LONDON attraction. These do not stand perpendicular to the water surface but make an angle of 63° with it owing to the position of the carboxyl group with respect to the rest of the molecule.

The lubrication of moving metal parts is produced by oriented layers, solidly anchored to the metal by carboxyl groups etc. Only the LONDON interaction between the hydrocarbon tails then still acts between the two metal parts, each with their layer of lubricating oil. A pure hydrocarbon (kerosene or paraffin oil) lubricates badly since this is forced away through inadequate adhesion to the metal. This is not only a consequence of too small a viscosity since a soap solution (potassium oleate, etc.) is serviceable (drilling oil).

The LONDON forces are predominant in the adsorption of gases on solid substances such as carbon. In the adsorption on ionic lattices such as salt layers ($CaF_2$ in electric lamps), silicic acid and aluminium oxide, the adsorption of the first layer depends mainly on polarization by electrostatic forces, in which isolated ions, corners and edges will give a larger heat of adsorption than a perfect crystal surface. The VAN DER WAALS-LONDON energy is, however, predominant in adsorption in multimolecular layers just as in the cohesion energy.

An empirical rule (DE BOER and CUSTERS, 1934), according to which the heat of adsorption of substance $A$ on the absorbent $B$ is proportional to $\sqrt{L_A L_B}$ in which $L_A$ and $L_B$ are the latent heats of evaporation of the two substances, is directly understandable both for LONDON and for KEESOM interaction of the pairs of molecules $AA$, $AB$ and $BB$ (see p. 390).

## § 43. MISCIBILITY AND SOLUBILITY

The mutual miscibility of liquids and the solubility of non-electrolytes, both solid and gaseous, in liquids are also governed by the VAN DER WAALS interaction. The solubility of non-polar gases, such as the inert gases, hydrogen, oxygen, nitrogen and the halogens, is theoretically a fairly simple problem. Here the interaction is based in the first place on LONDON forces; the DEBYE forces remain of minor significance even with polar solvents.

The solubility will, therefore, increase with increasing polarizability of the gas molecule (per unit volume) as well as with that of the solvent (among others, in the series of the homologous alcohols, ketones and benzene derivatives). These two influences will exhibit themselves most clearly when the other component is also readily polarizable. We see indeed that the variation is strongest in benzene on the one hand and in radon on the other (Table 32).

One must, however, also take the mutual interaction of the molecules of the solvent into account.

When a gas molecule dissolves in a liquid a hole must first be made in which it can be placed. The necessary energy will be proportional to the *specific* cohesion $U/V$ (or to the internal

TABLE 32

SOLUBILITY OF THE INERT GASES

Expressed as the molar fraction in solution at 1 atm*, $10^4\ n/(n+n_0)$
(According to SISSKIND and KASARNOWSKY, 1933; CLEVER *et al.*, 1957, 1958)

| | | Solvent | | | |
|---|---|---|---|---|---|
| | Polarizability | water 0° | ethanol 0° | acetone 0° | benzene 7° |
| He | 0.202 $10^{-24}$ cm³ | 0.177 | 0.599 | 0.684 | 0.55 |
| Ne | 0.392 | 0.174 | 0.857 | 1.15 | 0.87 |
| Ar | 1.629 | 0.414 | 6.54 | 8.09 | 8.66 |
| Kr | 2.460 | 0.888 | — | — | 28.9 |
| Xe | 4.000 | 1.94 | — | — | 140.7 |
| Rn | 5.419 | 4.14 | 211.2 | 254.9 | 638.1 |
| Dipole moment | | 1.84 | 1.70 | 2.85 | 0 D |
| Polarizability | | 1.48 | 5.29 | 6.59 | 10.87 $10^{-24}$ cm³ |

* This is also $10^4 k$; $k$ is the constant of HENRY's law, in the form $x = kp$ ($p$ in atm).

pressure). If the molecules of the solvent are not polar, this is proportional to $\alpha^2/v^3$ (p. 379). It will, therefore, be expected that the solubility of gases of small polarizability will decrease with increasing polarizability of the solvent; for gases of large polarizability, it is exactly the opposite.

The latter have already been mentioned above. The first case is illustrated by the relatively small solubility of hydrogen, nitrogen, etc. in carbon disulphide compared with the high solubility in pentane, which has a smaller polarizability.

The solubility will be small in solvents in which the cohesion is based for a great part on dipole-dipole interaction (in particular through hydrogen bonds). The large specific cohesion energy of the solvent is only compensated to a small extent by the DEBYE interaction with the solute molecule.

While atmospheric air contains 21% oxygen, air dissolved in water contains 34% oxygen. This is important in biology and is a consequence of the greater polarizability per unit volume of oxygen in comparison with nitrogen (the ratio is 1 : 0.77).

The mutual solubility of liquids involves first of all the thermal effect which occurs on mixing, namely, the heat of mixing $M$ (HILDEBRAND and SCOTT, 1950; VAN ARKEL and VLES, 1936; STAVERMAN, 1937, 1941; VAN ARKEL, 1946; GUGGENHEIM, 1952; HAASE, 1956; Discussions Faraday Soc., No. 15, *The equilibrium properties of solutions of non-electrolytes*, 1953). This quantity consists of the difference between the cohesion energy of the mixture and that of the pure components individually. Now it is plausible that the LONDON interaction of two molecules $A$ and $B$ is the geometrical mean of those between pairs of molecules $A$ and molecules $B$ where these three interactions are in fact proportional to $\alpha_A \alpha_B$, $\alpha_A^2$, and $\alpha_B^2$ (actually one must also take into account the differences in radius; however, $r_{AB} \approx \sqrt{r_A r_B}$ is a fairly good approximation as long as $r_A$ and $r_B$ do not differ too much). This is also reasonable for the KEESOM energy which is proportional to $\mu_A^2 \mu_B^2$ (see however p. 395). This does not mean, however, that the total interaction due to both effects could also be represented by the geometrical mean. Consider two substances $A$ and $B$ with approximately equal cohesion energies, *e.g.*, water and carbon tetrachloride. The first is composed practically exclusively of KEESOM energy ($K$), the second exclusively of LONDON energy ($L$). The interaction of an $H_2O$ and a $CCl_4$ molecule is not equal to the geometric mean of the two approximately equal individual quantities, thus approximately equal to that between the pairs $A$ and $B$ separately. This interaction is much less because both the KEESOM energy and the LONDON energy are small for the combination of the weakly polarizable, strongly polar water molecule and readily polarizable but dipoleless molecules such as carbon tetrachloride, bromine or benzene. The heat of mixing is thus strongly negative and the two substances are but slightly miscible.

For a mixture of $x$ mole $A$ and $(1 - x)$ mole $B$ the LONDON cohesion energy according to VAN ARKEL (1934) is $x^2L_A + (1 - x)^2L_B + 2\,x\,(1 - x)\sqrt{L_A\,L_B}$. $L_A$ and $L_B$ are the LONDON cohesion energies of $A$ and $B$ which are proportional to the interaction energies of pairs of molecules $AA$ and $BB$ respectively. The interaction of a pair $AB$ is proportional to $\sqrt{L_A A_B}$. The probability of pairs $AA$ is proportional to $x^2$, that of pairs $AB$ and also of pairs $BA$ is proportional to $x(1 - x)$, total $2\,x\,(1 - x)$. The sum of the cohesion energies of the components is $x\,L_A + (1 - x)\,L_B$. The heat of mixing is obtained by subtracting this latter amount from the former and rearranging and simplifying: $-\Delta U = M = -x\,(1 - x)\,(\sqrt{L_A} - \sqrt{L_B})^2$, that is to say an intrinsically negative quantity. In the above-mentioned case in which both LONDON and KEESOM energies play a part we have: $M = -x\,(1 - x)\,\{(\sqrt{L_A} - \sqrt{L_B})^2 + (\sqrt{K_A} - \sqrt{K_B})^2\}$. The expression is highly negative when $K_A \approx L_B$ but $L_A \ll L_B$, $K_A \gg K_B$; $M$ is only small for $L_A \approx L_B$, $K_A \approx K_B$.

As early as 1906 VAN LAAR had deduced the heat of mixing of a binary liquid mixture on the basis of the VAN DER WAALS equation of state.

According to VAN DER WAALS the cohesion energy of a liquid is $U = -a/V$ (p. 379). For a mixture of $x$ mol $A$ and $(1 - x)$ mol $B$, the cohesion energy is $U_M = -a_M/V_M$ with $a_M = x^2 a_A + 2x(1 - x) a_{AB} + (1 - x)^2 a_B$.

Again the probability of pairs $AA$ or $BB$ is proportional to $x^2$ or $(1 - x)^2$, respectively; that of pairs $AB$ as stated above to $2x(1 - x)$ if the molecules are distributed at random. The interaction between a molecule $A$ and a molecule $B$ is represented by $a_{AB}$. According to BERTHELOT's empirical relation we have:

$$a_{AB} = \sqrt{a_A \cdot a_B}$$

The volume $V_M = x V_A + (1 - x) V_B$ (no contraction). The negative heat of mixing, that is to say the heat which is absorbed on mixing, $\Delta U$, equals $\Delta H$ (since there is no volume effect).

$$-M = \Delta U = U_M - x U_A - (1 - x) U_B$$

After substituting the above expressions we have:

$$\Delta U = \frac{x(1 - x) V_A V_B}{x V_A + (1 - x) V_B} \left[\frac{\sqrt{a_A}}{V_A} - \frac{\sqrt{a_B}}{V_B}\right]^2 \quad \text{VAN LAAR}$$

Bearing in mind that the specific cohesion $U/V$ is $a/V^2$ for a liquid which obeys the VAN DER WAALS equation of state, this formula can be written more generally as:

$$\Delta U = \frac{x(1 - x) V_A V_B}{x V_A + (1 - x) V_B} \left[\left(\frac{U_A}{V_A}\right)^{1/2} - \left(\frac{U_B}{V_B}\right)^{1/2}\right]^2$$

HILDEBRAND-SCATCHARD

It is only for $V_A \approx V_B$ that this equation transforms into the above (simplified) expression of VAN ARKEL:

$$-M = \Delta U = x(1 - x)\left[\sqrt{U_A} - \sqrt{U_B}\right]^2$$

The volume factor in the formula of HILDEBRAND-SCATCHARD can also be written as $V_m \varphi_A \varphi_B$, in which $\varphi_A$ and $\varphi_B$ are the volume fractions of $A$ and $B$ and $V_m$ is the molar volume of the mixture; then

$$-M = \Delta U = V_m \, \varphi_A \, \varphi_B \left[ \left( \frac{U_A}{V_A} \right)^{1/2} - \left( \frac{U_B}{V_B} \right)^{1/2} \right]^2$$

It is again the specific cohesion energy $U/V$ which determines the behaviour of the substances. The square root of the specific cohesion energy is also called the solubility parameter (Table 33).

TABLE 33

SPECIFIC COHESION OF NON-ASSOCIATED LIQUIDS AT 25° C

| | $\Delta H$ kcal/mole | $\sqrt{U/V}$ (cal/mole cm$^3$)$^{1/2}$ | | $\Delta H$ kcal/mole | $\sqrt{U/V}$ (cal/mole cm$^3$)$^{1/2}$ |
|---|---|---|---|---|---|
| phosphorus | 12.6 | 13.1 | naphthalene | — | 9.9 |
| sulphur | — | 12.7 | $CH_3Cl$ | 4.76 | 8.6 |
| bromine | 7.34 | 11.5 | $CHCl_3$ | 7.6 | 9.3 |
| iodine | — | 14.1 | $CH_3Br$ | 5.63 | 9.4 |
| $CCl_4$ | 7.83 | 8.6 | $CHBr_3$ | 10.3 | 10.5 |
| $SiCl_4$ | 7.19 | 7.6 | $CH_3I$ | 6.7 | 9.9 |
| $SnCl_4$ | 9.55 | 8.7 | nitromethane | 9.15 | 12.6 |
| *n*-$C_5H_{12}$ | 6.32 | 7.05 | $CS_2$ | 6.7 | 10.0 |
| *neo*pentane | 5.21 | 6.25 | $(C_2H_5)_2O$ | 6.36 | 7.4 |
| *n*-$C_7H_{16}$ | 8.74 | 7.45 | dioxan | 8.7 | 9.7 |
| *n*-$C_{16}H_{34}$ | 19.3 | 8.0 | pyridine | 9.85 | 10.7 |
| cyclohexane | 7.90 | 8.20 | chlorobenzene | 9.83 | 9.5 |
| benzene | 8.09 | 9.15 | nitrobenzene | 14.5 | 11.6 |

The following hypotheses have been introduced into these deductions:

1. The cohesion energy is additively composed of the interaction energy of pairs of (two) molecules, that is to say this interaction is independent of the nature and the position of the other molecules and of the temperature, but depends only on the separation and the orientation of the molecules of the pair.

2. This interaction energy $\varepsilon_{AB}$ equals $\sqrt{\varepsilon_A \cdot \varepsilon_B}$. This is valid, as appears directly from the formulae concerned, both for the LONDON and for the KEESOM energy. The validity of BERTHELOT's relation is thus a consequence of the predominance of these types of interaction.

3. The distribution of the molecules is completely random ("randomness of mixing"), that is to say the probability of pairs *AA*, *AB* and *BB* is determined only by the ratios of the number of particles. This is only correct when the differences in interaction for these pairs are small compared with the thermal energy $kT$ and when the differences in size are not too large. In other words it is assumed that the entropy of mixing is equal to that for *ideal* (gas and liquid) mixtures:

$$\Delta S = -R\,[x \ln x + (1 - x) \ln (1 - x)].$$

4. No volume effect occurs on mixing. This is, in fact, correct to a good approximation for many liquid pairs in which no hydrogen bond formation occurs as it does in water-alcohol.

Solutions that satisfy conditions 3 and 4 and that show an ideal entropy effect and no volume effect on mixing but do show a thermal effect are called regular solutions (HILDEBRAND and SCOTT, 1950; GUGGENHEIM, 1952, HAASE, 1956). In ideal solutions the thermal effect is also absent.

The extended VAN ARKEL equation contains the same volume factor as that of HILDEBRAND-SCATCHARD. VAN ARKEL's extended equation is then as follows:

$$\Delta U = V_m \varphi_A \varphi_B [(\sqrt{L'_A} - \sqrt{L'_B})^2 + (\sqrt{K'_A} - \sqrt{K'_B})^2]$$

in which $L'$ and $K'$ are the contributions to the *specific* cohesion energy $U/V = L' + K'$, proportional respectively to

$$\frac{\alpha^2}{v^3} I \text{ and } \frac{\mu^4}{v^3} \frac{1}{kT}$$

The validity is restricted to those cases in which the field of the molecule can still be represented by a dipole moment at the centre of a sphere, thus where the external position, as in the OH and NH dipoles especially, does not play a part.

VAN ARKEL's formula has the advantage over that of SCATCHARD in that it can be seen from it that the heat of mixing does not become zero for liquids with the same specific cohesion if this cohesion has a different origin.

In general it can be said that similar compounds will mix; the solubility decreases however with increasing difference in volatility, that is in (specific) cohesion. By "similar" is meant that the cohesion energy belongs to the same type of interaction in both substances. Thus halogenated compounds are miscible with hydrocarbons; likewise lower alcohols and polyalcohols with one another and with water. The higher alcohols, for example cetyl alcohol $C_{16}H_{33}OH$ from spermaceti wax, high fatty acids such as palmitic acid $C_{15}H_{31}COOH$ and stearic acid $C_{17}H_{35}COOH$, are similar in many respects, even to the inexpert eye, to the corresponding paraffins. Again the fatty oils, the ethereal oils and mineral oil, however different from the chemical standpoint, show a striking similarity as expressed by the common name "oil". This similarity is the result of the predominance of the LONDON interaction in these compounds.

Incomplete miscibility at room temperature or above is rare with non-polar liquids. Only $SnI_4$, molten phosphorus and molten sulphur, all with a very high specific cohesion, and the fluorocarbons with a very low specific cohesion, are exceptions to this statement. With increasing cohesion of the second substance, for example of sulphur with benzene, naphthalene and anthracene, respectively, the critical solubility temperature falls below the melting line but the partial miscibility is present in the metastable state (KRUYT, 1909; KETELAAR and JIBBEN, 1948).

Although aniline does possess a dipole moment the cohesion energy is predominantly of the LONDON type. The critical solubility point—technically actually the 1 : 1 demixing point—with hydrocarbon mixtures (aniline point) is an important characteristic quantity. The aniline point rises with the molecular weight in a homologous series. For aromatic hydrocarbons the critical solubility point is the lowest, for paraffins the highest, olefins and cyclic hydrocarbons are intermediate in agreement with the variation of the specific cohesion (Table 33).

The condition for the critical solubility point $T_c$ can easily be derived from the thermodynamic conditions for a critical point:

$$\frac{\partial^2 \Delta G}{\partial x^2} = 0 \text{ and } \frac{\partial^3 \Delta G}{\partial x^3} = 0 \left[\text{or } \frac{\partial \mu_B}{\partial x} = 0 \text{ and } \frac{\partial^2 \mu_B}{\partial x^2} = 0 \text{ (p. 398)}\right].$$

$$\text{The result is: } 2\,RT_c = V\left[\left(\frac{U_A}{V_A}\right)^{1/2} - \left(\frac{U_B}{V_B}\right)^{1/2}\right]^2 \text{ and } x = 1 - x = 1/2$$

for the case $V_A \approx V_B = V$.

With $V = 100$ cm³, $\sqrt{U_A/V_A} - \sqrt{U_B/V_B}$ must, therefore, be at least 3.4 in order that $T_c \geqslant 300°$ K which indicates a very appreciable difference in specific cohesion energy, so that partial miscibility is rare in non-polar substances. In most systems of two liquids one of the components is associated.

The fact that absolute non-miscibility does not exist (at any rate not at temperatures above the absolute zero of temperature), is a consequence of the gain in entropy which occurs on mixing. According to thermodynamics it is not the change in energy $\Delta U$ but the change in free energy $\Delta F = \Delta U - T\Delta S$ which determines the course of an isothermal reaction at constant volume. $\Delta U$ on mixing is in general positive (that is to say energy must be supplied on mixing, corresponding to a negative heat of mixing; cooling occurs on mixing); nevertheless, when $\Delta S$ is positive, that is to say if there is a sufficient gain in entropy, $\Delta F$ can be negative so that mixing will occur.

Since the partial entropy contains a term $-R \ln x$, this entropy will always become large and positive for very small concentrations, so that a small mutual solubility will necessarily occur. Complete miscibility thus only occurs when $\Delta F$ can still be negative for all concentrations even though $\Delta U$ is positive. This can in general occur at higher temperatures and in fact the mutual solubility does generally increase with increasing temperature since the entropy term then gains in effect.

With "regular" mixtures, in which, therefore, no volume effect occurs on mixing, $\Delta F$ and $\Delta G$ are identical ($p\,\Delta V = 0$). According to the derivation given above we have in this case:

$$\Delta F = \Delta U - T\Delta S = V_m \varphi_A \varphi_B \left[ \left(\frac{U_A}{V_B}\right)^{1/2} - \left(\frac{U_B}{V_B}\right)^{1/2} \right]^2 + $$
$$+ RT\,[x \ln x + (1 - x) \ln (1 - x)]$$

Now it can be shown (see HILDEBRAND, 1950, p. 139) that when a volume effect does occur, the above expression for $\Delta F$ at constant volume is nevertheless equal to that for $\Delta G$ with volume change at constant pressure.

Thus $\Delta G_p = \Delta F_v$.

In another approximation *athermal* mixtures are discussed with a zero heat of mixing just as ideal solutions, but with a different entropy of mixing, owing to a difference in size of the two kinds of molecules. The most simple expression is that derived by FLORY (1942):

$$-\Delta F/T = \Delta S = -R[x \ln \varphi_A + (1 - x) \ln (1 - \varphi_A)].$$

This influence of the difference in size is important for solutions of macromolecules. By including this expression for the entropy in the expression given above for $\Delta F$, a (simplified) formula is obtained, applicable to non-regular solutions.

The empirical symmetrical relation of PORTER (HILDEBRAND and SCOTT, 1950; HAASE, 1951, 1956; GUGGENHEIM, 1952):

$$\Delta G = A(T)\, x\, (1 - x)$$

has been found to represent the experimental data very well, even in systems that show far from ideal behaviour and where, *e.g.*, $\Delta H$ and $\Delta S$ individually are by no means represented by symmetrical functions as given above on p. 390 and p. 392.

The mutually restricted miscibility can be very different as seen for example in the system ether-water; 4.9 mol % water dissolves in ether, but in water only 1.6 mol % ether dissolves. This occurs because water dissolved in ether forms hydrogen bonds with it (§ 45), but ether in water cannot form bonds and is also inferior to water as an acceptor.

The hypothesis of an interaction energy *AB* as the geometric mean of *AA* and *BB* for each of the types (p. 389) is unable to account for the occurrence of a positive heat of mixing, which is so obvious with acetone and water, for example.

If the interaction *AB* is much stronger than the mean of *AA* and *BB*, the heat of mixing will be positive; this is further strengthened because the pairs *AB* in the mixture with their low energy content will occur relatively more frequently than when a random distribution holds, as with equal interactions.

Such a case is present, for example, if the two components both have a dipole but in the one case the end which points to the outside is the positive pole, in the other molecule this is the case for the negative pole (LANGMUIR, STAVERMAN). An example of the first class is a molecule with an OH or NH dipole such as water, alcohol, amine and also chloroform (p. 407) and of the second class acetone, ether or pyridine. Combinations of substances from both groups give rise to a positive heat of mixing. If the interaction of dissimilar particles is especially pronounced, the mixture will consist largely of pairs (or more complicated, but not necessarily stoichiometrically constituted, complexes) and one can speak of the formation of a compound. The heat of mixing set free ($\Delta U$ negative!) then has the character of a heat of formation of a partially dissociated compound.

With water-alcohol, both molecules with an OH dipole, the cause of the positive heat of mixing is to be found elsewhere. In view of the strong volume contraction which occurs on mixing, the packing in water-alcohol mixtures is appreciably denser than in water and alcohol themselves. In particular, water has an open, partly ordered structure (p. 420). The introduction of alcohol molecules disturbs this structure and the dense packing itself gives rise to a low energy content; the formation of definite alcohol hydrates does not occur here.

In the light of considerations on the heat of mixing, it may seem surprising that there are also various cases in which only restricted miscibility exists in spite of a positive heat of mixing. In fact if the solubility decreases with increasing temperature, then, according to the VAN 'T HOFF-LE CHATELIER principle, the heat of mixing must be positive ($\Delta U$ negative!). Since the *free* energy of mixing, $\Delta F$, is, however, positive in view of the limited miscibility, the entropy of mixing must be strongly negative in these cases. This case of decreasing solubility occurs in all systems in which a lower critical solubility point is found, as for example with triethylamine-water. A closed region of partial miscibility even occurs in the system nicotine-water with both an upper and a lower critical solubility point.

It is incorrect to consider exclusively the energy effects. The strong interaction *AB* described above will result in a restriction of the number of complexions*, thus a lowering of the entropy. It even appears, also in the case of the solubility of gases, that an increase of the heat set free ($\Delta U$ more negative) is associated with a decrease of the entropy effect ($\Delta S$ lower). The influence of the energy on the free energy is thus partially compensated or sometimes even dominated by the entropy changes acting in the opposite direction.

It is indeed thermodynamically necessary that in mixtures in which the (temperature-dependent) orientation interaction energy plays a part the entropy is not given by the (temperature-independent) ideal entropy of mixing (or GIBBS term) given above.

The cause lies in the above-mentioned strong ordering of the molecules in the mixture by the attractive interaction so that an entropy loss is produced on mixing. At lower temperatures the influence of the entropy ($T\Delta S$!) is smaller; the influence of the positive heat of mixing is then predominant and a lower critical solubility point is produced. At high temperatures the liquids begin to bear more and more a normal character while the influence of the orientation interaction of the dipoles decreases through the thermal motion; thus the heat of mixing becomes negative at high temperatures, while the entropy change becomes positive. An upper critical solubility point now becomes possible.

In the solubility of a solid substance, the change in energy, and entropy in the solid-liquid transition must also be considered as well as the effect which occurs on mixing the liquids. The entropy of melting, like the evaporation entropy, is an approximately constant quantity (8–11 E.U.) in many cases. A high melting point is therefore associated with a high heat

* The number of complexions $W$ is the number of ways of distributing the molecules, among the various positions and energy-levels available that lead to the observed state of the system. In statistical thermodynamics the entropy is $S = k \ln W$, with $k = R/N$.

of fusion (p. 400); therefore the solubility of higher melting substances will be smaller than that of lower melting compounds with otherwise corresponding properties.

Further the solubility then depends on the same circumstances, as regards the nature of the interaction, as in the mixing of liquids; that is to say, similarity of interaction is also a condition for high solubility (fat in benzene and carbon tetrachloride; sugar in water).

For ideal solutions VAN 'T HOFF's law holds for the solubility of substance $B$:

$$\ln x_B = -\frac{\Delta H}{R}\left(\frac{1}{T}-\frac{1}{T_0}\right)$$

in which $\Delta H = H_L - H_S$ is the latent heat of fusion and $T_0$ the melting point, both of the pure substance $B$.

For regular solutions $\mu_B$, the partial free enthalpy (chemical potential) of substance $B$ in solution, calculated with respect to the solid state, also contains the partial heat of mixing $\Delta u$ (the entropy is equal to that of the ideal case). From the expression for $\Delta U$ on p. 392 we have for the partial heat of mixing:

$$\Delta u_B = \left(\frac{\partial \Delta U}{\partial n_B}\right)_{n_A}$$

$$\Delta u_B = V_B \varphi_A^2 \left[\left(\frac{U_A}{V_A}\right)^{1/2} - \left(\frac{U_B}{V_B}\right)^{1/2}\right]^2 \quad \text{and thus}$$

$$-\frac{\Delta \mu_B}{RT} = \ln x_B = -\frac{\Delta H}{R}\left(\frac{1}{T}-\frac{1}{T_0}\right) - \frac{V_B \varphi_A^2}{RT}\left[\left(\frac{U_A}{V_A}\right)^{1/2} - \left(\frac{U_B}{V_B}\right)^{1/2}\right]^2$$

For dilute solutions the volume fraction $\varphi_A$ varies parallel with $x_A = 1 - x_B$ and so the partial heat of mixing can also be written as $\Delta u_B = Cx_A^2$ in which $C$ is a constant. The change in $\Delta\mu_B$ is then likewise equal to $Cx_A^2$ and thus we also have $RT \ln f_B = Cx_A^2$, when $f_B$ is the activity coefficient of substance $B$. Such a variation of the activity coefficient had frequently been found in earlier experimental work.

Comparison of the above formula for $\ln x_B$ with the formula of VAN 'T HOFF shows that the solubility will follow the ideal law only if the solubility parameters $\sqrt{U/V}$ of solute and solvent are equal.

The above formula for the solubility, in which the corrections for the temperature dependence of the latent heat of fusion $\Delta H$ were taken into account, has been very extensively tested by HILDEBRAND (HILDEBRAND, 1949; HILDEBRAND and SCOTT, 1950; HILDEBRAND and GLEW, 1956) on the solubility of iodine in a very large number of solvents (violet solution, p. 374). Since the specific cohesion (p. 392) of iodine is very high ($\sqrt{U/V} = 14.1$), the solubility-temperature curve only approaches the ideal value for solvents with similarly large specific cohesion, such as $SnI_4$ (11.7) and $S_8$ (12.7), molten sulphur (Table 33).

The solubility is very much smaller for a solvent with smaller cohesion.

TABLE 34

SOLUBILITY OF IODINE AT 25° C

| Solvent | Mol. % iodine | Activity coefficient $f_{I_2}$ | $\sqrt{U/V}$ solvent |
|---|---|---|---|
| ideal | 25.8 | 1.00 | 14.1 |
| $CS_2$ | 5.46 | 4.73 | 9.9 |
| $CCl_4$ | 1.15 | 22.5 | 8.6 |
| $n$-$C_7H_{16}$ | 0.679 | 38.0 | 7.4 |
| $n$-$C_6H_{14}$ | 0.456 | 56.6 | 7.3 |
| $n$-$C_7F_{16}$ | 0.0185 | 1400 | 5.7 |

The solubility is increased by solvation (lowering of $\Delta U$) so that the brown solution (p. 374) in ether ($\sqrt{U/V} = 7.4$) shows a very much greater solubility than in heptane (namely 7.9 mol. %).

The solubility (degree of swelling) of polymers in solvents is only appreciable if the specific cohesion of polymer and solvent do not differ too much (MAGAT, 1949; MARK and TOBOLSKY, 1950). Thus rubber ($\sqrt{U/V}$ 7.9) is soluble in most solvents from Table 33, but not in neopentane (6.25), dioxan (10.1) and nitromethane (12.6). Polyvinyl chloride (9.5) is oil-resistant (hexadecane, 8.0) in contrast to rubber. With strongly polar solvents one must take account of the separate contributions (p. 390 and 396; the total specific cohesion (ethanol $\sqrt{U/V}$ 12.7, water 23.4) is not a valid measure of the interaction with the solute.

In gas chromatography (PHILLIPS, 1956; KEULEMANS, 1957) the retention of the solute molecules of the mobile vapour phase by the non-volatile stationary solvent phase is governed by the partition coefficient $k$ of the solute between both phases ($k$ is the ratio of solute per unit volume of the liquid phase to that in the gas phase) or the HENRY coefficient $h$. Only for an ideal solution is the HENRY coefficient equal to the vapour pressure $p_0$ of the pure solute. RAOULT's law is $p = xp_0$; HENRY's law is $p = hx$ with the Henry coefficient $h = f_B p_0$, where $x$ is the mole fraction of the solute and $f_B$ is the activity coefficient of the solute. It can be easily shown that for $x \ll 1$, $k = RT/V_A f_B p_0$ with $V_A$ the molar volume of the solvent.

The activity coefficient $f_B$ is derived as given above from the excess energy $\Delta U$ (for regular solutions) or more generally (p. 398):

$$-RT \ln f_B = \Delta u = V_B \left[(U_A/V_A)^{1/2} - (U_B/V_B)^{1/2}\right]^2$$

It is possible to determine the value of $f_B$ and the solubility parameters from the elution curves. It is also possible to predict the partition coefficient from a knowledge of the solubility parameters (LITTLEWOOD, PHILLIPS and PRICE, 1955; PIEROTTI, *et al.*, 1956; PORTER *et al.*, 1956; KWANTES and RIJNDERS, 1958).

As A is the non-volatile solvent we can state that $U_A/V_A \gg U_B/V_B$ and thus $\ln f_B = B + C(U_A/V_A)^{1/2}(U_B/V_B)^{1/2}$. As shown on p. 391 $(U_B/V_B)^{1/2} \propto \sqrt{a}_B/V_B$ and both $\sqrt{a}$ and $V$ increase linearly with the number of carbon atoms for hydrocarbons (p. 383). Thus it can be understood that a linear increase with the number of carbon atoms was found for the retention volume (or log $k$) (JAMES and MARTIN, 1952).

If the cohesion energies of $A$ and $B$ are of different origin, differences in $f_B$ and $k$ can arise even if the boiling points or solubility parameters of two solutes are equal. Thus the selective power of an immobile phase can be both understood and predicted from an insight in the nature of the cohesion energy.

The empirical relation of BRÖNSTED and KOEFOED (1946), $\log f = -D(n_1 - n_2)^2$ for a mixture of two hydrocarbon with $n_1$ and $n_2$ carbon atoms respectively can be understood as well.

## § 44. THE MELTING POINT

The melting point $T_f$ and the heat of fusion $\Delta H_f$ may vary very much, *e.g.*, hydrogen melts at 13.95° K, heat of fusion 28.2 cal/mole, platinum at 2028° K with a heat of fusion of 5310 cal/mole. However, the entropies of melting $\Delta S = \Delta H_f/T_f$ are closely similar 2.02 and 2.62 E.U. (EUCKEN, 1942; UBBELOHDE, 1950).

The melting point is connected with the cohesion energy; in general a high boiling point $T_b$ is connected with a high melting point $T_f$ but the ration $T_f/T_b$ varies between 0.5 and 1.1.

The entropy of melting is approximately constant and ranges between 1.5 and 3.5 E.U. for crystals composed of simple units, *e.g.*, the inert gases (3.26–3.43 E.U., except He, 1.5 E.U.), hydrogen, the metals (exceptions Ga, Sb, Bi etc. with low coordination numbers) and ionic crystals (alkali halides). For most simple polyatomic substances the entropy of melting ranges between 8 and 11 E.U. However, there are a rather large number of simple diatomic molecules ($O_2$, $N_2$, CO, HCl, HBr, HI) and polyatomic molecules ($H_2S$, $CH_4$, $CCl_4$) with a low entropy of fusion of 2–3 E.U. In all these cases transformations in the solid state are known and the combined entropies of transformations and fusion lead to a normal value of 5–10 E.U. (EUCKEN, 1942; UBBELOHDE, 1950).

The entropy of melting is $\Delta S = k \ln W_f/W_s$ where $W_f$ and $W_s$ are the probabilities or the numbers of complexions in the liquid and in the solid state respectively. This entropy is composed of a part due to the increase of translational degrees of freedom and of a part due to the increase in configurational and rotational degrees of freedom. At the transformations in the solid state the increase in entropy is due to this latter part. The first part of the entropy of melting is closely connected with the increase of volume at the melting point.

It is not possible to obtain general relations for the melting point or the entropy of melting of more complicated molecules. In the series of normal aliphatic hydrocarbons the entropy of melting per $CH_2$ group is about 2.5–3 E.U. However, an important influence of the molecular symmetry is observed. Symmetrical molecules, in which the entropy of fusion is lower because of the smaller number of different complexions in the liquid (and in the vapour), melt at a higher temperature than similar, less symmetrical molecules. However, in many cases the packing in the lattice is more favourable for symmetrical molecules and also a higher latent heat of fusion results.

The relation between melting point and structure is therefore fairly complicated. In many cases both causes counteract each other where we observe a low (high) heat of fusion and at the same time a low (high) entropy of fusion $\Delta S_f = \Delta H_f/T_f$ (Table 35). As the crystal structure is nearly always different for isomeric substances, it is not surprising that no exact general rules can be given for the melting point of a substance.

Nevertheless, it is a fixed rule that the *para* isomer of a disubstituted benzene melts at an appreciably higher temperature than the other isomers, although the differences in boiling

TABLE 35

| | M.P. | $\Delta H_f$ kcal/mole | $\Delta S_f$ cal/degr. mole | B.P. | $\Delta S_{vap}$ cal/degr. mole |
|---|---|---|---|---|---|
| benzene | + 5.53° | 2.351 | 8.436 | 80.10° | 20.81 |
| cyclohexadiene −1,3 | − 95.0 | — | — | 81.0 | — |
| cyclohexadiene −1, 4 | − 49.7 | — | — | 88.6 | — |
| cyclohexene | −103.51 | — | — | 82.98 | — |
| cyclohexane | + 6.55 | 0.637 | 2.28 | 80.74 | 20.30 |
| *o*-xylene | − 25.19 | 3.250 | 13.11 | 144.42 | 21.07 |
| *m*-xylene | − 47.87 | 2.765 | 12.27 | 139.10 | 21.10 |
| *p*-xylene | + 13.26 | 4.090 | 14.28 | 138.35 | 20.95 |
| *n*-butane | −138.33 | 1.114 | 8.26 | −0.50 | 19.63 |
| *n*-pentane | −129.72 | 2.011 | 14.02 | 36.07 | 19.92 |
| *iso*-pentane | −159.89 | 1.232 | 10.88 | 27.85 | 19.41 |
| *neo*-pentane | − 16.6 | 0.778 | 3.03 | 9.50 | 19.24 |
| *n*-hexane | − 95.32 | 3.114 | 17.51 | 68.74 | 20.17 |
| *n*-heptane | − 90.59 | 3.358 | 18.39 | 98.43 | 20.38 |
| *n*-octane | − 56.80 | 4.931 | 22.79 | 125.7 | 20.96 |
| 2-methylheptane | −109.04 | 2.451 | 14.94 | 117.6 | 20.55 |
| 3- ,, | −120.50 | 2.718 | 17.80 | 118.9 | 20.76 |
| 4- ,, | −120.95 | 2.592 | 17.03 | 117.7 | 20.72 |
| 2, 2-dimethylhexane | −121.18 | 1.625 | 10.69 | 106.8 | 20.34 |
| 2. 5- ,, | − 91.20 | 3.073 | 16.89 | 109.1 | 20.51 |
| 3, 3- ,, | −126.10 | 1.7 | 12 | 112.0 | 20.30 |
| 2. 2. 3-trimethyl-pentane | −112.27 | 2.063 | 12.82 | 109.8 | 20.08 |
| 2, 2, 4- ,, | −107.36 | 2.202 | 13.28 | 99.2 | 19.90 |
| 2, 3, 3- ,, | −100.70 | 0.366 | 2.12 | 114.8 | 20.06 |
| 2, 3, 4- ,, | −109.21 | 2.215 | 13.51 | 113.5 | 20.20 |
| 2, 2, 3, 3-tetramethyl-butane | +100.69 | 1.702 | 4.55 | 106.3 | 19.92 |

point are very small. For dibromobenzene, mentioned on p. 382, the melting points for *o*-, *m*- and *p*- respectively are −6°, −7° and +87°. For xylene these values are −25°, −48° and +13° with 144°, 139° and 138° as the boiling points. Tetramethylmethane or neopentane melts at −17° while normal and *iso*-pentane melt at −130° and −160° respectively. A

# ADDENDA AND ERRATA

p. 403, footnote, last line, add: *Rev. Modern Phys.*, 30 (1958) 94.

p. 408, line 17 from bottom, the first $NO_2$ should read $R_2O$.

p. 416, Table 37, fourth column, line 6 from bottom, 1725 should read 1775; fifth column, lines 4 and 5 from bottom, 4140 should read 3962.

p. 418, line 16, 4140 should read 3962.

p. 424, last line, add: GIGUÈRE, A. and IRENGI, N., *Can. J. Chem.*, 36 (1958) 1013.

comparison between benzene and its hydrogenated products is also interesting; the boiling points are equal but the symmetrical compounds possess much higher melting points (Table 35). Large differences in melting point also exist in the isomeric octanes (Table 35).

The series of the normal alkanes (Table 31) shows the alternation of the increase of melting point which is also seen in the fatty acids. This is a consequence of the difference in crystal structure of even and odd molecules resulting from a difference in symmetry (centre or plane through the middle).

In very symmetrical molecules (spherical or planar compact molecules, BACKER), such as for example tetramethylmethane (neopentane), hexachloroethane, hexamethylbenzene, camphor, sulphur hexafluoride, etc., a high melting point occurs for the above-mentioned reasons. Since the volatility is also great, these compounds have a small liquid range which may even be absent at 1 atm. In addition, however, one or more degrees of freedom (rotation) are excited even in the solid state, so that the entropy of melting is still further diminished. In Table 35 we find examples of this in cyclohexane, neopentane and 2,3,3-trimethylpentane. These substances will have a very high molecular freezing point depression $\Delta T \propto \frac{R\,T^2}{\Delta H}$ (application in the micromolecular weight determination in camphor according to RAST).

## § 45. THE HYDROGEN BOND*

Abnormal or associated liquids have long been distinguished from normal non-associated liquids on the basis of the deviations from various rules, *e.g.*, TROUTON's rule, EÖTVÖS' rule, etc. All molecules containing OH groups, *e.g.*, water, hydrogen

* Older reviews: HUGGINS, 1936; LASSETTRE, 1937; *Trans. Faraday Soc. Gen. Disc.*, "*The Hydrogen Bond*", 36 (1940) 851; PAULING, *The Nature of the Chemical Bond*, p. 284, ref. p. 425; HOYER, 1943. Recent reviews: DAVIES, 1946; HUNTER, 1946; RUMPF, 1948; BAUER, 1949; MECKE, 1950; DONOHUE, 1952; KELLNER, 1952; COULSON, 1957; CANNON, 1958.

peroxide, inorganic and organic acids, alcohols and, to a lesser degree, molecules containing NH groups, *e.g.*, amines, amides, etc., give abnormal liquids. Liquid HF and HCN also belong to the associated, abnormal liquids. On the other hand almost all other molecules with CH groups, *e.g.*, the hydrocarbons, behave normally.

Association is thus encountered in decreasing strength with the FH, OH and NH dipole, while in rare cases the CH dipole behaves similarly, although weakly. The electric dipole moments involved are rather small and molecules with much stronger or equally polar groups, *e.g.*, C—F, C—Cl, C—O—C, C=O, C—$NO_2$ etc., are not associated in the liquid state.

The discrepant behaviour of the hydrogen atom has led to the introduction by HUGGINS and by LATIMER and RODEBUSH of a special term "hydrogen bond" for the interaction, in which a hydrogen bound to an electronegative atom X (proton donor) gives rise to bonding with a second electronegative atom Y (proton acceptor), X—H......Y.

Two structurally different kinds of hydrogen bonds can be distinguished: *inter*molecular (external) bonds between atoms of different molecules and *intra*molecular (internal) hydrogen bonds between atoms X and Y of one and the same molecule.

Various explanations regarding the nature of this special form of bond, such as divalent hydrogen (with two electron pair bonds, though the K-shell can accommodate only one pair) or proton resonance or electron resonance as in benzene, have proved to be wrong.

The hydrogen atom in the O—H... O bridge (Fig. 32) has two non-equivalent positions of minimum energy, one near each of the two oxygen atoms separated by a potential hump. Thus there is a possibility for proton resonance (p. 212). However, the splitting of the energy levels, even in the most favourable case of two configurations of equal energy (compare $NH_3$, p. 213) is so small that no stabilization results (p. 134). This only means, however, that proton resonance has no influence on the bond energy. The proton resonance does

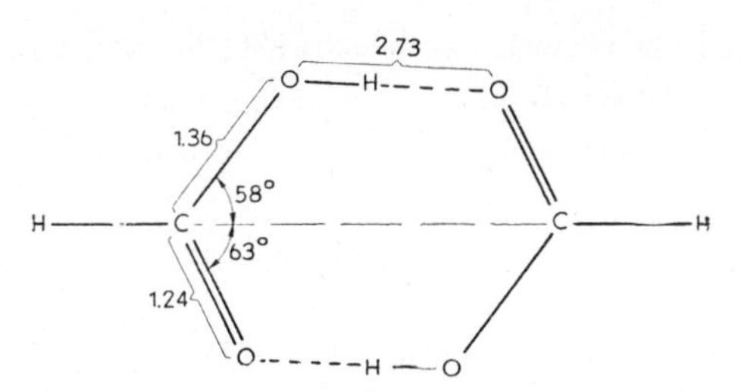


Fig. 32. The dimer of formic acid.
Distance O—H 1.07 Å, compared with 0.97 Å in the monomer.

play a part in other phenomena, as in the large mobility of $H^+$ and $OH^-$ ions in water and in the mechanism of the over-potential of hydrogen. Classical transfer of the proton as an $OH_3^+$ ion would lead to a mobility of the $H^+$ ion comparable to that of the $NH_4^+$ ion. Transfer by proton resonance (BERNAL and FOWLER, 1933), that is, tunnelling through the potential barrier separating the two positions of the hydrogen atom in the O—H...O bond, would be much faster than corresponds to the observed mobility. Moreover the ratio of the mobilities of $H^+$ and $D^+$ ions would be expected to be much larger than the observed value of 1.41.

The rate determining reaction (preceded and succeeded by fast tunnelling of protons) is probably the rotation of water molecules near the $OH_3^+$ ion to a position where the proton can jump over (CONWAY, BOCKRIS and LINTON, 1956).

The high dielectric constant of water, as well as that of ice, does not depend on proton resonance since it is high for both $H_2O$ and $D_2O$. In ice, as well as in "heavy" ice, it appears from the frequency- and temperature-dependence of the dielectric constant that the activation energy, associated with the orientation of dipoles in an alternating electric field, is equal to 13.2 kcal/mole (MAGAT, 1948; AUTY and COLE, 1952). This points to the rupture of three hydrogen bonds (p. 416).

From nuclear magnetic resonance spectra it can be concluded on the other hand, that in the absence of an electrolyte the mobility of the proton in alcohols and liquid ammonia is very small. However, traces of $OH^-$ ions in alcohol or of water in ammonia ($H_2O + NH_3 \rightarrow OH^- + NH_4^+$) cause rapid proton exchange by ionic reactions (ARNOLD, 1956; OGG, 1954, 1957).

Measurements of deuterium exchange in quinhydrone (GRAGEROV and BRODSKY cited by CANNON, 1958) and of conductivity in solids, *e.g.*, oxalic acid and benzoic acid (MCPOLLOCK and UBBELOHDE, 1956) have also led to high activation energies for proton transfer of 20–40 kcal.

The duality of the position of the hydrogen atom in a hydrogen bond leads to a large number of complexions for the possible distribution of the protons in ice; this furnishes an extra entropy of R ln 3/2 (PAULING, 1935; PITZER and POLISSAR, 1956). This random distribution has been confirmed by neutron diffraction from heavy ice (PETERSON and LEVY, 1953; 1957).

It has also been suggested that electron resonance might play a part in the hydrogen bond. It is then assumed that the bonds in Fig. 32 between hydroxyl oxygen and hydrogen and the second bonds between carbonyl oxygen and carbon are displaced one place in the ring similarly to the transition from the one KEKULÉ configuration to the other in benzene. This is, however, excluded in this case since this configuration has a much higher energy than the normal valence structure as a result of the abnormal bond distances such as OH: 1.76 Å. (Nuclei must be arranged in both configurations in the same way!) The contribution of this configuration has been estimated as 4% only. This contribution would be more important for a shorter, symmetrical hydrogen bond (p. 414).

The eccentric position of the dipole in these groups, to which attention had already been drawn by VAN ARKEL, gives a better indication regarding the cause of the effect.

The electrostatic, ionogenic explanation of the "hydrogen bond" has found general acceptance. We might replace the somewhat misleading term, which does not indicate a special type of bond, by "hydrogen bridge". This last term, however, is already used to indicate the special function of hydrogen in the boron-hydrides (p. 248).

VAN ARKEL and DE BOER regard the formation of the bifluoride ion $[HF_2]^-$ from KF and HF $\rightarrow KHF_2$ as an analogue of the reaction $KF + BF_3 \rightarrow KBF_4$. In the last case the coordination number of the trivalent boron with respect to fluorine is equal to four in agreement with the electrostatic calculation. The monovalent, but extremely small hydrogen ion also has a higher coordination number, namely two.

The same phenomenon of a coordination number two appears in the other groups OH and NH in so far as and to the extent that the hydrogen atom is present as a positive ion. The ability to form hydrogen bonds thus decreases with decreasing ionogenic character of the bond. As a consequence of decreasing electronegativity in the series FH, OH, NH, CH also the tendency decreases to form hydrogen bonds. The C—H bond is almost a pure atomic bond; only in rare cases (HCN) is there a possibility for the formation of hydrogen bonds. For example in chloroform $CHCl_3$ the hydrogen atom obtains a somewhat stronger positive charge through the strong electronegative character of the three chlorine atoms. In the systems chloroform-acetone and chloroform-dioxan this bridge formation C—H...O is seen from the positive heat of mixing, the infrared spectrum and other properties (HILDEBRAND and SCOTT, 1950; SAROLEA-MATHOT, 1953; HUGGINS, PIMENTEL and SHOOLERY, 1955; MCGLASHAN and RASTOGI, 1958). Again the high solubility of acetylene $C_2H_2$ in organic solvents (acetone!) indicates H-bond formation. GORDY has also shown that this solubility of $C_2H_2$ is a measure of the acceptor action. The charge distribution in $C_2H_2$ which causes this tendency to hydrogen bond formation has already been discussed on p. 240.

The tendency to form hydrogen bonds is much smaller in the elements of the second row of the Periodic System, such as chlorine and sulphur. The bond has a less ionogenic character here. The hydrogen atom is not situated much deeper in the electron cloud; compare the VAN DER WAALS radii of $F^-$, $O^{2-}$, $Cl^-$ and $S^{2-}$ of 1.35, 1.45, 1.80 and 1.90 A with the nuclear distance in the hydrogen compounds of 0.92, 0.97, 1.27 and 1.35 A, respectively.

Hydrogen sulphide (b.pt. —61.8°) is not associated like water (b.pt. 100°); no more than HCl (b.pt. —83.7°) compared with HF (b.pt. 19.4°). For a normal behaviour, the compounds mentioned in the second place ought to possess a lower boiling point since the LONDON contribution is lower for the atoms with a lower atomic number. $NH_3$ is only weakly associated; the b.pt. (—33.3°) is only a little higher than that of $PH_3$(b.pt. —87.4°); $CH_4$ boils, quite normally, at a lower temperature than $SiH_4$, namely at —161.5° compared with —111.8°.

Attention may be drawn to the fact that there is no direct connection between ionogenic character of the X-H bond and acidity as the degree of dissociation in water ($HCl > HF$, $H_2S > H_2O$); hydrogen bond formation depends on the first-mentioned property.

Further, mercaptan is not associated (however, see SPURR and BYERS, 1958) and also not miscible with water; $CH_3SH$ b.pt. +6°, $CH_3OH$ b.pt. +65°. However, HCl does form compounds by bridge formation, for example with ethers, $(CH_3)_2$ O.HCl. The sulphur and halogen atoms are also much less effective than oxygen and fluorine as acceptors. The sequence is $I < Br < Cl < F$, $NO_2$, $C = O$, $NO_2$. Thus in 6-chloro-2,4-dinitrophenol a hydrogen-bridge is only formed with the nitro group (HOYER, 1956).

The formation of hydrogen bonds is manifested most directly and most clearly in the infrared absorption spectrum. In crystals (from X-ray analysis) and molecules (electron diffraction) a distance between two oxygen atoms of different molecules or groups which is shorter than 2.85 Å is also an indication for the presence of a hydrogen bond. There is a close relation between the decrease in frequency of the association band (see below), the decrease of the O—O distance (p. 422) and the increase of hydrogen bond energy (Table 37). The accompanying increase of the O—H distance (Fig. 32) is less easily detected because of the difficulty of ascertaining the position of hydrogen atom by X-ray and electron diffraction methods. Neutron diffraction and proton magnetic resonance are more powerful (RICHARDS, 1956). The chemical shift in proton magnetic resonance changes also if the hydrogen atom takes part in the formation of a hydrogen bond (GUTOWSKY and SAIKA, 1953; HUGGINS, PIMENTEL and SHOOLERY, 1956).

The characteristic absorption band, which corresponds to the OH valence vibration for the free group, is situated at about 2.7 μ or 3600—3700 $cm^{-1}$. This is observed in the gaseous state and in very dilute solutions in non-polar solvents (such as $CS_2$, hexane and $CCl_4$, but not dioxan with two partial dipole moments) for water, alcohols and organic acids.

At higher concentrations and *a fortiori* in the pure liquid this band is replaced by a much broader band, the association band, at longer wave lengths (3.0 to 3.3 μ).

*Water:* vapour 3756, 3652 $cm^{-1}$; dilute solution 3702, 3611 $cm^{-1}$; liquid 3455, 3430 $cm^{-1}$; ice 3256, 3156 $cm^{-1}$; the number mentioned last is each time the frequency of the symmetrical vibration, observed in the RAMAN effect.

*Methyl alcohol:* vapour 3682 $cm^{-1}$, dilute solution 3660 $cm^{-1}$, liquid 3356 $cm^{-1}$, solid 3200 $cm^{-1}$.

*Formic acid* (see p. 405): monomer 3570 $cm^{-1}$, dimer 3080 $cm^{-1}$.

The frequency is lowered by 250–500 $cm^{-1}$ as a result of bridge formation; the restoring force of the normal OH bond is reduced by the electrostatic attraction acting in the opposite direction due to the acceptor atom of the bridge. The lengthening of the O—H distance also causes a decrease of the force constant (BAUER and MAGAT, 1938).

The frequency of the deformation vibration is connected with the motion of the hydrogen atom perpendicular to the direction of the bridge; this is raised through the attraction of the proton acceptor atom (1595 $cm^{-1}$ for $H_2O$ free, and 1640 $cm^{-1}$ for $H_2O$ liquid).

At suitably chosen concentrations the absorption bands of the free groups and of groups bound by the hydrogen bond formation are present simultaneously (Fig. 33). The former is a narrow band; the latter is appreciably broader owing to the appreciable fluctuations in distance and orientation of the groups forming the bridge, associated with the small bond energy of about 6 kcal/mole.

Another cause for the width of the association band in solution is the overlapping of the slightly displaced bands of polymers of different degree of polymerization. For methanol in $CCl_4$ solution the monomer band is found at 3662 $cm^{-1}$ with bands at 3525 $cm^{-1}$ and 3341 $cm^{-1}$ for the dimer and the trimer (KUHN, 1952, 1954). The results are derived from the changes in the fine structure of the association band with the increase of concentration. In a matrix of solid nitrogen at 20° K the monomer band of methanol is found at 3660 $cm^{-1}$ with bands at 3490, 3445, 3290 and 3250 $cm^{-1}$ for dimer, trimer, tetramer and higher polymers respectively. (VAN THIEL, BECKER and PIMENTEL, 1957).

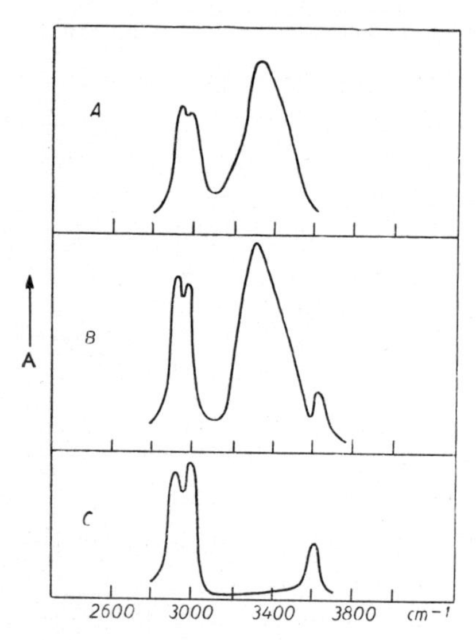


Fig. 33. Infrared absorption spectrum of ethanol in $CCl_4$ with the association band (3300 $cm^{-1}$, broad) and the band of the CH groups (about 2900 $cm^{-1}$, double: symmetric and antisymmetric vibration) and with the band of the free OH group (3600 $cm^{-1}$). A: pure liquid; B: 0.42 mole/l; C: 0.006 mole/l (BUSWELL, DEITZ and RODEBUSH, 1937).

It is possible to determine the concentration of the free groups as a function of the total concentration by careful intensity measurements. The association equilibrium can thus also be determined. This is especially interesting in linear association, *e.g.*, in phenol where polymeric molecules occur which can contain up to 10–20 molecules of phenol (KEMPTER and MECKE, 1940; MECKE, 1950). The percentage monomer $\alpha_m$ and the average degree of polymerization $\bar{n}$ in $CCl_4$ solutions of phenol was calculated at different concentrations:

| $c$ | $\alpha_m$ | $\bar{n}$ |
|---|---|---|
| 0.0375 mole/l | 86.1 % | 1.15 |
| 0.3 ,, | 47.0 % | 1.92 |
| 3.0 ,, | 10.1 % | 4.65 |
| 6.0 ,, | 5.4 % | ~ 8 |

Not only is the fundamental frequency of the OH vibration (~ 3500 $cm^{-1}$) displaced towards lower values, but also the harmonic vibrations at 7000 $cm^{-1}$ and 10500 $cm^{-1}$ show the same change on the formation of hydrogen bonds.

A similar displacement occurs with the NH frequency though to a lesser degree. The 2nd harmonic of the fundamental frequency (that is $3\nu_{NH}$) for aniline is situated at 9853 $cm^{-1}$ for the vapour, at 9825 $cm^{-1}$ for a dilute solution in $CCl_4$, but in the pure liquid the band is displaced to 9719 $cm^{-1}$ as a consequence of the formation of hydrogen bonds. The displacement is very small in ammonia: gas 3334 $cm^{-1}$, liquid 3300 $cm^{-1}$.

There are two possibilities of formation of hydrogen bonds in the solution of ammonia in water: N — H...O and N... H — O. The latter case is realized in agreement with expectation; in fact nitrogen is a better acceptor (more strongly basic) than oxygen, the OH group a stronger donor (more acidic) than NH. Therefore, ammonia hydrate occurs in a solution of ammonia but ammonium hydroxide does not exist (VAN VELDEN and KETELAAR, 1947).

*Intramolecular hydrogen bond*

The influence of the internal hydrogen bond formation on the absorption spectrum and the physical and chemical properties is manifested especially in the dilute state where this effect, in contrast to the formation of intermolecular hydrogen bonds, is still present. Thus the two kinds can be distinguished experimentally.

Besides a polarly bound hydrogen, as in the OH, NH and

$NH_2$ groups, a negative atom with a lone pair of electrons (usually oxygen or nitrogen, to a much smaller extent also chlorine) is necessary as proton acceptor (comparison of proton acceptor power, GORDY, 1939; GORDY and STANFORD, 1940, 1941).

The occurrence of this bridge formation or chelation (derived from the crab's claw as a picture of the hydrogen atom clamped between two atoms) is further dependent on spatial factors. In benzene derivatives an OH group will only be able to give hydrogen bond formation with another OH groups, with a carboxyl group (free or esterified), with a carbonyl group or with a nitro group when these groups are in the *ortho* position with respect to the OH group. Groups in the *meta* and *para* positions have no influence since the distance from the hydrogen atom to the other group becomes too great. Other steric factors can also play a part; thus in general the formation of a ring with five or six links is the most favourable for the formation of a bridge. With longer aliphatic chains, *e.g.*, with $\omega\ \omega'$ glycols, a closed ring could be formed without too much strain, but the probability of other conformations of the chain, in which the bridge-forming elements are remote from each other, then becomes predominant (again entropy versus energy!).

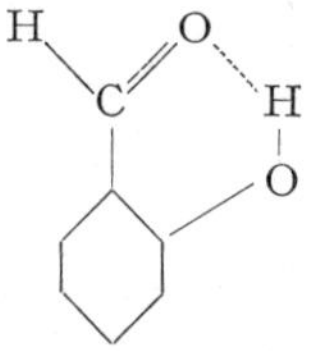

The intramolecular hydrogen bond formation has an important influence on the chemical properties. Thus the *ortho* isomer of the three isomeric hydroxybenzoic acids (salicylic acid) is, as a result of the formation of hydrogen bonds in this substance, less readily soluble in water but more soluble in ether than the other two isomers which themselves do not differ in their properties. The internal hydrogen bond formation has resulted in the outwards action of the OH dipole being diminished; salicylic acid is, as it were, less polar than the other isomers although its total moment is actually the largest. The same holds for the isomers of hydroxybenzaldehyde (salicylaldehyde and isomers), nitrophenol (Table 36), etc. The boiling point will also be lower as a result of the formation of an internal hydrogen bond since the energy of the free *ortho* molecule in particular is lowered, whereas in the liquid state all hydrogen atoms are engaged in hydrogen bonds, either internal or external bonds. Compare b.pt. catechol 245°, resorcinol 277°, hydroquinone 285°, although the total moment decreases again in these cases; and similarly *o*-, *m*- and *p*-nitrophenol, boiling points 214°, 290°, 279° (heat of sublimation: 17.5, 21.9 and 21.0 kcal/mole). The great volatility of *o*-nitrophenol is also evident from its odour and volatility with water vapour. The methyl ethers of the three isomers, on the other hand, all exhibit quite similar properties, as is to be expected.

The hydrogen bond formation has also an influence on the acidities of the above-mentioned hydroxybenzoic acids since the proton attraction of the carboxylate group is partially saturated and the basicity of the anion is therefore smaller. Salicylic acid and, more particularly, 2, 6-dihydroxybenzoic acid are stronger acids than the other isomers (HUNTER, 1953).

The absorption spectra of the vapour and of solutions of molecules such as *o*-iodophenol but not of the other isomers, indicate the presence of two forms, free and bound, or *trans* and *cis*, characterized by the absorption bands at 3650 $cm^{-1}$ and 3577 $cm^{-1}$ (ROSSMY, LÜTTKE and MECKE, 1953).

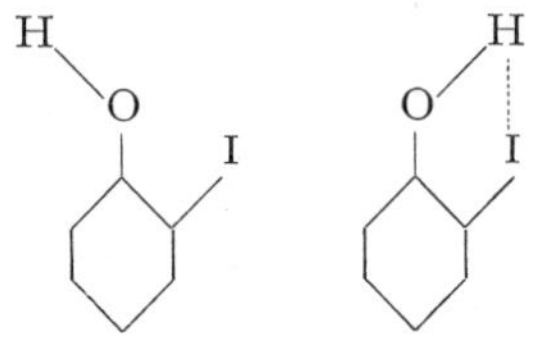

H O I H O I

The former frequency corresponds with that of phenol in dilute solution.

The ratio *cis: trans* is found to amount to 36 : 1 in the vapour at 125° C, from which we find $\Delta F = -2.8$ kcal/mole in favour of the *cis* form. From the change of the ratio *cis: trans* with the temperature it follows that the thermal effect on association amounts here to $\Delta H = -3.2$ kcal/mole. In solution $\Delta F = -1.4$ kcal/mole; the difference from the first-mentioned amount for $\Delta F$ must be attributed to the difference in solvation energy for the two forms, which is larger for the *trans* form. The association naturally decreases with rising temperature as an exothermal process.

Intramolecular hydrogen bonds with a very short O—O distance of 2.46–2.42 Å have been found by X-ray analysis in a number of cases, *e.g.*, nickel- and palladium dimethylglyoxim (GODYCKI, RUNDLE *et al.*, 1951, 1953; RUNDLE and PARASOL, 1952), nickel salicylaldoxime (MERRITT *et al.*, 1956), maleic acid (SHAHAT, 1952) and α, α′-dihydroxynaphtoquinones (BROCKMANN and FRANCK, 1955). The O—H frequency has been shifted to such low frequencies of 1775 $cm^{-1}$ in nickel dimethylglyoxime, that the broad association band is difficult to detect.

These very short hydrogen bonds might be symmetric or very nearly so (compare $HF_2^-$ where, however, the distance is still much shorter, p. 418). The short O—O distance in these molecules is in the first instance not due to the attraction between the hydrogen atom and the proton acceptor atom but to steric conditions, governed by the rest of the molecule. These conditions are, *e.g.*, the planar arrangement of the Ni—N $dsp^2$ bonds (p. 183), the planar *cis* conformation of the maleic acid which furnishes optimal resonance between the C=C bond and the C=O bonds and the plane structure of the naphthoquinone nucleus.

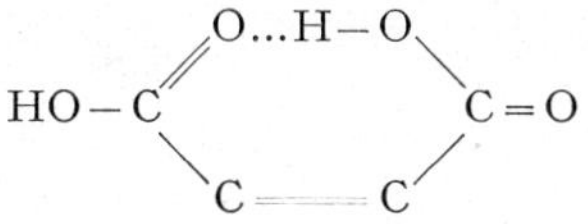

O...H–O
HO–C C=O
C=C

maleic acid (2.46 Å)

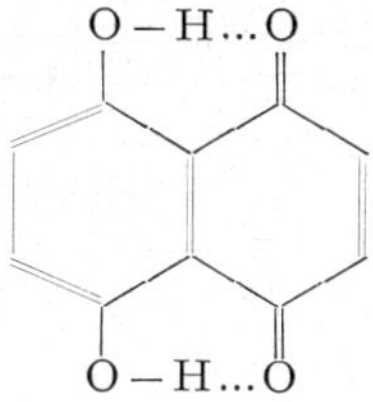

O–H...O
O–H...O

α, α′-dihydroxy naphthoquinone (2.42 Å)

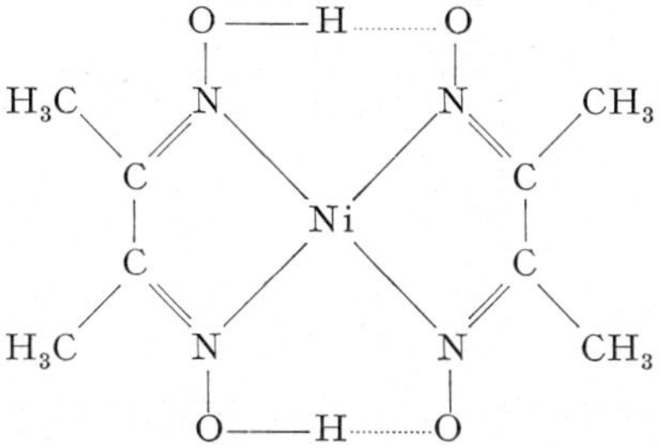

O—H...O
$H_3C$ N N $CH_3$
C C
Ni
C C
$H_3C$ N N $CH_3$
O—H...O

Ni-dimethylglyoxime (2.44 Å)

*Intermolecular hydrogen bonds*

The formation of *inter*molecular hydrogen bonds has a still more striking influence on the physical and chemical properties of the compounds in question (Table 36).

The association of water, hydrofluoric acid, the alcohols, the organic acids, etc., is a consequence of the formation of strong intermolecular hydrogen bonds with a dissociation energy of about 6 kcal/mole. As a result association can occur which leads to the formation of stoichiometrically constituted complexes, such as double molecules. This is the case with the organic acids such as formic acid (Fig. 32), acetic acid and benzoic acid. These double molecules have a small or no resultant dipole moment and the association thus leads to a reduction of the dielectric constant of the liquid. Because the dimer molecule has no free hydrogen atoms, association does not go further. These non-polar double molecules dissolve almost exclusively in the non-polar solvent in the distribution

TABLE 36

INFLUENCE OF HYDROGEN BONDS ON THE PROPERTIES OF ISOMERIC COMPOUNDS

Intramolecular

Solubility ratios *o*-, *m*- and *p*- nitrophenol at 20°

| | water | ethanol | benzene |
|---|---|---|---|
| *o* : *p* | 0.39 | 1.58 | 193 |
| *m* : *p* | 1.84 | 1.00 | 2.76 |

Intermolecular

| | ethanol $C_2H_5OH$ | dimethyl ether $(CH_3)_2O$ |
|---|---|---|
| Latent heat of evap. | 10.19 kcal/mole | 4.45 kcal/mole |
| Boiling point | 78° | — 25° |
| TROUTON constant | 29.0 cal/deg. | 17.9 cal/deg. |

TABLE 37

HYDROGEN BONDS

| | Distance (Å) | Energy (kcal) | Frequency | |
|---|---|---|---|---|
| | | | bound ($cm^{-1}$) | free ($cm^{-1}$) |
| O—H...O | | | | |
| $Ca(OH)_2$ | 3.36 | | 3590 | (3600) |
| $Y(OH)_3$ | 2.90 | | 3470 | (3600) |
| $\gamma$-$Al(OH)_3$ | 2.78 | | 3315 | (3600) |
| Water | 2.85 | 4.5 | 3453 | 3756 |
| Methanol (ethanol) | 2.7 | 6.2 | 3356 | 3682 |
| Ice | 2.76 | 4.5 | 3256 | 3750 |
| Formic acid (dimer) | 2.73 | 7.0 | 3080 | 3570 |
| Pentaerythritol | 2.69 | | 2939 | 3632 |
| $\gamma$-AlOOH | 2.66 | | 2875 | 3600 |
| Salicylic acid | 2.63 | | 2564 | 3700 |
| $NaHCO_3$ | 2.55 | | 2440 | (3533) |
| $KH_2PO_4$ | 2.49 | | 2320 | (3590) |
| Maleic acid | 2.46 | | 2000 | (3533) |
| Ni-dimethylglyoxime | 2.44 | | 1725 | (3590) |
| O—O free | 2.90 | | | |
| F—H...F | | | | |
| HF (gaseous polymer) | 2.55 | 6.7 | 3497, 3380 | 4140 |
| $KHF_2$ | 2.26 | 58 | 1450 | 4140 |
| F—F free | 2.70 | | | |
| N—H...O | | | | |
| Urea | 3.02 | | 3350 | 3448 |
| Diketopiperazine | 2.85 | | 3225 | 3460 |
| Uracil | 2.84 | | 3092 | 3460 |

equilibrium of the acid between, for example, water and benzene. The double molecules are still present in the vapour; consequently the TROUTON "constant" is abnormal in these substances and indeed is too low, so that the entropy of the vapour is lower than normal. However, in solutions where the solvent itself can function as the acceptor for the hydrogen bond (such as ether, dioxan), de-association of the dissolved substance takes place.

Molecular compounds can also be formed by hydrogen bond formation. This holds both for the numerous hydrates and alcoholates of organic compounds and for compounds of phenol, for example, with substances which possess $NH_2$, ROR or $C = O$ groups (HUNTER, 1946).

Non-stoichiometric association can lead to linear complexes or large rings, as in hydrofluoric acid and phenol, or to a three-dimensional spatial ordering as in water and the alcohols. This association gives rise in both cases to a greatly increased dielectric constant as in water, HF, $H_2O_2$, HCN and alcohols (to a much smaller extent in $NH_3$ and $CH_3NH_2$).

Not only the latent heat of evaporation but also the entropy of evaporation is raised (high TROUTON "constant"), because ordering in the liquid signifies a decrease of the entropy of this phase. The increased heat effect predominates, however, so that the boiling point is likewise too high; the viscosity is high (glycerol, sugar), the surface tension also.

The influence of steric factors is seen clearly in the primary, secondary and tertiary amyl alcohols; only the last one is not completely associated, as follows from the presence of a narrow infrared absorption band at a higher frequency. Indeed two molecules of *t*-amyl alcohol can hardly approach one another, but this is possible for the molecular pair *t*-amyl alcohol-methanol; the band of the free OH groups disappears on addition of the small methanol molecule.

The ordering by hydrogen bonds disappears more and more with rising temperature as a result of the increasing thermal agitation. All associated liquids, therefore, approximate more and more to a normal liquid at higher temperatures.

Intermolecular hydrogen bonds are also present in the solid state. The strongest hydrogen bond is found in the bifluoride-ion in $KHF_2$. The F—F distance is only 2.26 Å which is very small compared to 2.70 Å, twice the ionic radius of the fluoride ion. This is the only case in which a symmetric structure F—H—F is certain (WESTRUM and PITZER, 1949; KETELAAR and VEDDER, 1951; PETERSON and LEVY, 1953; WAUGH *et al.*, 1953). The bond energy of the $HF_2^-$-ion can be obtained from the lattice energy; a value of 58 kcal/mole is found (WADDINGTON, 1958). This experimental value is close to the results of calculations of the bond energy for an ionic model of the bifluoride ion with values of 45–57 kcal/mole (DAVIES, 1947; FYFE, 1953; WADDINGton, 1958). The very short distance found is accompanied by a very large shift in the frequency from 4140 $cm^{-1}$ in the HF molecule to 1450 $cm^{-1}$ in $KHF_2$.

In $KH_2PO_4$ a very short O—O distance of 2.49 Å is observed between oxygen atoms of two phosphate groups (see also p. 414 for short internal bonds). The short distance is associated with a considerable lowering of the OH frequency from about 3590 $cm^{-1}$ to 2320 $cm^{-1}$ for the maximum of the extremely broad absorption band of the crystal. The deformation frequency is raised, however, from about 1400 $cm^{-1}$ to 1575 $cm^{-1}$.

In the inorganic hydroxides hydrogen bond formation is detected again by a shift in the frequency of the OH infrared absorption band. In some hydroxides, *e.g.*, $Ca(OH)_2$ and $Mg(OH)_2$, this frequency is found at 3600 $cm^{-1}$ in the absence of hydrogen bonding; the O—O distance here is large: 3.3–3.2 Å. With decreasing O—O distance an influence on the OH frequency is already detected for the $OH^-$-ion at slightly larger distances than for the hydroxyl groups in organic molecules (Table 37) (GLEMSER and HARTERT, 1956). This must be attributed to a slightly greater size of the $OH^-$-ion.

A bridge of the type N—H. . . O=C, such as occurs in urea, uracil and diketopiperazine, is of interest for a correct concep-

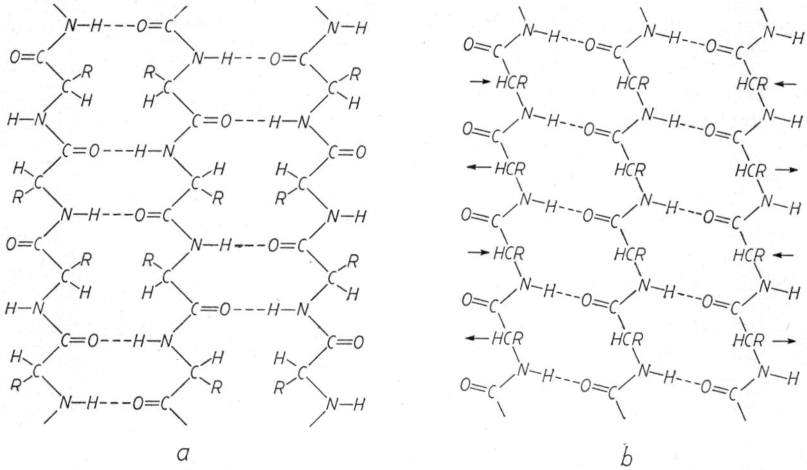

Fig. 34. Protein chains in the stretched state (silk, β-keratin) with O . . . H hydrogen bonds.

(a) Polypeptide layer with alternately oriented chains, according to ASTBURY (1933, 1940). The layer is entirely flat, the residues R point upwards and downwards alternately, so that the configurations around the optically active α-carbon atoms are the same.

(b) Polypeptide layer with similarly oriented chains, according to PAULING and COREY (1951). The plane through the two chain bonds of the α-carbon atom is vertical in (b) instead of horizontal as in (a). The layer is "pleated" about the lines indicated by → ← (down) and → ← (up).

The chains are folded in the contracted α-state or they form spirals through the presence of hydrogen bridges between a C = O group and a N—H group within the same chain (PAULING and COREY, 1953).

tion of the secondary bonds of the proteins besides the primary (principal) valence chains of the proteins. Intermolecular hydrogen bonds occur as bonds between the chains (backbone linkage of about 4.5 Å) Fig. 34. In hair (wool) there are in addition the S — S bonds of the cystine residues, which form a cross linkage ≈ 10 Å perpendicular to the plane of Fig. 34. (BERNAL and CARLISLE, 1955; *Fibrous Proteins and their Biological Significance, Symposia Soc. Exptl. Biol., Cambridge, 1955;* KAUZMANN, 1957).

*Ice and water.* The water molecule has an approximately tetrahedral charge distribution: two positive charges at the positions of the hydrogen atoms ($\angle$ HOH $= 104°27'$, O—H 0.958 Å) and two negative charges arising from the two pairs of lone electrons in hybrid orbitals with nearly an $sp^3$ character (p. 170 and 303) (BERNAL and FOWLER, 1933; MAGAT, 1936; VERWEY, 1941, 1942; BURNELLE and COULSON, 1957).

The crystal structures of the modifications of ice show a similarity to the structures of the modifications of $SiO_2$; each water molecule is tetrahedrally surrounded by four others (OWSTON, 1951). Each water molecule acts as a proton donor for two hydrogen bonds and as a proton acceptor for two other hydrogen bonds. Ordinary ice has an O—O distance of 2.76 Å and an O—H distance equal to 1.01 Å. The energy $\Delta U$ of sublimation of ice ($\Delta H = 12.23$ kcal/mole thus $\Delta U =$ 11.69 kcal/mole) contains about 3 kcal of cohesion energy due to London attraction, leaving 8.7 kcal for the energy of rupture of two hydrogen bonds per molecule. As the (latent) heat of fusion ($\Delta H \approx \Delta U$) is only 1.44 kcal/mole apparently, only a fraction of the hydrogen bonds is broken on melting. However, the heat of activation for dipole rotation in ice is considerably higher with 13.2 kcal/mole (p. 405) as now three bonds have to be broken.

Normal ice is analogous to tridymite; water is supposed to have mostly a quartz-like structure with a higher density (BERNAL and FOWLER, 1933). The occurrence of the density maximum at 4°, a unique property of water, must then be attributed to the gradual transition of the remaining tridymite structure into the quartzlike structure, while at higher temperatures the normal thermal expansion again predominates.

However, the average O—O distance as found from X-ray diffraction in water is about 3.1 Å and the shortest distances (hydrogen bonds) are probably around 2.85 Å and thus much longer than in ice. To reconcile these longer distances with the higher density of water as compared to ice, one is led to assume that water has a coordination number higher than four, *e.g.*, six with four neighbours at 2.85 Å joined by hydrogen bonds and two other water molecules at about 3.6 Å (VAN PANTHALEON VAN ECK *et al.*, 1957, 1958).

According to both of these pictures there is no question of definite stoichiometrically constituted associations such as dihydrol and trihydrol which were formerly assumed to be present in liquid water.

EUCKEN (1948), however, in his careful interpretation of the specific heat, compressibility etc. of water, assumes again the presence of $(H_2O)_2$, $(H_2O)_4$ and $(H_2O)_8$ polymers without excluding in principle the presence of intermediate ones. He ascribes to the 8-polymers a larger specific volume and thus these are equivalent to the tridymite groups mentioned. He calculated on the basis of the mass law that the mole fraction of the 8-polymers decreases from 0.376 at 0° C, 0.245 at 20° C, 0.0218 at 100° C to 0.008 at 200° C.

The same treatment leads to an average degree of polymerization for the chain-like polymers in ethanol of $\bar{n} = 4.6$ at 20° C (methanol $\bar{n} = 4.8$) which is in good accordance with infrared data.

According to X-ray investigation the lower alcohols also have partially a quasi-crystalline structure similar to that of water.

The formation of such a quasi-crystalline structure leads to the production of glasses at low temperatures for the same reasons as with inorganic glasses such as quartz and silicates. Indeed the lower alcohols and especially the poly-alcohols (*e.g.* glycerol) readily produce glasses on cooling. With water a glass is only formed under special conditions to ensure very rapid cooling to liquid air temperatures.

The hydrogen bond appears to be of essential importance for the physical and chemical properties of the vast majority of the compounds, in the first place water, and plays a significant part both in the living organism and in technical processes.

## § 46. THE NATURE OF THE HYDROGEN BOND

The electrostatic interaction of the proton with the electronegative proton acceptor atom Y forms undoubtedly the main contribution to the hydrogen bond energy for the so-called long bonds (O—O above 2.75 Å). However, for very short distances (2.42–2.45 Å) with a symmetric X—H—Y bond ($HF_2^-$, Ni-dimethylglyoxime, maleate ion) or a nearly symmetric hydrogen bond (maleic acid), (electron) resonance certainly will play an important part.

The relation between the X—H infrared absorption frequency and the X—Y distance has been shown to be a continuous function which for the O—H...O bond is very nearly linear if the hydroxides are excluded (Fig. 35). (LORD and MERRIFIELD, 1953; RUNDLE and PARASOL, 1952; NAKAMOTO,

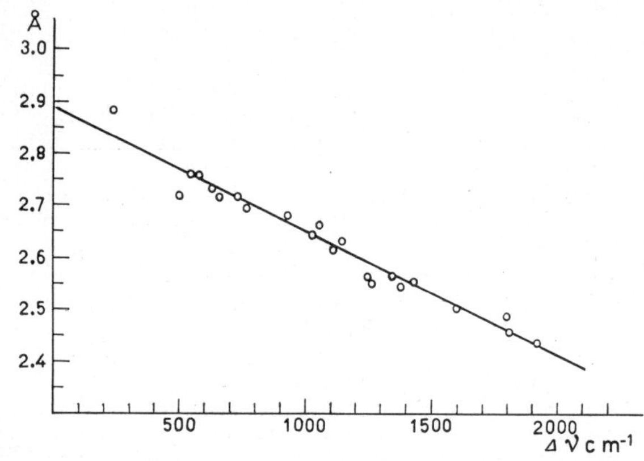


Fig. 35. Frequency shift versus O—O bond distance for O—H...O hydrogen bonds (NAKAMOTO, MARGOSHES and RUNDLE, 1955).

MARGOSHES and RUNDLE, 1955; PIMENTEL and SEDERHOLM, 1956; WELSH, 1957). Also a relation of the bond energy and of the X—H distance with the X—Y distance is found (WELSH, 1957). From the latter relation it can be deduced that the OHO band will be symmetric for an O—O distance of 2.45 Å. In $KH_2PO_4$ the OH and O—O distances as found by neutron diffraction are 1.07 Å and 2.49 Å respectively, so that a distance of only 0.35 Å would separate the two equilibrium positions for the hydrogen atom (BACON and PEASE, 1955; PETERSON *et al.*, 1954).

The OH infrared absorption band is not only shifted to longer wavelengths on association but also its (integrated) intensity is increased considerably (HUGGINS and PIMENTEL, 1956). The large width of the band, not only in liquids but also in crystals (even at low temperatures) has not yet found a satisfactory explanation (COULSON, 1957; CANNON, 1958).

Tsubomura (1955, 1956) has enumerated four possible contributions to the hydrogen bond energy which are for ice (Coulson, 1957):

| | |
|---|---|
| *a.* Electrostatic interaction | 6 kcal |
| *b.* London interaction | 2.7 |
| *c.* Exchange repulsion | —8.4 |
| *d.* Resonance or delocalization energy | 8 |
| For one bond total (theor.) | 8.3 kcal; exp. 5.85 kcal. |

An apparent correspondence between the observed energy and the value calculated for the energy of the electrostatic interaction might be fortuitous if, *e.g.*, (*c*) and (*d*) cancel, without both being much smaller than (*a*).

It will be necessary to consider the contribution (*d*) from resonance.

Pauling (1949) first considered the O—H. . .O system as a resonance hybrid of three configurations.

| | | |
|---|---|---|
| 1. valence bond | $O_A$—H | $\vert O_B$ |
| 2. ionic | $O_A\vert^{\ominus}$ $H^{\oplus}$ | $\vert O_B$ |
| 3. charge transfer, valence bond | $O_A\vert^{\ominus}$ H ——— | $O_B^{\oplus}$ |

He estimated the contributions of the three configurations as 65, 33 and 2% for an O—O distance of 2.8 Å. However, at a distance of 2.5 Å the third configuration would contribute to 10% to the charge distributions. Coulson and Danielsson (1954, Coulson, 1957) made more refined calculations and obtained for the contribution of the third configuration 3% at 2.8 Å and 6% at 2.5 Å. They concluded that the bonding is indeed essentially electrostatic.

However, the increase in intensity of the infrared absorption band indicates an appreciable change in the charge distribution of the $O_A$—H bond as a result of the increase of the $O_A$—H distance and the electrostatic attraction by $O_B$, which will lead to an increase of the effective charge on the hydrogen atom (and on the oxygen atom), *i.e.* an increase in the contribution of the second configuration.

The most complete quantitative discussion of the hydrogen

bond has been given by LIPPINCOTT and SCHROEDER (LIPPINCOTT and SCHROEDER, 1955; SCHROEDER and LIPPINCOTT, 1957). From a one-dimensional model based on an accurate potential function they were able to calculate the OH frequency shifts, O—H bond distances, hydrogen bond energies and the low OH....O frequencies ($\approx$ 200 $cm^{-1}$), all as a function of the O—O distance. Excellent agreement was obtained with the experimental data. A considerable increase of the effective charge on the oxygen atoms with decreasing O—O distance is also calculated. In these calculations essentially only the configurations 1 and 3 are taken into account, with the electrostatic interaction being included in the energy of configuration 1. According to LIPPINCOTT and SCHROEDER the electrostatic term does not make a major contribution of the energy but does allow a closer approach of the oxygen atoms.

However, this conclusion and that of COULSON (1957) cited above do not contradict each other.

It can be seen from the energy balance for ice given above that one may just as well say that the electrostatic attraction just overcomes the repulsion, so that the hydrogen bond energy is almost equal to the resonance energy or that the resonance energy and the repulsive energy cancel, so that the electrostatic energy provides the dominating contribution to the hydrogen bond energy!

The lone pairs of electrons on atom Y also play an important role in the formation of a hydrogen bond. If these electrons were to occupy an s-orbital with spherical symmetry, no directional influence would be exercised by atom Y. However, in most cases the lone pairs occupy hybrid orbitals (p. 170) and the negative charge protrudes in certain directions as discussed above for the water molecule. The effect of the directional influence exerted is illustrated by the zig-zag chain structure of the HF polymers in the vapour and the solid state with an angle of 120° (ATOJI and LIPSCOMB, 1954; SCHNEIDER, 1955; FYFE, 1953).

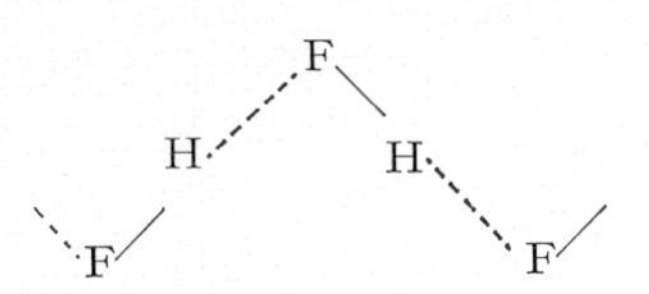


The criteria for the formation of hydrogen bonds: X—H...Y may now be summarized:

1. The hydrogen bond must be bound to an electronegative atom X, leading to a partial ionic character of the X—H bond. This also involves that part of the 1 s orbital on the hydrogen is available for overlap with the lone pair orbital of Y.

2. The Y-atom must have lone pair electrons in an asymmetric orbital, *e.g.*, $sp^3$ orbitals. This means both a dipole with an external negative pole and a greater overlap. A low ionization potential will promote resonance.

3. The X—H bond and the axis of the lone pair orbital must be collinear for maximum attraction by resonance because of maximum overlap, and by electrostatic interaction.

## LITERATURE

G. Briegleb, *Zwischenmolekulare Kräfte und Molekülstruktur*, Karlsruhe, 1949.
G. Darmois, *L'état liquide de la matière*, Paris, 1943.
J. H. Hildebrand and R. L. Scott, *The Solubility of Non-Electrolytes*, 3rd Ed., New York, 1950.
L. Pauling, *The Nature of the Chemical Bond*, 2nd Ed., Ithaca, 1944.

## REFERENCES

Andrews, L. J., *Chem. Revs.*, *54* (1954) 713.
Andrews, L. J. and Keefer, R. M., *J. Am. Chem. Soc.*, *72* (1950) 4677, 5170; *73* (1951) 463; *74* (1952) 458, 1891, 4500; *77* (1955) 2164.
Arnold, J. T., *Phys. Rev.*, *102* (1956) 136.
Astbury, W. T., *Trans. Faraday Soc.*, *29* (1933) 193; *36* (1940) 871.
Aten Jr., A. H. W., *J. Chem. Phys.*, *5* (1937) 260, 264, 598.
Atoji, M. and Lipscomb, W. N., *Acta Cryst.*, *7* (1954) 173.
Auty, R. P. and Cole, R. H., *J. Chem. Phys.*, *20* (1952) 1309.

Bacon, G. E. and Pease, R. S., *Proc. Roy. Soc. (London)*, *A 230* (1955) 359.
Barrer, R. M., *Nature*, *178* (1956) 1410.
Bauer, E., *J. chim. phys.*, *46* (1949) 420.
Bauer, E. and Magat, M., *J. phys. radium*, *9* (1938) 319.
Benesi, H. A. and Hildebrand, J. H., *J. Am. Chem. Soc.*, *70* (1948) 2832; *71* (1949) 2703.

BERNAL, J. D. and CARLISLE, C. H., *Ann. Repts. on Progr. Chem. (Chem. Soc. London)*, *52* (1955) 380.
BERNAL, J. D. and FOWLER, R. H., *J. Chem. Phys.*, *1* (1933) 515.
BIER, A., *Rec. trav. chim.*, *75* (1956) 866.
BRACKMAN, W., *Rec. trav. chim.*, *68* (1949) 147.
BRIEGLEB, G., *Zwischenmolekulare Kräfte und Molekülstruktur*, Karlsruhe, 1949.
BROCKMANN, H. and FRANCK, B., *Naturwissenschaften*, *42* (1955) 487.
BRÖNSTED, J. N. and KOEFOED, J. K., *Kgl. Danske Videnskab. Selskab., Mat.-fys. Medd.*, *22* (1946) Nr. 17.
BURNELLE, L. and COULSON, C. A., *Trans. Faraday Soc.*, *53* (1957) 403.
BUSWELL, A. M., DEITZ, V. and RODEBUSH, W. H., *J. Chem. Phys.*, *5* (1937) 501.

CANNON, C. G., *Spectrochim. Acta*, *10* (1958) 341.
CASIMIR, H. B. G. and POLDER, D., *Phys. Rev.*, *73* (1948) 360.
CLAUSEN, W. F., *J. Chem. Phys.*, *19* (1951) 1425.
CLEVER, H. L. *et al.*, *J. Phys. Chem.*, *61* (1957) 1078; *62* (1958) 375.
COLLIN, J. and D'OR, L., *J. Chem. Phys.*, *23* (1955) 397.
CONWAY, B. E., BOCKRIS, J. O. M. and LINTON, H., *J. Chem. Phys.*, *24* (1956) 835.
COULSON, C. A., *Research (London)*, *10* (1957) 149.
COULSON, C. A. and DANIELSSON, U., *Arkiv Fysik*, *8* (1954) 239, 245.
CRAMER, F., *Angew. Chem.*, *64* (1952) 347; *68* (1956) 115.
CRAMER, F., *Einschluszverbindungen*, Berlin, 1954.
CRAMER, F., *Rec. trav. chim.*, *75* (1956) 891.
CRAMER, F. and HERBST, W., *Naturwissenschaften*, *39* (1952) 256.
CROMWELL, T. M. and SCOTT, R. L., *J. Am. Chem. Soc.*, *72* (1950) 3825.

DALLINGA, G., *Acta Cryst.*, *7* (1954) 665.
DAVIES, M. M., *Ann. Repts. on Progr. Chem. (Chem. Soc. London)*, *43* (1946) 5.
DAVIES, M. M., *J. Chem. Phys.*, *15* (1947) 739.
DE BOER, J. H., *Trans. Faraday Soc.*, *32* (1936) 10.
DE BOER, J. H., and CUSTERS, J. F. H., *Z. physik. Chem.*, *B 25* (1934) 225.
DERYAGUIN, B. V., *Trans. Faraday Soc.*, *36* (1940) 203, 730.
DERYAGUIN, B. V. and ABRIKOSSOVA, I. I., *J. Phys. and Chem. Solids*, *5* (1958) 1.
DIJKGRAAF, C., 1957, not published.
DONOHUE, J., *J. Phys. Chem.*, *56* (1952) 502.

EUCKEN, A., *Die Chemie (Angew. Chemie)*, *55* (1942) 163.
EUCKEN, A., *Z. Elektrochem.*, *52* (1948) 255.
EVANS, D. and RICHARDS, R., *Proc. Roy. Soc. (London)*, *A 223* (1954) 238.
EVANS, D. F., *J. Chem. Soc.*, (1957) 1351, 3885.

FAHRENFORT, J. and KETELAAR, J. A. A., *J. Chem. Phys.*, *22* (1954) 1631.
FAIRBROTHER, F., *Nature*, *160* (1947) 87; *J. Chem. Soc.*, (1948) 1051.
FLORY, P. J., *J. Chem. Phys.*, *10* (1942) 51.
FYFE, W. S., *J. Chem. Phys.*, *21* (1953) 2.

GLASSTONE, S., LAIDLER, K. J. and EYRING, H., *The Theory of Rate Processes*, New York, 1941.
GLEMSER, O. and HARTERT, E., *Z. anorg. u. allgem. Chem.*, *283* (1956) 111.
GODYCKI, L. E., RUNDLE, R. E. *et al.*, *J. Chem. Phys.*, *19* (1951) 1205; *Acta Cryst.*, *6* (1953) 487.
GORDY, W., *J. Chem. Phys.*, *7* (1939) 93.
GORDY, W. and STANFORD, S. C., *J. Chem. Phys.*, *8* (1940) 170; *9* (1941) 204.
GUGGENHEIM, E. A., *Mixtures*, Oxford, 1952.
GUTOWSKY, H. S. and SAIKA, A., *J. Chem. Phys.*, *21* (1953) 1688.

HAASE, R., *Z. Elektrochem.*, *55* (1951) 29.
HAASE, R., *Thermodynamik der Mischphasen*, Berlin, 1956.
HAMAKER, H. C., *Physica*, *4* (1937) 1058.
HILDEBRAND, J. H., *Chem. Revs.*, *44* (1949) 37.
HILDEBRAND, J. H. and GLEW, D. N., *J. Phys. Chem.*, *60* (1956) 618.
HILDEBRAND, J. H. and SCOTT, R. L., *The Solubility of Non-Electrolytes*, New York, 1950.
HOARD, J. L., *Acta Cryst.*, *4* (1951) 396, 399, 405.
HOYER, H., *Z. Elektrochem.*, *49* (1943) 97.
HOYER, H., *Chem. Ber.*, *89* (1956) 146.
HUGGINS, C. M. and PIMENTEL, G. C., *J. Phys. Chem.*, *60* (1956) 1615.
HUGGINS, C. M., PIMENTEL, G. C. and SHOOLERY, J. N., *J. Chem. Phys.*, *23* (1955) 1244; *J. Phys. Chem.*, *60* (1956) 1311.
HUGGINS, M. L., *J. Org. Chem.*, *1* (1936) 407.
HUNTER, L., *Ann. Repts. on Progr. Chem. (Chem. Soc. London)*, *43* (1946) 141; *Chem. & Ind. (London)*, *17* (1953) 154.

JAMES, A. T. and MARTIN, A. J. P., *Biochem. J.*, *50* (1952) 679.

KALLMANN, H. and WILLSTÄTTER, M., *Naturwissenschaften*, *20* (1932) 952.
KAUZMANN, W., *Ann. Rev. Phys. Chem.*, *8* (1957) 413.
KELLNER, C., *Repts. Progr. Phys.*, *15* (1952) 1.
KEMPTER, H. and MECKE, R., *Z. physik. Chem.*, *B 46* (1940) 229.
KETELAAR, J. A. A., *J. phys. radium*, *15* (1954) 197.
KETELAAR, J. A. A., *Rec. trav. chim.*, *75* (1956) 857.
KETELAAR, J. A. A. and JIBBEN, B., *Rec. trav. chim.*, *67* (1948) 393.
KETELAAR, J. A. A. and LOOPSTRA, B. O., *Rec. trav. chim.*, *74* (1955) 113.
KETELAAR, J. A. A. and VAN DE STOLPE, C., *Rec. trav. chim.*, *71* (1952) 805.
KETELAAR, J. A. A., VAN DE STOLPE, C. and GERSMANN, H. R., *Rec. trav. chim.*, *70* (1951) 499.
KETELAAR, J. A. A., VAN DE STOLPE, C., GOUDSMIT, A. and DZCUBAS, W., *Rec. trav. chim.*, *71* (1952) 1104.
KETELAAR, J. A. A. and VEDDER, W., *J. Chem. Phys.*, *19* (1951) 654.
KEULEMANS, A. I. M., *Gas Chromatography*, New York, 1957.
KLAGES, F., *Ber.*, *76* (1943) 788.
KLEINBERG, J. and DAVIDSON, A. W., *Chem. Revs.*, *42* (1948) 601.
KLEMM, W. *et al.*, *Z. anorg. u. allgem. Chem.*, *300* (1931) 343, 367.
KORTÜM, G. and KORTÜM-SEILER, M., *Z. Naturforsch.*, *5a* (1950) 544.
KORTÜM, G. and VOGEL, W. M., *Z. Elektrochem.*, *59* (1955) 16.
KRUYT, H. R., *Z. physik. Chem.*, *65* (1909) 486.
KRUYT, H. R. *et al.*, *Colloid Science*, Vol. I, p. 264, Amsterdam, 1952.
KUHN, L. P., *J. Am. Chem. Soc.*, *74* (1952) 2492; *76* (1954) 4323.
KWANTES, A. and RIJNDERS, G. W. A., *Second Symposium on Gas Chromatography*, London, 1958.

LASSETTRE, E. N., *Chem. Revs.*, *20* (1937) 259.
LIFSCHITZ, E. M., *Zhur. Exptl. i Teoret. Fiz.*, *29* (1955) 94.
LIPPINCOTT, E. R. and SCHROEDER, R., *J. Chem. Phys.*, *23* (1955) 1099.
LITTLEWOOD, A. B., PHILLIPS, C. S. G. and PRICE, D. T., *J. Chem. Soc.*, (1955) 1480.
LONDON, F., *Z. Physik*, *63* (1930) 245; *Z. physik. Chem.*, *B 11* (1930) 222.
LONDON, F., *Trans. Faraday Soc.*, *33* (1937) 8.
LORD, R. C. and MERRIFIELD, R. E., *J. Chem. Phys.*, *21* (1953) 166.

MCGLASHAN, M. L. and RASTOGI, R. P., *Trans. Faraday Soc.*, *54* (1958) 496.

McPollock, J. and Ubbelohde, A. R., *Trans. Faraday Soc.*, *52* (1956) 1112.
Magat, M., *Ann. phys.*, *6* (1936) 108.
Magat, M., *J. chim. phys.*, *45* (1948) 93; *46* (1949) 344.
Mark, H. and Tobolsky, A. V., *Physical Chemistry of High Polymeric Systems*, New York, 1950.
Mecke, R., *Discussions Faraday Soc.*, No. 9 (1950) 161.
Merritt, L. L., Guare, Ch. and Lessor, A. E., *Acta Cryst.*, *9* (1956) 253.
Mulliken, R. S., *J. Am. Chem. Soc.*, *72* (1950) 600; *74* (1952) 811; *J. Phys. Chem.*, *56* (1952) 801.
Mulliken, R. S., *Rec. trav. chim.*, *75* (1956) 845.
Murakami, H., *J. Chem. Phys.*, *22* (1954) 367.

Nakamoto, K., Margoshes, M. and Rundle, R. E., *J. Am. Chem. Soc.*, *77* (1955) 6480.

Ogg, R. A., *J. Chem. Phys.*, *22* (1954) 560; *Helv. Phys. Acta*, *30* (1957) 89.
Orgel, L. E. and Mulliken, R. S., *J. Am. Chem. Soc.*, *79* (1957) 4839.
Overbeek, J. Th. G. and Sparnaay, M. J., *J. Colloid Sci.*, *7* (1952) 343.
Owston, P. G., *Quart. Revs. (London)*, *5* (1951) 344.

Pauling, L., *J. Am. Chem. Soc.*, *57* (1935) 2680.
Pauling, L., *J. chim. phys.*, *46* (1949) 435.
Pauling, L. and Corey, R. B., *Proc. Natl. Acad. Sci. U.S.*, *37* (1951) 205, 251; *Nature*, *171* (1953) 59.
Peterson, S. W. and Levy, H. A., *Phys. Rev.*, *92* (1953) 1082; *Acta Cryst.*, *10* (1957) 70.
Peterson, S. W., Levy, H. A. and Simonsen, S. H., *Phys. Rev.* *93* (1954) 1120.
Phillips, C. S. G., *Gas Chromatography*, London, 1956.
Pierotti, G. J., Deal, C. H., Derr, E. L. and Porter, P. E., *J. Am. Chem. Soc.*, *78* (1956) 2989.
Pimentel, G. C. and Sederholm, C. H., *J. Chem. Phys.*, *24* (1956) 639.
Pitzer, K. S. and Polissar, J., *J. Phys. Chem.*, *60* (1956) 1140.
Platteeuw, J. C. and Van der Waals, J. H., *J. Mol. Physics*, *1* (1958) 91.
Porter, P. E., Deal, C. H. and Stross, F. H., *J. Am. Chem. Soc.*, *78* (1956) 2999.
Powell, H. M. and Huse, G., *Nature*, *144* (1939) 77; *J. Chem. Soc.*, (1943) 435.
Powell, H. M., Huse, G. and Cooke, P. W., *J. Chem. Soc.*, (1943) 153.
Powell, H. M. *et al.*, *J. Chem. Soc.*, (1947) 208; (1948) 61, 571; (1950) 298, 300, 468; *Endeavour*, *9* (1950) 154.
Prosser, A. P. and Kitcher, J. A., *Nature*, *178* ( 1956) 1339; *Proc. Roy. Soc. (London)*, *A 242* (1957) 403.

Quayle, D. R., *Chem. Revs.*, *53* (1953) 439.

Redlich, O. *et al.*, *J. Am. Chem. Soc.*, *72* (1950) 4153.
Richards, R. E., *Quart. Revs. (London)*, *10* (1956) 480.
Rossmy, G., Lüttke, W. and Mecke, R., *J. Chem. Phys.*, *21* (1953) 1606.
Rumpf, P., *Bull. soc. chim. France*, (1948) 211.
Rundle, R. E. and Parasol, M., *J. Chem. Phys.*, *20* (1952) 1487.

Sarolea-Mathot, L., *Trans. Faraday Soc.*, *49* (1953) 8.
Schlenck, W., *Ann.*, *565* (1949) 204; *Fortschr. chem. Forsch.*, *2* (1951) 92.
Schneider, W. G., *J. Chem. Phys.*, *23* (1955) 26.
Schroeder, R. and Lippincott, E. R., *J. Phys. Chem.*, *61* (1957) 921.
Scott, R. L., *Rec. trav. chim.*, *75* (1956) 787.

SHAHAT, M., *Acta Cryst.*, *5* (1952) 763.
SISSKIND, B. and KASARNOWSKY, I., *Z. anorg. u. allgem. Chem.*, *214* (1933) 385.
SLATER, J. C. and KIRKWOOD, J. G., *Phys. Rev.*, *37* (1931) 682.
SMITH, A. E., *Acta Cryst.*, *5* (1952) 224.
SPURR, R. A. and BYERS, H. F., *J. Phys. Chem.*, *62* (1958) 425.
STACKELBERG, M. VON, *Naturwissenschaften*, *36* (1949) 327; 359; *J. Chem. Phys.*, *19* (1951) 1319.
STACKELBERG, M. VON and MÜLLER, H. R., *Naturwissenschaften*, *38* (1951) 456; *39* (1952) 20; *Z. Elektrochem.*, *58* (1954) 25, 40, 99, 104, 162.
STAVERMAN, A. J., *Physica*, *4* (1937) 1141; *Rec. trav. chim.*, *56* (1937) 885, 1189; *60* (1941) 827.
STEIN, R. S. and RUNDLE, R. E., *J. Chem. Phys.*, *16* (1948) 195.
SUGDEN, S., *Parachor and Valency*, London, 1930.

TSUBOMURA, H., *J. Chem. Phys.*, *23* (1955) 2130; *24* (1956) 927.

UBBELOHDE, A. R., *Quart. Revs. (London)*, *4* (1950) 356.
ULICH, H. *et al.*, *Z. physik. Chem.*, *Bodenstein Festschrift* (1931) 423; *B 16* (1932) 153; *B 17* (1933) 21.

VAN ARKEL, A. E., *Rec. trav. chim.*, *51* (1932) 1081; *52* (1933) 719, 733, 740; *53* (1934) 91, 246.
VAN ARKEL, A. E., *Chem. Weekblad*, *31* (1934) 490.
VAN ARKEL, A. E., *Trans. Faraday Soc.*, *42B* (1946) 81.
VAN ARKEL, A. E. and DE GROOT, W., *Physica*, *12* (1932) 215.
VAN ARKEL, A. E. and VLES, S. E., *Rec. trav. chim.*, *55* (1936) 407,
VAN NES, K. and VAN WESTEN, H. A., *Aspects of the Constitution of Mineral Oils*, Amsterdam, 1951.
VAN PANTHALEON VAN ECK, C. L., MENDEL, H. and BOOG, W., *Discussions Faraday Soc.*, No. 24 (1957) 200.
VAN PANTHALEON VAN ECK, C. L., MENDEL, H. and FAHRENFORT, J., *Proc. Roy. Soc., (London) Symposium on Physics of Water and Ice*, 1957; *Nature*, *181* (1958) 380.
VAN THIEL, M., BECKER, E. D. and PIMENTEL, G. C., *J. Chem. Phys.*, *27* (1957) 95.
VAN VELDEN, P. F. and KETELAAR, J. A. A., *Chem. Weekblad*, *43* (1947) 401.
VAN DER WAALS, J. H., *Trans. Faraday Soc.*, *52* (1956) 184.
VAN DER WAALS, J. H. and PLATTEEUW, J. C., *Rec. trav. chim.*, *75* (1956) 912.
VERWEY, E. J. W., *Rec. trav. chim.*, *60* (1941) 887; *61* (1942) 127.
VERWEY, E. J. W. and OVERBEEK, J. TH. G., *Theory of the Stability of Lyophobic Colloids*, Amsterdam, 1948.

WADDINGTON, T. C., *Trans. Faraday Soc.*, *54* (1958) 25.
WALLWORK, S. C. and HARDING, T. T., *Nature*, *171* (1953) 40.
WAUGH, J. S., HUMPHREY, F. B. and YOST, D. M., *J. Phys. Chem.*, *57* (1953) 486.
WEISS, J., *J. Chem. Soc.*, (1942) 245.
WELSH, H. K., *J. Chem. Phys.*, *26* (1957) 710.
WESTRUM, E. E. and PITZER, K. S., *J. Am. Chem. Soc.*, *71* (1949) 1940.

ZIMMERSCHMIED, W. J. *et al.*, *J. Am. Chem. Soc.*, *71* (1949) 2947.

# AUTHOR INDEX

# SUBJECT INDEX